HAEMOPOIETIC CELLS

NORTH-HOLLAND RESEARCH MONOGRAPHS

FRONTIERS OF BIOLOGY

VOLUME 24

Under the General Editorship of
A. NEUBERGER
London
and
E. L. TATUM
New York

Consultant for Immunology
E. J. HOLBOROW
Taplow

NORTH-HOLLAND PUBLISHING COMPANY
AMSTERDAM · LONDON

HAEMOPOIETIC CELLS

D. METCALF

and

M. A. S. MOORE

*Cancer Research Unit, Walter and Eliza Hall Institute,
Melbourne, Australia*

1971

NORTH-HOLLAND PUBLISHING COMPANY

AMSTERDAM · LONDON

Library of Congress Catalog Card Number: 79–157019
ISBN North-Holland: 0 7204 7124 9
ISBN American Elsevier: 0 444 10127 6

PUBLISHERS:

NORTH-HOLLAND PUBLISHING COMPANY - AMSTERDAM
NORTH-HOLLAND PUBLISHING COMPANY, LTD.-LONDON

SOLE DISTRIBUTORS FOR THE U.S.A. AND CANADA:

AMERICAN ELSEVIER PUBLISHING COMPANY, INC.
52 VANDERBILT AVENUE
NEW YORK, N.Y. 10017

PRINTED IN THE NETHERLANDS

Editors' preface

The aim of the publication of this series of monographs, known under the collective title of 'Frontiers of Biology', is to present coherent and up-to-date views of the fundamental concepts which dominate modern biology.

Biology in its widest sense has made very great advances during the past decade, and the rate of progress has been steadily accelerating. Undoubtedly important factors in this acceleration have been the effective use by biologists of new techniques, including electron microscopy, isotopic labels, and a great variety of physical and chemical techniques, especially those with varying degrees of automation. In addition, scientists with partly physical or chemical backgrounds have become interested in the great variety of problems presented by living organisms. Most significant, however, increasing interest in and understanding of the biology of the cell, especially in regard to the molecular events involved in genetic phenomena and in metabolism and its control, have led to the recognition of patterns common to all forms of life from bacteria to man. These factors and unifying concepts have led to a situation in which the sharp boundaries between the various classical biological disciplines are rapidly disappearing.

Thus, while scientists are becoming increasingly specialized in their techniques, to an increasing extent they need an intellectual and conceptual approach on a wide and non-specialized basis. It is with these considerations and needs in mind that this series of monographs, 'Frontiers of Biology' has been conceived.

The advances in various areas of biology, including microbiology, biochemistry, genetics, cytology, and cell structure and function in general will be presented by authors who have themselves contributed significantly to these developments. They will have, in this series, the opportunity of bringing together, from diverse sources, theories and experimental data, and of integrating these into a more general conceptual framework. It is unavoidable, and probably even desirable, that the special bias of the individual authors will become evident in their contributions. Scope will also be given for presentation of new and challenging ideas and hypotheses for which complete evidence is at present lacking. However, the main emphasis will be on fairly complete and objective presentation of the more important and more rapidly advancing aspects of biology. The level will be advanced, directed primarily to the needs of the graduate student and research worker.

Most monographs in this series will be in the range of 200–300 pages, but on occasion a collective work of major importance may be included exceeding this figure. The intent of the publishers is to bring out these books promptly and in fairly quick succession.

It is on the basis of all these various considerations that we welcome the opportunity of supporting the publication of the series '*Frontiers of Biology*' by North-Holland Publishing Company.

E. L. TATUM

A. NEUBERGER, *Editors*

TO OUR WIVES

for their patience and understanding

Preface

This monograph will record the overthrow of the established concepts of haemopoiesis which have held sway from the first identification of the various blood cells to the middle of the 20th century. In a dramatic revolution which is probably unique in modern cell biology, the introduction of a handful of new techniques has forced a complete revision of virtually every accepted concept in the field – and this in a span of little more than a decade.

What is almost as remarkable to those working in this burgeoning field is how little of this new information has yet reached the clinical haematologist or the undergraduate. While this monograph is not intended in any sense as a formal textbook, its preparation has certainly been motivated by a desire to catalyse the dissemination of this new information.

Like all monographs, the present work reflects the personal interests of the authors, perhaps to an undue degree. The subject of haemopoiesis is too large and diffuse to be covered adequately in a single volume and many aspects are outside the field of competence of the authors. We have attempted to cover most of the important aspects, at least in outline, but we are well aware that some subjects have received less attention than is warranted by their intrinsic importance. We apologise in advance to those of our friends and colleagues who may feel that their contributions to the field have been overlooked or underestimated.

While a clear pattern has now emerged of the general nature of the haemopoietic tissues, it will become evident from the account to follow that many questions remain unanswered. The authors will be more than satisfied if this monograph stimulates renewed efforts to answer these unresolved questions.

We are indebted to our many colleagues whose discussions and critical comments have assisted us in preparing this manuscript and particularly to Betty Hodgson whose untiring efforts allowed the manuscript to be completed.

Melbourne, 18th November, 1970   D. METCALF

M. A. S. MOORE

Contents

CHAPTER 1

General description of blood cells and haemopoietic organs

1.1 The blood cells – morphology and function

It is not proposed in this book to present a detailed morphological description of the various blood cells and the haemopoietic organs. However, a minimal amount of morphological description of these cells must be entered into for a proper understanding of the experimental studies to follow, and the functional properties of the different mature cells must be outlined since cell function is linked with the regulation of proliferation and differentiation of these cells.

It is usual to divide the mature blood cells into three broad classes – red cells, white cells and platelets. Within the white cell class there are further subdivisions into lymphocytes, granulocytes, eosinophils, basophils and monocytes. Three features characterise the population structure of blood cells in the body: (a) most cells within any one class are mature and usually highly differentiated, (b) most mature blood cells have a relatively short life span of days or weeks, and (c) with the exception of lymphocytes, all mature blood cells appear to be 'end cells' – that is, incapable of proliferative activity. This combination of characteristics is not unique in the body but for two blood cells – the red cell and the platelet – the end cell state is carried to the extreme limit in which the cell also lacks a nucleus – a situation unique in the body.

The finite life span of mature blood cells and their incapacity for self-replication necessitate the existence of a hierarchy of cells which generates the mature cells in each class of blood cells. These are termed 'poietic' cells – literally 'generating' cells, a prefix being attached to designate the mature cell type involved. Thus erythropoietic cells are the cells whose proliferative activity generates the mature erythrocyte (red cell), granulopoietic cells generate mature granulocytes, etc., and the whole system of cell populations generating blood cells is referred to collectively as the haemopoietic cell system. In this context, the lymphopoietic system cannot be separated from the remainder of the haemopoietic system in this definition and the haemopoietic system as discussed in this book embraces the whole lymphomyeloid complex.

In most tissues of the body the cells are arranged in fixed architectural patterns, and where the mature cells in these tissues are short-lived, e.g. the bowel or skin epithelial cells, the architectural pattern of the underlying cell populations which continuously generate new populations of mature cells is clearly evident. The situation with blood cells differs in that the mature cells circulate freely in the blood as individual cells which consequently have no permanent cell connections either with one another or with the cell populations generating them.

It is one of the many paradoxes of blood cells that while the remote ancestors of mature blood cells can, and do, circulate in the blood, the immediate ancestors (that is, the morphologically-recognisable proliferating cells in each cell series) do not normally circulate in the blood stream. Again, as we shall see later, lymphocytes and their ancestral cells are exceptional in this regard.

Certain generalisations can be made about the cells generating each class of mature blood cells. The production of each mature cell type is achieved by sequential mitotic divisions, starting from a restricted number of ancestral or haemopoietic progenitor cells. As the sequential divisions proceed within a cell class, the cells in general show a reduction in size, at the same time developing sufficient functional specialisation to allow the cells to be identifiable morphologically as belonging to a particular class. The earliest identifiable cells in a haemopoietic class are referred to as 'blast' cells. Thereafter further divisions progressively increase the population size of the class and at the same time more and more morphological and functional specialisation occurs. Usually the last few stages of specialisation occur without further cell division and typically these maturing cells are held at the site of haemopoiesis in the tissues for a final period before release to the blood stream.

These features and some of the specialised names applied to various cell populations are shown diagrammatically in an over-simplified fashion in Figure 1.1.

The cell class most readily dissectible into its component subpopulations is the erythropoietic series because the acquisition by the proerythroblast of the capacity to synthesise haemoglobin allows the use of the radioisotope

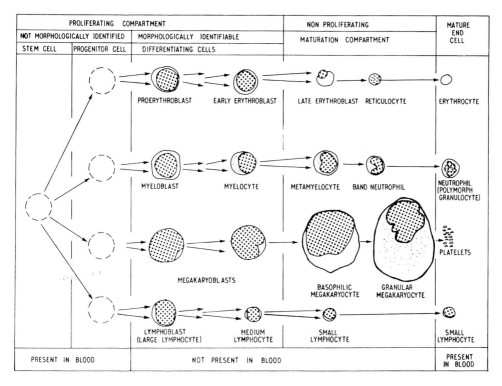

Fig. 1.1.   Schematic diagram indicating the nomenclature, morphology and some properties of the various blood cells.

[59]Fe as a functional marker which clearly separates precursor cells from erythroblasts. Furthermore, the dramatic changes in nuclear morphology which culminate in loss of the nucleus and development of the characteristic non-nuclear reticulocyte allow a precise characterisation of the non-proliferating or 'maturation' compartment of the erythropoietic series. Although no correspondingly specific isotopic markers have been developed for the granulocytic and megakaryocytic cell series, there are clear enough morphological changes in these cells which allow some precision in definition of the cell sequences for these cells. The lymphopoietic series presents particular problems because of the unspecialised morphology of both nucleus and cytoplasm combined with a lack of suitable specific isotopic markers. In the lymphoid cell series, tritiated thymidine uptake studies can distinguish dividing from non-dividing cells but determination of lymphocyte sub-population classes rests on the relatively unsatisfactory determination of

cell diameters or volumes and of minor changes in the nuclear-cytoplasmic size ratios and cytoplasmic basophilia.

Before leaving this brief survey of the blood cells it is necessary to refer to three other cell types which are closely related to blood cells but which do not normally circulate in mature form in the blood.

The plasma cells are closely related to lymphocytes and almost certainly share the same lineage of ancestral cells. Typically, they are restricted in location to the lymphoid tissues and do not enter the blood. A cell sequence from plasmablast to mature plasma cell can readily be discerned by inspection of these cells in the tissues and this cell sequence appears quite distinct from the parallel lymphoblast to lymphocyte sequence. However, recent functional and electronmicroscopic studies on antibody-producing cells have made it clear that the two cell classes merge imperceptibly into one another at all stages, and only the most extreme forms of both classes are readily distinguishable at the light microscope level. Most workers now are hesitant to place too much emphasis on distinctions between the lymphocyte and plasma cell series, preferring to regard them as a continuous spectrum of cells within the same cell class and often this class is referred to as the 'immunocyte' series, containing cells ranging from immunoblasts to immunocytes (Dameshek 1966). Within the immunocyte class the most mature cells can range in morphological appearance from small lymphocytes at one extreme to mature plasma cells at the other. Whilst the word 'immunocyte' is a convenient functional concept for the immunologist, it rather prejudges the potential functions of these cells and it is an open question whether the sole function of this cell class is to engage in immunological responses. As we shall discuss later, there is some evidence for trephocytic and growth regulatory functions for lymphocytes. Because of this, the term 'immunocyte' will not be used further in this book.

The second cell to share a close relationship with blood cells is the tissue macrophage. Recent studies have made it clear that many, perhaps most, tissue macrophages are derived from blood cells and originate from ancestors in the bone marrow, and this will be discussed later in more detail. Finally, the tissue mast cell probably shares a similar relationship with the blood basophil although here the evidence is less compelling.

The precise details of the specialised functions of the various blood cells are not pertinent to the theme of this book. However, brief mention needs to be made of the more obvious functions of the various blood cells because inevitably functional demands on these cells have repercussions on the proliferative activity of corresponding haemopoietic cells. Indeed, as shall be seen later, functional demands may be the major factor regulating haemopoiesis by a series of direct and indirect feedback mechanisms.

The functions of red blood cells are well established and involve essentially oxygen transport to the tissues and CO_2 transport from the tissues. This functional capacity is based on the haemoglobin molecule and the carbonic anhydrase enzyme system. The haemoglobin in embryonic red cells differs from that in adult cells and red cells appear to be the only blood cell class in which a clearly separate population of cells exists in the embryonic animal.

The functions of granulocytes are poorly understood. They demonstrate the capacity to phagocytose bacteria and have a high content of proteolytic enzymes. Their characteristic presence at sites of tissue injury has led to the conclusion that one of the chief functions of granulocytes may be to remove cell debris by local phagocytosis and digestion. It seems likely that other major functions of granulocytes may exist but these are so far uncharacterised.

Lymphocyte function appears to be related clearly to immunological responses to foreign antigens. As was mentioned earlier, many lymphocytes have been shown to actively produce antibodies and most are believed to carry small amounts of antibody on their surface which allows these cells to respond by proliferation when contact is made with the specific antigen. Current views are that lymphocytes are pre-programmed genetically only to react to one, or a limited number, of antigenic determinants and only to produce antibody to this restricted range of antigens. It seems likely that the primary immunological function of lymphocytes is to engage in cell-mediated immune responses in which intimate cell contact between the lymphocytes and the target cell exhibiting the appropriate antigen results in death of that target cell. Such cell-mediated immune responses are seen in delayed hypersensitivity, homograft rejection responses following the grafting of foreign tissues and in immune responses to tumour cells which are antigenic for the host. From time to time it has been speculated that lymphocytes may possess functions of a non-immunological nature – specifically growth promoting (trephocytic) or growth regulatory functions (Loutit 1962). There is little direct experimental evidence linking lymphocytes with non-immunological functions but recently it has been shown both *in vitro* and *in vivo* that lymphocytes can promote the proliferation of other haemopoietic cells and provide nuclear material which is reincorporated in proliferating granulocytes and macrophage cells.

Plasma cells appear to be highly specialised and to have a single function – the mass production of large amounts of specific antibody, individual cells producing antibody of only one type. These cells presumably contribute most of the antibody found in the peripheral blood during immunological responses to soluble or particulate foreign antigens.

Eosinophils are also involved in immunological responses, particularly of the allergic and hypersensitivity types but the exact role played by these cells is in dispute. Platelets, through their capacity to adhere to injured surfaces and to catalyse the formation of certain of the elements of blood clots, are intimately involved in the repair of minor defects in the walls of the vascular system and in major wound repairs. Basophils contain and release large amounts of heparin, histamine and 5-hydroxytryptamine. These substances have widespread pharmacological effects in the body and basophils and tissue mast cells appear intimately involved in acute vascular responses to injury, whether mechanical or chemical, and in immediate hypersensitivity reactions.

What is perhaps striking about this list of functions for the different blood cells is the relative absence of functions shared by two or more classes of blood cells. There are situations, e.g. at a site of inflammation, where different blood cell types become concentrated, but present evidence would suggest that each blood cell class tends to carry out its own specific functions in a combined action with other blood cells rather than that two or more classes of cells share common functions. E.g., an inflammatory focus due to bacterial invasion requires the presence of antibody-producing cells, cells with a scavenger function and cells with a digestive function. However, the lymphocytes and plasma cells which produce antibody are never phagocytic, and macrophages and granulocytes, although phagocytic, appear never to produce antibody. This degree of specialisation in blood cells is surprising in view of the common ancestral origin of blood cells (see later) and implies the existence of powerful differentiating influences which determine this individuality of cell structure and function.

It is appropriate at this stage to introduce and define the remaining cells in the hierarchy of haemopoietic cell populations. We have described the mature cells as seen in the blood and the morphologically-identifiable immediate ancestors of these cells which reside in certain haemopoietic organs. The description so far has implied that each cell lineage is separate and distinct from the others, with some reservations regarding probable lymphocyte-plasma cell and monocyte-macrophage interconversions which have been referred to. This concept that the cell lineages of morphologically-identifiable cells are distinct and non-interchangeable is supported by the vast bulk of experimental evidence. However, when one traces the lineage of these cell classes back beyond the earliest morphologically-identifiable stages it immediately becomes obvious that there is a merging together of the cell lineages. In other words, the same ancestral cells appear to be able to give rise to more than one lineage of identifiable blood cells. Because these ancestral cells are not morphologically identifiable and have not yet been separated from other cells as pure populations, there is dispute regarding the exact way in which the cell lineages are interrelated at the ancestral cell level.

No unified nomenclature has been established in this field and the titles 'stem cell', 'progenitor cell' and 'precursor cell' have been used to describe different functional states of ancestral haemopoietic cells. As discussed by Barnes and Loutit (1967) a dictionary definition of 'stem cell' is 'an unspecialised and usually embryonic cell, ancestral to one or more specialised cells' (*Webster's dictionary*, 1961). A 'progenitor cell' is defined by the same source as an ancestral cell in a direct line, while a 'precursor cell' is simply one that precedes another. Whether these definitions imply a hierarchy in the degree to which these cells are ancestral to the ultimate progeny is a problem of semantics. Lajtha et al. (1962) define stem cells as cells that 'can maintain their own number and give rise to differentiated cells'. Stem cell self-replication is not infinite, however (Siminovitch et al. 1964). Because of this, the definition of Caffrey-Tyler and Everett (1966) that a stem cell has 'the capacity for extensive proliferation, resulting in renewal of its own kind' is more valid. For the purposes of this review, stem cells are defined as primitive haemopoietic cells capable of extensive self-replication and endowed with a multiple differentiating capacity. A second class of ancestral cells is also recognised which is restricted in differentiating capacity to one or two lines of differentiation, has limited proliferative capacity, i.e. little or no self-replicative ability, and is sensitive to specific regulatory factors which are not thought to act on stem cells. Such cells have been variously termed 'precursor cells' (Morse and Stohlman 1966; Ebbe and Stohlman 1965; Bennett and Cudkowicz 1968), 'early differentiated cells' (McCulloch 1968) and 'progenitor cells' (Moore and Metcalf 1970; Haskill et al. 1970; Moore et al. 1970).

In the discussions to follow in this book, the terminology adopted is as follows:

Stem cells → Specific → Morphologically → Mature
progenitor identifiable cells
cells blast cells

The major historical controversy in haematology has been the opposing views regarding the nature of the stem cells. Conflicting opinions have centred on the morphological and functional characterisation of the so-called 'free' stem cells and their origins. The opposing viewpoints most favoured were the monophyletic theory most forcibly argued by Maximow, and various forms of the polyphyletic theory illustrated in Figure 1.2. In essence the monophyletic or unitarian concept recognised the existence of a single population of free pluripotential stem cells, variously termed haemocytoblasts or lymphoid wandering cells with the capacity to generate all the classes of differentiated haemopoietic cells. The polyphyletic theories variously recognised two, three or more separate types of stem cell, each restricted to one or two lines of differentiation. Adherence to any of these earlier concepts was determined by willingness to accept dubious histological characterisation and to interpret static morphological sequences in dynamic terms. For this reason no particular hypothesis could be unequivocably eliminated. However, the recent development of new methodological and conceptual approaches has materially assisted the resolution of this old controversy. What does appear to have been generally accepted by earlier haematologists is the concept that 'free' stem cells developed locally within each haemopoietic organ from a population of 'fixed' stromal cells. Perhaps most generally favoured as the source of haemopoietic stem cells has been

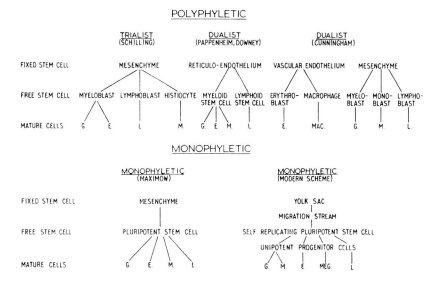

Fig. 1.2.   Schematic representation of the monophyletic and polyphyletic theories of the origins of haemopoietic cells.

the undifferentiated mesenchymal cell though vascular endothelium, reticulo-endothelial cells, epithelium and hepatic endoderm have received consideration. Despite such measures of agreement that have been achieved in the past with respect to the origin of the free haemopoietic stem cell it is now apparent that the earlier theories were invalid. A far more dynamic concept of haemopoiesis is now apparent, with active migration of stem cells occurring between different components of both the adult and embryonic haemopoietic systems.

It will be one of the primary objectives of this book to show that relatively simple experimental procedures have disproved many of these hotly championed theories regarding the origins of haemopoietic cells. It is to be hoped that soon these meticulously reproduced schemes with their confusing and contradictory terminologies will be dropped from text books of haematology, thereby ending the confusion of the hapless student.

As the experimental sections of this book unfold, it will become obvious that the concept of stem cells as having multipotent properties (that is, having the capacity to generate more than one class of specialised blood cell) is the one which agrees with experimental observations, with the reservation that hierarchies of these cells probably exist and that there may even be intermediate cell populations with a restricted capacity for the generation only of one or two cell classes.

It could be argued of course that this controversy was meaningless from the outset since all cells in the body are presumably derived from the single fertilised ovum – the ultimate stem cell. Nevertheless the haemopoietic stem cells represent multipotential cells which persist in adult life and by their proliferation are the *font et origo* of the whole dynamic system of blood-forming cells. It shall be seen later that the question of multipotent vs. unipotent stem cells is far from an academic one, and the basis of understanding and treating many disease states depends on establishing the essential unity or separateness of these haemopoietic stem cell populations.

1.2 Haemopoietic organs

The haemopoietic cells have a restricted distribution in the body and are concentrated in a limited number of organs, the haemopoietic organs. Taking the normal adult mouse as an example, the haemopoietic populations are restricted to the organs listed in Table 1.1.

There is some species variation in the location of various haemopoietic

TABLE 1.1

Distribution of haemopoietic cells in embryonic and adult life in the mouse

	Age in days	Erythropoiesis	Granulopoiesis	Lymphopoiesis	Megakaryo-poiesis
Embryo	0—7	0	0	0	0
	7—8	Yolk sac	0	0	0
	8—13	Yolk sac Liver	Liver	0	Liver
	13—15	Liver Spleen	Liver Spleen	Thymus	Liver Spleen
	15—20	Liver Spleen Bone marrow	Liver Spleen Bone marrow	Thymus Lymph nodes ($\pm$)	Liver Spleen Bone marrow
Adult		Bone marrow Spleen	Bone marrow Spleen	Thymus Spleen Lymph nodes Peyer's Patches Appendix Bone marrow	Bone marrow Spleen

cell populations. E.g., the mouse spleen is normally a site of erythropoiesis and granulopoiesis but the human spleen is not. Similarly in birds, classical lymph nodes do not exist, but diffuse lymphoid aggregates occur which appear to substitute in part for the missing lymph nodes. The bursa of Fabricius has no obvious equivalent in mammals. Most of the experimental studies to be discussed have been carried out in small laboratory mammals, particularly the mouse and rat and, to a lesser degree, the chicken. Unless otherwise qualified, the processes being described will be as observed in the mouse and it should be kept in mind that such species differences do exist. In most cases these will be of degree rather than nature but occasionally fundamental differences appear to exist and here specific qualifications will be made.

In the embryo the distribution of haemopoietic cells differs from that in the adult animal and varies widely according to the stage of development of the embryo as is shown in Table 1.1. In part this is due to the asynchronous development of various organs and in part to the existence of organs like the yolk sac which have no counterpart in the adult animal. The distribution of haemopoietic tissue in the embryo will be discussed in more detail later.

1.3 Structural features of haemopoietic organs

A brief description will now be made of the architectural features of the major haemopoietic organs, together with some comments regarding the growth of these organs at various stages of life. Certain special features of the structure of several of these organs will be discussed in more detail later.

1.3.1 Spleen

The spleen in the mouse appears first at day 15 of embryonic life and enlarges progressively until reaching maximum size in the 6–8 week old young adult animal. At this time, in conventional mice, its weight ranges from approximately 60–120 mg, and it contains approximately 2×10^8 nucleated cells. This makes the spleen the largest single haemopoietic organ in the adult mouse. Much of the bulk of the spleen is due to red cells trapped in sinusoids in the red pulp but the remainder of the spleen cells are arranged in a characteristic pattern whose significance will be referred to repeatedly later. The basic features of this pattern are (a) that lymphocytes are concentrated in spherical or ovoid lymphoid follicles surrounding central arterioles, (b) that erythropoietic tissue is present in scattered aggregates throughout the red pulp, in which are occasional megakaryocytes, and (c) that granulopoietic cells tend to be localised at the periphery of the red pulp, lying under the spleen capsule and along the fibrous trabeculae projecting inwards from this capsule. These regions are shown in Figure 1.3. One characteristic of the spleen which differentiates it from other organs is its lack of a lymphatic drainage system. All cells entering or leaving the organ do so via the blood.

In the normal spleen, mitotic activity is apparently distributed at random throughout the aggregates of erythropoietic and granulopoietic cells in the red pulp but this conclusion should only be regarded as provisional as the exact distribution of these mitotic cells has never been carefully investigated. Mitoses are infrequent in the spleen megakaryocytic series in the normal animal but can be common in tumour-bearing animals or animals with chronic infections or prolonged antigenic stimulation.

Lymphoid cells are undoubtedly present in large numbers in the red pulp,

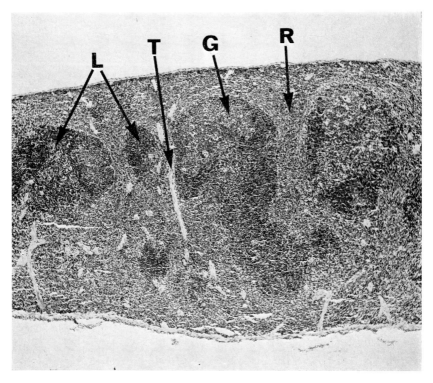

Fig. 1.3.   Photomicrograph of mouse spleen, showing several lymphoid follicles (L) with
germinal centres (G) surrounding red pulp (R) and fibrous trabeculae (T).
H and E × 25.

and possibly some of these exhibit mitotic activity. The complexity of the
cell populations in the red pulp makes it difficult to determine the existence
and magnitude of such red pulp lymphopoiesis. However, it seems likely that
the majority of the mitotic activity in lymphoid cells in the spleen is restricted
to the cells in lymphoid follicles and in particular to the cells in germinal
centres.

The spleen lymphoid follicles have a characteristic architectural pattern
shown in Figure 1.4. The roughly spherical cell aggregates are enclosed by a
peripheral complex of vascular channels, the perifollicular sheath, by which
antigens reach the lymphoid follicles and through which cells can enter or
leave the lymphoid follicles. The central region is pierced by a central
arteriole and the surrounding follicle is composed of densely-packed lymphocytes, the vast majority of which are mature small lymphocytes. The

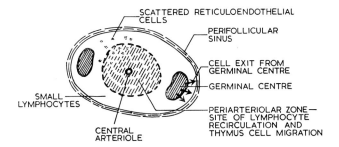

Fig. 1.4. Schematic diagram of a spleen lymphoid follicle.

shaded area in the figure is known as the peri-arteriolar zone and is the site of lymphocyte recirculation. At either pole of the follicle are discrete areas known as germinal centres which stand out from the general background of densely-staining small lymphocytes because of their content of more lightly-staining cells which are a mixture of large and medium lymphocytes, reti-culum cells and phagocytic macrophages. Many of the latter cells contain pyknotic nuclear material, presumably of lymphocyte origin. Mitotic activity in lymphoid follicles is usually concentrated in these germinal centres al-though occasional additional mitoses may be found in the densely-packed follicular aggregates of lymphocytes. The nature of the progeny of dividing germinal centre cells is somewhat uncertain but they probably are cells destined to become both lymphocytes and plasma cells. There is an internal structural specialisation within the germinal centre. Cells produced by the proliferative activity of germinal centre cells leave the outer aspect of the germinal centre – many passing direct to the red pulp (Hanna 1964). Kinetic studies have shown clearly that most small lymphocytes within the lymphoid follicle are *not* the recent progeny of germinal centre cells, but represent recirculating lymphocytes with a relatively long life span (Fliedner et al. 1964).

Precise estimates are difficult to obtain of the relative frequency of the various nucleated cells in the spleen. Differential counts on cells teased out of the spleen or from sieved cell suspensions may not be truly representative, since cells more firmly adherent to the structural framework of the spleen may not readily be released by these methods. With this qualification, typical data from an analysis of the cells present in an adult mouse spleen cell suspension are: lymphocytes 90.4%, nucleated erythroid cells 2.2%, granulocytic cells 5.2%, reticulum cells and macrophages 1.5% and plasma cells 0.7%.

1.3.2 Lymph nodes

Lymph nodes contain only a restricted range of haemopoietic and mature blood cells – lymphocytes, plasma cells, macrophages, reticulum cells and occasional mast cells. Specifically, erythropoietic and granulopoietic cells are not present in normal lymph nodes. In lymph nodes in the mouse which are draining sites of chronic inflammation it is common to find granulocytic cells in quite large numbers but even here mitotic activity is rare in such cells and most appear to be mature granulocytes.

Lymph nodes have a dual vascular system, lymphatic and blood, making it possible for cells entering or leaving the organ to do so either via the lymph or the blood. This is shown schematically in Figure 1.5. Lymphocytes entering or leaving the lymph node from the blood do so via a system of specialised post-capillary venules, a process first described by Gowans and Knight (1964). The unique feature of this cell transit is the fact that the cells pass *through* the cytoplasm of the cuboidal or columnar cells making up the vessel wall, rather than between the cells, as is the normal process for granulocytes and monocytes penetrating a vessel wall. The general location of these post-capillary venules and thus the major site of entry of lymphocytes into lymph nodes is shown in the hatched area in Figure 1.5.

The outer regions of the lymph node contain loosely packed areas of lymphocytes, predominantly small lymphocytes (loose cortex). These are interspersed by tighter aggregates of lymphocytes (lymphoid follicles or

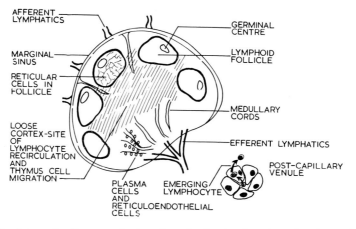

Fig. 1.5.   Schematic diagram of a lymph node showing location of major regions in relation to lymphatic drainage and lymphocyte recirculation.

primary lymphoid follicles). As in the spleen, these lymphoid follicles are the site of most mitotic activity in lymphoid cells of the lymph node and again, as in the spleen, mitotic activity is concentrated within germinal centres ('secondary lymphoid follicles') in these follicular aggregates of lymphocytes. The composition of lymph node germinal centres is essentially similar to that of the germinal centres of spleen lymphoid follicles.

The plasma cells in a lymph node tend to be concentrated in the medullary region of the node as cords of cells surrounding the efferent lymphatics and blood vessels at the hilum. In an antigenically-stimulated lymph node the proliferative activity in these plasma cell aggregates can be intense. The remaining component of lymph nodes requiring description is the diffuse network of phagocytic cells which are variously called macrophages or reticulum cells. These are dispersed throughout the organ but two regions of concentration of these cells are prominent in any lymph node draining foreign material. These are (a) the medullary region and the sinusoids under the capsule, and (b) the lymphoid follicles and germinal centres where a meshwork of dendritic reticulum cells is present in addition to more prominent phagocytic cells in the germinal centres themselves.

1.3.3 Peyer's patches

Peyer's patches are lymphoid aggregates in close association with the epithelium of the small bowel and have the same basic structure as that of spleen or lymph node lymphoid follicles. Their most obvious component is a large, usually single, germinal centre with a surrounding cuff of lymphocytes. Mitotic activity is usually marked in the germinal centres and there is a correspondingly high degree of phagocytic activity of scattered macrophages in these germinal centres. The lymphatic drainage system of Peyer's patches is somewhat uncertain but in general appears to be analogous with that of more typical lymph nodes – the efferent lymphatics draining through the mesentery to collecting lymph nodes along the major vessels.

1.3.4 Thymus

The thymus is a highly specialised lymphopoietic organ normally lacking erythroid and granulocytic cells and having a minimum of the reticuloendothelial cells usually associated with deposits of lymphocytes. The thymus is a bi-lobed organ, or more properly a paired organ, whose location is either in the upper chest as in most mammals, or in the neck as in the guinea pig and bird. Some Australian marsupials have both a thoracic and cervical thymus. Each lobe of the thymus has an outer region, the cortex, composed of dense aggregates of lymphocytes surrounding an irregularly-shaped central region, the medulla, in which lymphocytes although frequent are more obviously mixed with other cells, the medullary epithelial cells. In some species, e.g. the rat or human, it is clear that the thymus lobe is really a composite of a series of lobules each more or less spherical and having a central medullary area.

Detailed histological and electronmicroscopic studies have shown that the apparently homogeneous lymphoid cortex is in fact much more complex. The cortex is pierced by radial vessels passing from the medulla towards the outer capsule. These are ensheathed by tubes of flattened epithelial cells with a distinct space between the epithelial cells and the cells of the vessel walls. It is common to find lymphoid cells between these two layers apparently in transit between the cortical lymphoid aggregates and the vessel lumen. There is dispute regarding the direction of movement of such cells and possibly the cells may move in both directions.

The cells of the epithelial sheaths do not form a continuous layer and gaps exist between the cells which could allow free transit of cells or antigenic material between the blood vessels and the thymic parenchyma. The flattened epithelial cells continue as a layer under the thymus capsule, enclosing the outer aspects of the lymphoid cortex. Furthermore, a diffuse meshwork of epithelial cells (reticular-epithelial cells) extends through the lymphoid cell aggregates from one vascular sheath to the next. Thus the lymphoid cells in the cortex are enclosed in a mesh-work of cytoplasmic processes of epithelial cells and are in a sense enclosed in small epithelial packets (Figure 1.6). The significance of this intimate relationship between thymic epithelial and lymphoid cells in the cortex will be discussed later.

The lymphoid cells in the cortex appear to be the most mitotically-active of all haemopoietic cells, and mean cell cycle times for large and medium lymphocytes have been calculated to be, respectively, 6 and 7.5 hrs (Metcalf and Wiadrowski 1966). Although direct proof is difficult to obtain, it seems a reasonable assumption that large lymphocytes in the cortex generate by mitotic activity medium lymphocytes, which in turn generate small lymphocytes. The data suggest that the mitotic activity of large and medium lymphocytes must be almost self-sustaining in the sense that these cell populations do not expend themselves completely in the generation of medium or small lymphocytes.

Most thymic small lymphocytes do not incorporate tritiated thymidine

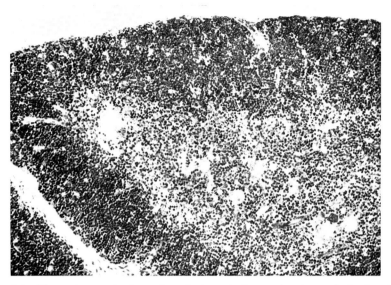

Fig. 1.6.   Photomicrograph of a portion of guinea pig thymus showing cortical and medullary areas with several radial vessels. Methylene blue × 125.

directly and thus appear not to be capable of division, although the total
population is replaced every 3–4 days by the mitotic activity of large and
medium lymphocytes. This observation that thymic small lymphocytes are
non-dividing cells must be qualified by saying that these cells may well be
capable of division, having first migrated elsewhere in the body. This question
will be re-examined later, in discussing the role of cell migration from the
thymus to other lymphoid organs.

The data indicate strongly that the loss of small lymphocytes from the
thymus is on an age-related basis, the first formed being the first to die or
leave the organ. The magnitude of cell migration from the thymus at various
stages in life will be discussed later but some comments need to be made
concerning the routes of exit of such cells. The thymus does have a lymphatic
drainage system, and studies have indicated that some lymphocytes appear
to leave the organ by this route (Kotani et al. 1966). Other studies, in which
cannulae were placed in the thymic arteries and veins revealed a net gain of
lymphocytes in the venous blood indicating that thymic lymphocytes also
leave the organ by this route (Ernström et al. 1965). The site of exit of such
cells into the venous system may be the medulla or the cortico-medullary
junctional region which has a relatively rich vascular system (Leblond and
Sainte-Marie 1960). The radial cortical vessels have been suggested as an

alternative site of exit of cells from the thymus. To a large degree, the difficulty in seeing convincing morphological evidence of the site of exit of lymphocytes from the thymus is due to the probability that relatively few of the small lymphocytes generated in the adult thymus actually leave the organ under normal conditions (Metcalf 1966).

Whilst reticulum cells are not prominent in the thymus cortex, appropriate histochemical techniques reveal moderately large numbers of these cells seeded throughout the dense cortical masses of lymphocytes. In a thymus in which excessive local destruction of lymphoid cells has been induced, e.g. by X-rays or cortisone, the whole cortex can be rapidly occupied by large phagocytic cells which have ingested the cell debris. Presumably most of these are derived from the inconspicuous reticuloendothelial cells normally present in the cortex.

One problem complicating efforts to completely thymectomise animals for experimental purposes in the existence of accessory thymus tissue. Most commonly this is embedded in the lobules of the thyroid but occasional deposits can be found along the length of the path taken by the epithelial cells in migrating from the third and fourth branchial pouches during embryogenesis. This accessory thymus tissue is more commonly seen in some mouse strains than others, e.g. BALB/c and F_1 hybrids of BALB/c, but it has been found less frequently in all mouse strains carefully examined.

Two features of the thymus warrant further comment. The thymus exhibits a characteristic growth curve, which is unique amongst haemopoietic organs in mammals. Thymus weight increases exponentially in early post-natal life and the weight of the organ reaches a maximum level in late pubertal or early adult life (5–8 weeks). Growth then ceases and there follows a characteristic weight loss, which is initially rapid and finally slows to a gradual loss which continues throughout adult life and old age. This phenomenon of thymus weight loss in early adult life is termed 'age-involution' and has as its cellular basis a diminution in proliferative activity of cortical lymphoid cells. The second feature of the thymus is that characteristic sex and strain differences occur in the weight of the organ within any one species. These differences are superimposed on the basic age-involution weight curve and do not modify the timing or the shape of this curve.

1.3.5   Bursa of Fabricius

The bursa of Fabricius is a cloacal epithelial-lymphoid organ unique to birds but sharing many structural similarities with the thymus. In newly-hatched chicks the bursa appears as a round or pear-shaped dorsal diverticulum of the cloaca. The organ increases rapidly in size and cellularity in the first few weeks after hatching attaining maximum size by the 5–12th week (depending on strain). At the onset of sexual maturity at 4–$4\frac{1}{2}$ months, the bursa undergoes involution and by 6–12 months has involuted completely, unlike the thymus which persists as a small atrophic organ. The epithelial connective tissue lining of the bursal sac is convoluted into a number of longitudinal folds or primary plicae which in turn are folded into numbers of secondary plicae. Large numbers of lymphoid follicles are present in each primary plicae within the connective tissue of the tunica propria lying beneath the columnar pseudostratified epithelial lining (Figure 1.7). The individual lymphoid follicles display a corticomedullary organisation similar to that seen in the thymic lobes, with a central medulla comprising an epithelial-reticular framework with dispersed large and medium lymphocytes, and a peripheral cortical region of densely-packed small lymphocytes liberally supplied by a capillary network.

Bursal follicular lymphopoiesis displays a similar maturation sequence with regard to cell size as in thymus, though mature bursal lymphocytes are larger than the thymic small lymphocytes (Peterson and Good 1965; Sherman and Auerbach 1966). Other similarities between bursal and thymic lymphopoiesis are (1) the very high proliferative activity which appears to be independent of antigenic stimulation, (2) a high incidence of local cell death, (3) intimate association between proliferating lymphocytes and epithelial cells, and (4) susceptibility to stress and age involution. Further

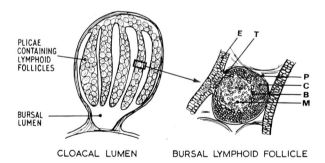

Fig. 1.7.   Diagram of the avian bursa of Fabricius showing plicae containing lymphoid follicles. Enlarged views shows the cortical (C) and medullary (M) organisation of a single follicle. E = bursal epithelial lining; T = epithelial tuft; B = row of bursal undifferentiated epithelial cells separating cortex from medulla; P = perifollicular mesenchyme.

parallels can be drawn between bursa and thymus in regard to embryonic development (see Chapter 4), and function in development of immunological capacity (see Chapter 6).

1.3.6   The primary lymphoid organs

The term 'primary lymphoid organs' has been introduced to cover a group of lymphoid organs whose basic role may be to generate lymphoid cells for immunological functions elsewhere in the body (Miller 1966). In its ultimate form this concept envisages a number of properties for the primary lymphoid organs: (a) they are important producers of lymphocytes and serve also as generating sites for lymphoid cells with the genetically pre-programmed ability to react to a restricted number of antigenic determinants, (b) they tend to involute in adult life, (c) they exhibit few or no signs of local immune responses in the form either of antibody-forming cells or plasma cells, and (d) they regulate lymphopoiesis in secondary lymphoid organs (lymph nodes and spleen) through cell delivery and by humoral factors elaborated by the epithelial components of the organs.

The immune system can be divided horizontally into the primary lymphoid organs, thymus and bursa (or bursal equivalent in mammals), controlling the development of the secondary lymphoid tissue in lymph nodes and spleen where the actual immunological reactions occur. A further vertical dissociation exists, with a thymus-dependent system concerned with manifestations of cellular immunity such as homograft rejection, graft vs. host reactivity and delayed hypersensitivity, and a bursal-dependent system concerned with immunoglobulin synthesis and humoral antibody formation.

The concepts of primary lymphoid organs and dissociation of the immune system have been useful but controversial questions remain. In particular, recent studies have revealed, in mammals, clear evidence for involvement of the thymic limb of the immune system in specific humoral antibody formation mediated via a collaboration process involving a thymic-independent population of cells. This latter population may be the elusive mammalian bursal-dependent population. Frequent attempts have been made to assign components of the mammalian gut-associated lymphoid tissue to the status of mammalian primary lymphoid equivalent of the avian bursa. Tonsils, appendix and Peyer's patches have all been nominated as possible candidates, as have the more diffuse lymphocyte populations of the gut and even of the skin (Fichtelius et al. 1970). The status of these proposed components of the primary lymphoid system is still uncertain and the experimental evidence will be reviewed in Chapter 6.

1.3.7 Bone marrow

The bone marrow is the most complex and, for many reasons, the most important of the haemopoietic organs in the adult animal. The haemopoietic cells do not uniformly fill the marrow cavity of all bones and recent technical innovations using isotoptic markers, have made it possible in large animals to produce myelograms of the distribution of the haemopoietic cells. In most species haemopoietic tissue is most abundant in the long bones and vertebrae, and because of this, in the mouse and rat the most commonly used source of bone marrow cells is the femur.

Calculations based on total ^{59}Fe uptake (Smith and Clayton 1970) have indicated that one femur shaft contains approximately 6% of the total bone marrow content of haemopoietic cells. Assuming that erythroid cells are distributed uniformly through bone marrow haemopoietic cells it was estimated that the total cell count in a single femur in an adult mouse was approximately 47×10^6 cells and that there was a total of 24×10^6 cells per gram body weight in all bone marrows combined.

The anatomical organisation of haemopoietic tissue in the marrow has not been fully analysed but it is probable that the function of this tissue depends to an unusual degree on the microanatomy of the vascular network. The arterial supply to the marrow ultimately breaks up into a network of inter-communicating sinusoids. Certain pecularities in the branching of the vascular system and the presence of venous throttling arrangements between draining terminal sinuses in the marrow and periosteal veins suggest the existence of blood flow-controlling mechanisms which may regulate haemopoietic activity and cell release.

The vascular sinusoids are lined by flattened endothelium with a supporting basement membrane and frequent fenestrations permit cell traffic between the parenchyma and the sinusoid lumen (Hudson and Yoffey 1967). However, the highly efficient retention of immature cell types within the marrow implies that the exit process is complex and may require active participation by the cells after an appropriate stage of maturation has been reached.

Few detailed studies appear to have been made on the possible regional segregation of different haemopoietic cells within the marrow. On gross inspection the different cells appear to be mixed in a random fashion and to have no specific spatial relationships with one another. Despite this, indirect evidence makes it certain that cell-cell inductive regulatory processes must operate in the bone marrow as in other haemopoietic organs. A careful search seems overdue to determine what are the distribution patterns of various cell types in the marrow as these cells are most unlikely to be randomly disturbed. In the chicken a striking segregation has been reported with the granulopoietic cells lying in aggregates outside the sinusoids and the erythropoietic cells confined to regions within sinusoids. However, in mammals both granulopoiesis and erythropoiesis appear to be entirely extravascular.

Differential cell counts on the major readily discernible cell populations in the mouse bone marrow give the following approximate pattern in the adult animal: granulocytes 47%; erythropoietic cells 27%; lymphocytes 22%; other cells 4% (Endicott and Gump 1947; Boggs et al. 1967). Thus granulopoiesis predominates over erythropoiesis in the mouse bone marrow although in total numbers most erythropoiesis in the body occurs in the marrow.

The small lymphocyte-like cells of the marrow present a particular problem. Like the small lymphocytes of the thymus, these cells appear not to be self-replicating but, as in the thymus, this population is rapidly renewed approximately every 3–4 days by the proliferative activity of other cells. The reason for classifying these cells as small lymphocytes is primarily based on their non-descript morphology. However, the response of bone marrow cells to phytohaemagglutinin has indicated that at least some of these lymphocyte-like cells must be functionally similar to comparable cells in lymph node populations.

1.3.8   The blood and lymph

The cell populations in the blood and lymph can be regarded collectively as constituting functional organs in their own right. However, in considering whether they represent haemo*poietic* organs it should be pointed out that the cell population in the blood exhibits a peculiarity which sets it apart from cell populations in other organs. As shall be shown later, multipotent haemopoietic stem cells are normally present in the blood. Despite the presence of stem cells in the blood, gaps exist in the lineages of cells between stem cells and mature or end cells. Thus the blood characteristically lacks proliferating cells from the blast stage to the maturation stage. This situation sets the blood apart from other organs containing stem and progenitor cells.

It should be kept in mind in later discussions based mainly on the mouse and rat that in adult animals the normal peripheral blood content of lympho-cytes is always in excess of that of granulocytes. In the mouse, a major switch occurs in the relative frequency of lymphocytes and granulocytes in the first week after birth. In the newborn, granulocytes and lymphocytes are equally frequent but there is a steady increase in lymphocyte levels with increasing age, leading to the characteristic predominance of lymphocytes in the adult animal.

Similar dramatic changes occur in the erythroid series. At birth and for the first week of postnatal life, large numbers of normoblasts (the last stage of erythrocyte formation in which the cells possess a nucleus) circulate in the peripheral blood. These disappear abruptly at about 7–10 days of age and never occur thereafter. The last stage in erythrocyte development, the non-nucleated reticulocyte, occurs normally in the peripheral blood at all ages. As might be anticipated, the frequency of these cells is high at birth and the adult frequency of 2–3% is reached some time between 2 and 3 weeks following birth.

The cellular composition of the thoracic duct lymph is almost purely lymphocytic and no granulocytic or erythroid cells are present in normal lymph. In the lymph draining from antigen-stimulated lymph nodes there can be a much higher percentage of more primitive lymphoid cells and reticulum cells. On electronmicroscopic examination, many of such cells exhibit a fine structure intermediate between that of classical lymphocytes and plasma cells.

Studies in the adult mouse after pulse labelling with tritiated thymidine indicate that no erythroid, granulocytic, eosinophilic or monocytic cells in the blood are in active cell cycle. However, a small percentage ($< 0.5\%$) of blood lymphocytes incorporates tritiated thymidine directly and can be presumed to be in the S phase of the cell cycle. One curious feature of the latter cells is that mitoses are *never* seen in the blood of normal animals and it must be presumed that as the S-phase cells enter G_2 or mitosis they either marginate in peripheral vessels or seed out in haemopoietic tissues. A similar comment can be made regarding the rarer stem and progenitor cells which are present in the blood and some of which are probably in active cell cycle.

1.4 Summary

This brief description of the blood cells and haemopoietic organs has indicated that blood cells occur in distinct classes and are usually non-dividing cells with short life spans. The cells are replaced by the proliferative activity of more immature, but identifiable, cells which in turn arise from smaller numbers of morphologically-unidentified progenitor and stem cells.

The haemopoietic populations are concentrated in a limited number of organs which exhibit specialisation in the type of blood cells contained in the organ. Cellular proliferative activity in haemopoietic organs is highly dynamic and can compensate rapidly for changing functional demands. From the complex architecture of the haemopoietic organs it is clear that haemopoiesis occurs only in highly specialised regions of the organs and that the structural cells forming these regions must have a profound regulatory influence on haemopoiesis.

References

Barnes, D. W. H. and J. F. Loutit, 1967, Lancet *2*, 1138.

Bennett, M. and G. Cudkowicz, 1968, Proc. Soc. Exp. Biol. Med. *129*, 99.

Boggs, D. R., P. A. Chervenick, J. C. Marsh, H. I. Pilgrim, G. E. Cartwright, and M. M. Wintrobe, 1967, Proc. Soc. Exp. Biol. Med. *125*, 325.

Caffrey-Tyler, R. W. and N. B. Everett, 1966, Blood *28*, 873.

Dameshek, W., 1966, Immunocytes and immunoproliferative disorders. In: The thymus. Experimental and clinical studies. CIBA Symposium, edited by G. E. W. Wolstenholme and R. Porter. London, Churchill, p. 399.

Ebbe, S. and F. Stohlman, 1965, Blood *26*, 20.

Endicott, K. M. and H. Gump, 1947, Blood *1*, 61.

Ernstrom, U., L. Gyllensten, and B. Larsson, 1965, Nature *207*, 540.

Fichtelius, K. E., O. Groth, and S. Liden, 1970, Int. Arch. Allergy *37*, 607.

Fliedner, T. M., M. Kesse, E. P. Cronkite, and J. S. Robertson, 1964, Annals N.Y. Acad. Sci. *113*, 578.

Gowans, J. L. and E. J. Knight, 1964, Proc. Roy. Soc. (*B*) *159*, 257.

Hanna, M. G., 1964, Lab. Invest. *13*, 95.

Haskill, J. S., T. A. McNeill, and M. A. S. Moore, 1970, J. Cell. Physiol. *75*, 167.

Hudson, G. and J. M. Yoffey, 1967, Interchange of lymphocytes between marrow and blood. In: The lymphocyte in immunology and haemopoiesis, edited by J. M. Yoffey. London, E. Arnold, p. 131.

Kotani, M., K. Seiki, A. Yamashita, and I. Horit, 1966, Blood *27*, 511.

Lajtha, L. G., R. Oliver, and C. W. Gurney, 1962, Brit. J. Haematol. *8*, 442.

Leblond, C. P. and G. Sainte-Marie, 1960, Models for lymphocyte and plasmocyte formation. In: Haemopoiesis. Cell production and its regulation. CIBA Symposium, edited by G. E. W. Wolstenholme and M. O'Connor. London, Churchill, p. 152.

Loutit, J. F., 1962, Lancet, 1106.

McCulloch, E. A., 1968, In: Proceedings XII International Society of Hematology N.Y., edited by R. Jaffe, p. 260.

Metcalf, D., 1966, The nature and regulation of lymphopoiesis in the normal and neoplastic thymus. In: The thymus. Experimental and clinical studies. CIBA Symposium, edited by G. E. W. Wolstenholme and R. Porter. London, Churchill, p. 242.

Metcalf, D. and M. Wiadrowski, 1966, Cancer Res. *26*, 483.

Miller, J. F. A. P., 1966, Brit. Med. Bull. *22*, 21.
Moore, M. A. S. and D. Metcalf, 1970, Brit. J. Haematol. *18*, 279.
Moore, M. A. S., T. A. McNeill, and J. S. Haskill, 1970, J. Cell. Physiol. *75*, 181.
Morse, B. S. and F. Stohlman, 1966, J. Clin. Invest. *45*, 1241.
Peterson, R. D. A. and R. A. Good, 1965, Blood *26*, 269.
Sherman, J. and R. Auerbach, 1966, Blood *27*, 371.
Siminovitch, L., J. E. Till, and E. A. McCulloch, 1964, J. Cell. Comp. Physiol. *64*, **23.**
Smith, L. H. and M. L. Clayton, 1970, Experimental Hematology *20*, 82.
Webster's 3rd new international dictionary, 1961, Springfield, Mass.

CHAPTER 2

Techniques in experimental haematology and their limitations

The purposes of this review are (a) to group together some of the major techniques used in experimental haematology, the original descriptions of which are scattered through the literature of a number of disciplines, and (b) to emphasise some of the limitations and common faults in using certain techniques in this field.

2.1 Cell morphology and size determinations

Virtually every procedure used in analysing haemopoiesis requires a parallel study of the morphology of the cells or organs being manipulated. No matter how sophisticated the experimental system, it is a foolish investigator who neglects to pay attention to the cellular composition of the populations being analysed.

Techniques for staining blood cells and criteria for their classification may be obtained from any handbook of haematology and these will not be dealt with here. The cells presenting the greatest difficulty in classification are lymphoid cells because of their failure to develop characteristic nuclear or cytoplasmic structures during maturation. Most workers classify lymphocytes according to nuclear and cell size and this approach has been vindicated by more recent studies on the proliferative activity of these cells using tritiated thymidine autoradiography.

The importance of cell size in the analysis of lymphoid cell populations has prompted the use of electronic size analysers (e.g. the Coulter Counter), which determine cell volumes and which if coupled with an automatic plotter will construct a histogram of the relative frequency of cells of various volumes in a cell suspension. Calibration of individual machines is essential since the aperture windows vary from one machine to another and a useful particle for calibration is the mature red cell. Coulter counter analyses are of most value in determining cell volumes in major subpopulations, e.g. in distinguishing small lymphocytes of the thymus from those of lymph nodes (Metcalf and Brumby 1966; Sherman and Auerbach 1966). This approach is less useful in dealing with less frequent cells in the tail of the distribution pattern, e.g. in the case of lymphoid cell suspensions, the medium and large lymphocytes. The cell volume is affected by pH and storage conditions and careful standardisation of the suspending medium is critical for some cells, e.g. erythroid cells, where the cell volume fluctuates widely with pH changes (Legge and Shortman 1968).

2.2 Isotopic markers and autoradiography

The introduction of tritiated thymidine (Hughes et al. 1958; Firket and Verly 1958) revolutionised the measurement of cell cycle times in dividing cell populations, particularly when combined with autoradiography which allows studies to be made on individual cells of different blood cell classes. The techniques involved and their limitations as applied to haemopoietic cells have been discussed by Clarkson (1969) and Cronkite (1969).

In principle the effectiveness of tritiated thymidine hinges on the fact that it is incorporated in large molecular weight form only in the nuclei of cells in the phase of DNA synthesis (the S phase). Recent work suggests that this simple statement may not be strictly true and that some turnover of DNA can occur in resting cells but for practical purposes, if a cell becomes labelled with tritiated thymidine, it indicates clearly enough that the cell was in the S phase of the cell cycle when the tritiated thymidine was available for incorporation. The fact that the half life of tritiated thymidine in the circulation is short, means that tritiated thymidine is an ideal substance for instantaneously characterising those cells in DNA synthesis in a mixed population ('pulse labelling') and subsequently for enumerating their progeny and following their life history.

Cell cycle times can be estimated using two general approaches: (a) determining the length of the S phase and also the proportion of cells in S at any one point in time, or (b) determining the rate of fall of grain counts in various cells, the grain count being halved in daughter cells following division of a labelled cell. In the first approach the percentage of labelled cells one hour after labelling is determined. This is coupled with data derived from plotting the percent of labelled mitoses in the population to determine the length of S. The length of S is the duration between the mid point in the rise to 100% of labelled mitoses and the subsequent fall to 50% of labelling in this population. Subsequent labelling patterns in the mitotic cells vary from one cell population to another, depending on many factors including asynchrony of chromosome replication and variation in individual cell cycle times, but these subsequent fluctuations do not detract from the validity of the estimation of S from the initial peak. The alternative method for determining the mean length of the cell cycle is to follow the fall in grain counts over cells of a particular class, establishing the mean time for the average grain count to be reduced to 50%. The technique is tedious and although offering independent corroboration of data from the mitotic labelling curve, it is less versatile as it provides data only on the length of the *whole* cell cycle. Furthermore, there is a serious technical problem in the interpretation of grain count data, particularly in lymphoid cells, due to the reutilisation by these cells of labelled material originating from the breakdown of other labelled cells (Mitchell et al. 1963; Metcalf and Wiadrowski 1966). To some extent this problem can be circumvented by flooding the body or cell system with unlabelled thymidine following pulse labelling (Weissman 1967).

The major problem in autoradiography is to ensure that cells are adequately labelled. This is achieved first by using a sufficiently high dose of tritiated thymidine and second by using exposure times which are sufficiently long to ensure that *all* labelled cells are detected and not just the most heavily-labelled cells. The literature abounds with misinformation from studies on underlabelled cells. To guard against such errors, replicate sets of auto-radiographs must be exposed for varying periods until the percent of labelled cells clearly reaches a plateau for *every* cell class being examined. To meet these requirements it will usually be found that an exposure time sufficient for the most lightly-labelled cells will be an over-exposure for the more heavily-labelled cells, requiring the use of replicate slides for scoring different cell classes.

Other radioisotopes have more specialised applications ^{59}Fe has proved invaluable for studying the general proliferative activity of erythropoietic cells. Unfortunately the beta and gamma emissions from ^{59}Fe have too much energy to be satisfactory for autoradiography. The use of [55]Fe allows adequate autoradiographs, although the cells in the smear need to be well separated from one another as the dispersion of grains is greater than for tritiated thymidine.

No correspondingly specific isotope exists for the granulocytic series although $DF^{32}P$ has proved to be a useful method for labelling mature granulocytes *in vitro* and for tracing their subsequent behaviour on re-injection (Athens 1969).

Lymphoid cells have no suitable isotopic markers at the present time except in the special case of antigen-reactive cells which can be labelled autoradiographically by pre-treatment with the appropriate [125]I- or ^{131}I-labelled antigen (Naor and Sulitzeanu 1967; Byrt and Ada 1969).

2.3 *Methods for selective cell killing*

Kinetic analysis of haemopoietic cell populations requires a knowledge of the fraction of the cells in particular phases of the cell cycle or in a non-cycling (G_0) state. In contrast to such non-specific cell killing agents as irradiation and nitrogen mustard which kill both resting and cycling cells, there are certain agents that act preferentially on proliferating cells through-out their cycle e.g. 5-fluorouracil, actinomycin-D and cyclophosphamide. Of more value are the phase-specific agents which kill cells at specific stages of the cycle, generally at the DNA synthesis S phase or at mitosis.

The S-phase killing agent most widely used is tritiated thymidine. The introduction of lethal, rather than marker, doses of this radioisotope into the DNA cells under study, during their S phase, results in 'suiciding' of the cells which subsequently die or lose their capacity for replication. The suiciding technique may be carried out *in vitro* by briefly exposing cell suspensions for 20 min to 200–500 μc of tritiated thymidine (Becker et al. 1965). Alternatively, a single massive dose (1 mc/20 gram mouse may be administered *in vivo*, or repeated doses of 166 μc of the tritiated thymidine, every 4 hours for a 24-hour period (Bruce and Meeker 1965). The brief exposure regime does not provide information on cell populations with a long generation time, but it avoids the disadvantage of prolonged exposure regimes where there is time for activation of resting cells into cycle, as a result of depletion of the proliferating pool, with consequent overestimation of the normal proliferative state of the cell population.

Hydroxyurea appears also to be a useful cytotoxic agent because of its selective lethal effect on cells in DNA synthesis when doses of 900 mg/kg are administered intravenously to mice (Morse et al. 1969). The S phase effect resides in inhibition of enzyme systems responsible for reduction of ribonucleotides to deoxyribonucleotides (Krakoff et al. 1968). *In vitro* use or very high dosage *in vivo* of this agent should however be avoided since there is evidence that it can produce a G_1 block in tissue culture if high cellular concentrations are maintained (Sinclair 1965). *In vivo*, the metabolic breakdown of hydroxyurea provides only a short period of effective concentration and consequently G_1 blocking is less significant, but should not be ignored.

The stathmokinetic agents, vinblastine, vincristine and colchicine have also been used to study cell kinetics because of their cytotoxic effects on cells passing into mitosis. Vinblastine and vincristine are two closely-related alkaloids prepared from the periwinkle *Vinca rosea*, vincristine possessing an N-formyl group and vinblastine an N-methyl. Cells exposed to either agent are blocked irreversibly in mitosis, possibly through dissolution of the mitotic spindle (Malawista et al. 1968). The duration of vincristine activity can be prolonged, with dividing cells continuing to accumulate in metaphase for 8 hours and with the mitotic index being greater than normal even up to 24 hours (Morse et al. 1970). The dose response curve for vinblastine *in vivo* in mice is discontinuous with a critical dose of 5 μg below which no cells die and above which 100% mortality occurs (Hodgson 1967). The *in vivo* half life of vinblastine is 3.5 hours (Valeriote and Bruce 1965), and from this and the dose response curve, the effective concentration of vinblastine to be given *in vivo* may be determined – between 40–80 μg/mouse, given intravenously. Much higher doses (1 mg/mouse intraperitoneally) have been used, and though clear differential killing has been obtained, certain drawbacks to the use of vinblastine emerge. Combined treatment with vinblastine and suiciding doses of tritiated thymidine produce no greater effect than either agent separately (Valeriote et al. 1966). However, *in vitro* studies have clearly shown the lethal action of both vinblastine and vincristine at high doses on cells in interphase (Madoc-Jones and Mauro 1968). Vinblastine caused an immediate interphase death by lysis, of cells treated in late G_1, and both agents, acting briefly on cells in S phase, allowed the cells to proceed at a normal rate to mitosis where they were arrested irreversibly. There is evidence that the cytotoxic effects of vincristine, other than the stathmokinetic action may be brought about by interference with nucleic acid and protein synthesis (Creasy and Markiw 1964).

The stathmokinetic effect of colchicine is used to advantage in determining the stathmokinetic index of accumulation of colchicine-blocked mitoses in tissue sections and smears, from which a calculation of cell generation times is possible. In addition, for chromosome marker studies, colchicine is used to accumulate increased numbers of mitoses blocked at an appropriately condensed metaphase stage. *In vivo*, colchicine has been used to determine when cells underwent mitosis prior to entering an erythropoietin-responsive stage (Hodgson and Eskuche 1968) though the reversibility of the colchicine-blocking of mitosis has limited the application of this drug as a phase-specific cytotoxic agent.

2.4 *Methods for studying stem-cell kinetics*

The most frequently used assay for haemopoietic stem cells is the *in vivo* spleen colony assay developed by Till and McCulloch (1961). In this system, haemopoietic cell suspensions are injected intravenously in low numbers (10^3–10^5 cells) into lethally-irradiated mice and 7–10 days later the recipient spleens are removed, fixed in Bouin's solution, and the number of macro-scopically visible nodules or colonies on the surface of the spleen is scored (Figure 2.1). Each nodule is the product of proliferation of a single stem cell or colony-forming unit (CFU). It is important to ensure that the dose of X– or gamma– irradiation given to the mice is sufficiently high so that formation of endogenous spleen colonies by surviving host stem cells does not introduce error in the exogenous assay. In practice between 800–1000 R is used. Spleen colony formation may also be assessed in histological sections prepared serially throughout the spleen. This approach, though tedious, is necessary if the morphological distribution of the different colony types is required. Minimum colony size is taken to be 100 cells per largest cross-section of a colony unless the colony is purely megakaryocytic in which case 6 cells per largest cross-section is accepted.

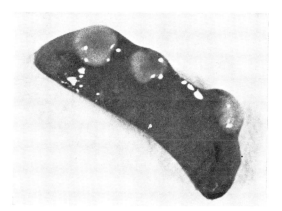

Fig. 2.1. Irradiated mouse spleen showing discrete spleen colonies 9 days after the injection of bone-marrow cells.

Radioisotope incorporation techniques can also be used to measure haemopoietic proliferation in irradiated mice injected with haemopoietic cells. Incorporation of the radioiodinated thymidine analogue, 5-iodo-2^1 deoxyuridine-^{131}I (^{131}IUdR) into regenerating marrow and spleen has been used to assay the repopulating capacity of grafted haemopoietic cells (Cudkowicz et al. 1964; Bennett and Cudkowicz 1967). 0.5 μc of ^{131}-IUdR is injected intraperitoneally to label cells synthesising DNA. One hour prior to injection each animal is given 10^{-7} moles of 5-fluoro-2^1-deoxyuridine to inhibit endogenous formation of thymidine precursors which compete with IUdR for incorporation into DNA. Mice are killed 18 hours later, and radioactivity retained in haemopoietic tissues is measured in a well-type scintillation counter and expressed as a percentage of radioactivity injected into each animal. This technique measures proliferating cells only, and furthermore various experimental conditions may alter the pattern of utilisation of administered IUdR, e.g. by changing the rate of hepatic breakdown of the compound.

Incorporation of ^{59}Fe into the erythroid series is also used to monitor erythroid regeneration. The 6-hour incorporation of ^{59}Fe into the femur or spleen (Smith 1964) as a measure of erythropoiesis in these sites, assumes that by 6 hours, the plasma has been cleared of radioiron and counts in the tissues are derived from iron incorporated into red cell precursors. This method has the disadvantage of also measuring iron storage capacity which may well vary in the course of regeneration. Repopulating capacity can also be measured by injecting radioiron 6–8 days after grafting, and assessing the appearance of radioiron in peripheral blood cells 48–72 hours later (Blackett et al. 1964; Hodgson 1962). A good correlation exists between the number of cells grafted and the blood iron incorporation.

The above measures of cell proliferation can also be applied to measure regeneration and stem cell kinetics in sublethally-irradiated animals and in autorepopulation systems where certain regions of haemopoietic tissue are shielded from an otherwise lethal dose of irradiation applied to the unshielded areas. In the autorepopulation system, colonising cells migrating from a shielded femur can be measured by their endogeneous colony-forming capacity in the unshielded spleen or by radioisotopic measurements of cell proliferation. Interpretation of this system is difficult since at least three factors operate: (1) the available stem cell reserve of the shielded area, (2) the rate of seeding or mobilisation of stem cells from the shielded area, (3) the receptivity of the irradiated tissue for colonising cells. Of these three factors, the seeding rate or mobilisation of stem cells is a more important consideration than the actual absolute number of stem cells in the shielded area (Lajtha et al. 1969).

2.5 Measurement of erythropoietin responsiveness

Erythropoiesis can be selectively suppressed for short periods in mice by a number of procedures (a) hypertransfusion, (b) starvation, (c) anoxia-induced polycythaemia, or (d) the use of anti-human erythropoietin anti-serum. In such mice, injected erythropoietin initiates a wave of erythropoiesis which can be measured by ^{59}Fe incorporation or reticulocyte counts. The suppressed animal is superior to normal animals for assay work since it is particularly sensitive to erythropoietin.

In the simplest system, mice are injected intraperitoneally at daily intervals for three days with 0.5 ml washed packed mouse red cells, preferably from lethally-irradiated donors. Erythropoiesis is suppressed by 5 days after commencement of treatment, with reticulocyte counts less than 0.1% and 72 hour radioiron incorporation less than 0.2% (Jacobson et al. 1959; Gurney et al. 1962). Suppression of erythropoiesis can be maintained by giving additional injections of packed red cells every 2–3 days and maintaining haematocrit levels at 70–75%.

The above types of suppressed animal can also be used to study the kinetics of the erythropoietin-sensitive cells (the progenitor cells of the erythropoietic series) since the magnitude of erythropoiesis induced by erythropoietin in suppressed animals is determined by the population size of the erythropoietin-sensitive cells (ESC). However, the situation is complex as the various methods for suppressing erythropoiesis differ somewhat in their effects on the stem cell and progenitor cell compartments. Furthermore the dose of erythropoietin used is important since with low doses, the short half-life of erythropoietin restricts its activity to directly erythropoietin-sensitive cells. With high doses of erythropoietin there is time for recruitment of additional ESC from more primitive precursors which can lead to an overestimation of the size of the immediately erythropoietin-responsive cell population.

2.6 In vitro culture of haemopoietic colonies

This technique will be described in some detail as it is relatively new and no single, complete, account exists of the various procedures involved. The technique for cultivation of haemopoietic cells in semi-solid agar was introduced independently by Pluznik and Sachs (1965) and Bradley and Metcalf (1966). The interpretation of the data obtained using this technique will be discussed in full later but here the usefulness of the technique can be summarised by saying that it allows the precise quantitation of the number of granulocyte progenitor cells and at least certain of the macrophage progenitors in any haemopoietic tissue.

These precursor cells reveal themselves in culture by proliferating to form discrete colonies, but in order for these cells to survive and proliferate *in vitro*, a factor known as the colony stimulating factor (CSF) must be incorporated in the agar medium. This can be achieved in a variety of ways, each with certain deficiencies, and this is the basis of a number of variations in the basic culture technique.

In its essentials, the agar culture technique involves mixing together equal volumes of double strength Eagle's medium and 0.6% agar held liquid at 37°C. To this liquid mixture is added the cell suspension to be cultured and aliquots of the resulting mixture are pipetted into petri dishes, allowed to gel, and incubated in 10% CO_2 in air for the required period – usually 7–10 days – without further media change. Colonies are scored unstained *in situ* simply by counting with a dissecting microscope, using indirect lighting.

Cells from any haemopoietic organ containing the above progenitor cells can be used as the source of colony-forming cells. These tissues are converted to a dispersed cell suspension in bone marrow collecting fluid by gentle pipetting, teasing with needles or sieving through a stainless steel sieve. The composition of bone marrow collecting fluid is: modified double strength Eagle's medium 40 ml; 3% trypticase soy broth 10 ml; glass distilled water 50 ml. This fluid can be stored for use at 4°C for up to 2 weeks. Where *in vivo* assays (spleen CFU assays) are being performed on the same cell suspension, Eisen's solution can be used instead of bone marrow collecting fluid and it is likely that many other balanced salt solutions would be equally effective. It does appear, however, that *in vitro* colony-forming cells are more sensitive to room temperature conditions than spleen colony-forming cells and cell suspensions not cultured immediately should be held in crushed ice.

Nucleated cell counts are performed on the suspensions using nigrosin for viability estimates and cell concentrations adjusted so that the volume of the cell suspension which must be added to the agar-medium does not exceed 10% of the volume of the agar-medium. Ideally, the volume of added cells should be even less, e.g. 1–2% of the final volume, as colony formation in agar is critically dependent on the concentration of the agar and 0.3% agar is the optimal concentration, 0.4% being quite inhibitory for colony formation and 0.2% agar not gelling adequately (Bradley and Metcalf 1966).

The modified double strength Eagle's medium has the following composition:

Eagle's minimal essential medium salts × 10	100	ml
NaH CO$_3$ (2.8%)	80	ml
Eagle's minimal essential medium vitamins × 100	10	ml
Eagle's minimal essential medium amino acids A × 100	10	ml
Eagle's minimal essential medium amino acids B × 100	10	ml
200 millimolar glutamine solution	10	ml
Sodium pyruvate (2.2%)	5	ml
Foetal Calf Serum (not heat inactivated)	100	ml
L-serine (21 mg per ml)	1	ml
Penicillin (200,000 units per ml)	0.58	ml
Streptomycin (200 mg per ml)	0.38	ml
Phenol red (1%)	2	ml
Horse Serum (not heat inactivated)	50	ml
Double glass distilled water	85	ml
Total	464	ml

These ingredients are mixed in the listed order, then millipore filtered and stored for use at 4 °C.

Other ingredients used in the culture medium are:

(1) Trypticase soy broth (Baltimore Biological Laboratories, Baltimore). 3% in distilled water, dissolved, autoclaved and then stored for use at 4 °C for a maximum period of 1–2 weeks.

(2) DEAE dextran (Pharmacia, Uppsala, Sweden) Dextran MW = 2 × 10^6/n/ = 0.70) made up as 50 mg per ml in water, millipore filtered and stored at 4 °C.

(3) L-asparagine made up in water as 6.6 mg per ml, millipore filtered and stored at 4 °C.

The agar used is Bacto Agar (Difco) and is made immediately before use by boiling a solution of 0.6% in water in an Erlenmeyer flask for 2 min then holding at 37 °C in a water bath. Other types of agar such as Noble agar, purified agar or agarose are less satisfactory for colony growth. Methyl cellulose (1.3%) or hydrolysed starch (7%) can also be used as the gelling material (Ichikawa et al. 1966).

For the preparation of the medium immediately before use, the following steps are performed. To make up 100 ml of agar-medium the following are mixed:

double strength Eagle's medium	40	ml
3% trypticase soy broth	10	ml
DEAE dextran (final concentration 75 μg per ml)	0.15	ml
L-asparagine (final concentration 20 μg per ml)	0.30	ml

To this mixture held at room temperature is then added 50 ml of 0.6% agar held at 37 °C to give a total volume of 100 ml of the final culture medium, which is then effectively single strength Eagle's medium in 0.3% agar with 10% foetal calf serum and 5% horse serum.

The cell suspension is immediately added to this agar-medium mixture and the cells uniformly dispersed. Depending on the type of experiment and the source of haemopoietic cells, usual cell doses plated vary from 10,000 to 100,000 per ml. The cell suspension in agar-medium is pipetted into 50 mm glass or 35 mm plastic petri dishes (Falcon Plastics, Los Angeles) using either pipettes or a Cornwall automatic 2 ml syringe fitted with plastic tubing.

The plates are agitated with a circular motion to obtain a uniform cell distribution and allowed to gel at room temperature for up to 20 min. These plates are then incubated in a fully humidified incubator at 37 °C in an atmosphere of 10% CO_2 in air, the pH being held at approximately 7.2 as judged by the phenol red indicator in the medium.

Colony counts are performed after 7 or 10 days of incubation using a

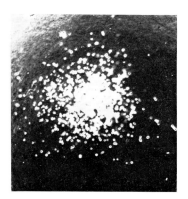

Fig. 2.2.   A loose macrophage colony growing in agar from mouse bone-marrow cells × 40.

dissecting microscope with indirect lighting. Colonies appear as discrete spherical aggregates of cells against a background of smaller aggregates of cells (clusters) (Figure 2.2). There is no fixed size criterion for the minimum number of cells which qualifies an aggregate to be scored as a colony since colony size depends on (a) the concentration of CSF, (b) the number of colonies per unit volume of the culture medium, (c) the number of cells initially plated, and (d) the adequacy of the media, the foetal calf serum, the batch of petri dishes and the efficiency of the CO_2 incubator in maintaining fully hydrated conditions at a constant pH. Under most culture conditions, colonies at 7 days of incubation will range in size from 50–1000 cells, colony size most often lying within the 200–500 cell range.

2.6.1 Colony-Stimulating Factor

The rate of initiation of proliferation of potential colony-forming cells is dependent on the concentration of CSF and CSF is required continuously in the medium for progressive colony growth (Metcalf 1969, 1970). Furthermore, as mentioned above, the growth rate of individual colonies is determined to a major degree by the concentration of CSF (Robinson et al. 1967; Metcalf 1969).

There are two general methods for supplying CSF to the above types of culture:

(a) A feeder layer of cells may be placed in the agar under the agar-medium layer containing the colony-forming cells (Bradley and Metcalf 1966; Pluznik and Sachs 1965). The cells in the feeder layer release or elaborate CSF which is freely diffusable in agar and penetrates the upper agar layer containing the colony-forming cells. The general advantages of this system are that colony growth is sustained longer than by other methods and that there is better survival of granulocytic colonies and the granulocytic cells in mixed colonies. The major disadvantage is that preparation of feeder layers is time consuming and although feeder layers can be stored at 37 °C in the CO_2 incubator for up to a week before use, there are practical limitations to the ready availability of such plates. A further disadvantage is that the density of cells in the underlayer obscures visualisation of the early events in colony growth and sometimes can even complicate colony counting.

Feeder layers are usually prepared using 0.5% agar, in part to restrict possible cell migration from the underlayer to the colony forming layer above. Many cell types have been shown to serve as adequate or good feeder layers for mouse bone-marrow cells. These include trypsinized embryo or neonatal mouse kidney cells, spleen cells, L cells, and some lymphoma or leukaemic cells. Underlayer cells can be pre-irradiated without loss of their feeder layer activity. For mouse colony-forming cells, feeder layer cells from any mouse strain appear to function equally well. However, there are some species barriers to the use of feeder layers from different species, e.g. rat cells will not stimulate mouse bone marrow cells and mouse cells are relatively poor stimulators of human cells. In the special case of human bone marrow cells, human peripheral white cells have been found to be superior to other feeder layer cells and for good colony growth an alternative medium (McCoy's modified medium) is required (Pike and Robinson 1970).

(b) A simple system for supplying CSF to agar cultures is to mix a small volume of fluid containing CSF with the agar-medium and cells before gelling occurs. With adequate concentrations of CSF in the fluid added initially, no further supply of CSF is required during a 7–10 day incubation period. In practice, 0.0125 to 0.2 ml of fluid containing CSF is pipetted into the empty petri dish before the agar-medium is pipetted in. Thorough mixing is carried out by agitation before gelling occurs. Alternatively, the CSF can be incorporated in an underlayer of agar-medium in a manner similar to the technique used for feeder layers.

Useful sources of CSF for stimulation of colony formation by mouse bone-marrow cells are:

(a) *Human urine.* – CSF is detectable in most unconcentrated urine samples from normal humans and is present in high concentrations in many leukaemic patients (see later). Human urine can be used unconcentrated after preliminary dialysis and millipore filtration in doses of 0.15 ml, but it is preferable to use a concentrated and partially purified preparation using techniques for the extraction and purification of CSF described by Stanley and Metcalf (1969). The advantages of urine as the source of CSF are its availability in large amounts (50 gallons of normal urine contains sufficient CSF to stimulate 1,500,000 1 ml cultures) and that initial colony formation is easy to follow because of the discrete, compact, nature of the developing colonies. The disadvantages are (a) that urine is more subject to variability than other sources of CSF, particularly to variations in the suitability of the foetal calf serum being used and the quality of the plastic petri dishes, and (b) that granulocyte survival is poor after 3–4 days of incubation and unless high concentrations of urine CSF are used, most colonies transform to macrophage colonies by 7 days of incubation.

(b) *Mouse or human serum.* – Sera from most strains of mice contain sufficiently high concentrations of CSF to be adequate for stimulating colony formation in doses of 0.1 or 0.05 ml in 1 ml cultures (Robinson et al. 1967). Serum CSF levels are even higher in mice with leukaemia or infections or following antigenic stimulation. The disadvantages with mouse sera are (a) that the sera of many strains contain large amounts of lipoproteins which inhibit colony formation. These can be removed by ether treatment and less satisfactorily by pre-bleeding, starvation, heating, centrifugation or dialysis of the serum against water, (b) that most 7 day colonies are purely macrophage in composition, and (c) that serum-stimulated colonies tend to be large, loose aggregates which sometimes render colony counting difficult when large numbers are present on a single plate.

Human serum also serves as an adequate source of CSF for stimulating mouse cultures. CSF is not detectable in untreated normal human serum but it is often present in high concentrations in sera from patients with leukaemia or other haemopoietic neoplasms and in patients with acute infections (Foster et al. 1968). CSF is present in normal serum but is masked by inhibitors which may be removed by centrifugation, ether treatment or dialysis against water (Chan et al. 1970). The disadvantages of human sera are (a) that activity is relatively weak compared with mouse serum, and (b) that 7 day colonies are again purely macrophage in composition and tend to be rather small in size.

(c) *Conditioned medium.* – Many cells can release or secrete CSF into the overlying fluid of conventional liquid tissue cultures (Ichikawa et al. 1966; Bradley and Sumner 1968). Use can be made of this property by simple preparing stationary mass cultures of cells in Eagle's medium in petri dishes. The fluid is harvested at 2–6 days, dialysed and millipore filtered. Useful cell types for producing conditioned medium are embryo, kidney, bone marrow, spleen and a variety of continuous cell lines and tumour cells. Most conditioned media have one advantage over serum or urine in that granulocytic colony growth and persistence can be as good as with feeder layers and conditioned medium is readily available, being stable indefinitely on storage at $-20\,°C$. The disadvantages are again that preparation of conditioned medium is time-consuming in comparison with the large amounts of factor available in human urine.

2.6.2 *Assay for in vitro colony-forming cells*

It is usual in an assay for colony-forming cells to culture cells at several concentrations. Linear relationships exist between the number of colonies and the number of cells plated over a wide cell range, e.g. 1–100,000 cells, but plating the cell suspension at a number of concentrations is an internal check on adequate mixing of the original cell suspension and on pipetting errors. Four to six replicate cultures at these different cell doses provide an adequate estimate of the incidence of colony-forming cells, which is usually expressed as the number of such cells per 10^4 or 10^5 cells.

The major difficulty in estimating *in vitro* colony-forming cells is that the number of colonies developing from a standard number of plated cells shows a sigmoid dose relationship with CSF concentration. Therefore care must be taken always to have a known excess of CSF in the culture system. Furthermore, standard preparations of CSF and standard bone marrow suspensions should always be included in any assay run to correct for general fluctuations in the efficiency of colony formation which may occur with different batches of media. In our laboratory, the commonly used standard is a pooled specimen of bone marrow cells from three, two-months old C57BL mice. Pooled C57BL bone marrow cells are assigned an arbitrary incidence of 100 colony-forming cells per 10^5 cells and the actual figure obtained in individual experiments is used to determine a correction factor which is applied to all data from test specimens in that experiment before calculating the incidence of colony-forming cells in these specimens. In actual fact, experimental estimates of the incidence of *in vitro* colony-forming cells in mouse bone marrow often give an incidence of 1 in 500 cells or even higher. Thus the use of an artificial standard can be a little misleading but it does allow comparison between results from different experiments. It is uncertain whether the above precautions adequately cover all possible failures in the culture system. E.g., it may be that the media and incubating conditions even at their best are not revealing the presence of all colony-forming cells. The plating efficiency of the culture system is unknown and will not be known until a pure population of colony-forming cells can be cultured. This question will be discussed further when the nature of cluster-forming cells is discussed in relation to *in vitro* colony-forming cells.

2.7 Assay systems for antibody-forming cells and antigen-sensitive units

Techniques for enumerating single antibody-producing cells in the presence of a large excess of non-antibody producers, have provided much quantitative information on the immune response and have added a new dimension to studies of the cellular dynamics of antibody formation.

The plaque-forming cell (PFC) assay, described independently by Jerne and Nordin (1963) and Ingraham and Bussard (1964) detects haemolysin-releasing cells by virtue of the appearance of pinpoint areas of haemolysis (plaques) in nutrient gels containing the appropriate erythrocytes mixed with cells obtained from immunised donors. Erythrocytes immediately surrounding a single antibody-producing cell within the semi-solid gel are lysed after incubation at 37 °C and addition of complement. Cunningham and Szenberg (1968) described a simpler and less time-consuming plaque-forming cell assay which is a modification of the Jerne assay that dispenses with the semi-solid agar supporting media. In this technique glass slides, 75 × 25 mm, are washed and rinsed. Three pieces of 'double sided' adhesive tape are laid across the ends and middle of one slide and another slide of similar size is pressed firmly onto the taped slide, forming two chambers of similar volume. The test cell suspension, in a volume of 0.1 ml of medium 199, is mixed with 0.01 ml of undiluted guinea pig serum as a source of complement, 0.01 ml of 25% erythrocytes in normal saline and 0.04 ml of 2.5% erythrocytes in medium 199. After mixing, the suspension is drawn into a fine pipette and expressed into the slide chambers which may be topped up if necessary, with the 2.5% erythrocyte suspension. The edges of the slide chamber are sealed with a molten paraffin – 'Vaseline' mixture (1 : 1) which is allowed to solidify. Slides are incubated at 37 °C for 30–45 min and the plaques are counted under a dissecting microscope. The only disadvantage of the method is the instability of the plaques and the chambers must consequently be handled with care, and plaques counted immediately (Figure 2.3).

A method has been described for the enumeration of cells producing antibody to a defined protein antigen – the polymerised flagellin of *S. adelaide* (Diener 1968). Cell suspensions from mice immunised with polymerised flagellin are mixed with *S. derby*, and coronas of bacteria form around the antibody-producing cells. Non-adherent bacteria are removed by layering the suspension over foetal calf serum and centrifuging. Cells are then re-suspended in nutrient agar, plated out in Petri dishes and incubated. During incubation the agar-embedded cells with adherent bacteria give rise to bacterial colonies (adherence colonies) and the plates can then be scored for the number of such colonies, which represent the number of cells in the plate that are producing antibody against the polymerised flagellin.

More recently a number of variations of the basic Jerne plaque technique have been developed which allow the detection of cells forming antibodies to bacterial or soluble antigens. In principle these techniques employ a

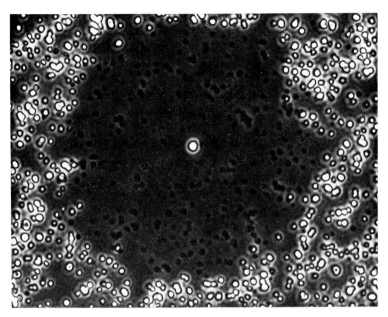

Fig. 2.3.   A haemolytic plaque-forming (antibody-producing) cell producing a zone of
lysis in surrounding sheep red cells.

detection system of red cells coated with the antigen in place of normal red
cells. Following reaction between antibody and this antigen in the presence
of complement, lysis of the carrier red cell occurs resulting in plaque formation.

Assays have been developed for the detection of the precursors of antibody-forming cells, variously termed antigen-sensitive cells (or units)
antigen-reactive cells or focus-forming cells (or units). The original assay
systems scored discrete foci of haemolysis developing in the spleens of
lethally-irradiated mice after cell injection and stimulation by heterologous
erythrocytes (Kennedy et al. 1965, 1966; Playfair et al. 1965; Papermaster
1967). Briefly, the technique consists of irradiating groups of recipient mice
with 900–950 rad and injecting intravenously the test cell suspension. Twenty-
four hours later heterologous red cells are injected intravenously and the
animals sacrificed 7–9 days after cell transfer and the spleens removed. The
spleens are placed on the stage of a tissue chopper and 250 μ sections are
cut sequentially throughout the spleen, and are transferred onto agar base
plates. The plates are then warmed to 37 °C and an overlayer of soft agar
in Eagle's medium containing the appropriate erythrocytes is then run over

the slices. After the layer has solidified, the plates are incubated at 37 °C for 1½–2 hours. Complement (1:10 guinea pig serum) is then added and incubation is continued for a further hour. Plates are then washed with saline and cooled. Zones of haemolysis or 'active areas' can be seen in the agar-erythrocyte layer in association with some spleen slices and can be scored as an index of clusters or foci of antibody-forming cells produced by precursor cells present in the original inoculum.

The focus-forming assay has also been adapted for protein antigens (Armstrong and Diener 1969). In this modification, polymerised flagellin replaces the heterologous erythrocyte antigen in the above system. 7–8 days after antigen injection the spleens are removed and sectioned. The spleen slices are laid on slides covered with a film of nutrient agar containing *Salmonella* bacteria and are covered with a thin layer of bacteria-free agar. After incubation, foci of inhibited bacterial growth, the result of antibody production by progeny of the antigen-sensitive or reactive cells, are counted with a low-power objective using reflected light on a black background.

2.8 The use of chromosome markers

Various chromosome markers have proved invaluable in experimental haematology since they allow permanent identification of cells regardless of their proliferation or differentiation. An inherent disadvantage of such marker systems is their restriction to dividing cell populations, apart from such interphase markers as are provided by the inactivated X-chromosome, expressed as a Barr body in the nucleus or as a nuclear drumstick appendage in neutrophils. This restriction limits analysis of slowly-dividing or non-dividing cell populations and makes difficult, if not impossible, morphological characterisation of the metaphase cells scored. Despite such qualifications, chromosome marker techniques have been extensively applied to the analysis of haemopoietic cell kinetics.

Four basic systems, enabling karyotypic analysis, are: (1) The use of species differences in karyotype, permitting e.g. identification of proliferating rat marrow cells in irradiated mouse recipients. (2) The generation and use of unique radiation-induced chromosome abnormalities as a marker system to identify the progeny of single cells. (3) Sex chromosome differences existing between male XY, and female XX mitoses. (4) The T6 translocation-marker system in mice. This latter system has been most extensively used and merits detailed consideration.

The T6 chromosome marker appeared as a reciprocal translocation in an irradiated male mouse and involved an unequal translocation between two medium-sized autosomes, with one of the two products being much smaller than the shortest pair of normal autosomes. This small chromosome is distinct in a somatic metaphase both because of its small size, and presence of a prominent secondary constriction near the centromere which gives the chromosome a characteristic tripartite appearance illustrated in Figure 2.4 (Ford 1966). The potential application of this marker was further enhanced by backcrossing the translocation heterozygote onto the genetic background of a standard inbred mouse strain – CBA/H resulting in production of a new strain, CBA/H-T6T6, syngeneic with CBA/H, but bearing two T6 marker chromosomes. The T6 marker system therefore provides a histocompatible system, suitable for grafting and immunological experiments where three separate cell populations can be identified, one bearing two T6 markers, a standard CBA population with none, and an F_1 hybrid population (CBA × CBA-T6T6)F_1, carrying only one T6.

Unique combinations of chromosome abnormalities can be induced in haemopoietic cells by irradiation. Cells with individual specific karyotypes offer advantages over even cells with T6 markers, since the clonal progeny

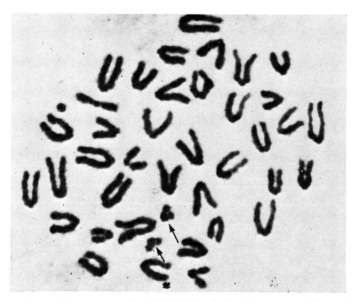

Fig. 2.4.   A metaphase spread of a CBAT6T6 cell showing the two characteristic T6 marker chromosomes (arrows).

of a single cell can be characterised. However, data obtained from the use of such cells need to be interpreted with caution as the possibility always exists that these cells may differ subtly from normal e.g. in enjoying a proliferative advantage over normal cells, or in failing to respond normally to humoral and microenvironmental regulation.

Innumerable procedures have been developed for chromosome preparation and consequently some flexibility in technique is possible without pre-judicing the outcome. It is certainly true that different species and even different tissues may require some variation in technique to ensure optimum results. The most popular and reproducible method is the air-dry technique which has many advantages over the earlier 'squash' method, both in terms of simplicity and number of scorable metaphases obtained (Rothfels and Siminovitch 1958). For mouse haemopoietic tissues, the technique described by Ford (1966) has been extensively used. In this procedure, mice are injected intraperitoneally with $10^{-5}M$ of colcemid (CIBA), equivalent to 0.01 ml of a 0.4% (weight/volume) solution in distilled water. Prior colcemid treatment results in accumulation of cells in an optimum condensed meta-phase stage. Animals are then sacrificed at various intervals, best determined empirically, that result in maximum metaphase accumulation without loss of metaphase quality. Approximately $1\frac{1}{2}$ hours has been found to be optimal for most mouse haemopoietic tissues, though up to 3 hours may be necessary with lymph node lymphocyte populations. If a number of tissues are to be sampled, cell suspensions should be prepared in isotonic media and subse-quent stages of preparation synchronised. Such cell suspensions are then gently centrifuged in small (0.5–1 ml) test tubes (excessive mechanical force both in preparation of cell suspensions and in centrifugation results in selective loss of mitotic cells). The supernatant is then removed with a fine pipette, and the cells resuspended in a fresh hypotonic solution of 0.95% sodium citrate (weight/volume). We have found that when only a few tissues are sampled, cell suspensions can be prepared directly in hypotonic citrate, thus avoiding a centrifugation step. The period of hypotonic treatment is required to swell mitotic cells and produces better chromosome spreading in the final preparation. Between 10–20 min of such hypotonic treatment is optimal for most haemopoietic tissues, though some variation in duration is permissible, particularly if a high proportion of poorly-spread metaphase figures is present in the final preparation. Following hypotonic treatment, the cells are recentrifuged with gradual acceleration and low peak speed not exceeding 500 rpm (47–50 g) for approximately 3–5 min. The following stage is perhaps most critical and requires the removal of as much of the aqueous hypotonic solution as is possible without disturbing the cell pellet. Freshly prepared fixative comprising 3 parts absolute ethyl alcohol to one part glacial acetic acid is then gently run down the side of the tube, avoiding disturbance of the cell pellet, and is then removed and replaced by fresh fixative. This replacement procedure is necessary to remove water adherent to the sides of the tube and ensures good fixation. In the event that the cell pellet is disturbed, an additional centrifugation step may be necessary in conjunction with fixative replacement. Round bottomed tubes and small pellets of cells further assist good fixation since rapid penetration of fixative is ensured and this greatly increases the quality of the final metaphase preparations. Fixation occupies between 30 min and 1 hour, but prolonging fixation does not adversely affect metaphase quality provided that the fixative is replaced prior to the final spreading stage. It is necessary to ensure that the cells are in suspension prior to spreading, and sharp flicking of the tube or very gently pipetting, avoiding bubbling, may be necessary if the cells become clumped during fixation. The final cell suspension is taken up into small, fine bored, Pasteur pipettes and single droplets dropped onto clean, grease-free slides. The droplets should expand evenly and then begin to retract as the fixative evaporates. When interference colour rings are seen at the edges of the contracting drops, gentle blowing should be instituted to assist the final rapid evaporation.

A modification of this technique has been described by Ford and Hamerton (1956) and applied to avian tissue by Owen (1965) and Moore and Owen (1965). The modification consists of an extension of the procedure by addition of a final stage of resuspension of cells in aqueous 45% acetic acid and spreading on warmed (60 °C) glass slides. The advantages of this final stage are that cells can remain for prolonged periods in the aqueous acetic acid prior to spreading, and the aqueous medium counteracts the cell clumping which frequently complicates the direct air-dry technique. By manipulating the evaporating droplets, the whole area of the slide can be used for cell spreading thus cutting down the number of slides to be scanned in order to obtain a given number of metaphase figures. The disadvantage of this final stage is a tendency for overspreading and disruption of metaphases, though with avian tissue the procedure overcomes the problem of underspreading or clumping of avian metaphases seen with conventional air-dry techniques.

The final preparations are stained in lactic-acetic orcein (Welshons et al. 1962) for 30 min, followed by rinsing in 45% acetic acid, dehydration in two changes of methoxy-ethanol and mounting in euperal. Preparations may be scored under normal or phase-contrast optics, the latter being necessary for adequate identification of avian chromosomes. An alternative staining procedure, less desirable from the standpoint of chromosome quality but technically easier, is the use of 15% Giemsa followed by washing and air drying.

The identification of chromosome markers is not in itself difficult, and in good preparations the T6 marker chromosomes can be identified at a glance, however, a number of sources of bias must be considered as discussed by Ford (1966). Not infrequently, even in good preparations, T6 chromosomes may lie in such a relationship to each other or to larger autosomes as to be missed on casual inspection. A second, and more important bias, is introduced in selection of metaphases for scoring. If, e.g., 10% (a not unreasonable figure) of all metaphases are unsuitable by virtue of poor quality, chromosome clumping, loss of chromosomes or juxtaposition to nuclei that may obscure certain chromosomes, inspection of such metaphases at high magnification, where T6 markers can be identified, may lead to bias in favour of T6 marked cells since the subjective tendency is to include metaphases where T6 markers are clearly seen (even if other chromosomes are obscured or missing), and to reject metaphases of similar quality where no markers are seen. To avoid such bias in favour of T6-marked cells, the assessment of suitability, or otherwise of a metaphase for scoring should be carried out at such a magnification that the T6 marker cannot be seen. Further complications involve confusion of the T6 with the Y chromosome or even some of the smaller autosomes bearing secondary constrictions. This is not a practical difficulty, however, if the observer is familiar with the normal mouse karyotype.

Sex chromosomes have been used as a marker system since in many species the X or Y chromosomes are clearly distinguishable from the autosomes. In birds, particularly in the chick embryo, sex chromosome markers have been extensively used to trace cell migration patterns throughout haemopoietic development. Unlike mammals, the female in the class *Aves* is the heterogametic sex possessing Z and W sex chromosomes, probably equivalent to the mammalian X and Y chromosomes, while the homogametic male has a pair of Z (or X) chromosomes. In Figure 2.5 a typical male metaphase from a chicken is shown and should be compared with the female karyotype on Figure 2.6. The ZZ sex chromosomes are the fifth largest pair of chromosomes in the male and are particularly distinct both because of their size and medially-situated centromeres. In the female only one Z chromosome is present and is partnered by a much smaller W chromosome, similar in size to the seventh pair but possessing a more medially-placed centromere. There

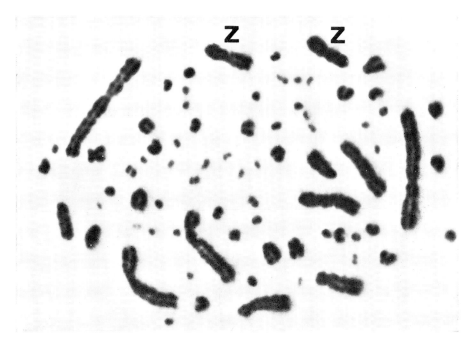

Fig. 2.5. *Metaphase spread from a male chicken cell. The large paired mediocentric (ZZ) sex chromosomes are indicated by (Z). Numerous microchromosomes can be seen.* × 4,500. (*From Owen 1965, reproduced by permission of Chromosoma.*)

is consequently no difficulty in sexing a metaphase on the basis of either one or two Z chromosomes (identification of the W chromosome is not practicable unless a karyotype is prepared). Bias in favour of the female population may be produced by loss of one Z chromosome from a male metaphase due to overspreading and breakage of the metaphase figure. Such overspreading is only rarely observed, but nevertheless the complement of large chromosomes should routinely be counted, and where the total complement is missing or obscured, the metaphase must be rejected – regardless of whether or not two Z chromosomes are present. The possibility of selective loss of one Z chromosome from an otherwise intact metaphase cannot be excluded, but in metaphases where chromosomes have been lost, these were invariably the first and second largest pairs.

Procedures have been developed for miniaturisation of the standard chromosome preparation technique so that analysis can be carried out on either single dividing cells or small populations. Nossal et al. (1968) described two methods, both employing micromanipulation of single cells, that have

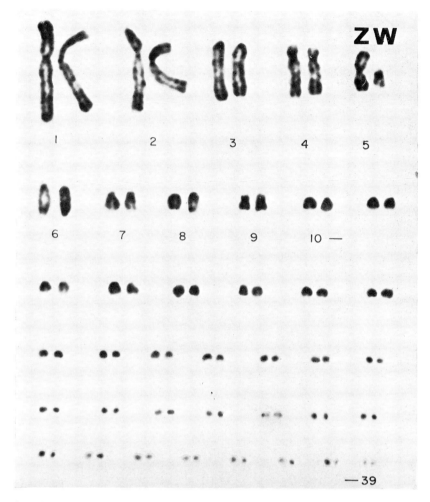

Fig. 2.6. Karyotype from a female chicken metaphase. Only one large mediocentric chromosome (Z) is present. The small W female sex chromosome is indicated. × 4,500. (From Owen 1965, reproduced by permission of Chromosoma.)

permitted T6 chromosome marker analysis of single antibody-forming cells. A procedure for chromosome preparation from colonies of normal and leukaemic haemopoietic cells growing *in vitro* in the agar culture system has also been described (Metcalf et al. 1969). This latter technique involves addition of colcemid (CIBA), at a concentration of $2\,\mu$g in a volume of 0.2 ml balanced salt solution, to culture plates containing colonies of haemopoietic cells after 2–8 days of culture. The cultures are returned to the incubator, and 3 hours later, individual colonies are picked from the agar and placed in 0.5 ml of 0.95% sodium citrate solution in small siliconised glass dishes. Individual colonies are then disaggregated under × 40 magnifications using an orally-controlled micropipette. The resulting suspension is then trans-ferred to 0.5 ml glass tubes and processed in the conventional manner with final spreading onto warmed slides from a 45% aqueous acetic acid sus-pension. This procedure, though not eliminating the agar, frees individual cells and disperses the agar over the entire slide. Staining is carried out with Giemsa which differentially stains metaphase figures but not the surrounding agar.

Radiation-induced chromosome markers develop as a consequence of alteration and rearrangement of the normal chromosome complement in-duced by high doses of irradiation. The unique combination of breakages, translocations and rearrangements of chromosomes initiated in a single cell provides a characteristic marker for all subsequent progeny of that cell and has proved invaluable in determining the differentiating capacity of single stem cells.

The procedure involves administration of near-lethal doses of irradiation to mice and rats. Chromosome analysis can then be performed on the haemopoietic tissue of any animals surviving 30–60 days, in a search for a 'clone' of cells common to the different tissues and carrying a unique com-bination of marker chromosomes. Difficulty arises with animal survival since high mortality is a necessary consequence of the high doses of irradiation. Grafting marrow from primary irradiated donors to a second group of lethally-irradiated recipients is one procedure for selecting and expanding chromosome-marked clones but here also, transfer of low numbers of mar-row cells results in poor survival. A two-stage technique which overcomes the survival difficulty yet generates haemopoietic cells with characteristic chromosome markers was described by Wu et al. (1967). In this method 850 rads of gamma radiation are administered to mice to generate chromo-somally-marked cells. Marrow cells from such mice are then injected at, or near, limiting dilutions, into groups of unirradiated, genetically anaemic mice of the genotype W/W^v. These recipients have a stem cell defect but support the growth of normal stem cells and the haemopoietic tissues of such mice are repopulated by marrow grafts too small to permit survival of heavily-irradiated mice. After 2 months the recipient's tissues are sampled for the presence of cells with abnormal karyotype, and, if found, the marrow can then be retransplanted into heavily-irradiated recipient mice where spleen colonies, and ultimately all the haemopoietic cell populations in the animal can be analysed for chromosome markers.

2.9 The use of antigenic markers

As was mentioned above, karyotypic identification of cells is only possible when cells are in mitosis and this approach cannot identify non-cycling cells or non-dividing mature cells. If specific blood cells could be shown to possess distinctive antigens, it should be possible to identify non-dividing cells of these classes in mixed populations of haemopoietic cells. Such an approach would be of great value in analysing cell migration streams and in determining the interrelationship between different cell classes. An even more obvious use of discriminatory antisera is in animals containing foreign grafted haemopoietic cells e.g. allogeneic or xenogeneic cells. In these latter situations extensive use has been made of specific antisera either to identify or to selectively kill chimaeric haemopoietic cells.

The use of antisera against antigens specific for a particular organ or blood cell class is still in its earliest stages. Most progress has been made with antigens characteristic of thymic lymphoid cells. In certain mouse strains, thymic lymphoid cells exhibit distinctive TL antigens which are absent from other lymphoid cells (Boyse et al. 1965). This antigenic marker has allowed an analysis of the migration of thymus-derived cells and the role of the thymus microenvironment in inducing the development of this antigen (Schlesinger 1970). Similar studies have been performed using the theta (θ) alloantigen described by Reif and Allen (1964). This antigen is not specific for thymic lymphoid cells being present also in the brain, but θ antibodies are more cytotoxic for thymic lymphoid cells than spleen or lymph node lymphocytes, apparently killing only thymus-derived cells in the latter populations (Raff 1969; Schlesinger and Yron 1970). Another antigen, the Ly-antigen described by Boyse et al. (1968) also appears to allow thymic lymphocytes to be discriminated from other lymphoid cells. H-2 alloantigens offer an additional means of discriminating between thymic lymphocytes and other lymphocytes, being present in higher amounts in the latter cells (Boyse and Old 1969).

Recently, it has been demonstrated by Takahashi et al. (1970) that immuno-globulin-forming normal and neoplastic cells can be distinguished from lymphoid cells, the former cells lacking TL, θ and Ly antigens but exhibiting a distinctive PC alloantigen.

Numerous investigators have prepared antisera in foreign species against semi-purified preparations of lymphocytes, granulocytes, macrophages, red cells and platelets. Such antisera have been used chiefly to produce acute depletion of the respective mature blood cells as a tool for investigating the response of the haemopoietic tissues during the regenerative period. Refinements of this general approach may ultimately allow the selective destruction of specific progenitor cells and an investigation of the inter-relationships between stem cells and progenitor cells.

2.10 Production of natural and artificial chimaeras

A chimaera has been defined as '... an organism whose cells derive from two or more distinct zygote lineages...' (Anderson et al. 1951), and is not synonymous with a mosaic, defined by the same authors as '... formed of the cells of a single zygote lineage'. Chimaeras, both natural and artificial, have been of immense value to experimental haematology, since the coexistence of genotypically distinct cell populations in the one individual has permitted analysis of haemopoietic cell differentiation potentials and cell migration streams.

Haemopoietic chimaerism occurs naturally in many species and is at-tributed to exchange of circulating stem cells between dizygotic twins united *in utero* by a placental vascular anastomosis. Unfortunately such experiments of nature cannot be predicted (though some species such as the marmoset have a very high incidence of natural chimaerism) nor can they be adequately controlled since the onset, magnitude and duration of vascular union is unknown. For this reason, techniques for artificial pro-duction of vascular anastomosis between pairs of embryonic or adult animals (parabiosis) have been developed.

Adult mice are parabiosed simply by suturing together cut skin edges along a line from the shoulder to the hip with several stronger holding sutures between the muscles of the shoulder and hip. The method relies entirely on the body's capacity to revascularise across cut surfaces and while it has proved remarkably successful in investigating migration streams of haemopoietic cells, a number of drawbacks must be recognised. The investigator has no control over subsequent events and has no guarantee that successfully united animals will be entirely uniform – particularly re-garding the volume of blood flow across the union. It must be assumed that the interchange of blood between the two members will always be limited in relation to the total cardiac output which probably means that if one member has a high blood level of a hormone or humoral regulator, a gradient will exist across the parabiotic union. A major difficulty that has been underestimated in the investigation of the adult parabiotic state is the presence of stress – at least in the initial weeks. According to how responsive the haemopoietic organs are to stress, there will be a correspondingly major or minor fluctuation in the total numbers, composition and mitotic activity of various haemopoietic populations. Following parabiotic union of adult mice, the thymus undergoes severe weight loss followed by a fairly complete regeneration and similar changes of lesser degree almost certainly occur in the cortisone-sensitive organs such as the lymph nodes and bone marrow. For these reasons the data from an analysis of parabiotic animals cannot really be regarded as being fully valid for an intact animal, a reservation which has to be applied to almost all other methods of introducing identifiable haemopoietic cells into an animal. Whenever there is a significant component of involution and tissue regeneration it is inevitable that these processes will exaggerate the magnitude of cell migration streams and repopulation processes which presumably occur continuously but at a lower level in the normal animal.

These problems were seen in extreme form in this laboratory when attempts were made to study behaviour of young and old C57BL mice joined in parabiosis. These attempts involved the use of animals with differing body weights, the old animals being considerably smaller than the young. Almost without exception the old partner fared badly with a fate ranging from having obvious and progressive stress to actual death. Under such circumstances, conclusions drawn from the behaviour of young haemopoietic cells in the old partners would almost certainly have been invalid.

The technique of chick embryo parabiosis which results in haemopoietic chimaerism, was developed by Hasek (1953) and modified by Moore and Owen (1965). Fertile eggs between 6–11 days of incubation are transilluminated (candled) and the most vascular region of the chorioallantoic membrane (CAM) identified. A small hole is then made through the shell into the air space, and a small triangle is cut through the shell overlying the most vascular region of the CAM. Great care must be taken when cutting and removing the triangle of shell so as not to inadvertently penetrate the shell membrane and damage the underlying CAM. A small drop of balanced salt solution is then placed on the exposed shell membrane which is then torn with the tip of a fine needle. When suction is applied to the air space, the fluid is drawn through the tear in the shell membrane and this produces a collapse of the CAM and an artificial air space results. Circular holes 0.5–1 cm in diameter can then be cut through the shell over the artificial air space without danger of damage to the CAM. Pairs of eggs of similar size and with matching holes can then be brought together, as shown in Figure 2.7. When the holes are aligned the CAM's bulge slightly out of the hole and make contact. The pairs of eggs can then be sealed together around the circumference of the holes with paraffin wax and returned to the incubator (Figure 2.8). Vascular anastomosis rapidly develops between the chorioallantoic blood vessels of the partner embryos and produces both immunological tolerance and haemopoietic chimaerism in the chickens hatching after a period of embryonic parabiosis.

A new technique (Moore and Owen 1967) was developed to produce embryonic vascular anastomosis even earlier than achieved with the above procedure. With this method, embryos of 4–5 days incubation can be parabiosed. Eggs are held horizontally in a fixed position in egg trays on the first day of incubation and by the 4th–5th day the developing area vasculosa and yolk sac have risen to the upper side of the egg and have become fixed. The site of fixation is marked on the shell and embryos parabiosed in the normal manner except in this situation the chorion, area vasculosa and yolk sac are brought into contact rather than the chorioallantois, which is too

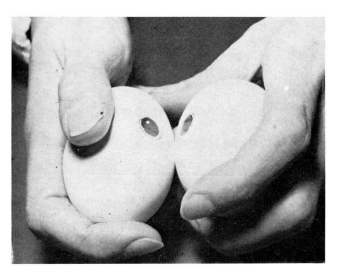

Fig. 2.7. Technique for chorioallantoic membrane parabiosis. Holes have been cut through the shells and shell membranes and eggs are being apposed. Note vascular nature of chorioallantoic membrane.

Fig. 2.8. Technique for chorioallantoic membrane parabiosis. Paired eggs have been united with wax and are in incubating position.

underdeveloped at this early stage. Vascular anastomosis rapidly develops between yolk sac blood vessels, and a typical pair of parabiosed embryos united by such a yolk sac union is shown in Figure 2.9.

A new and potentially valuable technique for production of chimaeras is that of aggregation of blastomeres of two mouse embryos of different geno-type into a single cluster and transfer of the developing aggregates to the uterus of a surrogate mother. The adult progeny of this manipulation are individuals that are potentially chimaeric in all tissues of the body and are called tetraparental or 'allophenic' mice. Through the incorporation of appropriate genetic markers into such mice, many new approaches to the analysis of haemopoietic problems are now possible. Methods for mouse embryo culture and production of such mice have been reported in the literature (Tarkowski 1961; Mintz 1964, 1965, 1967; Mystkowska and Tarkowski 1968; Biggers et al. 1969). The most effective method consists of removal of fertilised mouse eggs at the 4–8 cell stage of development from the oviducts of pregnant females. The accurate staging of fertilised eggs is assisted by hormone-induced ovulation before mating in the female. The zona pellucida surrounding each eggs at this stage, is removed by treatment with the enzyme pronase. Following a series of washing steps, pairs of eggs of genetically distinct strains are placed in contact in droplets of a defined culture medium with a high lactate and pyruvate concentration, contained under mineral oil (Biggers et al. 1969). Eggs begin to fuse after 4–6 hours

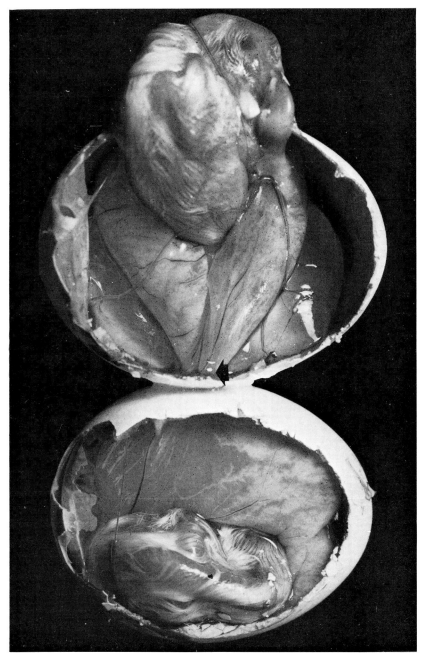

Fig. 2.9.   Pair of 14-day chick embryos with yolk sacs parabiosed at 4 days. Yolk sac and vessels can be seen at parabiotic union (arrow). (From Moore and Owen 1967, reproduced by permission of J. Exp. Med).

Fig. 2.10. Giant blastocyst formed by fusion of fertilised eggs from two genetically distinct strains of mice. × 36.

in culture and after 24–28 hours a single, giant blastocyst is produced (Figure 2.10). The mosaic blastocysts are then implanted into the uterus of a mouse rendered pseudopregnant by mating with a vasectomised male. The chimaeric (or allophenic) products of this procedure are readily identified, if a pigmentation marker is present in the system, by the presence of mixed hair colouring which produces a characteristic banded or striped appearance (Figure 2.11). Such mice differ from the usual form of haemopoietic chimaera since not only do they possess a mixed population of haemopoietic cells but also are chimaeric in the populations of cells which create the unique microenvironment within the various haemopoietic organs.

Permanent haemopoietic chimaeras can be produced by injection of haemopoietic cells, e.g. from spleen, marrow or foetal liver, into lethally-irradiated recipients. Chimaerism can be produced in many species with this

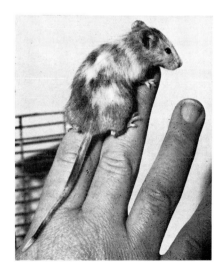

Fig. 2.11. An allophenic mouse produced by fusion of fertilised eggs from the strains (BALB/c × 129)F_1 and (C57BL × CBAT6T6)F_1.

procedure but survival of the recipients and stability of chimaerism are influenced by many factors (see Micklem and Loutit 1966). Frequently the complication of lethal gut damage sets an upper limit to the radiation dose, which consequently may be insufficient to produce complete haemopoietic aplasia and only partial chimaerism results. This difficulty is particularly relevant in allogeneic tissue grafting since residual host immunological competence results in graft rejection, which can be partially overcome by increasing the number of cells injected. This system is further complicated if the injected haemopoietic cells can react immunologically against the host causing secondary disease of varying severity. Under these conditions the behaviour of the haemopoietic cells may be quite abnormal.

Cytotoxic drug treatment has been used in place of radiation to prepare recipients for haemopoietic grafting. A combination of cyclophosphamide (350 mg/kg) and busulphan (50 mg/kg) treatment of mice, followed by marrow grafting, results in haemopoietic chimaerism. Here, allogeneic grafts are as efficient as syngeneic in repopulating the depleted haemopoietic tissue (Sensenbrenner et al. 1968).

Studies on the repopulation by haemopoietic cells of irradiated or drug-depleted animals and organ grafts all suffer from one serious defect. Haemopoietic cells are studied in a situation involving a greater or lesser degree of regeneration of haemopoietic tissue. There are reasons for suspecting that some of the information obtained may not be strictly relevant to a stable haemopoietic system as is present in an adult animal. These reservations will be discussed at length later, but they are sufficiently strong to warrant a search for some alternative system for introducing identifiable haemopoietic cells into an otherwise intact animal so that their subsequent behaviour can be compared with that in the experimental systems which have previously been used.

One possible approach which has not been exploited fully to date is the introduction of haemopoietic cells into neonatal animals. The very young animal increases in size at a very rapid rate and the total mass of haemopoietic tissue must similarly be increased very rapidly. Under such conditions, the body may exploit every available stem or haemopoietic cell, including cells introduced into the animal. This situation is less likely to occur in an adult animal with haemopoietic organs of stable size even though there is a continuous turnover of haemopoietic cells in these organs.

Injection of adult AKR spleen cells into neonatal AKR F_1 hybrid mice has been shown to result in permanent chimaeras with AKR cells being demonstrable up to one year later in the thymus, when thymic lymphomas develop from such cells (Metcalf 1963a). The potential disadvantage of parental cells in such a system is the risk of inducing graft-vs.-host disease but this can be largely avoided by careful attention to cell doses, the route of injection and the age at injection. Such disadvantages of course do not apply to the injection of CBA T6T6 cells into syngeneic neonatal CBA mice and this system seems worthy of investigation as a closer approach to a physiological system for studying the behaviour of haemopoietic cells in normal animals.

A similar situation may apply in old age, where at least in some mouse strains deficiencies of haemopoietic cells seem to occur. Here, however, the inability of some ageing organs to support actively proliferating haemopoietic cells may vitiate such attempts.

2.11 Organ grafting

The small size of the blood vessels of haemopoietic organs in the mouse and rat prevents vascular anastomotic-type organ grafting in what otherwise would be a perfectly suitable situation. This fact has limited the usefulness of grafts of intact haemopoietic organs from adult animals. The situation with neonatal and embryonic organs is more satisfactory as the small size of these organs makes it possible for grafted organs to obtain adequate vascularisation following invasion of the graft by small vessels from the periphery. Thus it is not only feasible, but technically very simple, to graft a whole day-old thymus, spleen or bone to recipient mice of any age. However, one penalty is paid for the dependence of the graft on active vascularisation by the host. There is an inevitable initial period of necrosis in the graft during which many haemopoietic cells die and, more importantly, during which the remainder may suffer subtle injury affecting their subsequent proliferative capacity and longevity.

Haemopoietic organ grafts can be placed in almost any site in the body, but the commonly used sites are the subcutaneous tissues, peritoneal cavity, spleen, anterior chamber of the eye and the subcapsular space of the kidney. So far as can be determined, grafts in all sites behave uniformly with the possible exception of grafts in the anterior chamber of the eye, where vascular connections with the body may, or may not, develop.

Of the various sites used the subcapsular space of the kidney is superior to all others in terms of the percent incidence of successful grafts, graft growth rate and shortness of the initial anoxic necrotic phase (Figure 2.12). This is

Fig. 2.12. A neonatal thymus graft 4 weeks after implantation under the kidney capsule.

presumably because of the relatively rich vascular network reaching the subcapsular space from the glomerular vessels.

For reasons to be discussed later the growth of thymus, spleen and bone marrow grafts is affected by the age of the donor and by far the most satisfactory donor is the neonatal animal – being the youngest animal readily available in which the organs have the full range of different haemopoietic cells. The age of the recipient is of less importance, and virtually any adult animal will support good graft growth. In the special case of the spleen, spleen graft growth is much greater if the host spleen is removed prior to grafting (Metcalf 1963b).

Neonatal organs are grafted intact and there is no need to mince the tissue to provide a greater surface area for vascularisation. Grafts can be introduced to the required site with a blunt trocar and cannula or more simply by placing them in this location with non-toothed forceps.

The extreme resistance of mice and rats to local infections makes it possible to carry out successful grafting with a clean but not sterile technique and without antibiotic cover. The hair is simply wet with 70% alcohol and the skin opened using boiled instruments on a clean work area. For grafts under the kidney capsule the kidney is exposed through the lateral abdominal wall and a small cut is made in the capsule over the lower pole of the kidney. A trocar is slid under the capsule to deposit the graft over the outer and upper aspects of the kidney. No closure of the capsule and the abdominal wall is required and the skin incision is closed with Michel clips.

For thymus and spleen grafts, the cycle of initial neocrosis and regeneration takes 1–2 weeks for grafts under the kidney capsule and 2–3 weeks for subcutaneous grafts. This period involves severe disruption of the internal architecture of the organ followed by regeneration of the haemopoietic tissues from stem cells entering the graft from the host. This repopulation by host cells is complete by 21–35 days, and from that time onwards all organ grafts are chimaeric organs being composed of a framework of supporting tissue derived from the graft and haemopoietic cells derived from the host (Metcalf and Wakonig-Vaartaja 1964; Metcalf et al. 1965).

2.12 Organ-culture techniques

Haemopoietic cells have been cultured *in vitro* both as dispersed cell cultures or as intact organs or organ fragments. In general, dispersed cell cultures have not proved successful in retaining haemopoietic functional differentiation, though considerable success has been reported in obtaining both primary and secondary immune responses *in vitro* (Mischell and Dutton 1967; Marbrook 1967; Diener and Armstrong 1967). Peripheral blood lymphocytes are also routinely cultured, either in the mixed lymphocyte reaction (Bach and Hirschhorn 1964) or with phytohaemagglutinin (Hungerford et al. 1959) both blast transformation and active proliferation is obtained over a period of 4–6 days. It is probable that the haemopoietic stroma or microenvironment is vital for normal haemopoietic differentiation, and some degree of organisation is necessary before continuing haemopoiesis can be obtained *in vitro*. To some extent, organisation does develop *in vitro* with dispersed cell cultures since cells aggregate within a few hours and distinct 'micro-organs' develop in static culture.

The organ-culture system described by Auerbach (Auerbach 1961; Globerson and Auerbach 1966, 1967) has proved particularly successful for culture of both embryonic and postnatal haemopoietic tissues and allows both growth, differentiation and function for a period of 1–2 weeks. With this method, small fragments of organs 0.2–0.3 mm thick and 0.5–1 mm^2 surface area (or indeed whole organs from early embryos) are explanted onto the surface of millipore filter-well assemblies. The filter-wells are prepared by glueing a TH millipore filter (pore size 0.45 μ, 25 μ thick) to the underside of a hole drilled through a thin plastic strip, creating a chamber 3 mm in diameter and 1 mm deep. The filter-well strip is then placed across the central well of a plastic organ culture dish (FALCON 3037) containing 1 ml of culture medium (Figure 2.13). The medium used in most studies is Eagle's basal medium supplemented with 10% horse serum and 5% 9-day chick embryo extract. For culture of certain tissues such as foetal liver, or yolk sac, foetal calf serum is more effective than horse serum and the chick embryo extract supplement may be reduced (Moore and Metcalf 1970). Cell and tissue interactions may also be investigated in this system using transfilter combination of tissues with chick plasma fixing the tissues in position.

Fig. 2.13.   Organ culture of a spleen fragment in a millipore filter-well assembly.

Since the filters are impermeable to cells, interaction between tissues in transfilter combinations is attributed to diffusible factors or inducing agents passing between the tissues. Living tissues may be observed *in situ* throughout the course of culture by transillumination. Histological preparations may be prepared by removing the filter membrane with tissue intact and either clearing and mounting the filter, or paraffin-embedding and sectioning the preparation.

2.13 Cell-separation techniques

For more precise evaluation of the functional capacity of various types of cells, it has been necessary to devise techniques for separating purified cell populations from the complex cell mixtures found in haemopoietic tissues. Cells may be separated on the basis of functional properties such as adherence capacity or on physical parameters such as size or density.

2.13.1 Equilibrium density-gradient separation

Cells, centrifuged in a density gradient, move into regions corresponding to their buoyant density and remain there. The development of a reproducible cell-separation procedure based on this phenomenon, has not been without its difficulties. The major technical difficulty has been the choice of gradient material, particularly since cell viability and constant osmotic pressure must be maintained throughout the gradient. For this reason, high molecular weight substances with a negligible osmotic pressure contribution must be used in an isotonic salt solution. Bovine serum albumin has been most frequently used in this technique but care must first be taken to remove salt contamination of commercial preparations by exhaustive dialysis. A further problem that arises, particularly when high molecular weight suspension media are used, is the tendency for cells to aggregate. This is overcome by lowering the pH of the albumin to 5.1, which surprisingly does not affect either the physical properties or biological activity of the cells. Cells are dispersed within the gradient rather than as a narrow zone at the top and this, together with the use of sufficiently high centrifugal forces to oppose the interaction between cells differing in density, further diminishes the risk of cell aggregation.

The most effective and standardised procedure for cell density separation has been developed by Shortman and detailed methodology is reported by Shortman (1968, 1969a). Briefly, between 10^7–10^9 cells are dispersed in a 13 ml volume linear gradient of bovine serum albumin (15–28 % BSA w/w) in balanced salt solution at pH 5.1. The gradient is generated by mixing dense albumin containing the cells, with a light density albumin solution in a mixing chamber and using a peristaltic pump to provide an outlet rate double the input rate. The linear gradient is run into nitrocellulose tubes containing a small quantity of 40% albumin which acts as a cushion. The tube is then spun at 4000 g for 45 min in a refrigerated centrifuge. Up to 30 fractions may then be collected from the top of the tube by upward displacement of the gradient. Three μl samples of each fraction are taken for density determinations which are carried out in a linear density gradient of bromobenzene and petroleum spirit calibrated with standard albumin solutions of known density.

The density distribution profile for any particular morphologically or functionally distinct population of cells can then be determined, with cells per density increment plotted against density and the curves normalised so that the peak value is 100%. The error in density measurement on the horizontal axis is negligible ($\pm$ 0.00006 g/cm^3 SD). The error in the vertical axis is $\pm$ 5% (SD) of the value at any particular point, and is a composite of errors in density measurement, fraction volume measurements and total

cell counts. The reproducibility of density peaks in separate density estimations on the same cell population or the same individual on separate
occasions is $\pm$ 0.0003 g/cm^3 or about $\frac{1}{4}$ of an average size fraction. Cell
recovery has averaged approximately 90% and recovery of biological activity
around 75% in numerous experiments on density separation of various
haemopoietic cell populations.

2.13.2 *Purification of erythroid cells by pH-induced density changes*

Density separation distinguishes between cells on the basis of physical
rather than functional differences, but in the case of erythroid cells, certain
density characteristics are directly related to a specific functional property.
Erythrocytes swell with decreasing pH of the suspending media. This is a
direct consequence of a specialised property of the erythrocyte membrane
and is related to the respiratory function of the cell. As pH is lowered, cell
protein is protonated and chloride anions enter the cell. The resulting increase in osmotic pressure causes reversible swelling of the erythrocyte
with change in both volume and density (Legge and Shortman 1968). Mouse
bone-marrow erythroid cells develop the ability to swell with pH reduction
at a stage when the cells are still nucleated. This property is displayed by
most small erythroblasts, and a separation procedure has been devised to
take advantage of this property (Shortman and Seligman 1969). In this
procedure bone marrow cells are first centrifuged in an albumin density
gradient at neutral pH, and regions containing erythroid cells are collected
and the recovered cells redistributed in a second albumin gradient run at
acid pH. The erythroid cells show a specific density shift which removes
them from contaminating cell populations and preparations containing
90–97% erythroblasts may be obtained by this technique.

2.13.3 *Velocity sedimentation separation*

Cell sedimentation at unit gravity in a density-stabilised system of hori-
zontally-flowing liquid layers has been used to achieve separation of granulocytic from erythroid cells (Mel et al. 1965). Improved resolution of cell
populations was obtained by Peterson and Evans (1967), who employed
velocity sedimentation in chambers containing a linear sucrose gradient.
The sucrose gradient was introduced into a sedimentation chamber and the
sample of cells introduced as a thin layer in the gradient. The cell sample is
rapidly lifted up the chamber by incoming sucrose and the cells fall through

the rising liquid and are collected in order of increasing sedimentation rate from the top of the chamber.

A further modification of the technique was described by Miller and Phillips (1969) and used by Worton et al. (1969) for separation of different subpopulations of haemopoietic stem cells. In this procedure, marrow cells suspended in 5% foetal calf serum (FCS) and culture medium are introduced under 30 ml of culture medium into the base of a cylindrical glass chamber 11.3 cm in diameter and 7 cm high with a conical base tapering to a 2 mm diameter opening at the bottom. A linear 15–30% FCS gradient of 500 ml is then introduced under the cell layer. Cells are allowed to sediment through the FCS gradient for $3\frac{1}{2}$ hours and the chamber then drained and the gradient is collected in 15 ml fractions.

The rate at which cells sediment in this system is related to the volume of the cell, with large cells sedimenting more rapidly than small cells. There is, however, a small dependence on cell density, and for this reason it is usual to express the cell distribution profiles in relationship to velocity rate in mm/hour rather than volume.

2.13.4 Two-dimensional cell separation

Since equilibrium density gradient and velocity sedimentation separation techniques resolve complex cell populations on the basis of two distinct physical characteristics (density and volume) then combination of the two procedures should produce greater resolution of heterogeneity than either alone. Haskill and Moore (1970) have applied such a two-stage separation to resolve differences between embryonic and adult haemopoietic stem cells. In this system haemopoietic cells of adult and embryonic origin were first separated in BSA density gradients, and fractions from both populations, containing cells of the same density, were then separated by velocity sedimentation into further subpopulations. Though stem cells were of the same density, the velocity profiles showed clear differences between the adult and embryonic stem cells, and since the small density component of the velocity sedimentation procedure was eliminated, the stem cells could be compared directly in terms of cell volumes.

2.13.5 Separation of cells using glass-bead columns

Siliconised glass-bead columns can be used to separate cells on the basis of size filtration with trapping of larger cells. They can also be used to separate cells on the basis of a temperature-dependent 'active adherence' of phago-cytic cells or a temperature-independent selective trapping by physical adherence. The prototype technique to exploit the adherence effect of glass bead, glass wool or nylon columns was that of Rabinowitz (1964) and was used to separate adherent cells from blood. In a modification of this tech-nique, Shortman (1969b) and Shortman et al. (1970) developed an active adherence column that minimized size filtration and selective trapping by physical adherence and is capable of producing, in less than 10 min, a preparation of mouse spleen lymphocytes > 500-fold depleted of active macrophages and 50-fold depleted of active polymorphs with good overall cell recovery and viability. The adherence column is prepared by introducing siliconised glass beads of 300–600 μ diameter (median diameter 450 μ) into water-jacketed columns 2.4 cm diameter and 14 cm high. Before use, the columns are brought to 37°C equilibrium and washed with medium 199 to pH equilibrium. The column is then washed through with 60% foetal calf serum and medium and then just before the cells are applied, 2 ml of 60% mouse serum and medium is run onto the column. 10^8–10^9 cells suspended in 4–5 ml of 50% mouse serum, and medium is then run onto the column followed by an equal volume of 50% mouse serum and medium. The cells are then washed through the column with one column of 25% mouse serum and medium and gentle stirring of the upper few millimetres of column beads to prevent blockage. The flow rate is adjusted so that the residence time for the main band of cells in the column is 8–10 min.

Four fractions are collected from the column: fraction I, the initial band of non-adherent cells; fraction II, the intermediate fraction off the column prior to elution with EDTA; fraction III, the adherent cells released by washing through the column with EDTA solution in media + 2% serum; and fraction IV, the cells released by combined EDTA washing and column disruption.

A different form of glass bead column separation has also been used to separate purified small lymphocytes from spleen cell suspensions (Shortman 1969b, 1966). This application of the size filtration properties of glass-bead columns employs columns 3.7 cm in diameter × 4 cm high, loosely packed with small (105–150 μ) glass beads maintained at 5–7°C. Cells are passed through such a column with a 10–15-min residence time, and the recovered cells then passed through a second column of smaller (60–90 μ) beads under similar conditions though with a more prolonged residence on the column (25–30 min). The final effluent is a size-filtered population of small lympho-cytes.

References

Anderson, D., R. E. Billingham, G. H. Lampkin and P. B. Medawar, 1951, Heredity Lond. *5*, 379.

Armstrong, W. D. and E. Diener, 1969, J. Exp. Med. *129*, 371.

Athens, J. W., 1969, Granulocyte kinetics in health and disease. In: Human tumor cell kinetics, edited by S. Perry. National Cancer Institute Monograph 30, p. 135.

Auerbach, R., 1961, Develop. Biol. *3*, 336.

Bach, F. and K. Hirschhorn, 1964, Science *143*, 813.

Becker, A. J., E. A. McCulloch, L. Siminovitch, and J. E. Till, 1965, Blood *26*, 296.

Bennett, M. and G. Cudkowicz, 1967, Functional and morphological characterization of stem cells: The unipotential role of 'lymphocytes' of mouse marrow. In: The lymphocyte in immunology and haemopoiesis, edited by J. M. Yoffey. London, Edward Arnold Ltd., p. 183.

Biggers, J. D., W. K. Whitten, and D. C. Wittingham, 1969, The culture of mouse embryos in vitro. In: Methods in mammalian embryology, edited by J. C. Daniel. New York, W. H. Freeman (in press).

Blackett, N. M., P. J. Roylance, and K. Adams, 1964, Brit. J. Haemat. *10*, 453.

Boyse, E. A. and L. J. Old, 1969, Ann. Rev. Genet. *3*, 269.

Boyse, E. A., L. J. Old, and E. Stockert, 1965, The TL (thymus leukemia) antigen: A review. In IV Internatl. Symposium Immunopathology, edited by P. Grabar and P. A. Miescher. Basel, Schwabe and Co., p. 23.

Boyse, E. A., M. Miyazawa, T. Aoki, and L. J. Old, 1968, Proc. Roy. Soc. *B. 170*, 175.

Bradley, T. R. and D. Metcalf, 1966, Aust. J. Exp. Biol. Med. *44*, 287.

Bradley, T. R. and M. A. Sumner, 1968, Aust. J. Exp. Biol. Med. *46*, 607.

Bruce, W. R. and B. E. Meeker, 1965, J. Nat. Cancer Inst. *34*, 849.

Byrt, P. and G. L. Ada, 1969, Immunology *17*, 501.

Chan, S. H., D. Metcalf and E. R. Stanley, 1970, Brit. J. Haematol. *20*, 329.

Clarkson, B. D., 1969, Review of recent studies of cellular proliferation in acute leukemia. In: Human tumor cell kinetics, edited by S. Perry. National Cancer Institute Monograph 30, p. 81.

Creasy, W. A. and M. E. Markiw, 1964, Biochem. Biophys. Acta *87*, 601.

Cronkite, E. P., 1969, Kinetics of granulopoiesis. In: Human tumor cell kinetics, edited by S. Perry. National Cancer Institute Monograph 30, p. 51.

Cudkowicz, G., A. C. Upton, L. H. Smith, D. G. Gosslee, and W. L. Hughes, 1964, Ann. N.Y. Acad. Sci. *114*, 571.

Cunningham, A. J. and Λ. Szenberg, 1968, Immunol. *14*, 599.

Diener, E., 1968, J. Immunol. *100*, 1062.

Diener, E. and W. D. Armstrong, 1967, Lancet *2*, 1281.

Firket, H. and W. G. Verly, 1958, Nature *181*, 274.

Ford, C. E., 1966, The use of chromosome markers. Appendix in Micklem and Loutit, (1966).

Ford, C. E. and J. L. Hamerton, 1956, Stain Technol. *31*, 247.

Foster, R., D. Metcalf, W. A. Robinson, and T. R. Bradley, 1968, Brit. J. Haematol. *15*, 147.

Globerson, A. and R. Auerbach, 1966, J. Exp. Med. *124*, 1001.

Globerson, A. and R. Auerbach, 1967, J. Exp. Med. *126*, 223.

Gurney, C. W., L. G. Lajtha, and R. Oliver, 1962, Brit. J. Haemat. *8*, 461.

Hasek, M., 1953, Ceskoslov. Biol. *2*, 25.

Haskill, J. S. and M. A. S. Moore, 1970, Nature *226*, 853.

Hodgson, G., 1967, Proc. Soc. Exp. Biol. Med. *125*, 1206.

Hodgson, G. and I. Eskuche, 1968, Ann. N.Y. Acad. Sci. *149*, 230.

Hodgson, G. S., 1962, Acta Physiol. Lat. Amer. *12*, 365.

Hughes, W. L., V. P. Bond, G. Brecher, E. P. Cronkite, R. B. Painter, H. Quastler, and F. G. Sherman, 1958, Proc. Natl. Acad. Sci. *44*, 476.

Hungerford, D. A., A. J. Donnelly, P. C. Nowell, and S. Beck, 1959, Amer. J. Human Genet. *11*, 215.

Ichikawa, Y., D. H. Pluznik, and L. Sachs, 1966, Proc. Natl. Acad. Sci. *56*, 488.

Ingraham, J. S. and A. Bussard, 1964, J. Exp. Med. *119*, 667.

Jacobson, L. O., E. Goldwasser, and C. W. Gurney, 1959, Control of red cell formation. In: The kinetics of cellular proliferation, edited by F. Stohlman Jr. New York, Grune and Stratton, p. 344.

Jerne, N. K. and A. A. Nordin, 1963, Science *140*, 405.

Kennedy, J. C., L. Siminovitch, J. E. Till, and E. A. McCulloch, 1965, Proc. Soc. Exp. Biol. Med. *120*, 868.

Kennedy, J. C., J. E. Till, L. Siminovitch, and E. A. McCulloch, 1966, J. Immunol. *96*, 973.

Krakoff, I. H., N. C. Brown, and P. Reichard, 1968, Cancer Res. *28*, 1559.

Lajtha, L. G., L. V. Pozzi, R. Schofield, and M. Fox, 1969, Cell Tissue Kinet. *2*, 39.

Legge, D. G. and K. Shortman, 1968, Brit. J. Haematol. *14*, 323.

Madoc-Jones, H. and F. Mauro, 1968, J. Cell. Physiol. *72*, 185.

Malawista, S. E., H. Sato, and K. G. Bensch, 1968, Science *160*, 770.

Marbrook, J., 1967, Lancet *2*, 1279.

Mel, H. C., L. T. Mitchell, and B. Thorell, 1965, Blood *25*, 63.

Metcalf, D., 1963a, Cancer Res. *23*, 1774.

Metcalf, D., 1963b, Aust. J. Exp. Biol. Med. Sci. *41*, 51.

Metcalf, D., 1969, J. Cell. Physiol. *74*, 323.

Metcalf, D., 1970, J. Cell. Physiol. *76*, 89.

Metcalf, D. and M. Brumby, 1966, J. Cell. Physiol. *67*, Suppl. 1, 149.

Metcalf, D. and R. Wakonig-Vaartaja, 1964, Proc. Soc. Exp. Biol. Med. *115*, 731.

Metcalf, D. and M. Wiadrowski, 1966, Cancer Res. *26*, 483.

Metcalf, D., R. Wakonig-Vaartaja, and T. R. Bradley, 1965, Aust. J. Exp. Biol. Med. Sci. *43*, 17.

Metcalf, D., M. A. S. Moore, and N. L. Warner, 1969, J. Natl. Cancer Inst. *43*, 983.

Micklem, H. S. and J. F. Loutit, 1966, Tissue grafting and radiation. New York, Academic Press.

Miller, R. G. and R. A. Phillips, 1969, J. Cell. Physiol. *73*, 191.

Mintz, B., 1964, J. Exp. Zool. *157*, 273.

Mintz, B., 1965, Science *148*, 1232.

Mintz, B., 1967, Mammalian embryo culture. In: Methods in developmental biology, edited by F. Wilt and N. Wessells. New York, T. Y. Cromwell Co., p. 379.

Mischell, R. I. and R. W. Dutton, 1967, J. Exp. Med. *126*, 423.

Mitchell, J., W. McDonald, and G. J. V. Nossal, 1963, Aust. J. Exp. Biol. Med. Sci. *41*, 411.

Moore, M. A. S. and D. Metcalf, 1970, Brit. J. Haemat. *18*, 279.

Moore, M. A. S. and J. J. T. Owen, 1965, Nature *208*, 956.

Moore, M. A. S. and J. J. T. Owen, 1967, J. Exp. Med. *126*, 715.

Morse, B. S., N. J. Rencricca, and F. Stohlman Jr., 1969, Proc. Soc. Exp. Biol. Med. *130*, 986.

Morse, B. S., N. J. Rencricca, and F. Stohlman Jr., 1970, Blood *35*, 761.

Mystkowska, E. T. and A. K. Tarkowski, 1968, J. Embryol. Exp. Morp. *20*, 33.

Naor, D. and D. Sulitzeanu, 1967, Nature *214*, 687.

Nossal, G. J. V., A. Cunningham, G. F. Mitchell, and J. F. A. P. Miller, 1968, J. Exp. Med. *128*, 839.

Owen, J. J. T., 1965, Chromosoma *16*, 601.

Papermaster, B. W., 1967, Cold Spring Harbor Symp. Quant. Biol. *32*, 447.

Peterson, E. A. and W. H. Evans, 1967, Nature *214*, 824.

Pike, B. L. and W. A. Robinson, 1970, J. Cell. Physiol. *76*, 77.

Playfair, J. H. L., B. W. Papermaster, and L. J. Cole, 1965, Science *149*, 998.

Pluznik, D. H. and L. Sachs, 1965, J. Cell. Comp. Physiol. *66*, 319.

Rabinowitz, Y., 1964, Blood *23*, 811.

Raff, M. C., 1969, Nature *224*, 378.

Reif, A. E. and J. M. V. Allen, 1964, J. Exp. Med. *120*, 413.

Robinson, W., D. Metcalf, and T. R. Bradley, 1967, J. Cell. Physiol. *69*, 83.

Rothfels, K. H. and L. Siminovitch, 1958, Stain Technol. *33*, 73.

Schlesinger, M., 1970, Prog. Exp. Tumor Res. *13*, (in press).

Schlesinger, M. and I. Yron, 1970, J. Immunol. *104*, 798.

Sensenbrenner, L. L., M. G. Beale, G. J. Elfenbein, and G. W. Santos, 1968, Exp. Hemat. *15*, 85.

Sherman, J. and R. Auerbach, 1966, Blood *27*, 371.

Shortman, K., 1966, Aust. J. Exp. Biol. Med. Sci. *44*, 271.

Shortman, K., 1968, Aust. J. Exp. Biol. Med. Sci. *46*, 375.

Shortman, K., 1969a, Equilibrium density gradient separation and analysis of lymphocyte populations. In: Modern separation methods of macromolecules and particles. Vol. 2: Progress in separation and purification, edited by T. Gerritsen. New York, Wiley-Interscience, p. 167.

Shortman, K., 1969b, The separation of lymphocyte populations on glassbead columns. In: Modern separation methods of macromolecules and particles. Vol. 2: Progress in separation and purification, edited by T. Gerritsen. New York, Wiley-Interscience, p. 91.

Shortman, K. and K. Seligman, 1969, J. Cell. Biol. *42*, 783.

Shortman, K., N. Williams, H. Jackson, P. Russell, P. Byrt, and E. Diener, 1970, J. Cell. Physiol. (in press).

Sinclair, W. K., 1965, Science *150*, 1729.

Smith, L. H., 1964, Amer. J. Physiol. *206*, 1244.

Stanley, E. R. and D. Metcalf, 1969, Aust. J. Exp. Biol. Med. Sci. *47*, 467.

Takahashi, T., L. Old, and E. A. Boyse, 1970, J. Exp. Med. *131*, 1325.

Tarkowski, A. K., 1961, Nature *190*, 857.

Till, J. E. and E. A. McCulloch, 1961, Rad. Res. *14*, 213.

Valeriote, F. A. and W. R. Bruce, 1965, J. Nat. Cancer Inst. *35*, 851.

Valeriote, F. A., W. R. Bruce, and B. E. Meeker, 1966, J. Nat. Cancer Inst. *36*, 21.

Weissman, I. L., 1967, J. Exp. Med. *126*, 291.

Welshons, W. J., B. H. Gibson, and B. J. Scandlyn, 1962, Stain Technol. *37*, 1.

Worton, R. G., E. A. McCulloch, and J. E. Till, 1969, J. Exp. Med. *130*, 91.

Wu, A. M., J. E. Till, L. Siminovitch, and E. A. McCulloch, 1967, J. Cellular Physiol. *69*, 177.

CHAPTER 3

Haemopoietic stem cells and progenitor cells

3.1 Introduction

Few fields of study in biological science have generated more controversy than that of haemopoiesis and specifically the problem of potentialities and interrelationships of the primitive haemopoietic cells. These questions have been hotly debated for over a century and the frequently opposing conclusions reached by various investigators were briefly referred to in Chapter 1. In the space of the last 10 years, reassessment of the various options has been made possible as a result of the development of techniques for the analysis of functional properties of primitive haemopoietic cells. In particular, valuable information has been obtained from such techniques as the polycythaemic mouse assay for erythropoietin-sensitive cells (Jacobson et al. 1960), the *in vivo* spleen colony (CFU) assay of Till and McCulloch (1961), the *in vitro* granulocyte-macrophage colony assay (Pluznik and Sachs 1965; Bradley and Metcalf 1966) and the focus assay for antigen-sensitive cells (Kennedy et al. 1966; Playfair et al. 1965). Such assays have broken the tyranny of classification of cells on dubious morphological criteria. This chapter will consequently review the results obtained using these new methods and an attempt will be made to present a unifying hypothesis of haemopoietic differentiation based on functional classification criteria.

3.2 In vivo colony-forming units (CFU; stem cells)

Till and McCulloch (1961) described a technique for the detection of certain primitive haemopoietic cells present in low frequency in mouse spleen and marrow. These cells have the capacity to form macroscopically visible colonies of differentiating erythroid, granulocytic or megakaryocytic cells in spleens of lethally irradiated mice and were termed '*in vivo* colony forming units (CFU)'. At that time the term 'unit' was considered preferable to 'cell' as the clonal origin of colonies had not been established and the macroscopic spleen colonies represented only a fraction of the total potential colony-forming cells present in the inoculum. Methodological details of the *in vivo* CFU assay have been given in Chapter 2.

3.2.1   Distribution of CFU's in the mouse

In vivo CFU's in adult mice are present in highest frequency in the marrow. From 5–30 CFU's per 10^5 marrow cells is the usual range observed (Barnes and Loutit 1967a; Till and McCulloch 1961; Kretchmar and Conover 1967), but considerable strain differences in the frequency of marrow CFU's have been noted (Warner and Moore 1970). Lower numbers are found in the spleen (1–3 CFU's per 10^5) (Till and McCulloch 1961; Micklem and Loutit 1966; Moore 1970). Circulating CFU's are present in the blood in small numbers, totalling 20–60 in the circulation, or 0.07–0.2 per 10^5 blood leucocytes (Barnes and Loutit 1967b; Cole and Maki 1968). A twofold diurnal variation in circulating numbers was noted by Micklem (1966), with maximum numbers in the morning and minimum in the afternoon. CFU's

TABLE 3.1

Calculated total content of CFU's in (C57BL × CBA) F_1 mice

Organ	Total CFU's	
	Neonatal mouse	Adult mouse
Bone marrow*	280	44,400
Spleen	660	7,000
Liver	2650	25
Blood	80	20
Thymus	6	5
Lymph node	—	12
Peritoneal exudate	—	8
Total	3,676	51,470

* Estimated from one femoral shaft assuming it to be 8.5% of total marrow.

are present also in peritoneal exudate cells (0.08 per 10^5 peritoneal exudate cells) (Cole 1963) but probably are not present (or at least only in very low numbers) in thymus or unstimulated lymph nodes (Goodman 1965; Micklem and Loutit 1966; Hege and Cole 1966; Mekori et al. 1965). Some typical values for the CFU content of various organs in the neonatal and young adult mouse are shown in Table 3.1. Further data on the distribution of CFU's in embryonic tissue are presented in Chapter 4. From the data in Table 3.1, an approximate calculation of CFU's in the mouse can be obtained using a seeding efficiency adjustment of 0.038 (Matioli et al. 1968). In the neonatal mouse the number is approximately 1×10^5 cells and in the young adult, approximately 1.4×10^6 cells.

3.2.2 Clonal origin of spleen colonies

The single cell origin of spleen colonies is implied by the linearity and absence of an initial threshhold of the curve relating the number of marrow cells injected to the number of colonies that develop in the spleen (Till and McCulloch 1961; McCulloch and Till 1962). Further indirect evidence was provided by the radiation survival curve of colony-forming cells which grossly resembles survival curves obtained for single cells in cell culture (Puck and Marcus 1956). More direct evidence of the clonal nature of macroscopic spleen colonies was obtained by the use of radiation-induced chromosome markers. Becker et al. (1963) generated spleen colonies with abnormal karyotypes by pre-irradiating the mice providing the bone marrow cells with 650R whole body irradiation. In some colonies uniquely abnormal karyotypes were observed and these same unique karyotypes were present in 95–99% of the metaphases obtained from 11-day colonies. This study was extended by Fowler et al. (1967) to 14-day colonies, at which stage the majority of colonies sampled would be of histologically mixed type. Eighty-three to 98% of mitoses were found to be of the same unique type in any one colony. However, such studies do not conclusively prove the clonal origin of mixed colonies as the small percentage of dividing cells (2–17%) of different karyotype from the majority would be sufficient to account for a morphologically different cell population. Proof of the clonal nature of mixed colonies was provided by Wu et al. (1967) using unirradiated W/W^v anaemic mice as recipients for irradiated bone-marrow cells. Marrow cells of recipients bearing a unique radiation-induced karyotype were then injected in low numbers into irradiated recipients and karyotypic studies made on 14-day colonies in conjunction with ^{55}Fe autoradiography and peroxidase staining.

Ninety-one to 100% of mitoses were found to be of unique type in any one colony and 10 out of 12 colonies showed the same unique marker in both ^{55}Fe-labelled (erythroid) and peroxidase positive (granulocytic) meta-phases.

Criticism of the above evidence can be directed at the normality of the colonies studied in so far as these were initiated by cells with radiation-induced damage manifest by chromosome rearrangement. Welshons (1964) used a translocation chromosome marker and observed no colonies with mixed karyotype following injection of a mixture of unirradiated normal and translocation-marked marrow cells. In contrast, Lewis et al (1967) using mixed CBA/T6T6 and non-T6 marrow grafts obtained evidence sug-gesting a two-cell origin for spleen colonies. However, the latter experimental design did not involve the isolation of discrete colonies but was based on the probability that any one spleen section contained a single colony. In a more extensive karyotypic analysis of colonies developing after injection of T6 and non-T6 marked marrow, Trentin et al. (1969) found 53 out of 55 colonies had a single karyotype at 7 and 10 days and that at 11 and 12 days, when colonies were histologically of mixed type, 42 of out of 45 colonies had a single karyotype.

These results did not eliminate the possibility that spleen colonies ori-ginated from 2 or more cells that had remained aggregated during the preparation of the marrow suspension. This problem was overcome by Chen and Schooley (1968), who analysed 10-day colonies produced by injection of haemopoietic cells derived from CBA radiation chimaeras, restored with mixtures of CBA, translocation-marked CBA/T6T6 and (CBA × CBA/T6T6)F$_1$ marrow cells. With this system, it may be anticipated that if colonies were derived from pairs of cells, by random chance half of the colonies would be composed of cells differing in karyotype. Analysis of 48 10-day colonies revealed that 41 were composed wholly of one or another karyotype, the remaining 7 showed 92–98% of one karyotype.

It can therefore be concluded with some confidence that the majority of macroscopic spleen colonies both of exogenous and endogenous origin are indeed clones and that since most colonies are of cytologically mixed type, the *in vivo* CFU can be considered to possess multiple differentiating po-tentiality. The clonal nature of the microscopic spleen colonies which are predominantly granulocytic or megakaryocytic, has not been demonstrated but is suggested from the data on the macroscopic (erythroid or mixed) colonies.

Barnes et al. (1968) have shown that although spleen colonies are clones, single cells from a donor marrow can produce more than one colony in a recipient spleen. Using donor marrow irradiated with 500–700 rads, karyotypic analysis revealed that in some recipients, 2, 3 or even 4 colonies in the spleen possessed the same unique, multiple karyotypic abnormalities. The possibility that identical distinctive karyotypes arose independently in more than one donor cell was negligible, and it was concluded that proliferation and secondary migration of colony-forming units had occurred in the recipients. The site of initial proliferation is unknown but it is possible that this occurs in the spleen or marrow followed by re-entry of the progeny into the circulation and subsequent re-seeding. Alternatively, the colony-forming unit may replicate in the circulation or when trapped in the vascular bed or lung or liver prior to localisation in the spleen. It is uncertain how often single CFU's give rise to more than one colony. One consequence of the ability of some CFU's to produce more than one colony would be an increase in the variance of the colony count relative to the mean and the generation of an over-dispersed distribution. Furthermore, it would lead to erroneous overestimates of CFU numbers if such CFU's are capable of extensive recirculation and/or rapid onset of proliferation within an irradiated recipient.

3.2.3 Morphology of spleen colonies

Three main lines of haemopoietic differentiation are exhibited in spleen colonies, erythroid, granulocytic and megakaryocytic. Erythroid colonies (Figure 3.1) are detectable histologically by 4–5 days within the spleen red pulp (but not the lymphoid follicles) and appear as surface colonies as early as day 6. Characteristically, more immature cells are observed at the periphery of the colony surrounding centrally-located more differentiated cells of the erythroid series (Curry and Trentin 1967a). Granulocytic colonies are found along the trabeculae of the spleen or in subcapsular regions and less frequently within the atrophic lymphoid follicles. The vast majority of such colonies are neutrophilic and grow more slowly and diffusely than the erythroid but can be detected histologically at 4 days and macroscopically at 7–8 days. Eosinophilic colonies constitute the rarest type (less than 0.5%) and cannot be detected macroscopically as they contain fewer than 200 cells (Curry and Trentin 1967a). Megakaryocytic colonies preferentially grow under the splenic capsule and generally appear as clusters of mature cells, but megakaryocytic colonies composed predominantly of small undifferentiated cells can be found.

Fig. 3.1. Section of irradiated spleen showing an erythroid colony 7 days after injection of 10-day yolk sac cells. H and E × 48. (From Moore and Metcalf 1970a, reproduced by permission of Brit. J. Haematology.)

Undifferentiated colonies appear as small foci of morphologically undifferentiated cells. Differing criteria of classification and histological techniques have resulted in extensive variation in the percentage of undifferentiated colonies recognised (see Table 3.2). Generally, the number of cells per spleen section in an aggregate of undifferentiated cells is fewer than the accepted minimum for defining a colony (less than 50–100 cells). Also some workers classify colonies as undifferentiated if fewer than 10% of the cells are differentiated (Curry and Trentin 1967a), but others if less than 2% are differentiated (Moore and Metcalf 1970a). Mixed colonies are the largest observed and are most frequently erythroid mixed with other types. Mixed colonies containing all three lines of differentiation are the most infrequent (Figure 3.2). With smear or imprint techniques, a higher proportion of colonies will be classified as mixed than with histological techniques due to the more efficient recognition of a small percentage of cells of a second type. In Table 3.2 data obtained on colony morphology by a number of investigators are shown.

Despite wide variation in technique and criteria of classification, there is agreement that between 6 and 10 days 'pure' erythroid colonies are in a majority (35–76%) with 'pure' granulocytic (11–36%), 'pure' megakaryocytic (0–24%), and mixed (6–30%) in a ratio of approximately 2:1:1:1.

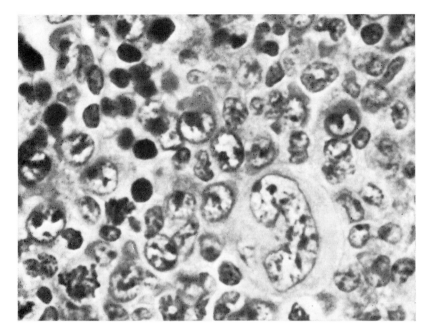

Fig. 3.2. Spleen colony of mixed type 7 days after injection of 10-day yolk sac cells. A single large megakaryocyte can be seen, together with darkly stained erythroblasts and some metamyelocytes. H and E × 1300. (From Moore and Metcalf 1970a, reproduced by permission of Brit. J. Haematology.)

Undifferentiated colonies, when they have been recognised, constituted 0–16% of the total. During the course of growth of colonies between 4–12 days, the proportion of mixed colonies increases relative to 'pure' colonies. The proportion of pure megakaryocytic colonies increased in this period however, whereas undifferentiated colonies, where recognised, decreased (Curry and Trentin 1967a).

The constancy of the relative proportion of colonies of different morphology, despite the diverse sources of the CFU's (marrow, spleen, blood or lymphoid tissue) suggests that direction of differentiation may be a property of the recipient rather than the donor cells. The multipotentiality of CFU's is further supported by the observation that 'pure colonies' become converted to mixed type at later stages of their development, a phenomenon not associated with colony crowding (Silini et al. 1968a). Moreover, it has been demonstrated that pure colonies of any one type contain CFU's that upon retransplantation produce colonies of all types with a morphological dis-

TABLE 3.2

Histological analysis of haemopoietic spleen colonies as reported in the literature

Source of CFU's	Colony age (days)	Percentage total colonies					Reference*
		Eryth-roid	Granu-locytic	Megakaryo-cytic	Undiffer-entiated	Mixed	
Marrow	4	66	22	0	12	0	Curry and Trentin (1967a)
Marrow	6	59	23	1	7	10	Curry and Trentin (1967a)
Marrow	7	60	22	3	0	15	Wolf and Trentin (1968)
Marrow	7	51	23	15	—	11	Moore and Metcalf (1970)
Marrow	8	51	20	14	5	10	Curry et al. (1967a)
Marrow	8	76	11	7	—	6	Duplan (1968)
Marrow	9	47	22	19	—	12	Lewis et al. (1968a)
Marrow	9	54	36	3	—	7	Brecher et al. (1967)
Marrow	9	52	17	10	5	16	Curry and Trentin (1967a)
Marrow	9	48	18	20	—	14	Silini et al. (1968a)
Marrow	9	42	21	21	—	16	Lewis and Trobaugh (1964)
Marrow	9	47	22	19	—	12	Trobaugh and Lewis (1964)
Marrow	9	62	13	2	7	17	Trainin and Resnitzky (1969)
Marrow	10	45	14	18	—	23	Juraskova et al. (1964)
Marrow	10	50	20	0	—	30	Mekori and Feldman (1965)
Marrow	10	35	15	6	16	28	Schooley (1964)
Marrow	12	31	10	12	0	47	Curry and Trentin (1967a)
Spleen	9	54	36	3	—	7	Brecher et al. (1967a)
Blood leukocytes	9	36	24	21	—	19	Lewis et al. (1968a)
Thymus and lymph nodes	8	44	22	19	6	9	Curry et al. (1967b)
10–18 day foetal liver	7	54	20	13	—	13	Moore and Metcalf (1970)
12–14 day foetal liver	8	70	0	8	—	22	Duplan (1968)
18–19 day foetal liver	8	62	14	10	—	14	Duplan (1968)
12½ day foetal liver	9	62	16	0	—	22	Silini et al. (1967; Silini (1967)
15½ day foetal liver	9	58	6	9	—	27	Silini et al. (1967); Silini (1967)

Haemopoietic stem cells and progenitor cells

TABLE 3.2 (continued)

Histological analysis of haemopoietic spleen colonies as reported in the literature

Source of CFU's	Colony age (days)	Percentage total colonies					Reference*
		Eryth-roid	Granu-locytic	Megakaryo-cytic	Undiffer-entiated	Mixed	
$17\frac{1}{2}$ day foetal liver	9	55	11	6	—	28	Silini et al. (1967); Silini (1967)
$19\frac{1}{2}$ day foetal liver	9	45	10	16	—	29	Silini et al. (1967); Silini (1967)
Foetal liver	6	87	7	3	0	3	Feldman and Bleiberg (1967)
Foetal liver	9	58	20	5	2	15	Feldman and Bleiberg (1967)
Yolk sac	7	52	18	11	—	19	Moore and Metcalf (1970)
Endogenous	8	62	8	4	25	0	Jenkins et al. (1969)
Endogenous	9	71	7	15	—	7	Silini et al. (1968a)
Endogenous	9	58	12	4	8	18	Curry and Trentin (1967a)
Endogenous	10	75	0	0	—	25	Mekori and Feldman (1965)
Endogenous	10	72	9	—	—	19	Curry et al. (1967a)
Endogenous	10	70	11	6	4	9	Feldman and Bleiberg (1967)
Endogenous	13	55	2	12	31	0	Jenkins et al. (1969)

* Data modified from cited authors.
— Colonies of this type not included in count.

tribution similar to primary colonies and not related to the morphology of the primary colony (Juraskova and Tkadlecek 1965; Lewis and Trobaugh 1964). Curry et al. (1967a) also showed that pure erythroid and granulocytic colonies gave rise to secondary colonies of differing morphological types but noted that the percentage of the erythroid secondary colonies was slightly, but significantly, higher among the progeny of erythroid primary colonies than among the progeny of granulocytic primary colonies. This observation indicates that the majority of CFU's are multipotential but that a very small percentage may be restricted to only one line of differentiation. Alternatively, passaged CFU's in secondary colonies, though multipotential, may differ from primary CFU's in their responsiveness to various differentiating stimuli.

Spleen colonies developing from embryonic CFU's may differ in morphology from those of adult origin although the data are conflicting. Duplan (1968) was unable to observe granulocytic colonies with 12–14-day foetal liver cells, but at later stages of liver development (18–19 days) CFU's in liver cell suspensions produced normal numbers of granulocytic colonies. Silini et al. (1967) and Moore and Metcalf (1970a) observed granulocytic colonies with early embryonic tissues, yolk sac and foetal liver, and found no significant difference in the ratios of different colony types throughout the course of foetal liver development. Duplan (1968) and Silini et al. (1967) found significantly more mixed colonies with foetal liver than with adult bone marrow cells but significant differences were not observed by Feldman and Bleiberg (1967) or Moore and Metcalf (1970a). In the latter study, colonies were scored at 7 days of development, and it is possible that differences between adult and embryonic-derived colonies may only become evident at later stages of colony development when the percentage of mixed colonies becomes increased. In an attempt to separate CFU's that may differ in differentiating capacity, Moore et al. (1970) analysed the morphology of colonies produced by CFU's separated from foetal liver and bone marrow on the basis of cell density using BSA density gradient separation. Five density increments covering the total density distribution profile of CFU's were analysed (Table 3.3). Significant differences in morphological distribution of spleen colonies were not obtained using cell density as a separating parameter, although with the pooled data, in 4 out of 5 fractions, there were more mixed colonies with foetal liver than with marrow. MacKinney and Korst (1967) presented preliminary data suggesting that following density separation of marrow cell populations, significant differences in the proportion of mixed and pure colonies could be obtained. The fraction giving an increased frequency of mixed types of colony appeared to be enriched for immature cells in rapid cell cycle as virtually all cells in this fraction were thymidine-labelling. Mixed colonies have been claimed to predominate also when regenerating marrow is used instead of normal (Schooley et al. 1968). These observations, in conjunction with the foetal liver data, suggest that the proliferative status of the CFU's may have some determining influence on colony morphology. This would not of course invalidate the conclusion that CFU's are multipotential since resting and dividing cells may differ in their localisation within the spleen, their susceptibility to differentiating stimuli and their self-replicating kinetics. The influence of these factors will be discussed in more detail in subsequent sections.

Other cell types appearing in the irradiated spleen following the injection

TABLE 3.3

Morphology of 7-day spleen colonies produced by CFU's from density fractions of foetal liver* and adult marrow

Density range (gms/cm³)	Tissue origin of CFU's	No. of colonies analysed	No. of spleens	% Total colonies			
				Eryth-roid	Granu-loid	Megakar-yocytic	Mixed
< 1.059	Liver	68	5	52.9	19.1	11.8	16.2
	marrow	69	8	58.0	17.4	14.5	10.1
1.059-1.063	Liver	75	6	64.0	16.0	5.3	14.7
	marrow	41	4	53.7	24.3	9.8	12.2
1.063-1.067	Liver	65	8	56.9	18.5	7.7	16.9
	marrow	149	12	51.0	20.1	17.0	11.9
1.067-1.070	Liver	100	7	66.0	19.0	8.0	7.0
	marrow	72	4	55.6	19.5	15.2	9.7
> 1.070	Liver	50	12	52.0	18.0	14.0	18.0
	marrow	76	5	50.0	22.3	15.8	11.9
Pooled fractions**	Liver	358	38	58.3	18.1	9.3	14.3
Unfractionated	Liver	240	18	54.3	20.0	12.8	12.9
Pooled fractions	Marrow	437	33	53.7	20.7	14.4	11.2
Unfractionated	Marrow	180	12	50.6	23.3	15.0	11.1

* Density fractions obtained from $10\frac{1}{2}$, 12, 14 and 18 day foetal liver profiles.
** Percentage of colony types are means of percentages of the five density increments.
(Reproduced from Moore et al. 1970, by permission of J. Cellular Physiology)

of haemopoietic cells include mast cells, which are not found as colonies but frequently appear in large numbers scattered throughout the spleen stroma. Phagocytic cells, detected by colloidal carbon uptake, are found scattered throughout the spleen but can also be observed in individual spleen colonies where they can constitute up to 1 % of the total colony cells and are more common in colonies primarily of granulocytic type (Moore 1970). Virolainen and Defendi (1968) cultured spleen colonies *in vitro* in the presence of conditioned medium from L-cell cultures and obtained extensive macrophage outgrowth from granulocytic colonies, but few or no macrophages from erythroid colonies. Karyotypic analysis of macrophage outgrowths confirmed that these cells were members of the spleen colony population and implicated a common origin of cells of the granulocyte and macrophage series.

The occurrence of spleen lymphoid colonies was claimed by Mekori et al. (1965) following the injection into irradiated recipients of large numbers of thymic or lymph node cells from phytohaemagglutinin (PHA)-treated donors. This claim was subsequently retracted, and similar experiments performed by other workers (Curry et al. 1967b; Curry and Trentin 1967b) failed to produce lymphoid colonies, although occasional erythroid and granulocytic colonies were observed. The earlier results were probably due to misclassification of erythroid colonies. The general pattern of lymphoid regeneration in the irradiated spleen following the injection of bone marrow cells is a gradual diffuse replenishing of lymphoid follicles of the white pulp by the 12th–14th day. This can be delayed for 4–5 weeks when only low doses of marrow cells are used.

Despite the failure of lymphoid colonies to occur, precursors of lymphoid populations do occur in spleen colonies, even in apparently pure erythroid colonies. Mekori and Feldman (1965) showed that spleen colonies did not contain immunologically-competent cells when tested for their capacity to produce red cell agglutinins or antibody to Shigella. The application of Simonsen's test for graft-vs.-host reactivity showed that colonies produced by marrow or spleen cells did not contain cells capable of detectable anti-host responses. However, Hege and Cole (1966) observed that plaque-forming cells to sheep red cells were present in 9–10 day colonies produced by lymph node cells. As many as 1 plaque-forming cell in 20 colony cells were found, and an average of 4 times more plaque-forming cells were found within colonies than in inter-colony areas. Celada and Wigzell (1966) also found a high frequency of antibody-forming cells in endogenous colonies developing in antigenically-stimulated animals. The frequency distribution of the cells was consistent with their clonal growth inside single colonies with a generation time of 7 hours. Evidence will be discussed later that clones of antibody-forming cells are generated in spleens from injected bone-marrow cells, but present evidence suggests that these are not located primarily in spleen colonies and that antibody-forming cells in spleen colonies are contaminants (Phillips 1968). CFU's can ultimately generate immunologically-competent cells, and Mekori and Feldman (1965) protected irradiated mice with cloned haemopoietic cells of marrow origin. The chimaeras thus produced regained immunological reactivity and on challenge after 3 months produced sheep red cell agglutinin titres similar to those of mice restored with non-cloned marrow. Moore and Warner (1970) observed a similar return of antibody-forming capacity to a wide variety of antigens (BSA, SRBC, *Brucella* and *S. adelaide* flagellin) in chimaeras between 1–3 months after restoration with single spleen colonies from both embryonic and adult haemopoietic CFU's.

Wu et al. (1968a) used radiation-induced chromosomal markers to identify the progeny of single haemopoietic stem cells after extensive proliferation following transplantation into mice of the genotype W/W^v. Cells with the same abnormal karotype were observed in lymph node, thymus and marrow of the recipient mouse and in spleen colonies produced by marrow grafted to irradiated recipients. Indeed lymph nodes containing more than 65% of metaphases with the unique markers were found to contain 5 10 times as many plaque-forming cells to sheep red cells as in normal mice. Therefore, cells belonging to the same clones as colony-forming stem cells, reached the lymph nodes of irradiated mice within 1 month and probably achieved the capacity to participate in an immune response. It is not known whether all CFU's can differentiate into both myeloid and lymphoid cells or whether CFU's and lymphoid cells have a common, as yet unidentified, precursor but it would appear likely that any cell with CFU's among its progeny would itself be capable of giving rise of a spleen colony.

3.2.4   Radiation sensitivity of in vivo CFU's

The gamma radiation survival curve for marrow CFU's was shown by McCulloch and Till (1962) to have a D_0 (dose required to reduce the surviving fraction of cells by a factor 0.37 on the exponential portion of the curve) of 105 ± 13 rads for *in vitro* radiation and 95 ± 9 rads for *in vivo* radiation either before removal from donor or after transfer to the recipient. Extension of this study (Siminovitch et al. 1965) showed that the D_0 of *in vivo*-irradiated CFU's in marrow was 95 rads, in spleen 90 rads and in foetal liver 146 rads. Similar results were obtained by Silini et al. (1967), but foetal liver was more radiosensitive when irradiated *in vitro* (D_0 126 rads) than *in vivo* (D_0 164 rads). Foetal liver-derived CFU's after proliferation for 14 days in adult spleen, showed increased radiosensitivity with a D_0 of 80 rads, similar to that of spleen (D_0 74 rads) and marrow (D_0 69 rads) proliferating in a similar situation (Siminovitch et al. 1965). This increased radiosensitivity of foetal liver-derived colony-forming units was not due to transplantation *per se*, since it was not observed 2 hours after transfer and was not maximum until 6 days after transfer.

The influence of ionizing radiation on colony-forming units and on their subsequent capacity to undergo differentiation is complex. It has been reported that irradiation of bone marrow, either *in vivo* or *in vitro* does not influence the morphological distribution of spleen colonies developing from the irradiated CFU's (Silini 1967, 1968a). Furthermore the slopes of the irradiation dose-response curves (between 350–500 R) for granulocytic or erythroid colonies are not significantly different (Jenkins et al. 1969). Differing results were reported by Brecher et al. (1967), Wolf and Trentin (1970) and Wolf et al. (1968), who found that sublethally-irradiated marrow CFU's produced a significantly lower proportion of erythroid to granulocytic colonies than did unirradiated marrow. It is unlikely that this result was due to selective destruction of monopotent erythroid CFU's since no change in the erythroid to granulocytic ratio was observed over an irradiation dose range of 300–450 R (Wolf et al. 1968). These latter workers provided a partial explanation for the differences in the various observations, since they noted that colonies from irradiated marrow showed a normal erythroid to granulocytic ratio by 10 days, but were deficient in erythropoiesis at 7 days. Furthermore, previously-established anaemia or large doses of erythropoietin in the recipient restored a normal E/G ratio in 7 day colonies derived from irradiated donor marrow cells. Possibly, delayed growth and/or maturation of colonies obtained from irradiated marrow cells may explain the observations.

3.2.5 Kinetic studies on CFU's after transfer to lethally-irradiated recipients and considerations of seeding efficiency (f)

McCulloch and Till (1964) tested the proliferation of CFU's after injection into irradiated recipients by both endogenous and exogenous assays. They noted a 24-hour lag phase after transplantation followed by an exponential increase in the number of CFU's in the spleen with a 20–25-hour doubling time. This suggested that CFU's may not proliferate in the first 24 hours after transplantation. A transient increase in D_0 of the CFU's was noted between 12 and 24 hours suggesting that synchrony of proliferation puts an increased proportion of the cells into a less radiosensitive portion of the cell cycle. Detailed analysis of early post-transplantation events showed that recovery of CFU's from the spleen and marrow falls between 2 hours and 2 days with a pronounced fall in the spleen, which was then followed by a period of exponential increase (Lahiri and Van Putten 1969). Similar results were obtained for CFU proliferation in the spleen by Moore and Metcalf

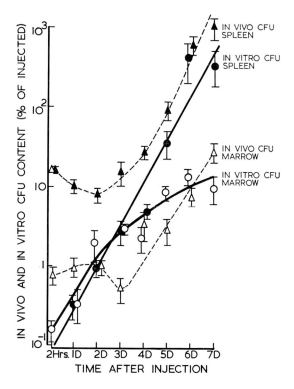

Fig. 3.3. Percentage recovery of CFU's and *in vitro* CFC's in spleen and bone marrow (one femur shaft) at different intervals after injection of 1×10^6–5×10^7 adult bone-marrow cells into lethally irradiated recipients. CFU spleen ▲----▲; CFU marrow △----△; *In vitro* CFC spleen ●——●; *In vitro* CFC marrow ○——○.

(1970b) (Figure 3.3). However, in the marrow a very low proportion of CFU's localised in the first 2 hours (0.4%) and a transient increase was noted at 1 and 2 days coinciding with the dip in the spleen content of CFU's. A significant fall in CFU's was noted on the third day in the marrow followed by a final exponential increase. Kretchmar and Conover (1968) obtained recovery data showing that CFU's decreased in the spleen in the first 24 hours, then doubled once between 24 and 72 hours, and doubled again between 72 and 96 hours.

The post-transfer fall in the recovery of CFU's in the spleen within the first 24–48 hours may be due to a number of factors: (1) the dip could indicate recirculation of CFU's and the abortive rise in CFU's in marrow during this period supports this view (Moore and Metcalf 1970b), (2) CFU's in cycle may be more sensitive to trauma and selectively die during transfer, (3) the dip may be due to abortive 'death' by differentiation without self-replication in the manner of the 'birth-death' model of Till et al. (1964) (see later). Much therefore depends on a detailed analysis of the initial fate of CFU's after transfer. Siminovitch et al. (1963) were the first to attempt to determine the seeding efficiency of CFU's using a double transfer system in which the fraction of CFU's localising in the irradiated spleen was determined by assay of the recipient spleen 2 hours after cell injection in a secondary group of irradiated recipients. This 2-hour recovery was termed '*f*' – the fraction of CFU's localising in the primary irradiated spleen. This fraction was found to be 0.17. Determination of this fraction has given essentially the same results in several strains of mice (Schooley 1966; Haskill et al. 1970) and was similar for CFU's proliferating 3–20 days in irradiated recipients (Valeriote and Bruce 1967).

The assumptions made in this assay are that recirculation is no longer significant after 2 hours and that the fraction of CFU's localising in the spleen of the secondary recipients ($f2$) is the same as the fraction localising in the spleen of the primary recipient ($f1$). Fred and Smith (1968) observed that the 3-hour f value equalled $0.20 \pm .01$ and produced good evidence that this value ($f2$) was probably representative of the fraction localising the first transfer since estimates of $f3$ in a third recipient as obtained by transfer of CFU's after 3 hours in the secondary recipient remained at 0.20, suggesting transfer *per se* was not selectively altering the fraction. The alternative objection to the assay method, namely the problem of CFU recirculation, does present a major, and probably irreconcilable, objection to the validity of the assumption that the f value a few hours after transfer reflects seeding efficiency of CFU's. Fred and Smith (1968) demonstrated the f value for normal marrow CFU's was similar when measured 1–5 hours after transfer, but CFU's from endotoxin-treated donors showed a lower f value at 1 hour than at 3 hours, suggesting that these cells did not lodge in the recipient spleen as quickly as the cells from the controls. Kretchmar and Conover (1969) investigated recovery of CFU's from different tissues at various intervals after injection of marrow and noted that the fraction recovered fell progressively in the spleen from 0.17 in the first 1–4 hours to a low of 0.059 at 16 hours and even at 3 days, was still less (0.093) than in the first few hours. In contrast the recovery fraction from the femur increased progressively from 16 hours onwards. It was considered unlikely that the fall in CFU's recovered from the spleen was due to death or differentiation of CFU's in the primary host, since the CFU's extracted from these hosts prior to the dip in recovery and injected into secondary recipients were perfectly capable of forming colonies, and it was considered more likely that emigration was responsible. Many CFU's initially seeding in the spleen and lung cannot be recovered from these tissues 8–24 hours later. CFU's in the circulation showed an initial decrease in the first 4–8 hours after injection but then remained at a constant level for at least 48 hours, suggesting that CFU's are continuously circulating between various tissues with equilibrium between emigration and immigration probably requiring 16–24 hours. The authors calculated that 80% of the number of colony-forming units injected will enter and leave the blood in the first 24 hours and consider it unlikely that CFU's will remain in any given tissue for the whole of the first day after transplantation. It has been reported that the f values in the first 24 hours after CFU injection varied linearly with the cellularity of the spleen of the irradiated recipient (Lord 1970). However, different linear relationships held for marrow- and spleen-derived CFU's and initially, fewer marrow than spleen CFU's got into the spleen although finally more marrow CFU's were retained. As mentioned earlier, evidence for redistribution of colony-forming units after initiation of proliferation within irradiated recipients, was obtained by Barnes et al. (1968), who found using chromosome markers, that a single cell could produce as many as 3–4 spleen colonies within a single recipient.

Despite the evidence for recirculation of colony-forming units, it remains evident that the number of CFU's recovered in the first 3 days after injection from all the likely tissues in which they could be sequestered (blood, lung, liver, spleen and marrow) is probably less than half the CFU's injected. For this reason, it seems likely that a number of injected CFU's may die or irreversibly differentiate in these early stages. Wolf and Trentin (1966), working with mice carrying multiple subcutaneous spleen grafts, observed that the total number of colonies developing in such grafted mice after irradiation and marrow injection was higher than in ungrafted mice. As many colonies developed in the grafted spleens as in the host's own spleen and there was no significant reduction in the number of colonies developing in the host's own spleen and marrow. The authors concluded that adding to the 'fertile soil bed' increased the number of CFU's detected and indirectly suggested that many of the injected CFU's did not normally proliferate for lack of a suitable environment.

Matioli et al. (1968) attempted to overcome the problem of recirculation of colony-forming units by utilising a direct intrasplenic injection technique, in which small numbers of haemopoietic cells were injected into the irradiated spleen using microneedles. This local assay technique indicated a dilution factor of 0.037 ± 0.014 for intravenously-injected CFU's. This contrasted with the intravenous retransplantation assay which gave values of 0.11–0.23 between 2–8 hours and a fall to 0.06–0.13 between 24 and 48 hours. If, however, the exponential phase of CFU regeneration determined by the exocolonising assay, between 2–9 days (stem cell doubling every 24.3 hours) is extrapolated and an assumption of a 24 hour lag time for proliferation is made, a dilution factor of 0.06 is obtained which slightly overlaps the directly-established value obtained by the local assay.

Despite the conclusion that the value of f determined 1–4 hours after injection may well be significantly influenced by circulation of cells in primary recipients, such determinations have revealed the existence of functional heterogeneity within the CFU compartment. Variations in f values can be induced by pretreatment of donor cells with various agents and are revealed in various cell separation techniques. Such variation may reflect the propensity of some CFU's to localise rapidly and permanently in a particular location or of others to recirculate between various components of the haemopoietic system. The short-term f estimates for embryonic colony-forming units are very low at early stages of development (0.05), but they show an increase in f at later stages of foetal liver haemopoiesis to values as high as 0.14 (Silini et al. 1967; Moore et al. 1970). Within the adult, differences have been noted between spleen-derived CFU's ($f = 0.11$) and marrow-derived CFU's ($f = 0.25$) (Lahiri and Van Putten 1969). Treatment with endotoxin, vinblastine or sublethal irradiation (200–300 R) 1–2 days prior to the transfer of marrow cells reduced the 3-hour f values to 0.12–0.08 and the combination of endotoxin treatment and 300 R 24 hours before transfer depressed f to 0.05. An even more profound depression was noted with vinblastine treatment and 200 R 24 hours before transfer ($f = 0.04$) (Fred and Smith 1968). It would appear that the CFU populations in active cell cycle either in embryonic tissues or in regenerating or stimulated adult organs, display an impaired spleen localisation potential as assessed at 2–3 hours. What influence this has on final seeding efficiency, remains to be determined. Separation of CFU populations in foetal liver (Moore et al. 1970) and in adult marrow (Haskill et al. 1970) using BSA density gradients has produced evidence for cell density-related differences in 2-hour f values. High density CFU's have on average a higher f value than those of lower density, and suggestive evidence for similar variations in f values following velocity sedimentation separation has been obtained by Worton et al. (1969a) with the most rapidly sedimenting (largest) cells having the lowest f values.

3.2.6   *Mitotic activity of the CFU population*

Administration of high specific activity tritiated thymidine in very high doses will kill cells that incorporate it (i.e. cells in S phase at the time of administration of the thymidine). The thymidine suicide technique has been used to determine what proportion of CFU's are in active cell cycle. Becker et al. (1965) noted no depression of CFU's in normal marrow cells exposed to tritiated thymidine for 20 min *in vitro*, suggesting that few CFU's in normal adult marrow were in cell cycle. A slight depression was noted in normal spleen (9–21%), but extensive killing of CFU's was observed with cells from rapidly regenerating spleen (65% depression) or near-term foetal liver (42% depression). Lajtha et al. (1969) administered a single large dose of tritiated thymidine *in vivo* and found a 10% depression of marrow CFU's after 2 hours and a 50% depression of CFU's in marrow regenerating after sublethal irradiation. This suggested that a high proportion of CFU's in the foetus or regenerating organs may be in active cell cycle. However, repeated doses of high specific activity tritiated thymidine *in vivo* depressed normal marrow CFU's to a plateau value of 20% of normal within 24 hours (Bruce and Meeker 1965) which suggested that most CFU's may normally be in cycle with a long generation time of 30–40 hours and therefore not many cells are lethally damaged by short-term tritiated thymidine treatment *in vivo* or *in vitro*. Alternatively, the majority of CFU's may be in a non-proliferating, G_0 state and due to prolonged thymidine treatment many dividing progeny cells will be killed. This deficit of more mature cells may trigger G_0 CFU's into cell cycle with a generation time of 10–12 hours and place an increasing percentage of the total CFU population at risk of tritiated thymidine suiciding.

Vinblastine induces irreversible mitotic arrest in cells, possibly by dissolution of the mitotic spindle (Malawista et al. 1968) and has been used to investigate CFU mitotic activity. Valeriote et al. (1966) found that high doses of vinblastine depressed CFU's to 19% in the marrow and 1% of the spleen within 24 hours and combined treatment with vinblastine and large doses of tritiated thymidine produced no greater depression than either agent separately. In regenerating marrow, vinblastine sensitivity was very high during the exponential phase of CFU proliferation with 98.5% of CFU's eliminated by 24-hour treatment with vinblastine. In contrast the transitional phase of regeneration was associated with less rapid increase in the CFU population which had a vinblastine-sensitivity similar to that in resting marrow (Valeriote and Bruce 1967). Silini et al. (1968b) obtained similar results with 1 mg of vinblastine which depressed marrow CFU's to 20–27% within 24 hours and to 3% in early stages of regeneration. However, the normal CFU survival curve differed from that presented by Valeriote et al. (1966) and Bruce and Meeker (1965), and there was an absence of a clear-cut tail or plateau in the survival curve. The existence of a plateau effect has been interpreted as evidence for two different CFU cell populations – one in cell cycle and the other in a G_0 or resting state. Silini and co-workers suggest that in normal mice, the spread in cell cycle times of proliferating CFU's is so large as to overlap the cycle time of the slowly dividing or dormant cells. The dose survival curve of Haskill et al. (1970) (Figure 3.4) indicates a possible plateau of vinblastine-resistant G_0 cells, but these constitute a much smaller percentage of the total population (5–9%) than observed by other workers. Possibly the difference may be accounted for by the use of young mice (8 weeks of age) in this study where a large fraction of the CFU compartment may be in cycle.

Vinblastine, particularly in large doses, is not without systemic effects, such as increased haematocrit, leucocytosis and inversion of the lymphocyte/ polymorph ratio (Silini et al. 1968b). The influence of such secondary effects on the CFU compartment is unknown. There is also evidence that high concentrations of vinblastine *in vitro* can kill cells at stages other than mitosis. Madoc-Jones and Mauro (1968) noted immediate interphase death by lysis in cultured cells treated with vinblastine in G_1, but cells treated in S phase proceeded at a normal rate to mitosis where they were arrested irreversibly. Finally, the *in vivo* administration of vinblastine, as with other cell poisons, may activate resting CFU's into cycle as a result of depletion of dividing progeny cells. All these considerations imply that the vinblastine data probably lead to an overestimate of the size of the rapidly proliferating CFU compartment at the expense of the slowly dividing or G_0 population.

The concept of resting, or dormant, G_0 cells was introduced by Lajtha et al. (1962). Such a resting period in the cell cycle between M and the completion of G_1 was also recognised by Quastler and Sherman (1959) as the phase of 'taking the decision', by Oehlert et al. (1962) as the 'reversible post-mitotic state', and by Bullough (1963) as 'dichophase'. These workers suggested that it was at this stage that a cell chose whether it divided or differentiated. Lajtha (1966) concluded that stem cells (CFU's) differentiated directly from G_0. This question has been extensively reviewed by Epifanova and Terskikh (1969), who concluded that 'no well-defined relationship has been established between cell differentiation and progression through the mitotic cycle'. It seems that in some cases a single stimulus is sufficient for a

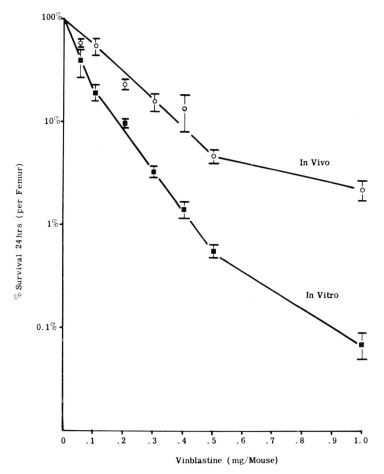

Fig. 3.4.   Percentage survival of femoral marrow CFU's and *in vitro* CFC's 24 hours after graded doses of vinblastine. Points represent means and standard errors of 2 to 5 experiments. (From Haskill et al. 1970, reproduced by permission of J. Cell. Physiology.)

cell to undergo differentiation directly from the G_0 state. However, more often the cells have to pass through a mitotic cycle prior to differentiation.

3.2.7   Influence of source and number of CFU's on the pattern of regeneration

Lahiri and Van Putten (1969) compared the regeneration of CFU's in recipient spleen and marrow following the injection of equal numbers of CFU's of either spleen or marrow origin. The percentage recovery of CFU's in spleen, blood and marrow seemed to be independent of the absolute number of CFU's infused in the range 47–8,800 CFU's during the 14-day period of observation. However, there was a consistent and significant difference in recovery of CFU's when spleen CFU's rather than marrow were injected. CFU's of marrow origin accumulated at a level about twofold higher than CFU's of spleen origin in both spleen and marrow of the recipient. Between 2–7 days the slope of increase in CFU's was similar with spleen-and marrow-derived CFU's and thus the proliferation rate was not the source of difference. Possibly, differences in onset of proliferation (i.e. differential lag periods) or, as the authors suggest, differential absolute seeding efficiency or differential self-replicating capacity, are responsible for spleen CFU's producing only half as many CFU's as marrow-derived CFU's. These latter mechanisms may relate to a greater propensity of spleen-derived CFU's to differentiate rather than self-replicate. In a study on individual spleen colonies dissected out and assayed for their content of CFU's, Moore and Metcalf (1970b) were unable to find any significant difference in CFU content or total cellularity between spleen-derived and marrow-derived colonies between 12 and 13 days of development (Figure 3.5).

Schofield and Lajtha (1969) and Schofield and Pozzi (1968), in contrast to the above study, observed an effect of graft size on kinetics of CFU proliferation. In a preliminary study, the CFU content of pooled spleen colonies was assessed with a range of colonies in the primary spleen (2–20 colonies per spleen) and the number of CFU's per colony was dependent on the number of colonies in the spleen. The data suggested that as the number of cells available for differentiation was reduced, differentiation of CFU's occurred at the expense of numbers of CFU's available for self-generation. Subsequent analysis (Schofield and Lajtha 1969) showed the rate of growth of CFU populations in spleen colonies during the exponential phase, was not dependent on the number of colonies present over a thirty-fold range and a doubling time of 23–25 hours was observed. However, increasing the number of colonies in the spleen accelerated the onset of CFU proliferation and subsequently, the time of onset of the plateauing-off of the exponential phase of CFU proliferation. The dose effect therefore appeared as a dose-dependent delay in the start of CFU proliferation inversely related to the size of the cell graft. There are reasons to doubt the magnitude of this effect, however, since it was not observed by Lahiri and Van Putten (1969) and Moore and Metcalf (1970b), who observed that CFU self-renewal was not strongly dependent on colony number in the range of 3–80 colonies per

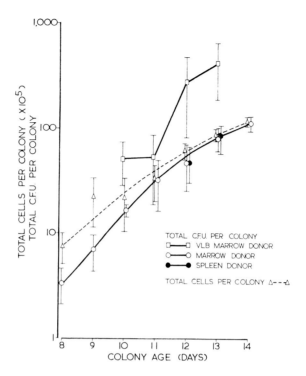

Fig. 3.5. CFU content and total cellularity of spleen colonies at different stages of growth. Spleen colonies derived from inocula of adult marrow, spleen or marrow from mice injected 24 hours previously with 1 mg vinblastine. Each point is mean with standard errors of separate estimates on 20–150 colonies.

spleen. The average doubling time of CFU's within spleen colonies over a 14-day period was 48 hours, including the initial lag phase and the plateau or transitional phase of growth (Figures 3.3 and 3.5) and during the exponential growth phase, the CFU population doubling time was 20–25 hours (Moore and Metcalf 1970b; McCulloch and Till 1964; Schofield and Lajtha 1969). If, however, seeding efficiency of CFU's and their extinction probabilities are considered, a much shorter doubling time is obtained (mean 19–21 hours) during the growth of 12 day colonies (Vogel et al. 1969). These workers estimated from the absolute CFU content of their colonies and their total cellularity, that if the generation time in the erythroid series was 8 hours and the number of steps in erythroid differentiation was eight, the previously unknown CFU generation time might be approximately 7 hours.

3.2.8 *Heterogeneity of CFU content of spleen colonies*

When individual colonies are dissected out of the spleen and assayed for their content of CFU's by injection into irradiated secondary recipients, the distribution of CFU's per colony is extremely heterogeneous (Siminovitch et al. 1964), even among colonies within the same spleen. In Figure 3.6, the distribution of CFU content of 443 colonies illustrates this heterogeneity which is observed at all stages when individual colonies can be isolated (9–14 days). No gross feature of colonies, such as their size or colour could be correlated with CFU content. The underlying cause of this heterogeneity is not clearly understood but a number of possibilities have been proposed as part of a general speculation on the nature and regulation of CFU self-renewal.

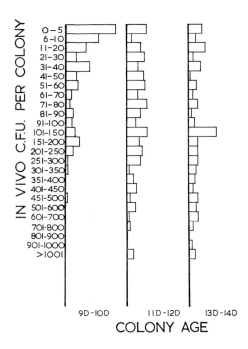

Fig. 3.6. Histogram showing distribution of spleen colonies with differing CFU contents at three stages of colony development. Data on 443 spleen colonies from both adult and embryonic sources.

3.2.9   Stochastic model of stem-cell regulation

As shall be discussed at the end of this section, the spleen colony assay detects a population of haemopoietic stem cells. For this reason the experimental data on CFU replication and differentiation, particularly within the clonally-expanding cell population of a spleen colony, have been used to test various models of control mechanisms which might operate on the stem-cell compartment. In particular, comparison of experimental data with theoretical models, has produced some insight into the balance between stem-cell differentiation and self-renewal, which is so vital to haemopoietic homeostasis.

The heterogeneity of CFU content of spleen colonies may reflect the operation of a purely random process governing stem cell self-replication and differentiation. The coefficient of variation, v, of CFU's per colony ($v =$ standard deviation over the mean CFU content per colony) has been variously estimated as 2 (Till et al. 1964) 1.86 $\pm$ 0.36 (Vogel et al. 1968, 1969) and 2.01 (Moore and Metcalf 1970b). A slight time dependence in v is suggested by Vogel et al. (1968). Comparison of the coefficient of variation of CFU content of 8–11-day colonies (1.79) and 12–14-day colonies (2.31) in the data of Moore and Metcalf does indeed indicate increase in v with colony age. This heterogeneous distribution in which variance greatly exceeds the mean does not correspond to the Poisson distribution and indicates that the variation from colony to colony is not due to sampling error alone (Till et al. 1964). These latter workers proposed that the pattern of development of colonies is strongly governed by the balance between two competing properties of stem cells, self-renewal and differentiation. During colony growth, all stem cells are therefore faced with a probability p of self-replication ('birth') or $1-p$ of differentiation ('death'). The variable composition of spleen colonies was assumed to reflect a random fluctuation in the frequency of occurrence of self-replication or differentiation of stem cells during the growth of the colony. Support for this model was provided by the similarity of the Gaussian distribution curve of CFU's per colony to a theoretical probability distribution of a large number of 'case histories' of possible stem cell generation mechanisms in colonies obtained by the Monte Carlo procedure.

Vogel et al. (1968, 1969) extended the analysis of stochastic models for stem-cell development, in their analysis of CFU production in spleen colonies. They were able to determine the self-renewal probability (p) for stem cells which determines the growth of the spleen colony and its stem-cell content and also the extinction probability omega (omega $= (1-p)/p$), which is the probability that at any one time all stem cells in a growing colony decide for differentiation rather than for self-renewal. The self-renewal and extinction probabilities can be calculated using the formula for single colonies

$$v^2 = \left(\frac{2-2p}{2p-1} \right) + \frac{1}{K},$$

where K = mean number of CFU's per colony, p = self-renewal probability and v = the coefficient of variation. The results of such calculations of these values are shown in Table 3.4. The data show that one-third of all stem cells which settle in the spleen of irradiated mice are capable of forming macroscopically-visible colonies. The remaining two-thirds are subject to extinction after one or a few divisions. It is probable that a number of these latter would be detected as microcolonies and in excess of 50% of total spleen colonies are not visible macroscopically (Lewis et al. 1968b).

It may at first appear surprising that the haemopoietic stem-cell compartment should be regulated by a seemingly random mechanism; howeverthe analogy with radioactive decay suggests that although the progeny of single cells display random features, a study of large populations of cells reveals the orderly behaviour of the whole system (Till et al. 1964).

The data from colonies produced by vinblastine-treated marrow (Table 3.4) suggest that self-renewal and extinction probabilities need not be uniform throughout the stem-cell population. On preliminary data Vogel et al. (1968) suggested that stem cells present in colonies developing in sub-lethally irradiated mice may have different self-renewal and extinction probabilities from non-irradiated stem cells. The relationship between possible environ-

TABLE 3.4

Calculations of stem-cell self-renewal (p) and extinction (ω) probabilities

CFU source	p	ω	Reference
Spleen	0.62	0.63	Vogel et al. (1968)
Marrow	0.62	0.63	Siminovitch et al. (1963); Till et al. (1964) – as calculated by Vogel et al. (1968)
Marrow	0.64	0.67	Moore and Metcalf (unpublished observations)
Foetal liver	0.62	0.61	Moore and Metcalf (unpublished observations)
Vinblastine-treated marrow	0.57	0.75	Moore and Metcalf (unpublished observations)

mental and intrinsic factors influencing self-renewal probabilities are at the moment incompletely resolved, but increasing evidence is accumulating and will be discussed in subsequent sections to show that regulation of stem-cell proliferation is multi-factorial.

3.2.10   Regulatory function of the haemopoietic microenvironment

Curry et al. (1967a), Trentin et al. (1967) and Curry and Trentin (1967a) theorised that the spleen is subdivided into a variety of microenvironmental areas, each inducing a single type of differentiation on the part of otherwise multipotent stem cells. Evidence is reviewed in Section 3.3, which shows in irradiated polycythaemic mice that suppressed presumptive erythroid colonies remain small and undifferentiated but do not become granulocytic colonies. The theory of microenvironmental regulation proposes that such microcolonies are developing from a stem cell lodged in an exclusive erythroid microenvironment and hence cannot become granulocytic. The increase with time in colonies of histologically mixed type is likewise explained by the encroachment of an expanding colony of 'pure type' upon adjacent different microenvironments.

Colonies of haemopoietic cells also develop in the marrow cavities of irradiated mice injected with bone-marrow cells, or appear as endogenous colonies in sublethally irradiated animals (Trentin et al. 1967). These marrow colonies are similar to those developing in the spleen, differing only in the frequency distribution of different morphological types. The erythroid to granulocyte ratio (E:G) of either endogenous or exogenous colonies is significantly different between spleen (3.5:1) and marrow (0.7:1). The predominance of granuloid colonies in marrow is consistent with the important role of the unirradiated marrow in granulopoiesis, and it was proposed that the marrow has proportionately more granulocytic microenvironmental regions than the spleen. When marrow CFU's which had seeded 18–24 hours earlier to the marrow cavity of irradiated primary recipients were retransplanted into irradiated secondary hosts, the E:G ratio of colonies in the spleen of the secondary host was typical of primary spleen colonies, and those colonies forming in the marrow cavity were typical of marrow colonies (Trentin et al. 1967; Wolf and Trentin 1968). This evidence refutes the possibility that selective distribution of pre-committed CFU's to either spleen or marrow was involved. Marrow stroma containing seeded CFU's was implanted with a trocar directly into the irradiated spleen and developed a normal marrow ratio of E:G colonies whereas CFU's that migrated from the marrow graft into contiguous or remote portions of the irradiated spleen, gave an E:G ratio characteristic of spleen. Irradiated marrow stroma and 1-mm cubes of unirradiated spleen were also implanted directly into spleens. Colonies developed from CFU's that migrated from the implanted spleen fragment and these were predominantly granuloid when located in the implanted marrow stroma and predominantly erythroid in the host-spleen tissue. Where colonies bridged the junction of the spleen and implanted marrow, in every case the erythroid portion of the colony was in the spleen stroma and the granulocytic portion in the marrow stroma (Trentin et al. 1967; Wolf and Trentin 1968). Similar results were obtained by Moore (1970) in a similar experimental system. Neonatal spleen fragments were cultured *in vitro* with neonatal marrow stroma and the resulting tissue mosaic was then grafted under the kidney capsule of normal or splenectomised adult mice. After 4–6 weeks the recipients were irradiated and injected intravenously with 10^5 marrow cells. Histological analysis of the grafts showed predominantly granulopoietic colonies in the marrow

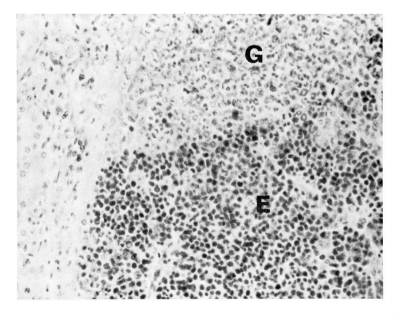

Fig. 3.7. Section of a colony developing in a mosaic spleen and marrow graft under the kidney capsule 10 days after injection of marrow cells into the lethally irradiated host. Note the distinct demarcation between the granulocytic (G) area of the colony developing in a marrow microenvironment and the erythroid (E) area in the splenic microenvironment. H and E × 200.

regions and erythropoietic colonies in the spleen tissue and the colonies overlapping the border between marrow and spleen tissue frequently exhibited a very sharp demarcation into erythroid and granulocytic areas (see Figure 3.7).

Microenvironmental influences may involve a direct cellular interaction between spleen stromal cells and stem cells or a very short range inductive interaction with differentiation elicited by a diffusible inducing agent. Such a regulative model where external factors determine differentiation is discussed in the context of the embryological development of haemopoiesis in Chapter 4. Microenvironmental factors regulating the direction of stem-cell differentiation could conceivably lead to heterogeneity of colony content of CFU's if, in the absence of an interaction between stem cell and stromal cells, self-replication occurred, or alternatively, certain microenvironments induced self-replication and blocked differentiation. Certain data suggest that CFU self-replication rather than differentiation may be favoured by a granulocyte-determining microenvironment since it has been reported that there is a significant association between colonies containing a high proportion of granulocytic cells and their content of CFU's (Fowler et al. 1967; Curry et al. 1967a). A weak correlation between CFU content and percentage of granulocytes was found by Moore and Metcalf (1970b). The value of the regression coefficient for 13-day colonies was 0.49 and for 14-day colonies 0.37, both values being significant at the 0.02–0.05 probability level.

3.2.11 *Intrinsic heterogeneity in CFU self-replication*

Both the stochastic and microenvironmental models are based on the assumption that the CFU population is homogeneous with respect to capacity to self-replicate or differentiate. Recently, evidence has accumulated to suggest that this assumption is not valid and that heterogeneity in CFU's per colony may reflect intrinsic differences in the CFU's themselves. Worton et al. (1969b) used a velocity sedimentation separation technique and resolved the marrow CFU population into a number of fractions essentially differing in cell size. The results of the assay for CFU content of 12-day spleen colonies derived from CFU's in the various fractions studied, indicated that CFU's in slowly sedimenting cell fractions (small cells) had a higher capacity to undergo self-renewal than rapidly sedimenting CFU's or unfractionated populations. In a second system the self-renewal capacity of marrow CFU's surviving in liquid culture for 48 hours was tested. If cells were cultured in the presence of a feeder layer of mouse kidney tubules, CFU recovery was 25% and the self-renewal capacity of these cells was normal (10–25 CFU's per colony at 12 days). Reduced survival was noted in cultures without feeder layers (10%), but self-renewal of the surviving CFU's was very high (up to 125 CFU's per colony). The sedimentation separation profile of CFU's cultured with feeder layers was similar to normal marrow, but some increase in CFU cell size was indicated. In contrast, CFU's from cultures without feeder layers exhibited a restricted size distribution and the cells were more slowly sedimenting (small cells).

Further support for the concept of intrinsic differences in capacity of individual CFU's for self-renewal emerged from an investigation of the self-replicative capacity of CFU's in different proliferative states (Moore and Metcalf 1970b). In these experiments vinblastine (1 mg per mouse) was used to eliminate cells entering mitosis within a 24-hour period. The surviving 5–10% of total CFU's in marrow represented CFU's with either a very long cell cycle or in a G_0 state (see Section 3.2.6). The self-replicating capacity of these vinblastine-resistant CFU's was tested by analysis of the CFU content of the spleen colonies they produced. The mean CFU content of these colonies at 12 and 13 days was 3–5-fold higher than normal (see Figure 3.5), although little significant difference was observed at earlier stages of colony development. Total cellularity of the colonies was slightly but not significantly higher than normal at all stages studied. The distribution of CFU's per spleen colony, comparing normal with vinblastine-treated CFU's was consistent with destruction of CFU's with low self-renewal capacity by vinblastine and consequent selective survival of CFU's with a high self-renewal capacity. An alternative, but less likely, possibility is that vinblastine did not discriminate between CFU's differing in self-renewal capacity but rather by some direct pharmacological influence altered the self-renewal probability of all surviving CFU's.

Further resolution of the CFU population was obtained using BSA equilibrium density-gradient separation techniques. Density distribution profiles of CFU's in normal and vinblastine-treated marrow-cell populations are compared in Figure 3.8. CFU distribution was altered qualitatively as well as quantitatively following vinblastine. The light density CFU population (less than 1.060) was only depressed to 42% of normal, whereas the major peaks of CFU activity at 1.063, 1.066 and 1.069 were depressed to 6%, 9.2% and 4.3% respectively. Less depression of high-density CFU's was also evident (15–18%). This qualitative difference indicates that CFU density heterogeneity may in part be related to heterogeneity in CFU cycle times

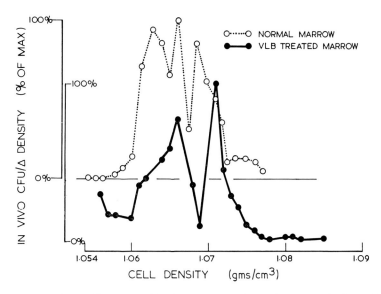

Fig. 3.8. Density distribution profile of CFU's in the femoral marrow of mice 24 hours after treatment with 1 mg vinblastine (lower graph). Compare with profile of CFU's in untreated marrow (upper graph). Profiles have been arbitrarily normalized so that the areas under the curves are equal.

and suggests that G_0 CFU's may be preferentially located in the light-density region of the gradient and also in the high-density regions, but not in intermediate regions.

The self-replicative capacity of CFU's different density in normal and vinblastine-treated marrow was determined using the experimental design outlined in Figure 3.9. Results of analysis of CFU content of 12-day spleen colonies produced by CFU's from six density regions covering the total density distribution of both normal and vinblastine marrow, are shown in Figure 3.10. Density separation failed to resolve populations of CFU's differing in self-renewal capacity in normal marrow (unlike size separation) with the exception of the very lightest density CFU's that had significantly reduced self-replicative potential. In contrast, separation of vinblastine-treated marrow revealed lighter density CFU's that had a 4–7 fold greater self-replicative capacity than CFU's with high density. Indeed the higher average self-renewal capacity of the unfractionated vinblastine-treated marrow must be due solely to vinblastine-resistant light density CFU's since CFU's in all increments of greater density than 1.068, which constitute 30–40% of the total survivors, were not significantly different in

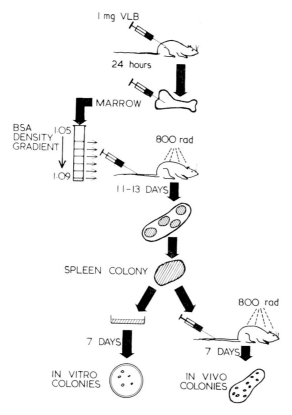

Fig. 3.9. Protocol of experiment in which normal marrow or marrow from donors given 1 mg vinblastine 24 hours previously is subjected to density gradient separation. Cells from various density increments of the marrow are then injected in low numbers into lethally-irradiated mice, and at intervals thereafter spleens are removed and individual spleen colonies isolated. Cell suspensions are prepared from each colony and aliquots of colony cells used for counting, assayed for *in vitro* CFC's or injected into a further group of irradiated recipients for CFU assay.

self-replicative capacity from normal marrow CFU's of similar density.

It is probable that these light-density G_0 CFU's are the same population of CFU's with high self-replicative capacity as Worton et al. (1969b) described. CFU's in a resting state may indeed be characterised by their small size and low density since cytoplasmic protein and RNA content may well be minimal during G_0. However, the possibility has not been eliminated that during the course of 24 hours' treatment with vinblastine, the small G_0 CFU's may enlarge and reduce their density in preparation for entry into

from normal or vinblastine-resistant CFU's that had proliferated for 12–13 days in the primary recipient. These data showed that in irradiated hosts CFU's endowed with high self-replicative capacity do not generate progeny with similar potentialities and do not sustain high self-replicative capacity beyond the first passage. The phenomenon of 'decline' in self-replication following serial passaging of CFU's is reviewed in Chapter 8, and evidence presented that this is related to the number of generations in which self-replication of CFU's has been maintained. It is unlikely that this decline phenomenon plays a role in heterogeneity of CFU self-replication in primary irradiated recipients since spleen colonies containing very few CFU's can produce secondary colonies containing more CFU's than in the primary colony.

The loss of high self-replicative capacity after only 48 hours' residence in an irradiated recipient is consistent with the proposal that this capacity is transitory and related to the G_0 status of CFU's. The absence of change after only 18–24 hours in the irradiated recipient may therefore reflect the time required to activate the CFU into rapid cell cycle. Supporting evidence for this conclusion was obtained following treatment of the primary ir-radiated recipient with 0.5 mg of vinblastine at the time of injection of vinblastine-resistant CFU's, or 24 hours after injection. No reduction in 24-hour CFU recovery was observed following vinblastine administration at the time of cell injection but complete elimination of CFU's was found at 48 hours when vinblastine was given 24 hours after cell injection.

The position of a CFU with respect to the cell cycle may be anticipated as having a profound influence on its initial differentiation or self-replication immediately following localisation in the spleen but it is difficult to see how such influences only become evident at late stages of colony development when the CFU's may have undergone in excess of 30–40 divisions (Vogel et al. 1969).

An alternative explanation for the data on high self-replicative capacity of certain CFU's revealed by vinblastine pretreatment or cell-separation techniques is that cell interactions can occur between CFU's and other cell types in the inoculum, and that such interactions can greatly influence stem cell self-replication. Inhibition of CFU self-replication may, on the basis of this theory, be due to interaction with a second cell population and this latter cell type or its precursor, may be selectively eliminated by vin-blastine treatment or cell separation. Alternatively, these procedures may produce enrichment of a promoting cell which facilitates CFU self-replication or inhibits differentiation. Cell-mixing experiments must be undertaken to resolve these possibilities but if cell interaction between two populations of injected cells occurs, then considerations of numbers of cells localising in the spleen (less than 1% of total injected marrow cells; Korst, 1966) and the numbers injected (as few as $5 \times 10^3-10^4$) necessitate proposing a very efficient interaction process.

Heterogeneity in CFU content of spleen colonies is also seen with CFU's from early embryonic tissues such as yolk sac and early foetal liver (see Chapter 4). Such CFU's are in rapid cell cycle with probably few cells in G_0 phase and are a relatively homogeneous population of light density, extremely large (600–1000 μ^3) cells (Haskill and Moore 1970). In this situation high self-replicative capacity of embryonic CFU's cannot be correlated with the small size and G_0 state which characterise adult CFU's having a similar capacity for self-replication.

3.2.12 Conclusions regarding CFU self-replication

It is apparent that regulation of CFU self-replication within spleen colonies cannot be adequately explained on the basis of one mechanism alone, and at least three factors are involved. Two of these involve intrinsic factors, which may be either purely random or predetermined. These influence self-replication and in this context, correspond to a 'mosaic' model of regulation of differentiation (Till 1968). The third factor corresponds to a 'regulative' model of differentiation where CFU self-replication is determined by extrinsic factors such as local microenvironment and feedback regulation, either humoral or involving cell interaction.

3.2.13 CFU regeneration after treatment with mitotic poisons

The recovery of the CFU population after vinblastine administration has been studied using the endogenous colony assay (Smith et al. 1968). The incidence of endogenous colonies in sublethally irradiated mice which had been treated with vinblastine 48 hours prior to irradiation was 30-fold higher than in control-irradiated mice. Mice treated with vinblastine 48 hours before 200 R sublethal irradiation showed recovery of spleen CFU's to normal between 2–4 days and a 6-fold overshoot by day 6. In contrast, irradiated controls showed a 27% recovery by day 10. Vinblastine given 2 days prior to 400 R eliminated the post-irradiation dip in marrow CFU recovery, and exponential growth was entered into immediately with no mitotic delay. These differences in recovery kinetics are qualitative and do not appear to depend on the number of CFU's surviving irradiation but rather on the readiness of CFU's to enter cell cycle.

Colchicine has an effect similar to vinblastine in promoting an increase ($\times$ 10) in endogenous colonies when administered 2 days before irradiation and also to a lesser extent ($\times$ 4–6) when given a few minutes before or after irradiation. A similar promoting effect on CFU regeneration after 400 rads was also noted. The immediate pre- and post-irradiation values for spleen CFU content were similar in irradiated controls and in mice given colchicine 2 days before, indicating that colchicine does not reduce sensitivity of CFU's to irradiation. An exponential increase in CFU's was initiated 24 hours after irradiation in colchicine pre-treated mice but was delayed until the third post-irradiation day in controls (Brecher et al. 1967). The effects of vinblastine and colchicine in promoting CFU regeneration may operate by preselection of CFU populations in G_0 endowed with a greater proliferative (self-replicative) capacity, or alternatively the regenerating CFU's after drug depression may be in more rapid cell cycle and may commence proliferation following sublethal irradiation without an intervening lag period. The third contributing factor is that these agents may exert an effect on the recipient similar to that described for the potentiating effect of prior sublethal irradiation on the proliferation of grafted CFU's in lethally-irradiated recipients (Blackett and Hellman 1966; Porteous and Lajtha 1968).

3.2.14   *Endotoxin effects on CFU's*

Endotoxin produces no change in spleen CFU content 24 hours after administration. Its effect on marrow varies and has been described as causing a decrease (Boggs et al. 1968) an increase (Hanks and Ainsworth 1967) or no change (Smith et al. 1966a, b) in bone marrow CFU's. However, a significant effect of endotoxin on haemopoietic regeneration and survival after irradiation has been noted. Regeneration of CFU's after 400 R was accelerated in mice receiving endotoxin 24 hours previously and both spleen and marrow recovery of CFU's was initiated 2 days earlier than in controls. Post-irradiation endotoxin treatment also augmented spleen and marrow CFU regeneration (Smith et al. 1966a, b).

Hanks and Ainsworth (1967) noted a maximum increase in endogenous colonies migrating from shielded hind quarters (in an autorepopulation system) when 25 μg of endotoxin were given as a single intravenous injection 24 hours before irradiation. The increase was 25-fold over controls and was associated with an approximate doubling in the migration rate of CFU's from shielded areas to the spleen 4–8 hours after endotoxin. The increase in spleen weight following endotoxin (Boggs et al. 1968) may also have increased the receptivity of the spleen and enabled it to accommodate an increased seeding rate of CFU's. Both augmented regeneration and seeding of CFU's may be related to an endotoxin-induced triggering of CFU's from a resting state into a state of active proliferation. This would reduce the time required for CFU's to begin proliferation after sublethal irradiation and promote early haemopoietic regeneration (Till and McCulloch 1967).

The effects of endotoxin pretreatment in promoting radiation survival do not correlate with the number of CFU's prior to irradiation, since these were not augmented. $LD_{50/30}$ was increased by 217 R following endotoxin and this would require an 11-fold increase in CFU's (Hanks and Ainsworth 1967). The slight increase in D_0 of CFU's and a slightly increased colony size following endotoxin could not produce this major protective effect, and it appears that the effect is due to the earlier onset of CFU proliferation following endotoxin which produces a CFU numerical advantage of 3–10-fold in spleen and marrow compared with controls (Hanks and Ainsworth 1967).

3.2.15   *Influence of miscellaneous factors on CFU's*

Antigenic stimulation in the form of pertussis vaccine (Barnes and Loutit 1967a, b; Cole and Maki 1968) mumps or influenza vaccine or sheep red cells (Boggs et al. 1967a, b) enhanced both endogenous and exogenous colony-formation in spleen and marrow and produced a 10–20-fold increase in CFU's in the circulation. Intraperitoneal administration of complete Freund's adjuvant also increased spleen CFU content 10–20-fold within a period of 7–9 days (Figure 3.12) but had a variable effect on marrow with on average little change in total marrow CFU's (Haskill et al. 1970). Multiple doses of foreign plasma given intraperitoneally to mice depressed the total marrow CFU content and reduced the relative and absolute incidence of CFU's in the spleen. However, endogenous colony formation and post-irradiation survival were significantly increased (Marsh et al. 1967a, b; Boggs et al. 1967a, b; 1968). The increase in endogenous colony-formation was explained by an increase in efficiency of the spleen as a trap for circulating CFU's due to plasma-induced spleen enlargement (Marsh et al. 1967a). Because of the dose-response relationship, this effect of plasma was unlikely to be mediated by antigenic effects. It was also unlikely to be a specific CFU growth-stimulating factor since human, rat or allogeneic mouse plasma

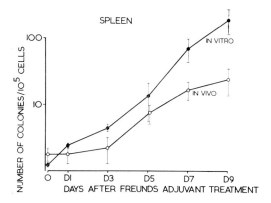

Fig. 3.12.   Effect of 0.2 ml of complete Freund's adjuvant on the concentration of CFU's and *in vitro* CFC's in the spleen. Each point is mean of four experiments with standard errors. Data not corrected for seeding efficiency. (From Haskill et al. 1970, reproduced by permission of J. Cell. Physiol.)

was effective but maternal or syngeneic mouse plasma was without effect (Boggs et al. 1967a, b).

Nettesheim et al. (1968) and Hanna et al. (1967) observed that a 19S alpha-2 macroglobulin in serum promoted post-irradiation survival and enhanced the recovery of CFU's in spleen and marrow. The effect was most marked when the macroglobulin was given shortly before irradiation. Phytohaemagglutinin (PHA) *in vivo* increased the CFU content of blood and lymph nodes (Micklem 1966) and has been claimed to increase the proportion of mixed and megakaryocytic spleen colonies where administered to irradiated mice given marrow cells (Curry and Trentin 1967b). Colonies developing in the presence of PHA were smaller with approximately half normal cellularity and contained only one-third the normal number of CFU's per colony. The question of toxicity mediating the *in vivo* effects of PHA must be considered. The number of endogenous colonies was also significantly augmented by 20–30-fold in PHA-treated mice subjected to irradiation. Curry and Trentin (1967b) have suggested a possible action of PHA on cell membranes, influencing cell-cell interactions or altering CFU seeding by inducing blast transformation.

3.2.16   Summary

From this discussion it is evident that *in vivo* CFU's can generate clones which can contain erythroid, granulocytic and megakaryocytic cells as well as precursors of lymphoid cells and additional CFU's. Indeed the progeny of a single CFU have been shown to be capable of completely repopulating the haemopoietic organs of a lethally-irradiated animal. The CFU therefore conforms to the characteristics of stem cells as defined in Chapter 1, having the capacity for extensive self-replication and generation of multiple lines of differentiating cells. It should be remembered, however, that although all spleen colonies are probably produced by stem cells, not all stem cells may be detected by the *in vivo* assay. It is possible that there may be a cell at a more primitive stage which is not detected by the assay (e.g. by failing to home to the spleen) yet has the capacity to generate *in vivo* CFU's. It is also possible that a cell population exists, endowed with extensive self-replicative ability but restricted to a lymphoid line of differentiation. There appears to be no evidence for either of these latter types of stem cell in the rodent, and until such evidence is available, the *in vivo* CFU assay remains the most reliable and valid technique for analysing the stem-cell population.

In the following sections, further types of primitive haemopoietic cells are described, and it is possible that some of these may be considered as stem cells, in the light of future information, particularly on the extensiveness of their self-replicative capacity. However, our present knowledge of such cells shows them to differ from the *in vivo* CFU, and they are consequently classified into an intermediate compartment of progenitor cells (as defined in Chapter 1) restricted in differentiating capacity to one or two lines of differentiation.

3.3 Erythropoietin-sensitive cells (erythropoietin-responsive cells; ESC)

The characteristics of the humoral regulating factor, erythropoietin, are discussed in detail in the chapter devoted to humoral regulation of haemopoiesis. This section will concentrate on reviewing the recent data on the target cells that are influenced directly by the action of this hormone.

Early studies concluded that erythropoietin acted on the 'stem cells' of the marrow inducing erythroid differentiation (Erslev 1959; Alpen and Cranmore 1959). With the development of the transfusion-induced polycythaemic mouse for assaying the effect of erythropoietin preparations (Filmanowicz and Gurney 1961; Jacobson et al. 1960) rapid progress was made in the understanding of erythroid differentiation. During the maintenance of an adequate level of polycythaemia the entire haemopoietic tissue of the mouse

remains apparently devoid of erythropoietic activity, but following the injection of material containing erythropoietin, an orderly sequence of
differentiation and maturation of erythrocyte precursors is seen with a
peak reticulocytosis in the blood at 3 days (Jacobson et al. 1960). Studies on
erythropoietin time/dose responses in hypertransfused and starved animals
showed that a given dose of erythropoietin exerted a greater erythroid
stimulating effect in the first 24 hours of erythroid suppression than after
prolonged erythroid aplasia had been induced (Gallagher and Lange 1960;
Hodgson and Eskuche 1962). Stohlman (1967) observed that the reticulocyte
response occurred earlier in normal than in hypertransfused mice and was
substantially greater in polycythaemic mice after four daily doses of erythropoietin than predicted from 4 times the response from a single dose
(Gallagher and Lange 1962; Gurney et al. 1961). These observations can be
reconciled with an action of erythropoietin on later phases of erythroid
differentiation or alternatively, may indicate the time required for recruitment of increased numbers of primitive cells into an erythropoietin-responsive
population when prolonged erythropoietic stimulation follows a prolonged
period of dormancy. There is evidence that erythropoietin not only initiates
haemoglobin synthesis but may actually govern the rate of haemoglobin
synthesis by virtue of an action on DNA-directed RNA synthesis in erythropoietic cells at various stages of differentiation. Stohlman et al. (1968,
1964) showed that massive doses of erythropoietin produced short-lived
macrocytic red cells in hypertransfused mice, and suggested that cytoplasmic
haemoglobin concentration may have been the actual factor terminating cell
replication. Thus with increased haemoglobin synthesis following large
doses of erythropoietin, critical haemoglobin concentrations were reached
prematurely before the last reduction division, resulting in macrocytes
rather than normocytes. Direct evidence on this question was provided by
Boorsook et al. (1968), who cultured *in vitro* fractions of rabbit marrow rich
in basophilic erythroblasts and showed an accelerated disappearance of
erythroblast cytoplasmic basophilia and increased cytoplasmic haemoglobin formation in the presence of erythropoietin, an effect nullified by
actinomycin D. Notwithstanding the above considerations, the major influence of erythropoietin is upon a primitive haemopoietic cell not morphologically classifiable as a member of the erythroid series which is induced by
erythropoietin to commence haemoglobin synthesis and enter the definitive
erythropoietic series. The following sections will review evidence that
this primitive erythropoietin-sensitive cell is closely related to, but more
differentiated than, the stem cell as detected by the *in vivo* spleen

colony assay and consequently belongs to the class of progenitor cells.

3.3.1 *Morphology of spleen colonies in polycythaemic mice*

Polycythaemia induced by administration of packed red cells either syngeneic or allogeneic (or even rat) into mice (Feldman and Bleiberg 1967) suppressed the development of differentiated erythroid cells in spleen colonies and resulted in the suppression of pure and mixed erythroid colonies (Curry et al. 1967a; Bleiberg et al. 1967; Lange et al. 1968; Schooley et al. 1968; Feldman and Bleiberg 1967; O'Grady et al. 1967a, b; Liron and Feldman 1965). Polycythaemia was also shown to suppress erythroid differentiation in endogenous colonies (Feldman and Bleiberg 1967; Curry et al. 1967a; Marsh et al. 1967b; Bleiberg et al. 1967). The extent of suppression of erythropoiesis was directly correlated with the haematocrit (Lange et al. 1968). Increased mass of red cells was not itself directly responsible for suppression since polycythaemic mice rendered hypoxic showed no suppression, suggesting that over-saturation with oxygen leading to suppression of endogenous erythropoietin formation might be an important factor (Feldman and Bleiberg 1967). This was supported by results showing reversal of erythroid suppression by exogenous erythropoietin administration (Curry et al. 1967a; Bleiberg et al. 1967; Lange et al. 1968; Feldman and Bleiberg 1967; Schooley et al. 1968; O'Grady et al. 1967a, b), or activation of endogenous erythropoietin production by bleeding (Feldman and Bleiberg 1967). It has been directly shown that antiserum against human erythropoietin can simulate the effects of polycythaemia when given to mice (Schooley 1965). O'Grady et al. (1966) and Lange et al. (1968) obtained a decrease in the number and volume of erythroid colonies similar to the result obtained with mild hypertransfusion.

Is the target cell for erythropoietin a multipotential colony forming unit and does this stem cell in the absence of erythropoietin differentiate into a granuloid or megakaryocytic colony? It has been suggested that the number of granulocytic and megakaryocytic colonies increases in the spleens of polycythaemic recipients (Curry et al. 1964; Liron and Feldman 1965; Feldman and Bleiberg 1967) but no increase was observed in subsequent studies or by other workers (Curry et al. 1967a; Lange et al. 1968; Schooley 1964; O'Grady et al. 1966) and an extensive study of 1800 colonies by O'Grady et al. (1967b) disclosed no increase in the number of megakaryocytic or granulocytic colonies in polycythaemic mice. Furthermore a regressional analysis showed complete independence between haematocrit and the numbers of non-erythroid colonies. The evidence that erythroid colonies do not convert to granuloid or megakaryocytic types is not at variance with the concept that the CFU is multipotential, since there is considerable evidence in polycythaemic mice that CFU's still become committed to erythroid differentiation after residence in the spleen but that this process is independent of erythropoietin.

In polycythaemic spleens after marrow transplantation, there is an increase in small undifferentiated colonies in place of the erythroid colonies. These colonies develop in the red pulp and contain 100–200 cells which have abundant cytoplasm, large pale nuclei with peripheral chromatin and large prominent nucleoli (Curry et al. 1967a; Schooley 1966). Activation of endogenous erythropoietin production by bleeding or hypoxia, or administration of exogenous erythropoietin at different stages of colony development has provided considerable information on the differentiation potential of the morphologically undifferentiated microcolonies. Early application of erythropoietin in the first 5 days resulted in the formation of erythroid colonies on day 7, but these had disappeared by day 9 (Feldman and Bleiberg 1967; Bleiberg et al. 1967; O'Grady et al. 1967a, b) suggesting that erythropoietin exerted a morphogenetic rather than a mitogenetic effect in this situation, inducing maturation of erythroid colonies and evacuation or dispersal of the small differentiated colony population. Delay in administration of erythropoietin to as late as 7–9 days in polycythaemic mice resulted in the formation of erythroid colonies within 2 days (Feldman and Bleiberg 1967; Schooley et al. 1968; O'Grady et al. 1967a, b). Such late-appearing erythroid colonies can contain $2\text{--}4 \times 10^4$ differentiated erythroid cells which have developed within 48 hours. If these were produced from a single cell in this time, a doubling time of 3–6 hours would be required, which is so short as to render this possibility most unlikely, and in fact the average doubling time of the cell population in erythroid colonies in the period up to 9–10 days was found to be approximately 12 hours (O'Grady et al. 1967a, b). It is probable therefore that erythropoietin acted upon clones of a few hundred cells generated by 8–9 divisions during the erythropoietin-independent phase of development from single CFU's. This clone size would correspond to the histological evidence for undifferentiated microcolonies in polycythaemic spleens.

3.3.2 *Possible influence of erythropoietin on CFU's*

The two alternative mechanisms of erythropoietin regulation, (a) a direct action on a multipotential stem cell (CFU), or (b) an action on a more differentiated erythropoietin-sensitive cell (ESC) only indirectly influencing the stem-cell compartment, can be resolved only by critical studies on the influence of erythropoietin or erythropoietin deprivation on the CFU population. Unfortunately, experimental results in this area are conflicting. In the preceding section, microcolonies of cells were described in the spleens of irradiated polycythaemic mice which could be converted to erythroid colonies under the influence of erythropoietin. If the ESC is indeed a CFU, an increase in the numbers of CFU's in the spleens of such polycythaemic irradiated mice may be anticipated, and Feldman and Bleiberg (1967) have reported that the CFU content of the irradiated spleen 4 days after marrow grafting was five-fold higher in polycythaemic than in control mice. No such difference was found in this period by O'Grady et al. (1967a, b) or by Pozzi and Silini (1968). Furthermore, at later stages between the 6th–9th day after marrow grafting, fewer CFU's could be recovered from the spleens of poly-cythaemic than of control mice (Schooley 1966; Schooley et al. 1968; Silini 1967). It would seem surprising, if CFU's were indeed susceptible to a differentiating influence of erythropoietin, that their numbers should fall in the polycythaemic spleen in the absence of a differentiating stimulus. More-over, administration of erythropoietin to such polycythaemic animals 4–6 days after marrow grafting augmented, rather than inhibited, the growth of the CFU population (Schooley 1966; Schooley et al. 1968), and the wave of resulting erythropoiesis could not be accounted for by an action of ery-thropoietin directly on CFU's even if all the CFU's in the animal were to differentiate.

The influence of exogenous erythropoietin on CFU regeneration has been studied in a system employing 5-fluorouracil rather than irradiation to eradicate erythroid cells and CFU's from mouse marrow (Reissman and Samorapoonpichit 1969). CFU regeneration was uninfluenced by the ad-ministration of large quantities of exogenous erythropoietin despite the induction of accelerated erythroid regeneration. The limb-shielded, irradi-ated, polycythaemic mouse failed to show increased splenic erythropoiesis during the early stages of splenic regeneration, despite administration of 20 times the dose of erythropoietin required to significantly increase splenic iron incorporation. This result showed that cells (CFU's) migrating from a shielded area and responsible for spleen colonisation are not themselves erythropoietin-sensitive (DeGowin 1967).

Erythropoietin-responsiveness has also been studied in *in vitro* systems where ^{59}Fe incorporation into the cultured cells was used as a measure of erythropoiesis. Cultures of irradiated spleen removed shortly after marrow-cell injection failed to show any erythropoietin stimulation of haem synthesis although CFU's were shown to be present in considerable numbers in the spleen cultures (Mizoguchi et al. 1968). Cultures of normal spleen cells showed a marked increase in haemoglobin synthesis in the presence of erythropoietin but the numbers of CFU's recovered from culture were unaffected and CFU's persisted in culture even after the stage when further erythropoietin responses could not be elicited (Kranz and Fried 1968).

3.3.3 *Influence of irradiation on erythropoietin-sensitive cells*

Erythroid regeneration following whole-body sublethal irradiation has been studied by assaying ^{59}Fe incorporation into polycythaemic mice following administration of erythropoietin at various times after irradiation. The early results were conflicting, with some studies reporting delayed recovery of erythropoietin responsiveness (Gurney et al. 1962, 1965; Gurney 1963; Gurney and Hofstra 1963), and others describing a more rapid return to normal responsiveness (Alexanian et al. 1963; Schooley et al. 1966). It is now apparent that estimates of the relative size of the erythropoietin-sensitive cell (ESC) population depend on the dose of erythropoietin used, with high doses (1.58–15.8 units) causing delayed recovery of normal responses and low doses causing rapid recovery (Lajtha 1967; Byron 1968; Byron and Lajtha 1968). A number of possibilities have been considered to explain this erythropoietin dose-response relationship: (a) it is possible that irradiation may alter the responsiveness of the ESC by decreasing its sensitivity to erythropoietin. In this context, spleen colonies developing from irradiated marrow CFU's exhibit delayed erythroid maturation which may be overcome by increasing erythropoietin levels (Okunewick et al. 1969; Wolf et al. 1968). If this possibility is correct, then high doses of erythropoietin should give the most reliable estimate of the size of the ESC population. However, if decreased erythropoietin responsiveness is due to radiation damage, then the use of high doses of erythropoietin may induce damaged cells to follow short-cut pathways of erythroid differentiation and be counted within the ESC population, whereas in more rigorous tests of reproductive integrity, they would not (Porteous et al. 1965). (b) Since 0.5 units of erythropoietin will have a much shorter period of biological effectiveness than 10 units, the low-dose erythropoietin assay measures the response of cells immediately sensitive to erythropoietin, whereas the high-dose assay provides time for recruitment of unresponsive cells into the ESC compartment. Evidence to support this view was provided by Porteous et al. (1965), who showed that the erythropoietic response to low doses of erythropoietin was more radio-sensitive than the response to high doses suggesting that the latter system measured an additional, and more radio-resistant, population of cells. More direct evidence was provided by Schooley et al. (1967) in mice, subjected to 200 R pre-irradiation. The response to low doses (1 unit) of erythropoietin 10 days after irradiation was considerably higher than in the unirradiated control mice, whereas with 12 units of erythropoietin, the pre-irradiated mouse response was considerably lower than in the control. If, however, the activity of the high dose of erythropoietin was terminated after 6 hours by administration of anti-erythropoietin serum, the same result was obtained as with the low dose, namely, the erythropoietin-sensitive population was significantly greater after pre-irradiation. A probable explanation for the result is that the cells which are immediately erythropoietin-sensitive rebound to a supranormal level in the regeneration phase but the population of potentially-responsive cells which can be recruited into the ESC compartment (and therefore can be detected with high doses of erythropoietin) remains depleted even 10 days after sublethal irradiation. The concept of recruitment is additionally supported by the observation that a low dose of erythropoietin (1 unit) given as a single dose produces a lower response in the normal animal than two doses of 0.5 units given 24 hours apart. Presumably here, the second dose of erythropoietin acts on new ESC's recruited into the compart-ment as a result of depletion of ESC's induced by the primary dose.

The major problem at this stage was whether erythropoietin-sensitivity was a property of a multipotential stem cell (CFU) or a more differentiated cell committed to erythroid differentiation (ESC). The above evidence does not distinguish between these possibilities since the CFU's may only be responsive to erythropoietin when in cell cycle and consequently recruit-ment from an erythropoietin-unresponsive population may simply reflect activation of resting, or G_0, CFU's into cell cycle. Alternatively, recruitment may involve differentiation of the CFU's into a progenitor cell compartment of ESC's. To distinguish between these alternatives the kinetics of the CFU, and ESC populations have been closely studied in various experimental systems.

Recovery of erythropoietin-responsiveness was shown to be similar to CFU recovery measured by endogenous colony formation in the irradiated, limb-shielded mouse (autorepopulation assay) (Weisman et al. 1967; Fried et al. 1966; Porteous and Lajtha 1966; Gurney and Fried 1965; Fried and Gurney 1968; Lajtha 1967; Lajtha et al. 1968). If, however, CFU's were measured by transplantation (exocolonising assay), the post-irradiation recovery kinetics revealed clear differences between the regeneration of CFU's and the recovery of erythropoietin responsiveness and furthermore indicated that the autorepopulating and exocolonising assays were not detecting the same cell population.

Following chronic irradiation (40–50R daily) the erythropoietin response was reduced to 10–15% of normal, whereas the CFU population of femoral marrow was more markedly depressed (0.17–1% of control) when assayed by the exocolonising method. If, however, the CFU's were assayed in an autorepopulation system with shielding of the chronically-irradiated femur and measurement of endogenous spleen colony formation, depression was similar to that seen with the erythropoietin response (10–11% of normal) (Lajtha 1967; Lajtha et al. 1969). The chronically-irradiated rat can maintain normal erythropoiesis, despite a two-thirds depression in haemopoietic recolonising capacity (Blackett et al. 1964).

The delayed recovery of CFU's after sublethal irradiation as detected by the exogenous transplantation assay contrasts with the recovery of erythropoiesis measured by erythropoietic responsiveness of polycythaemic mice and supports the concept that the repopulating cell (CFU) and the ESC are different, whereas the repopulating ability measured by the autorepopulation assay suggests the opposite, namely, that the CFU and ESC are the same. Consequently, considerable importance must be attached to an understanding of the possible differences between the autorepopulating and exogenous assay systems. Four major factors must be taken into account:

(a) The autorepopulation assay measures the rate of seeding of repopulating cells from the shielded region, whereas the exocolonising assay measures the population size. There is considerable evidence that the rate of seeding need not be closely dependent on the absolute size of the repopulating cell compartment of the shielded area. Hanks (1964) e.g. showed that the rate of seeding of CFU's from a shielded limb was not altered by prior sublethal irradiation, which reduced the CFU population to only a few percent of normal. Furthermore, in the early stages following half-body irradiation the rate of CFU seeding from a shielded area was increased to levels in excess of normal (Hellman 1965). The CFU population measured in the autorepopulation assay is predominantly the rapidly mobilisable CFU pool in marrow which has been estimated to be only 0.25% of the total marrow CFU population (Hellman and Grate 1968a).

(b) The exocolonising assay involves handling of cells both in preparation of cell suspensions and in grafting, and may preferentially lose CFU's in cycle.

If so, the exocolonising assay may grossly under-estimate the rate of regeneration of CFU's in rapidly proliferating tissue when compared to assays that do not involve handling of cells (Porteous and Lajtha 1968). However, cell cycle analyses using tritiated thymidine suiciding demonstrated that CFU's detected both by the exogenous assay and by the autorepopulation assay showed a similar degree of depression (43–50%) in animals recovering from sublethal irradiation (Lajtha et al. 1969). If the exogenous assay selected for non-proliferating CFU's, little or no depression of the CFU's would have been anticipated in such preparations following thymidine suiciding.

(c) The autorepopulation assay depends on the receptiveness of the irradiated environment for either seeding or proliferation of the immigrant CFU's and there is evidence that this receptivity is influenced by pre-irradiation (Hellman and Grate 1968b; Lajtha et al. 1968, 1969). Pre-irradiation may increase the physical or physiological space available in the spleen for seeding and proliferation, but the effect is probably not of sufficient magnitude to account for observed differences, nor does it correspond in time with the differences observed between the exogenous and autorepopulation assays.

(d) The results obtained in the autorepopulation assay depend on the particular region shielded and Weisman et al. (1967) found no correlation between erythroid regeneration and endogenous colony formation if the sublethally-irradiated tail, rather than the femur, was shielded.

The exogenous and autorepopulation assays therefore measure two different parameters of the CFU compartment, population size and seeding rate respectively. With moderate radiation-induced depopulation, the autorepopulation assay gives a fair picture of the animal's capacity for haemopoiesis but if irradiation depletion is severe, the exocolonising assay provides a more realistic index of haemopoietic status (Lajtha et al. 1969). We may conclude that the similarity in kinetics of erythroid and CFU regeneration revealed in the autorepopulation assay need not in any way prove that the CFU is erythropoietin-sensitive. Furthermore, the data do not support the view that the exocolonising assay grossly underestimates the size of the stem cell compartment. This consequently strengthens the conclusion drawn from the comparisons of erythroid regeneration and CFU recovery measured by the exogenous assay, that CFU's differ from erythropoietin-sensitive cells.

3.3.4 *Influence of hypoxia on CFU's and erythropoiesis*

If the erythropoietin-sensitive cell is a more differentiated progeny of the multipotential CFU, then chronic erythropoietin stimulation may ultimately result in depletion of the CFU's by differentiation into erythropoietin-sensitive cells (ESC). This possibility was apparently supported by the study of Bruce and McCulloch (1964), who showed that the splenic CFU content (detected by a transplantation assay) fell to 10% of normal over a 10–15 day period of hypoxia. Intermittent hypoxia also decreased spleen CFU content (Stohlman 1967) and in both studies, the initial fall in splenic CFU content followed, rather than preceded, the erythropoietic response.

Okunewick et al. (1969) proposed that hypoxic stress for erythroid differentiation initially depleted the number of ESC's which in turn decreased the CFU pool but as stress increased with continuous hypoxia, both the ESC and CFU pools increased in size to balance the increased demands for red cell output. Cessation of the differentiating stimulus by removal of mice to a normal atmosphere resulted in a short-lived excess of CFU's which was detected by an increase in the radio-resistance of the animal and increase in endogenous colony formation 3 days after cessation of hypoxia. It is relevant in this context to consider that any experimental design that attempts to perturb haemopoiesis to study normal homeostatic mechanisms may produce a change in the normal control mechanism. Thus the investigator may eventually draw a conclusion on the basis of long-term adaptive processes rather than the short-term physiological responses.

A direct effect of hypoxia on CFU's, independent of erythropoietic demand has been suggested by Schooley et al. (1968), who also noted a reduction in the splenic CFU content of hypoxic mice but found a more profound depression in CFU's when anti-erythropoietin serum was administered to hypoxic mice. In this latter instance the antiserum removed the endogenous erythropoietin stimulation and revealed a direct suppressive effect of hypoxia on CFU's independent of pressure for differentiation into an ESC compartment. This conclusion is further supported by studies on the influence of elevated erythropoietin levels produced by exogenous erythropoietin administration (rather than endogenous, hypoxia-induced, erythropoietin) on splenic CFU's (Kubanek et al. 1968a, b). Prolonged administration of high doses of erythropoietin augmented splenic erythropoiesis and increased spleen CFU content by 5-fold within 8–16 days, which was in marked contrast to the hypoxic-induced suppression of CFU's. Marrow CFU's were not significantly changed in this period and may have contributed to the increase in the spleen CFU population by migration (Kubanek et al. 1968b). A word of caution should be introduced here, since exogenous erythropoietin preparations are not completely purified and it is well documented that many non-specific foreign proteins can induce a marked increase in splenic CFU content.

Further evidence that the CFU response to hypoxia does not necessarily correlate directly with the degree of erythroid response was presented by Shadduck et al. (1968). These authors compared two strains of mice with differing responses to hypoxia. One strain developed a modest polycythaemia due to poor erythropoietin production, whilst the other showed a substantial polycythaemia and a markedly increased erythropoietin level. The strain with the least erythroid response showed a marked decrease in splenic CFU's after intermittent hypoxia and an even greater depression with continued hypoxia, whereas the strain with the greatest erythroid response showed no decrease in spleen CFU's after intermittent hypoxia and indeed a slight increase with continuous hypoxia (Kunabek et al. 1968a, b). Since both strains showed elevated splenic CFU levels after exogenous erythropoietin administration at normal atmospheric pressure, it would appear that in both strains, hypoxia counteracts the influence of erythropoietin in elevating CFU's and supports the view that hypoxia has a direct, possibly damaging or inhibiting, influence on the CFU's.

It is evident that the fall in CFU numbers in hypoxia cannot be simply explained by pressure for differentiation into an ESC compartment, but the concept of an ESC compartment distinct from the CFU as suggested by Bruce and McCulloch (1964) remains valid. Indeed recent studies have shown that demand for erythroid differentiation will feed back eventually to the stem-cell level, since turnover of splenic and femoral CFU's was increased markedly in polycythaemic mice following re-establishment or erythropoiesis by exogenous erythropoietin treatment (Guzman and Lajtha 1970).

3.3.5 Kinetic studies on erythropoietin sensitive cells

Early models of erythropoiesis e.g. Lajtha and Oliver (1960) suffered from uncertainty about the status of the morphologically-unrecognisable erythroid progenitor population, and it is only since the introduction of the various assay systems that can characterise this population that the early differentiation events in erythropoiesis have been subject to scrutiny.

Erythropoietin-sensitive cells (ESC) have been analysed indirectly using ^{55}Fe and tritiated thymidine autoradiography. This latter approach is based on the assumption that the labelling index of pro-erythroblasts in the marrow 24–48 hours after tritiated thymidine administration reflects the labelling index of the precursors, since sufficient time is allowed for maturation of pro-erythroblasts labelled directly at the time of tritiated thymidine treatment (Hanna 1967). Using this technique the mean cycle time of pro-erythroblast precursors in both normal and polycythaemic rats was shown to be approximately 30 hours (Blackett 1968; Hanna 1967). Both bleeding and the production of protracted anaemia with phenylhydrazine markedly increased the rate of red-cell production and the rate of proliferation of pro-erythroblast precursors (Blackett 1968). Estimates of cell cycle times of repopulating cells (CFU's) detected in a transplantation assay, and of the pro-erythroblast precursors (ESC's) revealed that in protracted anaemia the cell cycle time of the repopulating cells (CFU's) did not change, in contrast to the increased rate of proliferation of the pro-erythroblast precursors. The reverse situation was evident in chronically-irradiated animals, where the repopulating cells decreased their mean cell cycle time to 12 hours with no change in proliferative activity of the pro-erythroblast precursors (Blackett 1968). Other experimental studies using agents to kill cells at specific stages of the cycle, have confirmed that the ESC population can be distinguished from the stem cell (CFU) compartment on the basis of proliferative activity. Large doses of high specific activity tritiated thymidine depressed the erythropoietin responsiveness of polycythaemic mice by 70% within 2 hours, whereas the CFU population showed hardly any depression when measured by the exocolonising assay (Lajtha 1967; Porteous and Lajtha 1968; Lajtha et al. 1969). Even when the CFU's had been activated into cell cycle in sublethally irradiated mice, the S phase killing agent hydroxyurea (see Chapter 2) also suppressed the erythropoietin responsiveness of polycythaemic mice but failed to reduce CFU numbers over a 4-hour period of observation (Morse et al. 1970). These studies provide further evidence that the ESC's are a different cell population from the CFU's since the former but not the latter are in cell cycle, even in polycythaemic suppressed mice in which no erythropoiesis is occurring. It may be necessary to propose that the total numbers of ESC's in the body are regulated by a death control process since the population continues to proliferate but does not increase in total number in the absence of erythroid differentiation.

It has been suggested that the committed ESC compartment is to a large extent self-maintaining (Morse and Stohlman 1966). In the face of increasing pressure for differentiation, the ESC compartment may decrease its turnover time by increasing the proportion of cells in cycle or by shortening the cell cycle time. In addition, cells may be recruited from the more undifferentiated stem-cell compartment by an irreversible differentiation step with the magnitude of the recruitment being controlled by a feedback mechanism sensitive to population size. Such proposals must remain speculative until more detailed knowledge is available on the kinetics of both the stem-cell and progenitor compartments. However, recent studies have provided considerable insight into the nature and timing of interaction between erythropoietin and its target cell. Two early and conflicting models were proposed to explain erythropoietin action on the ESC compartment. Lajtha (1964) proposed that erythropoietin caused the differentiation of G_0 or resting precursor cells, with cells in cycle being for the most part unavailable for differentiation. The second model proposed that erythropoietin was able to enter the ESC's during the G_1 phase of the cycle (Kretchmar 1966). Homeostasis could then be maintained by varying the duration of G_1; e.g. when G_1 is lengthened, the time in G_1 may exceed the biological life span of intracellular erythropoietin resulting in insufficient carry-over of the erythropoietin into the S phase where it is postulated to exert its initial differentiation action. Further increase in the rate of ESC proliferation would eventually reduce the duration of G_1 resulting in a decrease in effective interplay between the ESC's and erythropoietin, thus preventing depletion of the population.

The evidence, mainly derived from experiments using cell cycle poisons supports this latter model. The influence of vinblastine on the erythropoietic response of polycythaemic mice induced by erythropoietin administration indicated that most ESC's appeared to be in cell cycle with a cycle time of 9 hours, responded to erythropoietin during the G_1 period and subsequently entered mitosis within a few hours (Hodgson 1967; Kretchmar et al. 1970).

Schooley (1965) on the basis of colchicine treatment data and tritiated thymidine labelling also suggested that erythropoietin acted after metaphase and before the S phase. In studies on the erythropoietic response of sublethally irradiated polycythaemic rats given erythropoietin, it was shown that ESC's entered a period of extreme sensitivity to actinomycin D at a time of least sensitivity to ionising radiation, suggesting that the RNA synthesising stage, triggered by erythropoietin, is not especially radiosensitive (Hodgson and Eskuche 1968). Furthermore, colchicine sensitivity studies revealed that the ESC's were undergoing mitosis about 4 hours before entering an erythropoietin-responsive stage, which involved RNA synthesis and lasted about 8 hours. Following differentiation to pro-erythroblasts, the cells then entered a radiosensitive stage preparatory to the S phase which began about 16 hours after erythropoietin action.

Experiments using hydroxyurea as a specific cytotoxic agent for cells in S phase showed that when hydroxyurea was given to polycythaemic mice at the same time as erythropoietin, the marrow erythroid response was slightly reduced and more prolonged. Therefore, some ESC's were clearly in S phase rather than in a G_0 state, but the fraction was small, indicating a population in cell cycle with a long G_1. When, however, the interval between erythropoietin treatment and hydroxyurea administration was lengthened, a greater erythroid depression was seen, indicating that a larger fraction of ESC's was in S phase (Morse et al. 1970). Since S phase is usually constant in mammalian haemopoietic cells, the shortening of apparent ESC generation time is best explained by a cell population with a variable G_1 period which shortens in response to the increased demand imposed by erythropoietin. This data is not incompatible with the observation of Hodgson (1967) that most ESC's appear to have a cell cycle time of 9 hours since if only the first wave of reticulocytes appearing after erythropoietin stimulation is considered, the depression obtained with hydroxyurea is similar to that seen following vinblastine treatment (Hodgson, G., personal communication). The experimental design could not, however, distinguish between an ESC compartment with all cells in cycle with prolonged G_1 or with some cells in G_0 and the remainder in active cycle. Nor could it accurately determine the rate of recruitment from the multipotential stem-cell compartment. It did appear, however, that CFU's were committed to the ESC compartment as a result of hydroxyurea-induced ESC depletion. Though CFU numbers did not fall initially as a result of a direct cytotoxic effect of hydroxyurea, the population was depleted by 14 hours at a time when the ESC compartment had completely regenerated and indeed even showed a degree of overshoot (Morse et al. 1970).

3.3.6 Summary

The proposal that the ESC's reside in a separate progenitor cell compartment, distinct from, and more differentiated than, the stem-cell (or CFU) compartment appears to conform with the majority of experimental observations. However, it should be borne in mind that the alternative concept of a stem cell responsive to inducers of differentiation only at a certain stage of its cell cycle, is not readily distinguishable from the concept of a separate ESC in the many experiments where kinetics of recovery of erythropoietin-sensitivity have been studied. Until a suitable single cell assay system for ESC's can be developed, our knowledge of this cell population remains at best second-hand. It is to be hoped that techniques for cell separation, e.g. velocity sedimentation separation, which has already been used to separate ESC's in rat bone marrow (McCool et al. 1970), will be used to distinguish ESC's from stem cells or other progenitor cells in order to provide a definitive answer to this problem.

The concept of a discrete compartment of ESC's does not of necessity imply uniformity of behaviour of all cells in the compartment with respect to such parameters as susceptibility to differentiation or capacity to undergo self-renewal. Indeed it is most probable that a hierarchy of cells will emerge, at different levels of differentiation, and which at the moment are placed within a single compartment. It has further been suggested that there may also be other populations of cells, intermediate between stem cells and the ESC's (Lamerton 1970).

Ultimately, studies using purified populations of ESC's and erythropoietin will provide invaluable information of general application, on the very intimate relationship between cell division and cell differentiation at the molecular level.

3.4 *In vitro colony-forming cells (in vitro CFC's)*

This section will discuss another group of haemopoietic cells, which appears to belong to the progenitor group of cells, in this case progenitors of granulocytes and macrophage-monocytes. Two independent studies (Pluznik and Sachs 1965, 1966; Bradley and Metcalf 1966) indicated that when suspensions of bone marrow or spleen cells were cultured under suitable conditions in agar, colonies of cells developed, which analysis showed to be composed of granulocytes and/or macrophages (Bradley and Metcalf 1966; Ichikawa et al. 1966). The general technique of agar culture has been described in Chapter 2. The dependence of colony formation in this *in vitro* culture system on a special factor – the colony stimulating factor (CSF), will be discussed at length in a subsequent chapter, together with an analysis of the cellular processes involved in colony formation. In the present discussion, attention will be concentrated on the nature of the cells initiating colony formation *in vitro*.

3.4.1 *Cellular composition of in vitro colonies*

When agar cultures of cell suspensions containing colony-forming cells are examined after an incubation period of 7–10 days, three distinct morphological types of colony can be observed. These are indicated in Figure 3.13 and

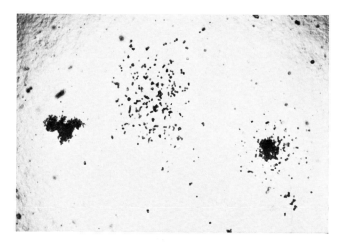

Fig. 3.13.   Low power view of an agar culture of mouse bone-marrow cells stimulated by serum from an endotoxin-injected mouse. Note compact granulocytic colony (left), mixed colony (right), and loose macrophage colony (centre). Unstained × 40.

are (a) compact, globular aggregates or grape-like clusters of three or four dense cellular aggregates which consist of pure populations of granulocytes in varying stages of differentiation from myeloblasts to polymorphs; (b) aggregates with a dense central core of cells surrounded by a looser peripheral mantle of cells. These usually consist of a central core of tightly-packed granulocytes, with an outer mantle composed of macrophages or a mixture of macrophages and granulocytes; and (c) loose globular aggregates of widely separated cells which are usually pure populations of macrophages, each with a single excentric nucleus and bulky vacuolated cytoplasm. This morphological description of the different types of *in vitro* colonies suggests that colonies can be typed from their gross morphology. Unfortunately under some culture conditions, e.g. when using low concentrations of CSF or highly purified urine CSF, granulocytic colonies can occur as loose aggregates and macrophage colonies as compact globular aggregates. It is necessary therefore always to sample colonies and type them from stained preparations for accurate colony classification.

A more detailed analysis of the sequence of changes in colonies developing in agar has indicated (a) that most colonies early in development are composed of pure populations of granulocytic cells regardless of whether, when fully developed, they are composed of granulocytes and/or macrophages (Metcalf 1969a), and (b) that macrophages begin to appear in some developing colonies after the second day of incubation (Metcalf 1969a) and depending on the type of stimulus used to provoke colony formation, some or most colonies eventually become composed of pure populations of macrophages (Metcalf et al. 1967).

It is uncertain at the present time how much significance can be attached to the obviously different morphological types of colony seen in routine 7 or 10 day cultures, although the differing morphology clearly indicates some sort of heterogeneity amongst colony-forming cells. It has been tacitly assumed by some workers that the cells forming granulocytic, mixed or macrophage colonies represent separate populations of colony-forming cells (Ichikawa et al. 1966; Paran and Sachs 1968). While it is clear that there is extreme heterogeneity amongst *in vitro* colony-forming cells, to date cell separation techniques have not produced pure populations of cells forming one morphological type of colony or another. At present therefore there is not sufficient evidence to justify the conclusion that there are three distinct types of *in vitro* colony-forming cells. For this reason, in the discussion to follow, all *in vitro* colony-forming cells will be discussed together, with the reservation that subsequent work in this field may necessitate a re-examination of the data and a subdivision of *in vitro* CFC's into three or more subclasses.

Unlike the *in vivo* situation with spleen colonies, there is no minimal size for an *in vitro* colony and as discussed in a subsequent chapter, colonies can vary in size from 50–5,000 cells, depending on the culture conditions used. In general, however, with most culture conditions, colonies increase in size progressively for at least 7–10 days, mitotic activity decreasing rapidly after this time and with increasing cell death, colony size can actually decline after 10 days of incubation.

Occasional colonies at 5–10 days of incubation contain cell populations showing a high degree of uniformity of differentiation e.g. all cells are myeloblasts or all are polymorphs but typically, colonies contain a mixed population of cells, some cells remaining primitive and exhibiting high mitotic activity whilst others differentiate to non-dividing cells. With increasing incubation, there is an overall drift in colony composition towards progressively more mature cells which exhibit decreasing mitotic activity. In the granulocytic series, differentiation can proceed to mature polymorphs with multilobular nuclei, but often differentiation ceases at the metamyelocyte or band stage. Granulocyte cells reaching the polymorph stage of differentiation appear to have a limited survival capacity in the cultures and usually disintegrate after 2 or 3 days.

The identification of cells in these colonies as granulocytes has been made using Leishman- or orcein-stained preparations (Metcalf et al. 1967) by the demonstration of peroxidase reactivity in human colony granulocytes (Senn et al. 1967) and by identifying typical neutrophil granules in electron-micrograph sections of colony cells (Figure 3.14). The macrophages usually

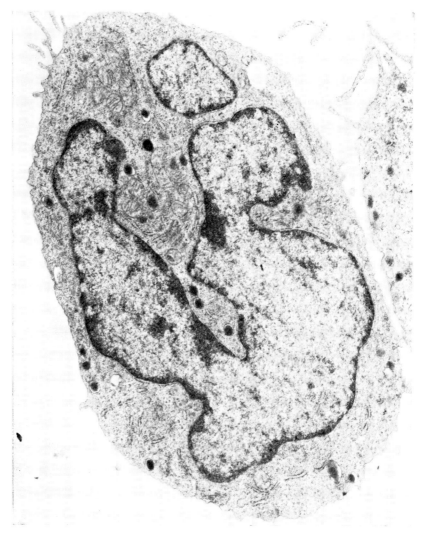

Fig. 3.14.   Electronmicrograph of a single granulocytic cell from an agar colony, showing typical neutrophil granules × 21,000. (Photograph by courtesy of Dr. T. Mandel.)

have a single round, excentric, nucleus and a bulky vacuolated cytoplasm. Less commonly, macrophages have two round excentric nuclei. In developing colonies, the macrophages exhibit high mitotic activity, but as the colonies mature, macrophages lose their proliferative capacity and paralleling this,

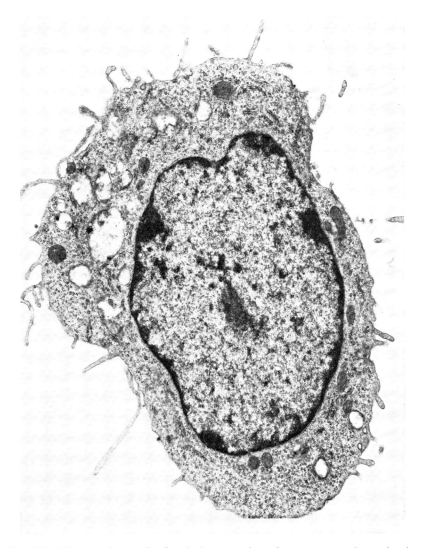

Fig. 3.15. Electronmicrograph of a single macrophage from an agar colony, showing phagosomes and numerous polyribosomes × 25,600. (Photograph by courtesy of Dr. T. Mandel.)

their nuclei tend to reduce in volume and become progressively more ex-centric. Both dividing and mature macrophages can be shown to be actively phagocytic for carbon and for the surrounding agar (Metcalf et al. 1967; Ichikawa et al. 1966). The phagocytosis of agar, which is metachromatic in Leishman-stained preparations, sometimes results in these cells containing metachromatic granules in their cytoplasm and having an appearance resem-bling mast cells (Pluznik and Sachs 1965, 1966). In electronmicrographs, the macrophages exhibit phagosomes in the cytoplasm together with irregular dense aggregates of ingested material, presumably ingested agar-medium (Figure 3.15).

Eosinophilic colonies have not been observed in cultures of normal mouse bone-marrow cells, but these do not appear to have been searched for ex-haustively and may have been missed, as the morphology of eosinophils in the mouse in rather similar to that of other early granulocytic cells. Small eosinophilic colonies have recently been observed in cultures of human bone-marrow cells (Senn, J., personal communication). Occasional small colonies have been observed which were composed of large cells with multiple round nuclei and these had some resemblance to megakaryocytes. However, the phagocytic activity of these cells makes it probable that they were multi-nucleate macrophages. Erythroid colonies have never been observed in agar cultures of normal bone marrow or spleen cells or even in cultures derived from mice with erythroleukaemia induced by the Friend virus (Metcalf, D. and Foster, R., unpublished data). The addition of erythropoietin to the cultures did not result in the development of erythroid colonies (Bradley et al. 1969; Paran and Sachs 1968).

Thus the agar-culture technique in its present form seems capable only of growing colonies of the granulocytic and/or macrophage type.

3.4.2   *Clonal nature of in vitro colonies*

Colonies growing in agar are usually discrete and culture conditions can be arranged so that only a few, widely-separated, colonies are present in a culture. It is tempting to assume that these colonies are clones derived from single colony-forming cells. However, the incidence of colony-forming cells is only of the order of 1 in 500 bone-marrow cells, which means that sur-rounding each developing colony there are potentially large numbers of other cells in the agar which might enter a developing colony and proliferate there. If this happens colonies could no longer be regarded as clones even if initiated by a single cell. This question is of particular relevance for the understanding of the nature of mixed colonies, where populations of both granulocytes and macrophages are present.

The capacity of the agar-culture system to support discrete colony growth in a semi-solid microenvironment theoretically allows the possibility of rigid proof of the clonal nature of colonies by the culture of single colony-forming cells. Techniques such as glass-bead column fractionation, BSA gradient sedimentation and velocity sedimentation have been employed in an attempt to obtain pure populations of *in vitro* colony-forming cells (Moore et al. 1970; Worton et al. 1969a). While some success has been achieved in enriching fractions for colony-forming cells, the techniques are not sufficiently advanced to obtain pure populations of these cells and it has not yet been practicable to carry out such single-cell cloning experiments.

To date the evidence on the clonal nature of *in vitro* colonies is indirect. Titration curves for colony incidence using varying numbers of plated cells extrapolate with a regression line consistent with a single cell origin (Pluznik and Sachs 1965; Bradley and Metcalf 1966). The kinetics of the radiation sensitivity curves for *in vitro* CFC's are consistent with a single hit effect, again suggesting that colonies are initiated by single cells (Robinson et al. 1967; Senn and McCulloch 1970).

In view of the fact that most colonies, regardless of the type of cells in the final colony, initially develop as small aggregates of primitive granulocytes, it is important in establishing the likelihood that mixed colonies could be clones, to demonstrate that granulocytic cells in early colonies can transform to macrophages. This question has been analysed by transferring single cells from developing 2-day colonies (containing 4–16 cells) to recipient agar cultures and then studying their subsequent behaviour (Metcalf 1970a). An analysis of donor colony cells showed that at the time the transfers were undertaken, more than 99 % of the cells involved were granulocytic. Analysis of 239 single cells 3–5 days after transfer showed that 48 had transformed to typical macrophages without cell division or had divided to form clusters of macrophages or mixed clusters of macrophages and granulocytes (Tables 3.6 and 3.7). This study established that some granulocytes at some stage in differentiation can transform to macrophages and that it is at least feasible that a mixed colony could represent a clone derived from a single colony-forming cell. However, this work has not eliminated the possibility that macrophages, which can be found in these agar cultures between developing colonies, might also be able to enter and proliferate in developing granulocytic colonies. Further evidence on this question will be discussed in Chapter 7.

TABLE 3.6

Transformation of single granulocytic cells to macrophages after transfer to recipient
cultures
Analysis of control 2-day colony cells = 461/466 (99%) granulocytes

Days after transfer	No. recovered/ No. transferred	Percent of recovered cells or clusters		
		Granulocytes	Mixed	Macrophages
1	8/11 (73%)	100	0	0
2	9/17 (53%)	75	12	13
3	49/112 (44%)	47	16	37
4	26/76 (34%)	33	8	59
5	9/51 (18%)	11	0	89

TABLE 3.7

Analysis of cells or clusters recovered 3–5 days after transfer of single granulocytic cells

	Single cells		Clusters		
	Granulocytes	Macrophages	Granulocytes	Mixed	Macrophages
Number	9	16	27	11	21
Mean size (range)	—	—	8 (2-27)	4 (3-7)	4 (2-12)

At the present time it seems reasonable to assume that at least some *in vitro*
colonies are clones derived from single colony-forming cells and that
virtually all colonies are at least *initiated* by single colony-forming cells.
On this basis, the enumeration of colonies in cultures serves as a satisfactory
assay system for determining the occurrence and frequency of this type of
cell in various haemopoietic populations.

3.4.3   *Location and incidence of in vitro colony-forming cells*

There are certain technical problems in determining the true incidence of
in vitro CFC's in various tissues. The number of colonies developing *in vitro*

from a constant number of haemopoietic cells is dependent on the concentration of CSF in the culture medium and to a lesser degree on the general adequacy of the culture conditions. A sigmoid dose response relationship exists between CSF concentration and colony numbers (Metcalf and Stanley 1969) and not all surveys to determine the frequency of *in vitro* CFC's in various tissues have been performed using sufficiently high concentrations of CSF to guarantee that plateau numbers of colonies were being obtained. Furthermore, it has been impossible so far to estimate the general 'plating efficiency' of current culture conditions. However, it seems likely that these cultures under optimal conditions detect a high proportion of colony-forming cells. In cultures using bone-marrow cells from Freund's adjuvant-treated mice separated on glass-bead columns and BSA gradients, some cell fractions contained as many as one colony-forming cell in five, and these fractions were certainly not pure cell populations.

With these reservations, regarding the ability of agar cultures to detect *all* colony-forming cells, repeated assays on bone-marrow cells using a variety of techniques for colony stimulation have yielded incidence figures of one *in vitro* colony-forming cell per 500 bone-marrow cells and this figure ($2/10^3$ cells) should be used as a reference figure in considering incidence figures of colony-forming cells quoted for other organs (see later), which were often obtained using culture conditions with less efficient colony stimulation and where incidence figures were standardised to an arbitrary figure of 1 colony-forming cell per 10^3 control bone marrow cells.

In the adult mouse, *in vitro* CFC's occur only in the bone marrow ($2/10^3$ cells) spleen ($1-2/10^5$ cells) and blood ($1/5 \times 10^5$ cells). No *in vitro* colony-forming cells have been detected in the thymus or in lymphoid organs. The location and incidence of *in vitro* CFC's in embryonic tissues will be considered in detail in a later chapter, but in brief, these cells are first detected in the 7-day yolk sac, then subsequently in the developing liver and finally in the developing spleen and bone marrow.

3.4.4   *Relation of stem cells to in vitro colony-forming cells*

In the adult mouse the distribution of stem cells (CFU's) and *in vitro* colony-forming cells is restricted to the same three organs – bone marrow, spleen and blood. Furthermore, studies which were undertaken to analyse the content of *in vitro* colony-forming cells and CFU's in spleen colonies gave initial results which suggested a certain linearity of relationship between the frequency of the two cell types in individual colonies. Because of this, the suggestion was made that *in vitro* CFC's and spleen colony-forming (stem) cells were identical (Wu et al. 1968b).

Subsequent observations have made it most unlikely that the cells forming spleen colonies *in vivo* (CFU's) are in fact identical with cells forming colonies *in vitro*:

(a) Wu et al. (1968b) used a radiation-induced chromosome marker system to prove that cells forming colonies in culture and in the spleen belonged to the same clone. Although analysis of some 96 spleen colonies for both CFU and *in vitro* CFC content revealed a very extensive heterogeneity in spleen colony content of the cells detected in these two assays, a highly significant correlation was noted in spleen colony content of CFU's and *in vitro* CFC's making it highly improbable that this association was occurring by chance. Furthermore, linear regression analysis showed that a straight line fitted the data from all colonies which had a slope of 0.91 and an intercept not significantly different from zero (after adjusting for CFU seeding efficiency by an *f* value of 0.17). These results were not incompatible with the conclusion that both assays were detecting the same cell type or at least two very closely related populations. In a more extensive analysis of spleen colonies for their content of CFU's and *in vitro* CFC's, Moore and Metcalf (1970b) also

TABLE 3.8

Correlation in individual spleen colonies between CFU and *in vitro* CFC content

Age of colonies (days)	Donor cells	Number of colonies	Correlation coefficient R CFU/*in vitro* CFC	p	Log ratio CFU/*in vitro* CFC**
9–11	Adult marrow	70	0.568	0.001	0.33 $\pm$0.22
	Yolk sac or foetal liver	82	0.354	0.001	0.89 $\pm$0.24
	Vinblastine-treated bone marrow*	14	0.760	0.001	0.52 $\pm$0.29
12–14	Adult marrow	78	0.339	0.001	0.45 $\pm$0.24
	Vinblastine-treated bone marrow	24	0.711	0.001	0.036$\pm$0.012

* 1 mg vinblastine 24 hours previously.
** $\pm$ standard error.

demonstrated a highly significant correlation between the CFU and *in vitro* CFC populations in colonies derived from embryonic, adult or adult G_0 (vinblastine-resistant) CFU's (see Table 3.8). Pooled results from a large number of spleen colony assays are shown in Figure 3.16, without adjustment of the data in any way for seeding or plating efficiency. It would appear that spleen colonies containing large numbers of CFU's have in general 5–10-fold more *in vitro* CFC's, whereas colonies containing only a few CFU's have even fewer *in vitro* CFC's. The ratio of CFU's to *in vitro* CFC's is shown in Table 3.8. There does not appear to be any significant difference in this ratio during the period of colony development between 9–14 days, but there were some differences in colonies from an embryonic source which had on average fewer *in vitro* CFC's than adult colonies with the same CFU content. A highly significant difference in this ratio was seen in colonies developing from the vinblastine-resistant CFU's when compared with embryonic or normal adult colonies and was due to a very considerable excess of *in vitro* CFC's found in such colonies. These results argue strongly that *in vitro* CFC's and CFU's are indeed members of a different cell popu-

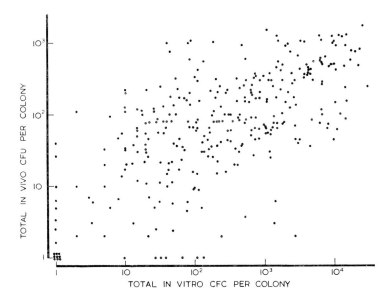

Fig. 3.16.   A log-log plot of total CFU and *in vitro* CFC content of individual spleen colonies. Each point is mean data for a single spleen colony. Colonies assayed between 8–14 days of growth and CFU source was adult marrow and spleen or foetal liver and yolk sac. CFU values not adjusted for seeding efficiency.

TABLE 3.9

Correlation in spleen colonies derived from normal bone-marrow cells between granulocyte content and CFU or *in vitro* CFC content

Colony age (days)	Mean percent granulocytes	CFU		in vitro CFC	
		Correlation coefficient R	p	Correlation coefficient R	p
13	2.09	0.49	0.02	0.76	0.001
14	4.07	0.37	0.05	0.71	0.001

lation but that a very close relationship, probably that of parent to progeny exists.

The *in vitro* CFC content of the colony is probably highly dependent on the growth of the CFU population, but also shows a highly significant correlation with the granulocytic content of the colony (Table 3.9), whereas the CFU's showed only a poor and barely significant correlation. Such a correlation may be anticipated in view of the granulocytic differentiation seen in the colonies *in vitro*.

If the true seeding efficiency of CFU's in the spleen is 0.04 (see Section 3.2.5) then in colonies between 12–14 days of growth which are derived from adult CFU's the CFU population will out-number the *in vitro* CFC's by approximately 11 to 1. It is most unlikely that the plating efficiency of the *in vitro* CFC's is as low as 0.09 and thus, on average, colonies must contain more stem cells (CFU's) than *in vitro* CFC's. Since the majority of colonies sampled were predominantly erythroid this result is perhaps not surprising.

(b) When normal mouse bone-marrow cells were passed through glass-bead columns under conditions favouring active cell adherence and assayed for CFU's and *in vitro* colony-forming cells, no correspondence in the behaviour of the two cell types was observed (D. Metcalf, M. A. S. Moore, K. Shortman and H. Janoshwitz, unpublished data). Overall recovery of CFU's from the columns was 82% and of *in vitro* colony-forming cells, 66%. As may be seen from Table 3.10, the cell population in the filtrate (Fraction I) was enriched for CFU's and depleted of *in vitro* colony-forming cells. Furthermore in the adherent fractions (Fractions III and IV) there was depletion of CFU's and considerable enrichment for *in vitro* colony-forming cells. A similar type of separation was observed using glass bead columns at

TABLE 3.10

Differential behaviour of CFU's and *in vitro* colony-forming cells on glass-bead columns

Fraction number	Number per 10^5 nucleated cells		Ratio CFU's to *in vitro* colony-forming cells
	CFU's	*In vitro* colony-forming cells	
Original	46	108	0.43
Fraction I	88	56	1.57
II	125	232	0.54
III	40	347	0.12
IV	28	100	0.28

4 °C. The most useful fraction of these column-separated populations appeared to be Fraction III, which contained 17% of total CFU's and 29% of total *in vitro* CFC's present in the starting population. Analysis of the differential cell counts from these column fractions (Table 3.11) indicated that the Fraction I population had been enriched for small lymphocyte-like cells and depleted of primitive granulocytes, whereas Fraction III populations showed depletion of small lymphocytes and an enrichment for primitive granulocytes.

(c) When normal mouse bone-marrow cells were centrifuged in BSA

TABLE 3.11

Distribution of cells of different morphology in column-separated fractions of normal mouse bone marrow

	Distribution as percentage of input cells					
	All nucleated cells	Blasts	Myeloblasts and myelocytes	Metamyelo-cytes and polymorphs	Lympho-cytes	Nucleated erythroid cells
Fraction						
I	19	0	0	3	47	15
II	4	0	0	2	6	7
III	20	30	26	31	8	7
IV	29	26	76	36	19	22
Overall recovery	72	56	102	72	80	51

density gradients, CFU's and *in vitro* colony-forming cells were found to be widely distributed throughout different density regions (Haskill et al. 1970). The distribution of both cell types was able to be resolved into a series of reproducible peaks. Although most density fractions contained cells of both types the density profiles of the two cell populations did not match. These differences were exaggerated in mice injected with Freund's complete adjuvant. The total content of CFU's in the bone marrow was not increased by this treatment, whereas *in vitro* CFC's rose 4–5-fold. Similarly in the spleen, CFU numbers rose 13-fold but *in vitro* CFC's rose 128-fold. Of more interest was the observation that with bone-marrow cells from mice injected 7 days previously with Freund's adjuvant an almost complete separation of the density profiles of the two cell types was apparent (Figure 3.17).

Similar observations on differences in density distribution patterns between CFU's and *in vitro* colony-forming cells were made in a study of haemopoietic cell populations in the developing foetal mouse liver (Moore et al. 1970). At 10.5 days of development, both cell types had similar density profiles, but by the 14th day, distinct differences were apparent.

(d) Similar evidence of dissimilarity between CFU's and *in vitro* CFC's was obtained by Worton et al. (1969a) using the velocity sedimentation technique for separating cells on the basis of cell size. *In vitro* colony-forming cells moved with a higher sedimentation velocity than most CFU's, although as with density gradient separation, most fractions contained cells of both types. The data obtained indicated that most *in vitro* colony-forming cells tended to have a large cell volume.

(e) As discussed above, the injection of lethal doses of tritiated thymidine to normal adult animals kills only a small fraction of bone-marrow CFU's when these populations are assayed 2 hours after injection. This fraction has been estimated at about 10% (Becker et al. 1965; Lajtha et al. 1969). In contrast, assays on *in vitro* colony-forming cells in the same animals revealed a reduction of 43% (Lajtha et al. 1969). A similar difference was obtained by Rickard et al. (1970), who employed hydroxyurea as a selective toxic agent for cells in S phase. Two hours after treatment of mice with hydroxyurea, CFU's were depressed 15–20% but *in vitro* CFC's approximately 50%. On the other hand, Iscove et al. (1970), using an *in vitro* exposure of bone-marrow cells for 20 min to tritiated thymidine, reported only a 35% reduction in *in vitro* CFC's, which increased to 75–80% in regenerating marrow. The experiments indicate clear differences between CFU's and *in vitro* colony-forming cells with respect to their status in the cell cycle in normal animals, most CFU's being in a G_0 state. Most *in vitro* colony-forming cells are in

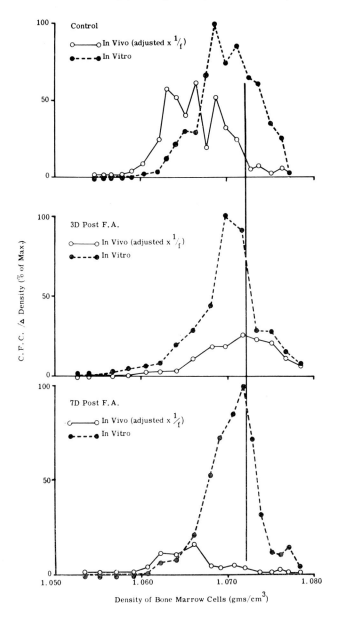

Fig. 3.17.   Density distribution profiles of CFU's and *in vitro* CFC's in normal marrow and in marrow 3 and 7 days after complete Freund's adjuvant (F.A.) treatment (0.2 ml i.p.). CFU profiles adjusted for seeding efficiency. Profiles normalized so that the areas under the curves are related to the absolute numbers of CFU's and *in vitro* CFC's per femoral shaft. (From Haskill et al. 1970, reproduced by permission of J. Cell. Physiol.)

active cell cycle, but it is possible that a smaller subpopulation of these cells may be in a G_0 state or a more prolonged cell cycle.

(f) Indirect evidence that CFU's must be different from *in vitro* colony-forming cells was provided by Bennett et al. (1968), who assayed both cell types in W^v/W^v and W/W^v mice with genetically-determined anaemia. Marrow cells from these mice produced very few spleen colonies and these were also of small size, but the same marrow-cell suspensions contained normal numbers of *in vitro* colony-forming cells which formed colonies of normal size in agar.

(g) A further difference in the behaviour of CFU's and *in vitro* CFC's was revealed in experiments designed to investigate the recovery of both these cell types from various tissues and at various time intervals following the injection of marrow cells into lethally-irradiated recipients. The recovery of CFU's has been described in Section 3.2.5, and as previously reported, between 15–20% of injected CFU's could be recovered from the spleen within 2 hours after injection, and 0.7–0.8% from the femoral shaft. Approximately 50% of all injected CFU's could be recovered from the various tissues in the animal 2 hours after injection. In contrast, no *in vitro* CFC's could be recovered from the spleen at this stage (despite the presence of 1–2×10^4 *in vitro* CFC's in the marrow inoculum) and only 0.3% could be recovered in femoral marrow and these latter may have been host cells that survived the irradiation. The reason for such a rapid disappearance of the vast majority of injected *in vitro* CFC's is puzzling, but it is possible that they underwent rapid differentiation or death in the irradiated environment. The regeneration of the *in vitro* CFC population was first evident by 24 hours after injection and the population increased exponentially in the spleen with a doubling time of approximately 14 hours (Figure 3.3). A slower rate of regeneration was evident in the marrow with a doubling time of 24 hours. The early stages of *in vitro* CFC recovery in the spleen coincided with the dip in spleen recovery of CFU's and the 48 hour lag period that preceded exponential expansion of the CFU population. Differentiation of CFU's into *in vitro* CFC's during this period may well have contributed to this dip and lag period (Moore and Metcalf 1970b).

(h) The cytotoxic drug vinblastine, which blocks cells entering mitosis, has a differential effect on the survival of CFU's and *in vitro* CFC's. The effect of 24 hours of treatment with different doses of vinblastine on the absolute number of both CFU's and *in vitro* CFC's in the mouse femoral marrow is shown in Figure 3.4. CFU's were depleted with increasing doses of vinblastine until a plateau of approximately 3–5% of control values was obtained

with doses of 0.5 mg and greater. In contrast, *in vitro* CFC's fell progressively
with dosage to less than 0.07% of control values 24 hours after treatment
with 1 mg of vinblastine. Consequently, in marrow 24 hours after administration of 0.5 mg of vinblastine, a 15–20-fold excess of CFU's relative to
in vitro CFC's existed, and after 1 mg, a 60–70-fold excess was present
(Haskill et al. 1970).

A prolonged high-dose regime of vinblastine does not provide information
directly on normal cell cycle parameters both because of its possible toxic
effects on stages of the cell cycle other than mitosis, and because elimination
of proliferating cells may activate a normally dormant population into cycle
thus placing them at risk to the vinblastine killing effect. The results do,
however, reveal a differential sensitivity of the cells detected in the *in vivo*
and *in vitro* assays and clearly demonstrate that vinblastine-resistant CFU's
are incapable of forming colonies in agar.

Density distribution analysis of marrow 24 hours after 0.5 mg of vinblastine
revealed a depression of CFU's throughout the entire density range, and an
almost complete elimination of *in vitro* CFC's. In the density region 1.068 to
1.071 gm per cm^3, no *in vitro* CFC's could be detected, whereas considerable
numbers of CFU's were present (18 per 10^5). Cells were transferred from this
density region into lethally irradiated recipients, and 7 days later their
regenerating marrow was removed and subjected to density separation and
in vivo and *in vitro* colony assay. The results are shown in Figure 3.18 and

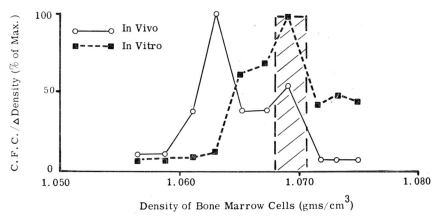

Fig. 3.18. Density profiles of CFU's and *in vitro* CFC's obtained from femoral marrow of
irradiated recipients 7 days after transfer of cells from density region 1.068–1.071 of a
density gradient of vinblastine-treated marrow (0.5 mg for 24 hours). (From Haskill et al.
1970, reproduced by permission of J. Cell. Physiol.).

clearly revealed that CFU's can generate a population of *in vitro* CFC's in marrow, and that the majority of the latter were detected in the density region devoid of such cells upon original transfer (Haskill et al. 1970). The relationship between the CFU and the *in vitro* CFC is therefore most probably that of parent to progeny, with CFU's differentiating into the *in vitro* CFC compartment.

The unique capacity of CFU's surviving 24 hours of treatment with 1 mg of vinblastine to produce spleen colonies with an exceptionally high content of CFU's has been discussed in detail in Section 3.2.11. It is only necessary at this stage to point out that when such colonies were assayed for *in vitro* CFC's they contained very large numbers of these cells, higher even than the colony content of CFU's (see Table 3.12). The mean *in vitro* CFC content of 12 day spleen colonies derived from vinblastine-resistant CFU's was 80–90 times greater than the mean value of normal colonies. Further evidence that CFU's are a heterogeneous population with respect to their capacity to generate *in vitro* CFC's is shown in Figure 3.19. In this experiment described in Section 3.2.11, normal or vinblastine-resistant CFU's were separated into a number of density subpopulations, and the spleen colonies produced from such CFU's were assayed for *in vitro* CFC content. No density difference was evident in the normal CFU population in the cells' capacity to produce *in vitro* CFC's. However, the vinblastine-resistant CFU's in the light density region of the gradient only, were endowed with the capacity to produce

TABLE 3.12

Total content of CFU's and *in vitro* CFC's in spleen colonies derived from marrow cells from normal or vinblastine-treated donors*

Colony age (days)	Type of donor	Number of colonies	Mean total CFU**	Mean total *in vitro* CFC+
11	Normal	26	31.8 ± 28.8	64.5 ± 29.3
	Vinblastine-treated	28	52.7 ± 34.2	102.3 ± 203.7
12	Normal	87	47.9 ± 22.5	58.9 ± 16.4
	Vinblastine-treated	42	276.7 ± 197.1	5012.0 ± 1276.0

* Treated with 1 mg vinblastine 24 hours previously.
** ± standard errors.

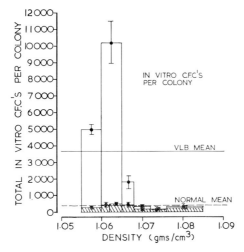

Fig. 3.19. *In vitro* CFC content of 12 day spleen colonies produced by injection of cells from 6 or 7 density increments of a BSA density separation of normal marrow (hatched columns) or marrow from mice given 1 mg vinblastine 24 hours previously (open columns). Each block is the mean with standard error of *in vitro* CFC assays on 20–40 individual spleen colonies which were simultaneously assayed for CFU's (see Figure 3.10). The lines representing mean values for the unfractionated population have been calculated from the density profiles of the CFU population and the *in vitro* CFC content of spleen colonies in each density increment.

within a spleen colony very large numbers of *in vitro* CFC's and these were the same cells that also produced colonies with large numbers of CFU's (compare Figure 3.10 with Figure 3.19).

The above experiments have shown that CFU's are different cells from *in vitro* CFC's and have proved that at least some CFU's can generate *in vitro* CFC's *in vivo* but not *in vitro*.

The data from tritiated thymidine and hydroxyurea experiments indicated that the majority of *in vitro* CFC's are in cell cycle which raises the question of the nature of the immediate progeny of these cells. Are *in vitro* CFC's capable of self-replication? Repeated attempts have been made to detect *in vitro* CFC's in *in vitro* colonies. These experiments can be difficult to interpret if early colonies, containing only a few cells, are examined because there is great heterogeneity in the size of colonies and no universally accepted minimum size for an *in vitro* colony. However, it seems clear that the vast majority of 7–10-day colonies lack detectable *in vitro* CFC's, suggesting strongly that these cells are not capable of self-generation *in vitro*.

It is more difficult to determine the capacity of these cells for self-generation *in vivo*, but there is suggestive evidence that here also they may not be capable of self-generation. Following bleeding in adult mice, erythropoiesis increases in the bone marrow. This is associated with a marked fall in the incidence of *in vitro* colony-forming cells (Bradley et al. 1967; Metcalf 1969b). Conversely, hypertransfusion with red cells from irradiated donors (lacking viable stem cells) leads to a suppression of erythropoiesis and a 3–4-fold increase in the number of *in vitro* colony-forming cells. A combination of both treatments does not alter the level of either cell type in the bone marrow (Metcalf 1969b). These experiments allow two likely conclusions: (a) that *in vitro* CFC's share common ancestral cells with erythropoietic cells and that the level of demand for erythropoiesis can divert significant numbers of ancestral cells into erythropoiesis whereas normally these would generate *in vitro* colony-forming cells and (b) that the *in vitro* CFC's seem unable to maintain equilibrium levels by self-generating proliferation.

3.4.5   *Morphology and properties of in vitro colony-forming cells*

Since cell separation procedures used so far have not succeeded in obtaining pure populations of *in vitro* CFC's no definite statement can be made regarding the morphology of these cells. Moreover, the heterogeneity of these cells with respect to cell size and density makes it improbable that they have a uniform morphological appearance. Some generalisations can be attempted regarding the possible morphology of many of these cells. Since most are in active cell cycle, the many cells in S or G_2 can be expected to be large, possibly blast-like, cells and this agrees with velocity sedimentation data indicating that most are of large size. Enrichment or depletion of column fractions of bone marrow cells for *in vitro* CFC's was paralleled by similar changes in the population of blast cells and early granulocyte forms.

In vitro CFC's are highly radio-sensitive and the *in vivo* D_{37} for mouse cells was estimated as 85 rads (Robinson et al. 1967) and 95 rads by Chen and Schooley (1970). Estimates for the *in vitro* sensitivity of mouse and human cells of 160 rads and 137 rads (D_0) have been made by Senn and McCulloch (1970). Discordant results have been presented on the rate of re-accumulation of those cells in the mouse bone marrow following whole-body irradiation. Hall (1969) reported that levels did not return to normal until 16 days after 250 rads, whereas Chen and Schooley (1970) reported a very rapid, but abortive, return to normal levels within 4 days of 200 R irradiation.

Levels of *in vitro* CFC's in the mouse bone marrow were depressed by 2 mg of cortisone acetate and *in vitro* 10 μg significantly inhibited colony formation (Metcalf 1969c). The proliferative activity of colony-forming cells *in vitro* is asparagine-dependent and colony growth was inhibited by 1-asparaginase (Harris 1969).

3.4.6 Other factors affecting the number of in vitro colony-forming cells

As mentioned earlier, the injection of Freund's complete adjuvant to mice elevates the number of *in vitro* CFC's in the bone marrow and particularly the spleen (McNeill 1970; Haskill et al. 1970). Changes of similar type have been observed to follow the injection of various antigens: pertussis vaccine (Bradley et al. 1969), *S. adelaide* flagellin, sheep and guinea pig erythrocytes and *E. coli* endotoxin (McNeill 1970; Metcalf 1970b). Elevation in the number of colony-forming cells was highest in the spleen and usually persisted for 5–7 days after a single injection.

More long-lasting elevations of colony-forming cells were observed for up to 8 months following the intraperitoneal injection of mineral oil in BALB/c mice (Hibberd, A. D., unpublished data). Elevation of colony-forming cells was observed in the bone marrow and spleen of mice bearing a variety of spontaneous and transplanted tumours (Hibberd and Metcalf 1970) and in neonatal F_1 hybrid mice with graft-vs.-host disease induced by the injection of parental spleen cells (Hibberd, A. D., unpublished data).

Germfree Swiss mice were found to have the same average content of *in vitro* colony-forming cells in their bone marrow as conventional Swiss mice, although levels of these cells showed less variability than in conventional mice (Metcalf and Foster 1969).

3.4.7 Heterogeneity of in vitro colony-forming cells

Before leaving this discussion of *in vitro* CFC's, some comments need to be made about the heterogeneity of this cell population. In the discussion to follow it should be kept in mind that the heterogeneity of *in vitro* CFC's which is so easy to demonstrate because of the availability of a simple *in vitro* culture system, probably applies equally to erythropoietin-sensitive cells and to the progenitor cells of other cell classes. Until satisfactory techniques are developed for analysing these latter cell populations *in vitro*, the heterogeneity in these cell populations can only be presumed by inference and not really be documented experimentally.

It is a characteristic feature of colony growth *in vitro* that colonies vary widely in size even in a single culture dish. Since the environment and distribution of stimuli can be assumed to be reasonably constant throughout the culture dish, this variation in colony size implies an intrinsic heterogeneity of the proliferative capacity of colony-forming cells or their progeny. This heterogeneity may represent a hierarchy within *in vitro* CFC populations, cells capable of giving rise to very large colonies possibly being ancestral to other *in vitro* CFC's.

As shall be discussed in a later chapter there is a second striking type of heterogeneity exhibited by *in vitro* CFC's related to the concentration of CSF required to initiate and maintain cellular proliferation. These two features, coupled with the heterogeneity in morphology of colonies and the heterogeneity of cell adhesiveness, volume and density all indicate that this cell class, delineated by the common capacity to form colonies *in vitro*, embraces an almost continuous spectrum of cells.

Cultures containing *in vitro* colonies characteristically contain smaller aggregates lying between the large aggregates scored as colonies (Metcalf 1969a). An analysis of one such culture from which every aggregate of 3 or more cells was removed and counted is shown in Figure 3.20. The heterogeneity in colony size is obvious in this figure as is the fact that the small cell aggregates ('clusters') outnumber colony-forming cells usually by 8–10:1. In other words, one in 500 bone-marrow cells is an *in vitro* CFC but approximately one in 50 cells will form *in vitro* a cluster of one size or another. The types of cells in clusters parallel those in colonies. Early in the incubation

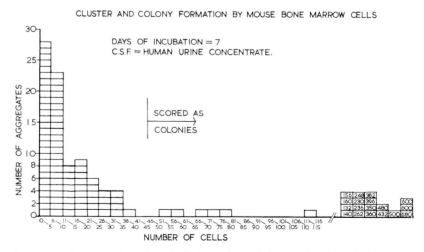

Fig. 3.20.   Histogram of total number of colonies and clusters of various sizes in a single culture of 25,000 mouse bone-marrow cells, stimulated by human urine CSF.

period all clusters are granulocytic, but after 3 days some are of mixed morphology and after this time progressively larger numbers of clusters are pure populations of macrophages. Although there is an obvious break in the continuity of aggregate sizes in Figure 3.20, which allows clusters to be distinguished from colonies, under some culture conditions clusters and colonies can form an almost continuous size spectrum. This raises serious questions regarding the nature of cluster-forming cells and their relation to *in vitro* CFC's. Are the two cells essentially similar and differing only in their proliferative capacity or are they qualitatively different cells?

This question has not been fully resolved at the present time, but some experimental evidence exists that the two cell types may differ by measurable properties: (a) with culture conditions using high concentrations of CSF and particularly with cultures stimulated by feeder layers, colony size can be greatly increased without causing a comparable enlargement of cluster size, clearly separating clusters from colonies. (b) Most *in vitro* CFC's die or lose their proliferative capacity within 24–48 hours if cultured in the absence of CSF, whereas cluster-forming cells survive these conditions much better (Metcalf 1970c). Here it may be, however, that culture in the absence of CSF causes a uniform reduction in proliferative capacity and colony-forming cells are capable only of generating clusters. (c) Separation of bone-marrow suspensions on glass-bead columns and BSA gradients consistently leads to a partial segregation of *in vitro* CFC's from cluster-forming cells. Thus, if cluster to colony-forming cell ratios are calculated for fractions separated on glass-bead columns, clear differences are noted between different fractions (Table 3.13). Similarly, if these ratios are calculated for fractions from BSA

TABLE 3.13

Effects of cell separation on glass-bead columns on *in vitro* colony-forming cells and cluster-forming cells in mouse bone marrow

Fraction	Cells per 10^5 nucleated cells		Ratio of clusters/ *in vitro* CFC's
	In vitro colony-forming cells	Cluster-forming cells	
Original	108	800	7.4
I	56	280	5.0
II	232	435	1.9
III	347	1550	4.5
IV	100	1420	14.2

gradients, the ratio falls continuously along the gradient from the least dense to the most dense fractions. (d) Clusters removed from 4–7-day cultures are not capable of continued proliferation when transferred to new cultures and cannot generate colonies regardless of the concentration of CSF used or the length of the second incubation period.

These observations have led to the tentative conclusion that the cells forming clusters may be the immediate progeny of *in vitro* colony-forming cells and may in fact be members of the morphologically-identifiable granulocytic series. With an incidence of 2 % in bone-marrow cell populations, these cluster-forming cells may include promyelocytes and myeloblasts, a population group with a similar incidence (approximately 2 %) in the normal bone marrow. If these conclusions are correct, then the capacity of these cells only to generate progeny numbering 3–50 cells is not surprising and would be anticipated from kinetic studies on myeloblasts and myelocytes carried out *in vivo* (Cronkite 1969; Athens 1969).

3.4.8   Résumé

In vitro colony-forming cells (CFC's) appear to be progenitors of granulocytes and at least some monocytes/macrophages and are identifiable by their capacity to form colonies of granulocytes and/or macrophages in agar cultures. Most are large cells in active cell cycle and are the progeny of stem cells (CFU's). Other cells exist in the bone marrow and spleen (cluster-forming cells) which are about 10 times more numerous than *in vitro* CFC's and may represent the progeny of *in vitro* CFC's. These are also capable of proliferating in agar but only form small aggregates of granulocytes or macrophages.

In vitro CFC's are only able to proliferate *in vitro* if stimulated by the specific humoral regulator, colony-stimulating factor (CSF). It is not yet certain whether CSF acts as an inducer of differentiation in *in vitro* CFC's as appears to be the case for erythropoietin and ESC's. Other differences may exist between ESC's and *in vitro* CFC's, e.g. with respect to their capacity for self-replication and to whether the respective regulators also stimulate proliferation of the progeny of these cells. In general, however, ESC's and *in vitro* CFC's seem to be roughly comparable cell populations being pre-committed to a restricted pathway of differentiation and lying in an intermediate position between stem cells and morphologically-differentiated blood cells.

3.5　*Megakaryocyte progenitor cells*

Unlike the erythroid and granulocytic series, clear experimental evidence for
the existence of a specific progenitor cell compartment for the megakaryocytic series is lacking, despite a number of studies that have speculated on
such a compartment under the control of a humoral regulator, thrombopoietin
(see Chapter 7). This situation results partly from an insufficient understanding of the nature of megakaryocyte maturation which until recently,
was considered to be due to an increase in ploidy brought about by successive
DNA endoreduplications *concomitant* with the development of cytoplasmic
granulation and other characteristics in mature megakaryocytes. Recent
experimental observations employing microspectrophotometry to estimate
single cell DNA content on Fuelgen-stained preparations, in conjunction
with tritiated thymidine labelling and morphological typing, are difficult to
reconcile with this concept.

Megakaryocytes are classified into three maturation stages, type I the most
immature are the megakaryoblasts and comprise 10% of the total population
in mice, type II, the intermediate stage of promegakaryocytes and basophilic
megakaryocytes are most frequent (86%) and type III, the most mature and
infrequent (4%) are large cells with multilobulated nuclei with dense coarse
chromatin and granulated cytoplasm (Odell et al. 1969a). Tritiated thymidine
labelling experiments have demonstrated that only the youngest type I
megakaryocytes can synthesise DNA (Ebbe and Stohlman 1965; Odell and
Jackson 1968). Consequently differentiation of the cytoplasm can continue
in the more mature megakaryocyte in the absence of nuclear replication.
Furthermore, estimates of DNA content have shown that the class of young
megakaryocytes contains cells of all ploidy values and thus the highest
ploidy (32–64 N) can be obtained without cytoplasmic maturation (Odell
and Jackson 1968). Furthermore, more mature morphological stages can
include cells of an 8 and 16 N ploidy value showing that megakaryocytes
need not reach the highest ploidy values before cytoplasmic maturation and
platelet production.

Studies in the rat have shown that two-thirds of all megakaryocytes have
a 16 N ploidy with the percentage of cells with lower ploidy falling progressively in the three stages of maturation and the 16 and 32 N values increasing.
The type I group can be divided into two subcompartments on the basis of
thymidine labelling, one consisting of endoreduplicating cells and the other
comprising cells in a post-DNA synthesis phase after endoreduplication has
permanently ceased (Odell and Jackson 1968; Odell et al. 1970). Over half of

the megakaryocytes in the labelled subcompartment of group I had 8 N values, whereas in the unlabelled group, ploidy values were significantly higher. Size characterisation can be used to classify megakaryocytes into maturation stages (Ebbe et al. 1968), and it is also possible to distinguish size groups corresponding to ploidy classes within a single maturation stage (Odell et al. 1970).

The total maturation time in recognisable megakaryocytes is 50–57 hours in mice (Odell et al. 1969a) and 48–75 hours in the rat, with 8–14 hours spent in stage I, 11–19 hours in stage II, and 24–42 hours in stage III, with an estimate of the precursor cell-generation time of approximately 16 hours (Ebbe and Stohlman 1965).

Many studies have demonstrated a homeostatic control of megakaryopoiesis and platelet production (see Abildgaard and Simone 1967). Experimental approaches used the production of thrombocytopenia either by bleeding, exchange transfusion with platelet-depleted blood or treatment with anti-platelet serum. In each instance a variable period of thrombocytopenia was followed by a rise in circulating platelets to supranormal levels. The lag period of thrombocytopenia prior to the recovery of platelet levels was species-related, ranging from 1–2 days in rats (Odell et al. 1962) to 3–5 days in man (Krevans and Jackson 1955). The lag period further indicates a lack of a significant platelet reserve.

Recovery from thrombocytopenia is associated with increase in DNA content with accompanying increase in size of the megakaryocytes and an increase in the absolute number of megakaryocytes in spleen and marrow. The increase in megakaryocyte size (macromegakaryocytosis) was first evident 8–24 hours after the stimulus of thrombocytopenia, in the type I compartment, but size increase was most evident by 48 hours (Ebbe et al. 1968; Penington and Olsen 1970). The increase in size was due to an increase in DNA content associated with increased endomitotic indices. In the reverse situation of thrombocytosis produced by platelet transfusion, there was a striking reduction in numbers of very large megakaryocytes and a significant reduction in mean diameter of all megakaryocytes with a reduction in ploidy values (Penington and Olsen 1970). This form of regulation is probably not operating on the progenitor compartment but rather, on the differentiated cell population of megakaryoblasts, regulating their endomitotic activity.

The increase in megakaryocyte numbers in thrombocytopenia is seen within 24–32 hours and a 3–4-fold increase in numbers of type I megakaryoblasts has been reported (Odell et al. 1969b). This increase could be brought about by cell division of the type I megakaryocyte or may be due to recruitment of diploid cells from a morphologically undifferentiated progenitor population. The possibility of cell division cannot be excluded from results of studies with tritiated thymidine labelling because of the problem of reutilisation of this label. However, studies employing 5-Iodo ^{125}-2-deoxyuridine, which is not reutilised, as a tracer has shown at least in normal animals that cell division of megakaryoblasts is most unlikely (Feinendegen et al. 1966). It is therefore more probable that in thrombocytopenia, a regulatory agent acts on a diploid progenitor cell which differentiates into the immature megakaryocyte compartment and a wave of differentiating megakaryocytes moves as a cohort of cells through the maturation process (Odell et al. 1969b).

Thrombocytopenia is found following sublethal irradiation with maximum depression on the 8–9th day in mice, though a lag period of 4 days was found following irradiation before the platelet count increased substantially. This lag period can be accounted for by the radio-resistance of the non-dividing megakaryocytes that maintain thrombopoiesis (Ebbe and Stohlman 1970). If the progenitor cells for thrombopoiesis are damaged by irradiation, with resulting failure of replacement of the pre-existing megakaryocytes, the time of onset of platelet reduction is an approximate transit time for the megakaryocyte series between the proliferating precursor compartment and platelet-producing megakaryocytes. This 4-day lag period is rather longer than the estimated transit time obtained with tritiated thymidine labelling (less than 3 days) and suggested that a pool of unrecognised megakaryocyte progenitor cells existed, and perhaps were in a non-dividing stage. Chronic stimulation with anti-platelet serum increased the radiosensitivity of the progenitor compartment, presumably because of activation of cells into more active cycle (Ebbe and Stohlman 1970).

Further observations have indicated that the megakaryocyte progenitor population may not be in active cell cycle and therefore may be different from the ESC or *in vitro* CFC populations. Boggs et al. (1964) noted that platelet and megakaryocyte levels appeared unchanged in dogs receiving vinblastine, despite marked suppression of erythropoiesis and granulopoiesis. Similar conclusions were reached in the hypertransfused, vincristine-treated rat where megakaryocytes appeared relatively unaffected, despite the striking depopulation of the erythroid compartment and during a 2–4-day period in which time erythroid progenitor cell differentiation could not be achieved with massive doses of erythropoietin (Morse and Stohlman 1966; Stohlman et al. 1968). Odell et al. (1966) presented some conflicting results in vinblastine-treated rats. In this study, a sharp fall in platelets (10% of normal) and a decline in megakaryocytes (to 25% of normal) was seen by 5 days, and thrombopoiesis therefore did not appear to be differentially resistant to vinblastine.

In conclusion, there appears to be evidence to indicate that a regulatory factor can control thrombopoiesis by action on a population of diploid cells, inducing differentiation into the megakaryoblast compartment. Evidence is conflicting on the exact proliferative status of the precursor compartment and little information is available as to the nature of this compartment. It may consist of multipotential stem cells, but is more probably an intermediate compartment of megakaryocytic progenitor cells, more differentiated than the stem cells (CFU's) and restricted to megakaryocyte differentiation.

3.6 Lymphoid progenitor cells

In the lymphoid series, cells appear to exist which can properly be regarded as progenitor cells and as equivalents of ESC's or *in vitro* CFC's. However, as shall be discussed shortly, the situation with lymphoid cells appears to be more complex than with the other cell lineages since, in the system most intensively studied (cells reacting to sheep RBC), it is apparent that two distinct lineages of progenitor cells must interact with each other, before one is capable of generating mature cells (antibody-forming cells). It is unfortunate that in the development of the concepts of the lymphoid progenitor cells and in the experimental analysis of this system identical terminology (antigen-sensitive, or antigen-reactive cells) has been used to describe two distinct populations of progenitor cells.

The original conception of lymphoid progenitor cells envisaged that antigens could trigger the proliferation of certain ancestral lymphoid cells leading to the generation of a clone of antibody-forming progeny. This postulated ancestral cell was termed the 'antigen-sensitive, or antigen-reactive cell' (Burnet 1959; Kennedy et al. 1966). As we shall see shortly, this term is now applied by common usage to another type of lymphoid progenitor cell, derived from the thymus, which does not actually give rise to antibody-forming progeny, and another term 'antibody-forming cell precursor' (AFC-P) applied to the actual progenitors of antibody-forming cells.

The original conception of a lymphoid progenitor cell which could generate a clone of antibody-forming progeny following contact with a specific antigen received experimental support following the development of the haemolytic spleen focus-forming assay. In this system, spleen cells are transferred into lethally irradiated animals injected with heterologous red cells, and 7–8 days later the recipient spleens are removed, sectioned and assayed for regions of haemolytic antibody formation. Each region of haemolysis in the spleen is produced by a focus of antibody-forming cells (plaque-forming cells (PFC)). The linear relationship between numbers of donor cells injected and numbers of active foci per spleen suggested a single cell origin for the foci and at limiting dilutions the frequency distribution of foci in the spleen conformed to a Poisson distribution (Playfair et al. 1965; Kennedy et al. 1965, 1966; Papermaster 1967). However, subsequent analysis has revealed that the foci are not the product of the clonal expansion and differentiation of a *single*, non-antibody secreting, antigen-sensitive cell, but develop as a result of collaboration between at least two cell types. For this reason, the nomenclature antigen-sensitive unit (ASU) or *focus-forming unit* (FFU) should be adopted. It has been calculated in the sheep red cell system that the frequency of FFU's is 0.5–2 per 10^6 spleen cells but estimation of seeding efficiency of injected FFU's has revealed that by 2 hours a fraction of 0.15 of the FFU's have localised in the spleen (Kennedy et al. 1966) and this fraction falls to 0.04 by 24 hours (Playfair et al. 1965). It is questionable whether these seeding efficiency values represent the true incidence of seeding because of difficulty in estimating the magnitude of recirculation and there is evidence that FFU's are indeed actively recirculating (Chaperon et al. 1968).

The number of plaque-forming cells produced in a single haemolytic focus is not fixed, and while the number of FFU's is linearly related to the number of spleen cells injected, the plaque-forming cell response increases allometrically with total graft size, implying that the rate or number of divisions is not fixed during the generation of plaque-forming cells within foci (Gregory and Lajtha 1968). This cell dose phenomenon was termed the 'premium effect' by Celada (1967) and with optimum colonising density of cells the number of plaque-forming cells per haemolytic focus was in the range of 90–800 (Bosma et al. 1968). FFU's to heterologous erythrocytes can be detected in the spleen and lymph nodes but are rare in marrow and thymus (Papermaster 1967). They are present, however, in the recirculating lymphocyte pool in the thoracic duct of normal mice but they are grossly reduced in numbers in neonatally thymectomised mice (Miller et al. 1967). The magnitude of the deficiency in thymectomised mice is apparent when the total FFU's in the 48-hour lymphocyte pool mobilisable by chronic thoracic duct drainage is calculated, there being 4000 in a normal CBA mouse and approximately 10 in a neonatally thymectomised mouse of the same strain. The defect in antibody response to sheep red cells, the greatly reduced recirculating lymphocyte pool and the depleted FFU content of neonatally-thymectomised mice all indicate that the thymus is intimately involved in the genesis of haemolytic foci.

3.6.1   Evidence for cell collaboration

Thymectomised irradiated mice given chromosomally-marked marrow and thymus grafts have both donor thymus and donor marrow mitoses in the lymphoid tissue (Dukor et al. 1965). Though the majority of dividing cells are of marrow origin, the proportion of thymus donor cells was observed to increase sharply for a short period after antigenic stimulation (Davies et al. 1967). This experiment provides evidence that thymus-derived (T) cells are able to proliferate following contact with antigen. The cells involved are now referred to as thymus-derived, antigen-reactive cells (ARC). However, using an anti-H-2 serum the antibody-forming cells produced as a result of antigenic stimulus appeared to be of marrow donor type.

From these results thymus cells, or thymus-derived cells appeared to be involved in the response to antigens but were not themselves antibody-forming cells. The original thymus graft experiment was unable to distinguish between the possibilities (a) that marrow-derived precursors of antibody-forming cells matured under the influence of a thymic humoral factor, (b) that these cells needed to mature locally in the microenvironment of the thymus, or (c) that thymus-derived cells interacted in the lymph nodes and spleen with bone marrow-derived cells, allowing the latter to generate antibody-forming cells.

The possible involvement of a thymic humoral factor in this process will be discussed in Chapter 7. In general, most workers at present feel that if a thymic humoral influence exists, it may be only a minor component of the potentiating influence exerted by the thymus on immune responses. Since thymic cells are ultimately of bone-marrow origin, ARC's can be considered to originate in the bone marrow. Osoba (1968) has reported that ARC's can be generated in irradiated thymectomised mice grafted with bone-marrow cells and implanted with thymus tissue in cell-impermeable chambers. This might suggest that a humoral factor could allow the progression of some bone-marrow cells to 'thymus-derived' ARC's without actual residence in the thymus.

Most experimental analyses of the role of the thymus in antibody formation have studied the potentiating effects of added thymic cells on antibody formation by bone-marrow cells in irradiated and/or thymectomised recipients.

Claman et al. (1966) found that mixtures of thymus and marrow cells were more effective in producing a haemolysin response in irradiated recipients than could be accounted for by summation of the activities of either population alone. In a modification of the Claman design, thymus cells with antigen were incubated for one week in lethally irradiated mice in the absence of marrow protection and the spleen cells from these mice (in which the only cells capable of proliferation were thymus-derived) then injected into a second group of irradiated recipients with antigen alone or with marrow cells and antigen. A significant plaque-forming cell response was seen only in mice given marrow as well as the spleen (thymus-derived) cells (Miller and Mitchell 1967; Mitchell and Miller 1968a). Furthermore, no significant response occurred if thymus cells had been incubated without antigen in the first irradiated host. This suggested that thymus cells had to react with antigen before interaction with marrow cells in order to elicit a significant antibody response. Furthermore, this interaction between thymus cells and antigen was specific, since thymus cells incubated with horse erythrocytes failed to produce a significant plaque-forming cell response to non-cross-reacting sheep red blood cells in a secondary host (Mitchell and Miller 1968a; Miller and Mitchell 1969a).

The peak haemolysin-forming response per spleen following sheep red cell antigen stimulation was depressed to 7–8 % of normal values in neonatally thymectomised mice. However, addition of syngeneic or allogeneic thymus cells together with the antigen reconstituted a normal plaque-forming response in these mice. Thymus cells were as effective as thoracic duct lymphocytes in reconstituting the response in this system (Mitchell and Miller 1968b) and the activity of the thymus cells appeared to depend on intact and undamaged cells since irradiated thymic cells were unable to potentiate the generation of antibody-forming cells. It is relevant that though thymus cells were as effective as thoracic duct lymphocytes in the unirradiated neonatally thymectomised animal, they were markedly less effective in collaborating with marrow-derived cells 2 weeks after irradiation in the adult thymectomised mouse (Miller and Mitchell 1968). This may be due to differential homing or survival of thymic and thoracic duct lymphocytes in the irradiated regenerating spleen in comparison with the neonatally-thymectomised spleen environment or alternatively, may be explained by the absence of a third cell type required for antigen handling which is deficient in the irradiated spleen and absent from the thymus inoculum but present in the thoracic duct lymphocyte population.

Estimates of the number of haemolytic foci produced by thoracic duct lymphocytes in irradiated recipients showed that one million thoracic duct lymphocytes produced 5 foci per spleen but the foci were considerably smaller than produced by spleen cell inocula and contained approximately 20 plaque-forming cells per focus by 8 days. Mixing 10^7 marrow cells with the thoracic duct lymphocytes did not increase the number of foci produced but greatly increased the size of each focus with numbers of plaque-forming cells per focus increasing to an average of 160 (Mitchell and Miller 1968a).

The crucial question at this stage was the origin of antibody-forming cells, namely whether they were of thymus or marrow origin. A definitive answer was obtained in three systems. In the first, specific alloantisera directed against either host or donor were incubated with haemolysin-forming cells, developing in neonatally-thymectomised mice reconstituted with allogeneic thymic or thoracic duct lymphocytes. It was clear that the majority, if not all, the antibody-forming cells developing in this system were derived from the host and not from the thymic or thoracic duct lymphocyte donors (Mitchell and Miller 1968a). Furthermore, in adult irradiated parental mice given F_1 hybrid thoracic duct lymphocytes, plaque-forming cells were of thoracic duct lymphocyte origin, whereas the plaque-forming cells in irradiated thymecto-mised mice given thoracic duct lymphocytes and marrow were predominantly of marrow type (Mitchell and Miller 1968a). In a third system an analysis of single antibody-forming cells was performed using T6 marker chromosomes in syngeneically reconstituted mice. In neonatally-thymectomised mice given thymic or thoracic duct cells (TDL), all plaque-forming cells were of host type. In irradiated mice given thymic and bone marrow cells, plaque-forming cells were shown to be of marrow type, whereas when TDL and marrow were given, plaque-forming cells were of mixed origin with some derived from the thoracic duct cells and the majority from the bone marrow. Cells producing antibody to polymerised flagellin were similarly shown to be of thoracic duct lymphocyte origin in irradiated mice reconstituted with thoracic duct lymphocytes alone (Nossal et al. 1968). From these results, it seems likely that the antibody-forming cells are derived from a bone-marrow pre-cursor which differentiates into an antibody-forming cell in the presence of the antigen as a result mainly of collaboration with the thymus-derived antigen-reactive cell.

Evidently both marrow-derived and thymus-derived cells are present in thoracic duct lymph, since TDL can not only generate antibody-forming cells in the absence of marrow cells but can also stimulate the differentiation of antibody-forming cell precursors from marrow cells.

The present conception of a focus-forming unit (FFU) is that each unit

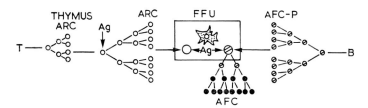

Fig. 3.21. Schematic diagram of the cellular components of a haemolytic focus-forming unit (FFU). Antigen reactive cells (ARC) derived from thymus interact with antibody-forming cell precursors (AFC-P) from the bone marrow in presence of antigen (Ag) and macrophages. AFC-P's proliferate, generating a clone of antibody-forming cells (AFC).

includes a minimum of two interacting cells, one thymus-derived and the other bone-marrow-derived, which are stimulated to proliferate after making contact with antigen – often presented in a special manner by reticulum cells (Figure 3.21). Further aspects of this problem will be discussed in Chapter 6, but at this stage the essential point is that it is within such foci that antibody-forming cell progenitors become activated to produce antibody-forming cells.

3.6.2   Proliferation of progenitors of antibody-forming cells

Various growth models of antibody-forming cells (PFC) have been proposed. At one extreme multiple recruitment of non-proliferating progenitors of antibody-forming cells can occur with functional transformation in the absence of cell division (Bussard and Lurie 1967), while at the other extreme the primary response has been attributed entirely to exponential division of antibody-forming cells in a single recruitment model involving asynchronous division with the magnitude of the response depending on the rate of division of cells responding to antigenic stimulation (Rowley et al. 1968). However, in *in vitro* systems apparent plaque-forming cell doubling times of less than 3 hours, were sometimes observed and as this is much shorter than the minimum cell-division time, the exponential growth curves of plaque-forming cells must be due in part to recruitment and differentiation of precursors not able themselves to form antibody (Dutton and Mischell 1967). These workers used tritiated thymidine suiciding techniques to show that virtually all plaque-forming cells arose from precursors that divided after an initial lag period of 24–32 hours following antigenic stimulation and that the original number of precursors limited the ultimate size of the plaque-forming cell population. Such recruitment of asynchronously dividing antibody-forming cell precursors in a multiple non-random manner would account for the linear expansion of plaque-forming cells.

However, detailed observation of PFC growth kinetics employing short intervals between estimations has revealed a divergence from linearity with a stepwise increase in PFC's suggesting significant synchrony in early primary responses in the spleen. Such data best fit a non-random multiple recruitment (synchronous) model (Perkins et al. 1969; Makinodan et al. 1969).

Models of production of antibody-forming cells must take into account interaction of thymus-derived antigen-reactive cells and marrow-derived antibody-forming cell precursors (AFC-P). Dose response data reveal a parabolic function when the range of spleen cells grafted is limiting, a relationship consistent with interaction between two cells (Bosma et al. 1968; Celada 1967; Gregory and Lajtha 1968). However, a transition to a linear function at higher dose levels indicates a limit to the degree of interaction with saturated interaction complexes possibly representing the chief class of immunologically-competent unit (Groves et al. 1969; Makinodan et al. 1969). In this latter model, it was proposed that thymus-derived antigen-reactive cells had a multiple but finite number of interaction sites, whereas the marrow-derived AFC-P's had a single interaction site. At upper doses, saturation of the antigen-reactive cell interaction sites would account for the transition to a linear function with dose. Recent studies have demonstrated that many haemolytic foci in the spleen produce antibody of a very high degree of homogeneity as judged by electrophoretic mobility (Luzzati et al. 1970) and capacity to bind antigen (Klinman 1969). Some foci, however, produced two and probably more electrophoretically distinct antibodies, which were either IgG or IgM or both of the IgG class (Luzzati et al. 1970). From these data it would appear that many foci are derived from the interaction of a single AFC-P with one ARC, a conclusion verified by Saunders (1969), who observed such a one-to-one interaction *in vitro*. Focal antibody heterogeneity may be due in part to an IgM to IgG switch in a single antibody-forming cell clone, and some evidence in favour of such a transition has been presented by Nossal et al. (1971). Alternatively, or possibly additionally, some foci may normally develop as a result of interaction of one ARC with two or more AFC-P's.

3.6.3 *Differentiation in thymus-derived cells*

Though only tentative conclusions can be drawn at the present time, some similarities are evident in the differentiation sequence of the immunocompetent cells (both thymus-derived and bone marrow-derived) and the erythroid and granulocytic series. The thymus-dependent limb of the immune system reveals a maturation sequence commencing in the thymus environment with differentiation of the stem cells seeding in the thymus. The product of differentiation is not directly the antigen-reactive cell, but is a progenitor cell whose differentiation within the thymus environment leads eventually to the emergence of antigen-reactive cells capable of proliferation in the peripheral tissues when brought into contact with antigen.

The product of thymic lymphoid differentiation is the small lymphocyte which emerges into the peripheral lymphocyte pool and can function as the classic effector cell in immune reactions such as delayed hypersensitivity and tissue graft rejection. The cellular immunity mediated by specifically-altered, or sensitised, lymphocytes requires antigenic recognition. The recognition site on the lymphocyte is thought to be an immunoglobulin molecule (Sell and Asofsky, 1968; Raff et al. 1970; Mason and Warner 1970), perhaps only a surface light chain (Mason and Warner 1970) though it is possible that the H chain of a whole immunoglobulin molecule may be present but buried deep in the cell membrane (Greaves and Hogg 1971). Recognition of antigenic determinants results in lymphocyte transformation to pyroninophilic blast cells which proliferate to produce a clone of small lymphocytes. These sensitised thymus-derived lymphocytes can directly act as killer cells in cell-mediated immunity and there is no evidence of a requirement for collaboration with marrow-derived cells (Stutman and Good 1969; Miller et al. 1971). Thymus-bone-marrow synergism has been demonstrated in graft-vs.-host splenomegaly elicited in 500 R-irradiated hybrid mice injected with parental marrow and thymus cells (Hilgard 1970). This synergism differs from that demonstrated in the SRBC system since the marrow cells play a non-immunological proliferative role in the splenomegaly and only the thymus cells carry out the immunological attack.

The ARC which leaves the thymus requires 'education' by interaction with antigen prior to collaborating with marrow-derived cells in humoral antibody formation. This process occurring in the spleen, is associated with a wave of proliferation with each thymus-derived cell being capable of generating 80–800 more cells in 4 days by clonal expansion involving a minimum of 6–10 divisions (Shearer and Cudkowicz 1969). This proliferation, which is antigen-specific and does not occur in response to a tolerated antigen, is associated with transformation of the small thymus-derived lymphocyte into a pyroninophilic blast cell with proliferation and further small lymphocyte production (Miller and Mitchell 1969b; Miller 1971). The difference between the 'virgin' ARC and the thymus 'educated' cell could simply be quantitative since considerably more cells would be available for collaboration after antigen-induced expansion. Alternatively the period of residence in the spleen in the presence of antigen may bring about further differentiation of the thymus-derived cells and possibly antigen-specific receptors of higher affinity develop. Antigen-induced proliferation of ARC's may also be the stage of production of memory cells since some memory clearly resides in the thymus ARC line (Cunningham 1969). Any cell not collaborating with a marrow-derived cell, or directly mediating cytotoxic reactions, may enter a prolonged G_0 state and enter the recirculating pool from which cells may again be reactivated by reaction with antigen (Syeklocha et al. 1966).

3.6.4 *Differentiation in bone-marrow- and bursal-derived cells*

The non-thymus-derived cells implicated in humoral immunity have been termed the B cell series to distinguish them from the T or thymus-derived (or dependent) cell series (Roitt et al. 1969). B cells in the mammalian cell collaboration studies are marrow-derived, but since ultimately the T cells also develop from stem cells of marrow origin, B cells should be considered the bursal equivalent component in mammals.

As discussed earlier, B cells are the direct progenitors of antibody-forming cells and the allotype markers of the immunoglobulins synthesised are of the genotype of the marrow donor (Jacobson et al. 1970). The differentiation sequence of antibody-forming cells in the bird has been well worked out in comparison with the mammalian situation, with a basic dichotomy of the immune response into a thymus-dependent system of cell-mediated immunity, and a bursal dependent system of humoral antibody formation (see Chapter 4). Stem cells of marrow origin (in the adult) or of yolk sac and spleen origin (in the embryo) enter the bursal epithelial environment and are induced to differentiate, in the absence of antigenic stimulation, within 24–48 hours into immunoglobulin-synthesising cells (Thorbecke et al. 1968; Kincade and Cooper 1970), which constitute the lymphoid progenitor population of the B cell series. The bursa does not produce antibody-forming cells following conventional antigenic stimulation (Dent and Good 1965), but bursal lymphocytes are capable of transferring the capacity to produce antibody to *Brucella* to neonatally-irradiated recipients (Gilmour et al. 1970). Thymus cells, or spleen cells from bursectomised donors, were incapable of transferring antibody-forming capacity. The bursal cells function in this system as AFC-P's, probably equivalent to the marrow-derived AFC-P's in mammals;

however, direct proof that the bursal lymphocyte differentiates into an anti-body-forming cell must await application of immunogenetic or chromosome marker techniques. No evidence of cell collaboration between bursal- and thymus-derived cells was obtained with *Brucella* antigen which may involve a thymus-independent response. However, Gilmour et al. (1970) noted that with SRBC, bursal cells were quite inefficient in transferring antibody for-mation, whereas spleen cells were quite competent. It is possible that certain antibody responses require a thymus-bursal cell collaboration and if such is proved to be the case, it would considerably strengthen the validity of referring to the marrow-derived AFC-P population of mammals as the 'bursal-equivalent' series.

A direct demonstration of interaction of antigen with lymphocytes was the observation that iodinated BSA specifically bound to a small percentage of spleen lymphocytes (Naor and Sulitzeanu 1967). A reaction has been shown between labelled flagellin or haemocyanin and lymphocyte-like cells in mouse spleen, lymph nodes, TDL and peritoneal exudate (Byrt and Ada 1969) and in human blood (Dwyer and Mackay 1970). Prior treatment with anti-immunoglobulin sera showed anti-μ and anti-L chain sera specifically blocked the binding, implicating an IgM molecule as the antigen-binding site. Evidence for specific immunological commitment of antigen-binding cells was the demonstration that heavily radioiodinated antigen could specifically eliminate cells capable of adoptively transferring an immune response to that antigen but did not inhibit transfer of the response to a closely related, but non-cross-reacting, antigen (Ada and Byrt 1969).

The rosette technique also measures antigen binding cells specific for sheep red cell antigens, but it is not clear whether only B cells or both B and T cells are capable of rosette-formation. Anti-theta serum has been claimed to suppress rosette formation by non-immune cells (Greaves and Hogg 1971) but was without effect in another study (Schlesinger 1970).

Antigen-binding lymphocytes may be a heterogeneous population of cells with specific immunoglobulin receptors though the possibility exists that many such cells are binding cytophilic antibody. Although generally considered that lymphocytes do not carry Ig cytophilic receptors, some recent studies suggest that this may not be completely correct (Basten, H., N. L. Warner, and J. F. A. P. Miller, personal communication; Dwyer and Warner 1971).

Some antigen-binding cells may be AFC-P's of the B series and ARC's of the T series since both populations carry antigen-recognition sites. Other antigen-binding cells may be long-lived memory cells both of the T series in the case of some T-dependent antigens and of the B series for thymus-independent antigens. It seems highly likely that memory can reside in the marrow-derived AFC-P line (Gowans 1971) and develop either as a consequence of clonal expansion of the AFC-P pool with regulation so that only a proportion differentiate into antibody-forming cells. Indeed it is not impossible to consider that AFC's could cease antibody formation and return to a memory pool of AFC-P's (Nossal and Lewis 1971).

Both the B- and T-cell systems produce cells recognising antigen by virtue of immunoglobulin receptors. It is possible that in this dual system, the T cell series is producing cells carrying small amounts of high affinity antibody and generating a considerable diversity of immunoglobulin receptors. The B cell series may then be segregated to generate cells producing potentially large quantities of low affinity antibody which can be secreted. The nature of the antigen and its form of presentation may then determine whether either or both cell lines are involved in an immune response. An antigen may only evoke a T cell response such as delayed hypersensitivity, or only a B cell response (as with antibody formation to flagellin in mice) or may require collaboration between both B and T cells in, e.g., the haemolysin response to heterologous erythrocytes. It should be remembered, however, that thymus independence of an immune response may be quantitative rather than qualitative, and furthermore, species differences in degrees of thymus independence of antibody formation to certain antigens undoubtedly exist. It remains to be seen whether cell collaboration developed phylogenetically with the appearance of the T- and B-cell series or whether it was a further and, phylogenetically, more recent adaptation superimposed on the basic dichotomy.

3.6.5 *Summary*

Evidence has been presented in this section which indicates the existence of two separate, but parallel, lines of lymphoid differentiation. The two lines diverge at the level of the common stem cell and two progenitor cell compartments develop under the influence of two distinct microenvironments, one the thymus epithelial environment and the other the bursal equivalent, which at least in birds is also epithelial and developmentally very similar. Both progenitor compartments produce lymphocytes which can recognise antigen by virtue of immunoglobulin receptors on their surface, and undergo proliferation and probably further differentiation. The clonal expansion of these lymphocytes, induced by antigen, serves to expand the population of reactive cells by self-replication possibly without further differentiation. In this respect, other progenitor cell populations differ since they apparently enter into an irreversible differentiation pathway after interaction with haemopoietic factors. Irreversible differentiation does of course occur in the immune system with production of mature plasma cells and lymphocytes mediating cytotoxic reactions. This differentiation is not, however, a necessary consequence of antigen recognition, but in the case of antibody-forming cell production in response to certain antigens, cell collaboration between the two lymphoid series is required. Furthermore, the demonstration of immunological memory requires that cells be diverted from an irreversible maturation pathway, enter a potentially long-lived phase, and be available for subsequent restimulation. The factors determining whether a lymphoid progenitor population enters a memory pool or differentiates further are unknown, but by analogy with mechanisms of stem-cell regulation (see Section 3.1) stochastic, microenvironmental and intrinsic mechanisms may determine whether cells differentiate or not.

3.7 General summary

The experimental data discussed in this chapter have clearly demonstrated the existence in haemopoietic tissues of multipotential stem cells. The evidence for this conclusion rests basically on two facts: (a) that the progeny of a single identifiable cell can completely repopulate all the haemopoietic tissues of an irradiated animal, and (b) that single stem cells (CFU's) can produce colonies containing mixed populations of blood cells in the spleen or bone marrow of irradiated recipients. The same type of evidence has clearly indicated the capacity of such stem cells to self-replicate, although, as shall be seen in a subsequent chapter, this capacity for self-replication is not unlimited.

The factors which determine whether stem cells self-generate or give rise to differentiated progeny are not fully understood, but on present evidence these factors are multiple and interacting and include (a) a random birth/death (self-generating/differentiation) process, (b) differing susceptibility of individual stem cells due to their intrinsic heterogeneity and their past history of mitotic activity, and (c) microenvironmental influences (probably cell-contact interactions with adjacent stromal cells), which may or may not commit stem cells to a specific pathway of differentiation depending on factors (a) and (b).

Multipotential stem cells are clearly heterogeneous with respect to physical characteristics and whether they are in active cell cycle or a G_0 state. Because of this it is likely that they are heterogeneous in morphological appearance although evidence is emerging that stem cells in adult animals may differ in general morphology from apparently similar cells in the foetus.

No firm evidence has yet been obtained for the existence of an intermediate type of stem cell with a partial or complete commitment to a single pathway of differentiation but retaining the capacity for extended self-generation. It is not impossible that such committed stem cells exist, particularly in view of the known heterogeneity of stem cells but in the absence of proof of their existence, such concepts can only be speculative.

Several cell populations have now been characterised as belonging to the progenitor class of haemopoietic cells. These include the erythropoietin-sensitive cell (ESC) and the *in vitro* colony-forming cell (*in vitro* CFC). These cells are characterised by an apparently permanent commitment to restricted pathways of differentiation, the ESC to the erythropoiesis and the *in vitro* CFC to granulopoiesis and monocyte/macrophage formation. Evidence is conflicting on the capacity of these cells for self-generation. The *in vitro* CFC's do not appear to have this capacity, but ESC's may have a limited capacity. Certainly both cell types differ from stem cells in adult animals in that the majority are in continuous cell cycle. Whereas the evidence favours the conclusion that stem cells are committed to differentiate by microenvironmental influences, humoral factors appear to be the primary differentiating influence for progenitor cells. These questions will be discussed in more detail in subsequent chapters.

In the lymphoid cell series an increasing body of evidence suggests that thymus-derived ARC's and bone marrow-derived AFC-P's also belong to the progenitor cell class. These cells may be committed to an even more restricted pathway of differentiation than ESC's or *in vitro* CFC's, at least in their responsiveness to specific antigenic determinants. The relevant antigen appears to substitute for humoral regulators as the mechanism triggering differentiation but the possibility that humoral regulators also exist for lymphoid progenitor cells is not excluded.

Little is known of megakaryocyte progenitors, although there is some indirect evidence for the existence of such a cell class.

As in the case of stem cells, clear evidence exists for the heterogeneity of cells within any one progenitor class.

Progenitor cells are induced to differentiate to morphologically- or functionally-characterisable primitive cells in the various cell classes. These cells in turn generate the more mature cell elements in each blood cell class. Much is known of the proliferative patterns exhibited by the various blast cells in generating populations of mature blood cells but the details of these sequences are outside the scope of the present book.

The present apparent interrelationships of the various ancestral blood cells are summarised in Figure 3.22. Diagrams such as this must be viewed realistically as representing only an outline of the probable processes and much more work will be required to finally establish whether subpopulations exist within the various cell classes and what additional interrelationships exist between the diverging cell classes during differentiation.

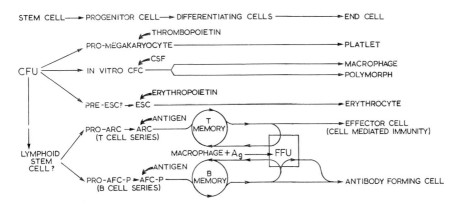

Fig. 3.22. A schematic diagram of the organization of the haemopoietic system into stem cell, progenitor cell and differentiating cell compartments. Target progenitor cells are shown with their appropriate humoral regulators. ESC – erythropoietin sensitive cell; PRO – progenitor; ARC – antigen reactive cell of T (thymus dependent) cell series; AFC-P – antibody forming cell precursor in the B (bursal equivalent) cell series. FFU – haemolytic focus forming unit or antigen sensitive unit – site of B and T cell collaboration. T and B – memory-pool of long lived; probably recirculating, memory cells for thymus-dependent or bursal-equivalent cell series.

References

Abildgaard, C. F. and J. V. Simone, 1967, Thrombopoiesis. In Seminars in Hematology *4*, 424.

Ada, G. L. and P. Byrt, 1969, Nature *222*, 1291.

Alexanian, R., D. D. Porteous, and L. G. Lajtha, 1963, Int. J. Radiat. Biol. *7*, 87.

Alpen, E. L. and D. Cranmore, 1959, Observations on the regulation of erythropoiesis and on cellular dynamics by Fe^{59} autoradiography. In: The kinetics of cellular proliferation, edited by F. Stohlman, Jr., New York, Grune and Stratton, p. 290.

Athens, J. W., 1969, Granulocyte kinetics in health and disease. In: Human tumor cell kinetics, edited by S. Perry. National Cancer Institute Monograph 30, p. 135.

Barnes, D. W. H. and J. F. Loutit, 1967a, Lancet *2*, 1138.

Barnes, D. W. H. and J. F. Loutit, 1967b, Nature *213*, 1142.

Barnes, D. W. H., E. P. Evans, C. E. Ford, and B. J. West, 1968, Nature *219*, 518.

Becker, A. J., E. A. McCulloch, and J. E. Till, 1963, Nature *197*, 452.

Becker, A. J., E. A. McCulloch, L. Siminovitch, and J. E. Till, 1965, Blood *26*, 296.

Bennett, M., G. Cudkowicz, R. S. Foster, and D. Metcalf, 1968, J. Cell. Physiol. *71*, 211.

Blackett, N. M., 1968, Changes in proliferative rate and maturation time of erythroid precursors in response to anaemia and ionizing radiation. In: Effects of radiation on cellular proliferation and differentiation. Proceedings of International Atomic Energy Agency Symposium, p. 235.

Blackett, N. M. and S. Hellman, 1966, Nature *210*, 1284.

Blackett, N. M., P. J. Roylance, and K. Adams, 1964, Brit. J. Haemat. *10*, 453.

Bleiberg, I., M. Liron, and M. Feldman, 1967, Blood *29*, 469.

Boggs, D. R., J. W. Athens, O. P. Haab, P. A. Cancilla, S. O. Raab, G. E. Cartwright, and M. M. Wintrobe, 1964, Blood *23*, 53.

Boggs, D. R., J. C. Marsh, G. E. Cartwright, and M. M. Wintrobe, 1967a, Exp. Hematol. *12*, 49.

Boggs, D. R., J. C. Marsh, P. A. Chervenick, C. R. Bishop, G. E. Cartwright, and M. M. Wintrobe, 1967b, J. Exp. Med. *126*, 851.

Boggs, D. R., J. C. Marsh, P. A. Chervenick, G. E. Cartwright, and M. M. Wintrobe, 1968, Rad. Res. *35*, 68.

Borsook, H., K. Ratner, B. Tattrie, D. Teigler, and L. G. Lajtha, 1968, Nature *217*, 1024.

Bosma, M. J., E. H. Perkins, and T. Makinodan, 1968, J. Immunol. *101*, 963.

Bradley, T. R. and D. Metcalf, 1966, Aust. J. Exp. Biol. Med. Sci. *44*, 287.

Bradley, T. R., W. Robinson, and D. Metcalf, 1967, Nature *213*, 511.

Bradley, T. R., D. Metcalf, M. Sumner, and E. R. Stanley, 1969, Characteristics of in vitro colony formation by cells from haemopoietic tissues. In: In Vitro 4, edited by P. Farnes. Baltimore, Williams and Wilkins, p. 22.

Brecher, G., W. W. Smith, S. Wilson, and S. Fred, 1967, Rad. Res. *30*, 600.

Bruce, W. R. and E. A. McCulloch, 1964, Blood *23*, 216.

Bruce, W. R. and B. E. Meeker, 1965, J. Nat. Cancer Inst. *34*, 849.

Bullough, W. S., 1963, Nature *199*, 859.

Burnet, F. M., 1959, The clonal selection theory of acquired immunity. Cambridge, University Press.

Bussard, A. E. and M. Lurie, 1967, J. Exp. Med. *125*, 873.

Byron, J. W., 1968, Recovery of the erythropoietin-sensitive stem cell population following total-body x-irradiation. In: Effects of radiation on cellular proliferation and differentiation. Proceedings of International Atomic Energy Agency Symposium, p. 173.

Byron, J. W. and L. G. Lajtha, 1968, Brit. J. Haemat. *15*, 47.

Byrt, P. and G. L. Ada, 1969, Immunol. *17*, 503.

Celada, F., 1967, J. Exp. Med. *125*, 199.

Celada, F. and H. Wigzell, 1966, Immunol. *10*, 231.

Chaperon, E. A., J. C. Selner, and H. N. Claman, 1968, Immunol. *14*, 553.

Chen, M. G. and J. C. Schooley, 1968, Transplantation *6*, 121.

Chen, M. G. and J. C. Schooley, 1970, J. Cell. Physiol. *75*, 89.

Claman, H. N., E. A. Chaperon, and R. F. Triplett, 1966, Proc. Soc. Exp. Biol. Med. *122*, 1167.

Cole, L. J., 1963, Amer. J. Physiol. *204*, 265.

Cole, L. J. and S. E. Maki, 1968, Exp. Hematol. *15*, 82.

Cronkite, E. P., 1969, Kinetics of granulopoiesis. In: Human tumor cell kinetics, edited by S. Perry. National Cancer Institute Monograph 30, p. 51.

Cunningham, A. J., 1969, Immunol. *17*, 933.

Curry, J. L. and J. J. Trentin, 1967a, Dev. Biol. *15*, 395.

Curry, J. L. and J. J. Trentin, 1967b, J. Exp. Med. *126*, 819.

Curry, J., J. Trentin, and N. Wolf, 1964, Exp. Hemat. *7*, 80.

Curry, J. L., J. J. Trentin, and N. Wolf, 1967a, J. Exp. Med. *125*, 703.

Curry, J. L., J. J. Trentin, and V. Cheng, 1967b, J. Immunol. *99*, 107.

Davies, A. J. S., E. Leuchars, V. Wallis, R. Marchant, and E. V. Elliott, 1967, Transplantation *5*, 222.

De Gowin, R. L., 1967, J. Lab. Clin. Med. *70*, 23.

Dent, P. B. and R. A. Good, 1965, Nature *207*, 491.

Dukor, P., J. F. A. P. Miller, W. House, and V. Allman, 1965, Transplantation *3*, 639.

Duplan, J. F., 1968, Nouvelle Revue Française d'Hématologie *8*, 445.

Dutton, D. W. and R. I. Mischell, 1967, J. Exp. Med. *126*, 443.

Dwyer, J. M. and I. R. MacKay, 1970, Lancet *1*, 164.

Dwyer, J. M. and N. L. Warner, 1971, Nature *229*, 210.

Ebbe, S. and F. Stohlman, Jr., 1965, Blood *26*, 20.

Ebbe, S. and F. Stohlman, Jr., 1970, Blood *35*, 783.

Ebbe, S., F. Stohlman, Jr., J. Overcash, J. Donovan, and D. Howard, 1968, Blood *32*, 383.

Epifanova, O. I. and V. V. Terskikh, 1969, Cell Tiss. Kinet. *2*, 75.

Erslev, A. J., 1959, Blood *14*, 386.

Feinendegen, L. E., V. P. Bond, and W. L. Hughes, 1966, Exp. Cell. Res. *43*, 107.

Feldman, M. and I. Bleiberg, 1967, Studies on the feedback regulation of haemopoiesis. In: CIBA Foundation Symposium on Cell Differentiation, edited by A. V. S. de Reuck and J. Knight. London, Churchill, p. 79.

Filmanowicz, E. and C. W. Gurney, 1961, J. Lab. Clin. Med. *57*, 65.

Fowler, J. H., A. M. Wu, J. E. Till, E. A. McCulloch, and L. Siminovitch, 1967, J. Cell. Physiol. *69*, 65.

Fred, S. S. and W. W. Smith, 1968, Proc. Soc. Exp. Biol. Med. *128*, 364.

Fried, W. and C. W. Gurney, 1968, Exp. Hematol. *15*, 50.

Fried, W., D. Martinson, M. Weisman, and C. W. Gurney, 1966, Exptl. Hematol. *10*, 22.

Gallagher, N. I. and R. D. Lange, 1970, Clin. Res. *8*, 280.

Gallagher, N. I. and R. D. Lange, 1962, Proc. Soc. Exp. Biol. Med. *110*, 422.

Gilmour, D. G., G. A. Theis, and G. J. Thorbecke, 1970, J. Exp. Med. *132*, 134.

Goodman, J. W., 1965, Concerning the capacity of lymphocytes to give rise to erythropoiesis. In: La greffe des cellules hématopoiétiques allogéniques. Colloques Internationaux du Centre National de la Recherche Scientifique *147*, 31.

Gowans, J. L., 1971, In: Summary discussion. In: Cell interactions in immune responses. Third Sigrid Juselius Foundation Symp., edited by A. Cross, T. Kosunen, and O. Makela. New York and London, Academic Press (in press).

Greaves, M. F. and N. M. Hogg, 1971, Antigen binding sites on mouse lymphoid cells. In: Cell interactions in immune responses. Third Sigrid Juselius Foundation Symp., edited by A. Cross, T. Kosunen, and O. Makela. New York and London, Academic Press (in press).

Gregory, C. J. and L. G. Lajtha, 1968, Nature *218*, 1079.

Groves, D. L., W. E. Lever, and T. Makinodan, 1969, Nature *222*, 96.

Gurney, C. W., 1963, Perspectives in Biology and Medicine *6*, 233.

Gurney, C. W. and W. Fried, 1965, Proc. Nat. Acad. Sci. *54*, 1148.

Gurney, C. W. and D. Hofstra, 1963, Rad. Res. *19*, 599.

Gurney, C. W., N. Wackman, and E. Filmanowicz, 1961, Blood *17*, 531.

Gurney, C. W., L. G. Lajtha, and R. Oliver, 1962, Brit. J. Haemat. *8*, 461.

Gurney, C. W., D. Hofstra, and A. Mangalik, 1965, Physiological studies of primitive hemopoietic cells. In: La greffe des cellules hématopoiétiques allogéniques. Colleques Internationaux du Centre National de la Recherche Scientifique *147*, 19.

Guzman, E. and L. G. Lajtha, 1970, Cell Tissue Kinet. *3*, 91.

Hall, B. M., 1969, Brit. J. Haematol. *17*, 553.

Hanks, G. E., 1964, Nature *203*, 1393.

Hanks, G. E. and E. J. Ainsworth, 1967, Rad. Res. *32*, 367.

Hanna, I. R. A., 1967, Nature *214*, 355.

Hanna, M. G., P. Nettesheim, W. D. Fisher, L. C. Peters, and M. W. Francis, 1967, Science *157*, 1458.

Harris, J. E., 1969, Nature *223*, 850.

Haskill, J. S. and M. A. S. Moore, 1970, Nature *226*, 853.

Haskill, J. S., T. A. McNeill, and M. A. S. Moore, 1970, J. Cell. Physiol. *75*, 167.

Hege, J. S. and L. J. Cole, 1966, Exp. Hematol. *9*, 30.

Hellman, S., 1965, Nature *205*, 100.

Hellman, S. and H. E. Grate, 1968a, Kinetics of circulating hematopoietic colony-forming units in the mouse. In: Effect of radiation on cellular proliferation and differentiation. Proceedings of International Atomic Energy Agency Symposium, p. 187.

Hellman, S. and H. E. Grate, 1968b, J. Exp. Med. *127*, 605.

Hibberd, A. D. and D. Metcalf, 1970, Israel J. Med. Sci. (in press).

Hilgard, H. R., 1970, J. Exp. Med. *132*, 317.

Hodgson, G., 1967, Proc. Soc. Exp. Biol. Med. *125*, 1206.

Hodgson, G. A. and I. Eskuche, 1962, Time course of effects of erythropoiesis stimulating factor(s). In: Erythropoiesis, edited by L. O. Jacobson and M. A. Doyle. New York, Grune and Stratton, p. 222.

Hodgson, G. and I. Eskuche, 1968, Ann. N.Y. Acad. Sci. *149*, 230.

Ichikawa, Y., D. H. Pluznik, and L. Sachs, 1966, Proc. Natl. Acad. Sci. *56*, 488.

Iscove, N. N., J. E. Till, and E. A. McCulloch, 1970, Proc. Soc. Exp. Biol. Med. *134*, 33.

Jacobson, L. O., E. Goldwasser, and C. W. Gurney, 1960, Transfusion-induced Poly-cythaemia as a model for studying factors influencing erythropoiesis. In: CIBA Symposium on Haemopoiesis-cell production and its regulation, edited by G. E. W. Wolstenholme, and M. O'Connor. London, Churchill, p. 423.

Jacobson, E. B., J. L'Age-Stehr, and L. A. Herzenberg, 1970, J. Exp. Med. *131*, 1109.

Jenkins, V. K., A. C. Upton, and T. T. Odell, 1969, J. Cell. Physiol. *73*, 141.

Juraskova, V. and L. Tkadlecek, 1965, Nature *206*, 951.

Juraskova, V., L. Tkadlecek, and V. Drasil, 1964, Folia Biol. *10*, 381.

Kennedy, J. C., L. Siminovitch, J. E. Till, and E. A. McCulloch, 1965, Proc. Soc. Exp. Biol. Med. *120*, 868.

Kennedy, J. C., J. E. Till, L. Siminovitch, and E. A. McCulloch, 1966, J. Immunol. *96*, 973.

Kincade, P. W. and M. D. Cooper, 1970, Fed. Proc. *29*, 503 (Abs.).

Klinman, N. R., 1969, Immunochemistry *6*, 757.

Korst, D. R., 1966, Exp. Hematol. *10*, 25.

Krantz, S. B. and W. Fried, 1968, J. Lab. Clin. Med. *75*. 157.

Kretchmar, A. L., 1966, Science *152*, 367.

Kretchmar, A. L. and W. R. Conover, 1967, Exp. Hematol. *14*, 48.

Kretchmar, A. L. and W. R. Conover, 1968, Proc. Soc. Exp. Biol. Med. *129*, 218.

Kretchmar. A. L. and W. R. Conover, 1969, Transplantation *5*, 576.

Kretchmar, A. L., T. P. McDonald, and R. D. Lange, 1970, J. Lab. Clin. Med. *75*, 74.

Krevans, J. R. and D. P. Jackson, 1955, J. Am. Med. Ass. *159*, 171.

Kubanek, B., L. Ferrari, W. S. Tyler, D. Howard, S. Jay, and F. Stohlman, Jr., 1968a, Blood *32*, 586.

Kubanek, B., W. S. Tyler, L. Ferrari, A. Porcellini, D. Howard, and F. Stohlman, Jr., 1968b, Proc. Soc. Exp. Biol. Med. *127*, 770.

Lahiri, S. K. and L. M. van Putten, 1969, Cell Tissue Kinet. *2*, 21.

Lajtha, L. G., 1964, Medicine *43*, 625.

Lajtha, L. G., 1966, J. Cell. Comp. Physiol. *67*, Suppl. 1, 133.

Lajtha, L. G., 1967, Bone marrow stem cell kinetics. Seminars in Hematology *4*, p. 293.

Lajtha, L. G. and R. Oliver, 1970, Studies on the kinetics of erythropoiesis: a model of the erythron. In: CIBA Symposium on haemopoiesis: cell production and its regulation, edited by G. E. W. Wolstenholme and M. O'Connor. London, Churchill, p. 289.

Lajtha, L. G., R. Oliver, and C. W. Gurney, 1962, Brit. J. Haematol. *8*, 442.

Lajtha, L. G., Pozzi, L. V., and R. Schofield, 1968, Comparison of methods of study of stem cell kinetics. In: Proliferation and spread of neoplastic cells. M. D. Anderson Hospital 21st Symp. on Fundamental Cancer Research. Baltimore, Williams and Wilkins, p. 247.

Lajtha, L. G., L. V. Pozzi, R. Schofield, and M. Fox, 1969, Cell Tissue Kinet. *2*, 39.

Lamerton, L. F., 1970, Adaptation of hemopoietic systems to environmental conditions. In: Plenary Session, Scientific Contributions XIII International Congress of Hematology. Munich, J. F. Lehmanns Verlag, p. 132.

Lange, R. D., L. F. O'Grady, J. P. Lewis, and F. E. Trobaugh, Jr., 1968, Ann. N.Y. Acad. Sci. *149*, 281.

Lewis, J. P. and F. E. Trobaugh, Jr., 1964, Nature *204*, 589.

Lewis, J. P., L. F. O'Grady, M. Passovoy, J. Simmons, and F. E. Trobaugh, Jr., 1967, Exp. Hemat. *13*, 15.

Lewis, J. P., L. F. O'Grady, F. E. Trobaugh, Jr., 1968b, Cell Tissue Kinet. *1*, 101.

Lewis, J. P., M. Passovoy, M. Freeman, and F. E. Trobaugh, Jr. 1968a, J. Cell. Physiol. *71*, 121.

Liron, M. and M. Feldman, 1965, Transplant. *3*, 509.

Lord, B. I., 1970, A comparison of the abilities of bone marrow and spleen cells to produce haemopoietic spleen colonies. In: Abstract Volume, XIII International Congress of Hematology. Munich, J. F. Lehmanns Verlag, p. 164 (Abs.).

Luzatti, A. L., R. M. Tosi, and A. O. Carbonara, 1970, J. Exp. Med. *132*, 199.

MacKinney, A. A., Jr. and D. R. Korst, 1967, Exp. Hematol. *13*, 17.

Madoc-Jones, H. and F. Mauro, 1968, J. Cell. Physiol. *72*, 185.

Makinodan, T., T. Sado, D. L. Groves, and G. Price, 1969, Current Topics in Microbiology and Immunology *49*, 80.

Malawista, S. E., H. Sato, and K. G. Bensch, 1968, Science *160*, 770.

Marsh, J. C., D. R. Boggs, G. E. Cartwright, and M. M. Wintrobe, 1967a, Exp. Hematol. *12*, 54.

Marsh, J. C., D. E. Boggs, C. R. Bishop, P. A. Chervenick, G. E. Cartwright, and M. M. Wintrobe, 1967b, J. Exp. Med. *126*, 833.

Mason, S. and N. L. Warner, 1970, J. Immunol. *104*, 762.

Matioli, G., H. Vogel, and H. Niewisch, 1968, J. Cell. Physiol. *72*, 229.

McCool, D., R. J. Miller, R. H. Painter, and W. R. Bruce, 1970, Cell Tissue Kinet. *3*, 55.

McCulloch, E. A., 1968, Plenary Session Papers, In: XII Congress International Society of Hematology, edited by R. Jaffe, p. 260.

McCulloch, E. A. and J. E. Till, 1962, Rad. Res. *16*, 822.

McCulloch, E. A. and J. E. Till, 1964, Rad. Res. *22*, 383.

McNeill, T. A., 1970, Immunology *18*, 61.

Mekori, T. and M. Feldman, 1965, Transplantation *3*, 98.

Mekori, T., L. Chieco-Bianci, and M. Feldman, 1965, Nature *203*, 367.

Metcalf, D., 1969a, J. Cell. Physiol. *74*, 323.

Metcalf, D., 1969b, Brit. J. Haematol. *16*, 397.

Metcalf, D., 1969c, Proc. Soc. Exp. Biol. Med. *132*, 391.

Metcalf, D., 1970a, J. Cell Physiol. (in press).

Metcalf, D., 1970b, Immunology (in press).

Metcalf, D., 1970c, J. Cell. Physiol. *76*, 89.

Metcalf, D. and R. S. Foster, 1969, In Vitro colony-forming cells in the bone marrow of germfree mice. In: Germfree biology: experimental and clinical aspects. New York, Plenum Press, p. 383.

Metcalf, D. and E. R. Stanley, 1969, Aust. J. Exp. Biol. Med. Sci. *47*, 453.

Metcalf, D., T. R. Bradley, and W. Robinson, 1967, J. Cell. Physiol. *69*, 93.

Micklem, H. S., 1966, Transp. *4*, 732.

Micklem, H. S., and J. F. Loutit, 1966, Tissue grafting and radiation. New York and London, Academic Press.

Miller, J. F. A. P., 1971, Interaction between T cells and B cells in humoral antibody responses. In: Proceedings of III International Conference on Lymphatic tissues and Germinal centers in immune response. Uppsala (in press).

Miller, J. F. A. P. and G. F. Mitchell, 1967, Nature *216*, 659.

Miller, J. F. A. P. and G. F. Mitchell, 1968, J. Exp. Med. *128*, 801.

Miller, J. F. A. P. and G. F. Mitchell, 1969a, Transp. Rev. *1*, 3.

Miller, J. F. A. P. and G. F. Mitchell, 1969b, Interaction between two distinct cell lineages in an immune response. In: Lymphatic tissue and germinal centres in immune response. Adv. Exp. Med. Biol., edited by H. Cottier and C. C. Congdon. New York, Plenum Publishing Co., p. 455.

Miller, J. F. A. P., G. F. Mitchell, and N. S. Weiss, 1967, Nature *214*, 992.

Miller, J. F. A. P., K. T. Brunner, J. Sprent, and P. J. Russell, 1971, Thymus derived cells as killer cells in cell mediated immunity. In: Transpl. Proceedings III International Congress of Transplantation Soc. *3*, 915.

Mitchell, G. F. and J. F. A. P. Miller, 1968a, J. Exp. Med. *128*, 821.

Mitchell, G. F. and J. F. A. P. Miller, 1968b, Proc. Nat. Acad. Sci. *59*, 296.

Mizoguchi, H., Y. Miura, F. Takaku, and K. Nakao, 1968, Blood *32*, 271.

Moore, M. A. S., 1970, Unpublished observations.

Moore, M. A. S. and D. Metcalf, 1970a, Brit. J. Haematol. *18*, 279.

Moore, M. A. S. and D. Metcalf, 1970b, unpublished observations.

Moore, M. A. S. and N. L. Warner, 1970, unpublished observations.

Moore, M. A. S., T. A. McNeill, and J. S. Haskill, 1970, J. Cell. Physiol. *75*, 181.

Morse, B. S. and F. Stohlman, Jr., 1966, J. Clin. Invest. *45*, 1241.

Morse, B. S., N. J. Rencricca, and F. Stohlman, Jr., 1970, Blood *35*, 761.

Naor, D. and D. Sulitzeanu, 1967, Nature *214*, 687.

Nettesheim, P., M. G. Hanna, and W. D. Fisher, 1968, Rad. Res. *35*, 378.

Nossal, G. J. V. and H. Lewis, 1971, Immunology (in press).

Nossal, G. J. V., A. Cunningham, G. F. Mitchell, and J. F. A. P. Miller, 1968, J. Exp. Med. *128*, 839.

Nossal, G. J. V., N. L. Warner, and H. Lewis, 1971, Incidence of cells simultaneously secreting IgM and IgG antibodies to sheep erythrocytes. Cellular Immunology (in press).

Odell, T. T. Jr. and C. W. Jackson, 1968, Blood *32*, 102.

Odell, T. T. Jr., T. P. McDonald, and M. Asano, 1962, Acta Haemat. *27*, 171.

Odell, T. T., M. Jefferson, C. W. Jackson, and R. S. Reiter, 1966, Exp. Hematol. *10*, 36.

Odell, T. T., E. A. Burch, Jr., C. W. Jackson, and T. J. Friday, 1969a, Cell. Tissue Kinet. *2*, 363.

Odell, T. T. Jr., C. W. Jackson, T. J. Friday, and D. E. Charsha, 1969b, Brit. J. Haemat. *17*, 91.

Odell, T. T. Jr., C. W. Jackson, and T. J. Friday, 1970, Blood *35*, 775.

Oehlert, W., P. Lauf, and N. Semayer, 1962, Naturwissenschaften *49*, 137.

O'Grady, L. F., J. P. Lewis, R. Lange, and F. E. Trobaugh, Jr., 1966, Exp. Hematol. *9*, 77.

O'Grady, L., J. P. Lewis, and F. E. Trobaugh, Jr., 1967a, Exp. Hemat. *12*, 62.

O'Grady, L. F., J. P. Lewis, and F. E. Trobaugh, Jr., 1967b, Exp. Hemat. *12*, 70.

Okunewick, J. P., K. M. Hartley, and J. Darden, 1969, Rad. Res. *38*, 530.

Osoba, D., 1968, Proc. Soc Exp. Biol. Med. *127*, 418.

Papermaster, B. W., 1967, The clonal differentiation of antibody producing cells. In: Cold Spring Harbor Symp. Quant. Biol. *32*, 447.

Paran, M. and L. Sachs, 1968, J. Cell. Physiol. *72*, 247.

Penington, D. G. and T. E. Olsen, 1970, Brit. J. Haemat. *18*, 447.

Perkins, E. H., T. Sado, and T. Makinodan, 1969, J. Immunol. *103*, 668.

Phillips, R. A., 1968, The immune response as a model system for studies on cellular differentiation. In: Differentiation and immunology, edited by K. B. Warren. Symp. Int. Society of Cell. Biology 7, p. 111.

Playfair, J. H. L., B. W. Papermaster, and L. J. Cole, 1965, Science *149*, 998.

Pluznik, D. H. and L. Sachs, 1965, J. Cell. Comp. Physiol. *66*, 319.

Pluznik, D. H. and L. Sachs, 1966, Exp. Cell. Research *43*, 553.

Porteous, D. D. and L. G. Lajtha, 1966, Brit. J. Haemat. *12*, 177.

Porteous, D. D. and L. G. Lajtha, 1968, Ann. N.Y. Acad. Sci. *149*, 151.

Porteous, D. D., S. C. Tso, K. Hirashima, and L. G. Lajtha, 1965, Nature *206*, 204.

Pozzi, L. V. and G. Silini, 1968, Kinetics of multiplication and differentiation of haemopoietic progenitor cells transplanted into irradiated mice. In: Effects of radiation on cellular proliferation and differentiation. Proceedings of International Atomic Energy Agency Symposium, p. 139.

Puck, T. T. and P. I. Marcus, 1956, J. Exp. Med. *103*, 653.

Quastler, H. and F. G. Sherman, 1959, Exp. Cell. Res. *17*, 420.

Raff, M. C., M. Steinberg, and R. Taylor, 1970, Nature *225*, 553.

Reissman, K. R. and S. Samorapoompichit, 1969, J. Lab. Clin. Med. *73*, 544.

Rickard, K. A., R. K. Shadduck, D. E. Howard, and F. Stohlman, 1970, Proc. Soc. Exp. Biol. Med. *134*, 152.

Robinson, W. A., T. R. Bradley, and D. Metcalf, 1967, Proc. Soc. Exp. Biol. Med. *125*, 388.

Roitt, I. M., M. F. Greaves, G. Torrigiani, J. Brostoff, and J. H. L. Playfair, 1969, Lancet *2*, 367.

Rowley, D. A., F. W. Fitch, D. E. Mosier, S. Solliday, L. W. Coppleson, and B. W. Brown, 1968, J. Exp. Med. *127*, 983.

Saunders, G. C., 1969, J. Exp. Med. *130*, 543.

Schlesinger, M., 1970, Nature *226*, 1254.

Schofield, R. and L. G. Lajtha, 1969, Cell Tissue Kinet. *2*, 147.

Schofield, R. and L. V. Pozzi, 1968, Growth rate of CFU population determined by bone marrow graft size. In: Advances in transplantation. Proceeding 1st International Congress of Transplantation Society, edited by J. Dausset, J. Hamburger, and G. Mathe. Copenhagen, Munksgaard, p. 423.

Schooley, J. C., 1964, Exp. Hematol. 7, 79.

Schooley, J. C., 1965, Blood *25*, 795.

Schooley, J. C., 1966, J. Cell. Physiol. *68*, 249.

Schooley, J. C., L. N. Cantor, and V. W. Havens, 1966, Exp. Hematol. *9*, 55.

Schooley, J. C., J. M. Hayes, L. N. Cantor, and V. W. Havens, 1967, Rad. Res. *32*, 875.

Schooley, J. C., J. F. Garcia, L. N. Cantor, and V. W. Havens, 1968, Ann. N.Y. Acad. Sci. *149*, 266.

Sell, S. and R. Asofsky, 1968, Progr. Allergy *12*, 86.

Senn, J. S. and E. A. McCulloch, 1970, Blood *35*, 56.

Senn, J. S., E. A. McCulloch, and J. E. Till, 1967, Lancet *2*, 597.

Shadduck, R., D. Howard, and F. Stohlman, Jr. 1968, Proc. Soc. Exp. Biol. Med. *128*, 132.

Shearer, G. M. and G. Cudkowicz, 1969, J. Exp. Med. *130*, 1243.

Silini, G., 1967, Control of haemopoiesis and the action of radiation on the blood forming organs. In: Effects of ionizing radiations on the haemopoietic tissue. Int. Atomic Energy Agency Panel Proceedings Series, p. 52.

Silini, G., L. V. Pozzi, and S. Pons, 1967, J. Embryol. Exp. Morph. *17*, 303.

Silini, G., S. Pons, and L. V. Pozzi, 1968a, Brit. J. Haemat. *14*, 489.

Silini, G., R. Elli, G. Siracusa, and L. V. Pozzi, 1968b, Cell Tissue Kinet. *1*, 111.

Siminovitch, L., E. A. McCulloch, and J. E. Till, 1963, J. Cell and Comp. Physiol. *62*, 327.

Siminovitch, L., J. E. Till, and E. A. McCulloch, 1964, J. Cell and Comp. Physiol. *64*, 23.

Siminovitch, L., J. E. Till, and E. A. McCulloch, 1965, Rad. Res. *24*, 482.

Smith, W. W., G. Brecher, R. A. Budd, and S. Fred, 1966a, Rad. Res. *27*, 369.

Smith, W. W., G. Brecher, S. Fred, and R. A. Budd, 1966b, Rad. Res. *27*, 710.

Smith, W. W., S. M. Wilson, and S. S. Fred, 1968, J. Nat. Cancer Inst. *40*, 847.

Stohlman, F. Jr., 1967, Some aspects of erythrokinetics. In: Seminars in hematology *4*, p. 304.

Stohlman, F. Jr., G. Lucarelli, D. Howard, B. Morse, and B. Leventhal, 1964, Medicine *43*, 6.

Stohlman, F., S. Ebbe, B. Morse, D. Howard, and J. Donovan, 1968, Ann. N.Y. Acad. Sci. *149*, 156.

Stutman, O. and R. A. Good, 1969, Proc. Soc. Exp. Biol. Med. *130*, 848.

Syeklocha, D., L. Siminovitch, J. E. Till, and E. A. McCulloch, 1966, J. Immunol. *96*, 472.

Thorbecke, G. J., N. L. Warner, G. M. Hochwald, and S. H. Ohanian, 1968, Immunol. *15*, 123.

Till, J. E., 1968, Prospects in the study of stem-cell kinetics. In: Effects of radiation on cellular proliferation and differentiation: Proceedings of International Atomic Energy Agency Symposium, p. 117.

Till, J. E. and E. A. McCulloch, 1961, Rad. Res. *14*, 213.

Till, J. E. and E. A. McCulloch, 1967, Stem cell function related to the repair of radiation damage. In: Brookhaven Symposia in Biology *20*, p. 161.

Till, J. E., E. A. McCulloch, and L. Siminovitch, 1964, Proc. Natl. Acad. Sci. *51*, 29.

Trainin, N. and P. Resnitzky, 1969, Nature *221*, 1154.

Trentin, J. J., J. C. Curry, N. Wolf, and V. Cheng, 1967, Factors controlling stem cell differentiation and proliferation: The hemopoietic inductive microenvironment (HIM). In: The proliferation and spread of neoplastic cells. M.D. Anderson Hospital 21st Annual Symposium on Fundamental Cancer Research, Baltimore, Williams and Wilkins, p. 713.

Trentin, J. J., B. A. Braaten, N. Amend, N. Prasad, N. S. Wolf, and V. K. Jenkins, 1969, Fed. Proc. *28*, 295 (Abs.).

Trobaugh, F. E. Jr. and J. P. Lewis, 1964, Exp. Hematol. *7*, 8.

Valeriote, F. A. and W. R. Bruce, 1967, J. Nat. Cancer Inst. *38*, 393.

Valeriote, F. A., W. R. Bruce, and B. E. Meeker, 1966, J. Nat Cancer Inst. *36*, 21.

Virolainen, M. and V. Defendi, 1968, Nature *217*, 1069.

Vogel, H., H. Niewisch, and G. Matioli, 1968, J. Cell. Physiol. *72*, 221.

Vogel, H., H. Niewisch and G. Matioli, 1969, J. Ther. Biol. *22*, 249.

Warner, N. L. and M. A. S. Moore, 1970, unpublished data.

Weisman, M., D. Martinson, W. Fried, and C. W. Gurney, 1967, J. Lab. Clin. Med. *69*, 438.

Welshons, W. J., 1964, Detection and use of cytological anomalies in the mouse. In: Mammalian cytogenetics and related problems in radiobiology. Oxford, Pergamon Press, p. 233.

Wolf, N. S. and J. J. Trentin, 1966, Fed. Proc. *25*, 296 (Abs.).

Wolf, N. S. and J. J. Trentin, 1968, J. Exp. Med. *127*, 205.

Wolf, N. S. and J. J. Trentin, 1970, J. Cell. Physiol. *75*, 225.

Wolf, N. S., J. J. Trentin and V. Cheng, 1968, Exp. Hematol. *15*, 88.

Worton, R. G., E. A. McCulloch, and J. E. Till, 1969a, J. Cell. Physiol. *74*, 171.

Worton, R. G., E. A. McCulloch, and J. E. Till, 1969b, J. Exp. Med. *130*, 91.

Wu, A. M., J. E. Till, L. Siminovitch, E. A. McCulloch, 1967, J. Cell. Physiol. *69*, 177.

Wu, A. M., J. E. Till, L. Siminovitch, and E. A. McCulloch, 1968a, J. Exp. Med. *127*, 455.

Wu, A. M., L. Siminovitch, J. E. Till, and E. A. McCulloch, 1968b, Proc. Nat. Acad. Sci *59*, 1209.

CHAPTER 4

Embryonic aspects of haemopoiesis

4.1 Introduction

Problems of the development of both the lymphoid and myeloid components of the haemopoietic system can be resolved into a number of issues concerning the origins and developmental potentialities of blood-forming cells, their relationship to haemopoietic organs, and the regulation and interrelationships of the different components of the system. (The term 'myeloid' is not used in this discussion in its literal sense of 'marrow' but as a useful collective term embracing those tissues containing stem cells, erythropoietic, granulopoietic and megakaryopoietic cells. At various stages in the embryo, yolk sac, liver, spleen and bone marrow can be so defined as 'myeloid'. The term is usually used to distinguish such tissues from 'lymphoid' tissues containing no stem cells and only lymphopoietic cells.) A considerable body of descriptive data exists, which is based on histological observations of developing haemopoietic organs and as such is within the sphere of descriptive embryology. The introduction of radioisotopic labelling and chromosome marker techniques now permits tracing of cells and cell populations in the haemopoietic system without necessitating the interpretation of ambiguous histological data. Application of tracer techniques in the adult system has revealed the dynamic nature of this system as a whole and the importance of cellular migration streams between different components. In this chapter, recent work using tracer techniques in embryonic systems is reviewed, and the validity of the conclusions reached by a considerable body of haematologists using histological methods will be re-evaluated. For reasons of availability and accessibility of embryological material, much of our knowledge of haemopoietic development has come from studies of non-mammalian vertebrates. In Table 4.1, the main stages of haemopoietic development and immunological maturation are compared in both mammals and lower

TABLE 4.1

Development of the haemopoietic system – comparative chronology[a]

Time of initiation (in days)	Mouse[b]	Lamb	Pig	Man	Opossum	Chicken[c]	Lizard[d]
Yolk-sac erythropoiesis (blood islands)	7		15–16	21–28	9–10	2	6;ST28
Liver haemopoiesis	11	30	28	42	—Birth	None	
Spleen rudiment appears	13	40	22	48	Birth	8	14;ST30
Spleen erythropoiesis	15	65	32–36	90–100	+ 5	11	24;ST33
Spleen lymphopoiesis	17	65	48	140	+21–23	19	48;ST40
Marrow haemopoiesis	15		51	140	+ 5	11	
Pharyngeal pouch formation	8	17	15	28–35		2	6;ST28
Epithelial thymus rudiment	10–11	30	21–22	40	—Birth	6–7	28;ST34
Large lymphocytes in thymus	12–13	43	28	70	+ 1	9	35;ST36
Lymph-node lymphopoiesis	18	45	52	70–120	+ 2–3	None[e]	
Lymphoid cells in Peyer's patches	+ 1	75	77				
Circulating small lymphocytes	18	50	38	120	+12	Hatch	

[a] Adapted from Auerbach, R., 1970 (personal communication).
[b] Based on 19-day gestation period. Add up to 24 hours for some strains, and 36 hours for the rat.
[c] Based on 21-day incubation period at 37–38 °C.
[d] *Calotes versicolor* – days approximate, staging according to V. Muthukkaruppan.
[e] No regular lymph nodes in chicken. The bursa of Fabricius appears as an epithelial thickening on day 4–5, becomes a separate rudiment on day 7–8. Stem-cell entry between days 12–14 and lymphoid cells appear on day 14.

vertebrates. There are clearly points of close similarity and some points of difference. In the comparison of birds and mammals e.g., the yolk sac is the first haemopoietic organ to develop at an early stage in both. In birds, however, the yolk sac persists for most of the incubation period as the major embryonic site of erythropoiesis, whereas in mammals it is rapidly superseded in this role by the embryonic liver. Primary lymphoid development is in all species initiated in the thymus, but in birds a second primary lymphoid organ, the bursa of Fabricius develops shortly thereafter. A homologous gut-associated organ may exist in mammals, but has not been clearly defined.

4.2 Yolk-sac haemopoiesis

It is unfortunate that the role of the mammalian yolk sac has been under-estimated, relegated to the status of an atavistic organ of transitory importance in mammalian development and considered a classic example of ontogeny recapitulating phylogeny. In two particular respects, in the development of the haemopoietic system and in production of primordial germ cells, such pessimism is hardly warranted, and there are excellent grounds for believing that the yolk sac has a unique role to play in the development of these two systems. In both instances this may be due to the early development of the yolk sac in an extraembryonic situation removed from the pressures of early embryonic differentiation. It would be singularly disastrous for the development of the embryo and the survival of the species if the first haemopoietic stem cells and primordial germ cells were to rapidly and completely succumb to differentiation pressures, such as exist within the early embryonic environment.

Haemopoiesis is first observed in blood islands generally confined to yolk-sac mesoderm, although in human embryos isolated foci of erythropoiesis are sometimes observed throughout the extraembryonic mesoblastic tissue (Bloom and Bartelmez 1940). In some lower vertebrates the intermediate cell mass is described as the first and chief site of blood formation (Stockard 1915) and is probably homologous with the blood-forming yolk-sac mesoderm of other meroblastic types, which has become incorporated into the intermediate cell mass. The early events preceding the establishment of blood islands have been extensively studied in organ-culture experiments using fragments of chick-embryo blastoderm. The early studies of Murray (1932) and Rudnick (1938) reported the migration of blood island precursor cells or haemangioblast precursors from the primitive streak region of the early blastoderm into the developing area vasculosa, and Murray (1932) concluded that '... the mesenchyme cells which form the haemangioblasts must be regarded even while they are still in the primitive streak, as self-differentiating cells, predetermined or at least strongly biased, towards the formation of the group of cell types which are derived from the haemangioblasts'. Settle (1954) confirmed these observations and showed that cells destined to form blood islands are organised in a horseshoe-shaped region surrounding the posterior and posterior-lateral region of the area pellucida (see Figure 4.1). Furthermore, haemopoietic potential is determined at the very early pre-primitive streak blastoderm stage, and is relatively uninfluenced by the course of the subsequent movement of the tissue to its definitive site. It is generally accepted that the mesodermal cells that ultimately form blood islands originate from epiblast, invaginate through the primitive streak and produce, by lateral migration, the middle germ layer. Spratt and Haas (1965) questioned this interpretation and proposed that mesoderm arises primarily by mitotic proliferation of the upper cell layer to form the mesodermal layer

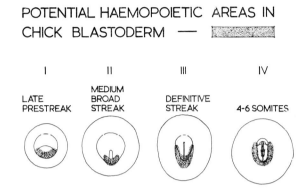

Fig. 4.1. The distribution of potential erythropoietic areas in chick blastoderms at various stages of development. (Figure redrawn from Settle (1954). Courtesy of the Carnegie Institute of Washington.)

which then migrates laterally from the streak area. However, tritiated thymidine labelling experiments have confirmed that invagination through the primitive streak, and subsequent lateral migration does occur and is probably the exclusive source of the mesodermal layer of the area vasculosa (Rosenquist 1966).

The mesenchymal cells of blood islands in most cases differentiate in two directions. The peripheral cells consist of a flattened irregular network of elongated spindle-shaped cells which join to form endothelial tubes, while the central cells of the island round up, become detached from peripheral cells and develop an intense cytoplasmic basophilia. These blood island precursors possess desmosomal connections or areas of increased density at various sites along their closely-opposed cell boundaries, and this is the case even in groups of cells floating free in the developing lumen (Edmunds 1964, 1966). Since endothelial-like capillaries can develop in the absence of haemopoiesis and some erythrocytic foci develop without vascular endothelium, dissociation probably exists between endothelium-forming potency and blood-cell forming potency of the yolk-sac mesenchyme. In this context, Murray (1932) proposed that the term 'angioblast' should be reserved for the forerunner of the vascular endothelium, while 'haemangioblast' should be restricted to blood cell precursors, and indeed the term 'blood island' has been restricted to the groups of cells in the lumen of the developing endothelial tubes (Sabin 1921). Some contribution by the endothelium of vessels of the yolk sac to erythropoiesis has been proposed (Jordan 1916; Houser et al. 1961), but studies in lower vertebrates (Stockard 1915) and electronmicroscopic studies of chick-embryo yolk sac (Edmunds 1964, 1966) do not support this view.

Although the haemangioblast precursors are probably predetermined to form blood cells, this capability is only expressed in the favourable milieu presented by the interacting endoderm and mesoderm layers. Studies in urodeles have shown the need for the presence of endoderm if erythropoiesis is to be satisfactorily initiated in the mesodermal blood islands (Finnegan 1953). More recent studies of definitive primitive streak chick embryos have confirmed this observation (Wilt 1965; Miura and Wilt 1969). In these experiments, fragments of the area opaca vascula near the pellucida-opaca junction of the embryo were removed prior to the establishment of haemopoiesis and separated into ectomesoderm and endoderm. Isolated fragments were cultured in transfilter combinations for 48 hours and assessed for haemoglobin formation. Erythroblast differentiation was suppressed in cultures of ectomesoderm alone but the presence of endoderm acting across a cell-impermeable filter, induced haemopoiesis in the ectomesoderm. The endodermal activity was not restricted to the areas of haemopoietic potential since anterior area opaca endoderm was just as effective. Miura and Wilt (1969) did not consider this to be a typical inductive interaction, since erythropoiesis though suppressed could occur without endoderm, but rather

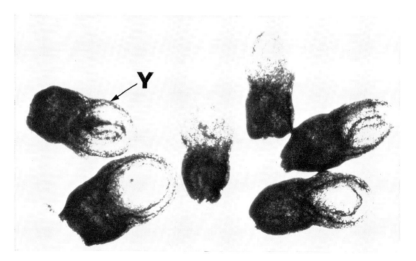

Fig. 4.2. Normal 7-day mouse embryos. The presomite stage embryo can be seen within the yolk sac (Y). The dark end of the embryo terminates in the ectoplacental cone ($\times$ 57). (From Moore and Metcalf 1970, reproduced by permission of the Brit. J. Haemat.)

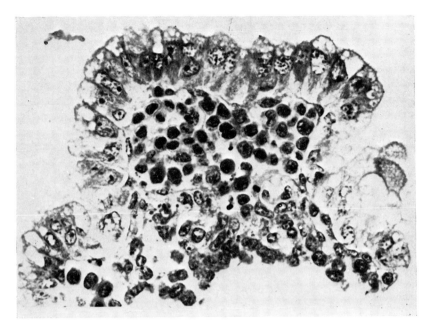

Fig. 4.3. Mouse yolk-sac blood island 7½ days' gestation. Note the accumulation of cells of the primitive erythroid series and undifferentiated blast cells in contact with the yolk-sac endoderm (Haematoxylin and Eosin 5 μ section × 480). (From Moore and Metcalf 1970, reproduced by permission of the Brit. J. Haemat.).

considered that endoderm provided a more favourable permissive micro-milieu for erythropoiesis. In electronmicroscopic studies of area opaca vascula, condensation of cells can be seen in the splanchnopleuric mesoderm in close association with the yolk-filled underlying endoderm with electron-dense material accumulating in the interspace between the two tissue layers (Mato et al. 1964). Explants of a homogeneous mixture of mesodermal, ectodermal and endodermal cells from the area opaca vasculosa of 19 hour chick embryos rapidly developed aggregates of haemangioblasts with a frequency of 64–183 aggregates per 10^6 cells (Miura and Wilt 1970). That these erythroblastic foci or islands which subsequently developed were not clones was shown in tritiated thymidine-labelling and cell-mixing experiments. Dilution of the culture with cells from non-haemopoietic areas reduced the frequency and size of blood islands. Since cell aggregation and sorting out undoubtedly play important roles in blood-island development, the number of actual haemopoietic precursor cells present at this stage cannot be determined, but it is clearly considerably larger than the number of haemangioblast aggregates.

The development of the mouse embryo is not typical since the embryonic area is invaginated into the yolk cavity with inversion of the relationship of ectodermal and endodermal layers. This inversion of germ layers results in the egg cylinder stage consisting of a double walled embryo with an outer endoderm and an inner ectoderm, which is the reverse of that seen in most other chordates. The yolk sac consists of extra-embryonic splanchnopleure which by $7\frac{1}{4}$-days' gestation is limited to an area forming a central or ecto-dermal-free portion of the egg cylinder wall (Figure 4.2). Blood islands develop in the yolk-sac mesoderm by $7\frac{1}{2}$-days' gestation and appear initially as regions of thickening in the inner or mesodermal layer of the yolk sac in contact with the extraembryonic endoderm. Initially aggregates of un-differentiated mesoblastic cells, the yolk-sac haemangioblasts rapidly develop into basophilic, morphologically undifferentiated, blast cells and basophilic erythroblasts (Figures 4.3 and 4.4). At later stages, polychromatic erythro-

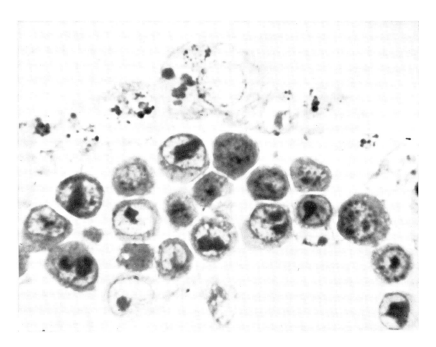

Fig. 4.4. Mouse yolk-sac blood island $7\frac{1}{2}$ days' gestation (1 μ section Toluidine Blue $\times$ 1,200). (From Moore and Metcalf 1970, reproduced by permission of the Brit. J. Haemat.).

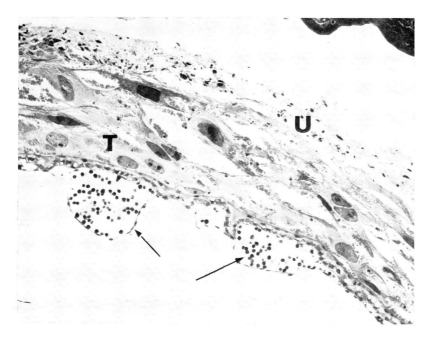

Fig. 4.5. Section of a 10-day yolk sac *in utero*. Note the dilated yolk-sac vessels filled with cells of the primitive erythroid series (arrowed) and the relationship of the yolk sac to the trophoblast (T) and uterine endometrium (U), × 120. (From Moore and Metcalf 1970, reproduced by permission of the Brit. J. Haemat.)

blasts at all stages of primitive generation erythropoiesis are evident. By the 9th day of gestation, blood islands are connected by an extensive capillary network and with initiation of cardiac contraction, circulation of blood between yolk sac and embryo commences. By the 10th day, blood islands develop into erythropoietic sinusoids (Figure 4.5) in free communication with the circulation and containing accumulations of large nucleated primitive generation erythrocytes. The primitive generation erythroid cells in mouse yolk sac are initially large proerythroblasts containing large nuclei with nucleoli, and cytoplasm containing abundant ribosomes and polyribosomes. At later stages of differentiation, nuclear volume decreases and the nucleus becomes increasingly pyknotic. Though the nucleus is not extruded, by the 14–15th day of gestation, circulating primitive generation erythroblasts do not incorporate tritiated thymidine and the cytoplasm may be devoid of ribosomes and detectable protein synthesis.

Haemoglobin synthesis in development has been extensively investigated, and it is known that in human embryos at least four types of haemoglobin are produced. At the earliest stage of human yolk-sac haemopoiesis, embryonic haemoglobins 'Gower I' and 'II' appear. Normal haemoglobins consist of two pairs of identical polypeptide chains, 'Gower II' haemoglobin consists of paired alpha and epsilon chains, while 'Gower I' consists probably solely of epsilon chains (Huehns and Shooter 1965). Since human yolk sac is also the site of definitive erythropoiesis initiated on the 6th week of gestation (Bloom and Bartelmez 1940) it is not unexpected therefore that transition from embryonic to foetal haemoglobin production should occur in this organ. Human foetal haemoglobin consists of pairs of alpha and gamma chains and comprises 85% of the total haemoglobin present at birth. Adult haemoglobin (alpha-2, beta-2) production apparently occurs simultaneously with that of foetal haemoglobin in embryonic liver, marrow and spleen, and it has been shown in hereditary persistence of foetal haemoglobin that both gamma and beta chains can be formed in the same cells (Shepherd et al. 1962). In the chick embryo at least two distinct embryonic haemoglobin types have been reported as early as at 48-hours' incubation using high-resolution vertical starch gel techniques, and three types at 5-days' using polyacrylamide gel electrophoresis. These are probably minimum numbers and there may be as many as three embryonic and five adult haemoglobin types in developing embryos with analysis complicated by asynchrony of cessation of embryonic haemoglobin synthesis and initiation of adult haemoglobin production (Wilt 1967). In most vertebrates, haemoglobin class expression does not show clear-cut organ restriction in contrast to the situation in the mouse embryo. Here, cell-separation studies and analysis of circulating primitive erythroid cells have shown conclusively that yolk-sac erythropoiesis produces solely foetal haemoglobin, while the intermediate generation of erythropoiesis in liver and all subsequent erythropoietic tissues produce adult haemoglobin (Craig and Russell 1964; Kovach et al. 1967; Barker 1968a). Mouse foetal haemoglobins comprise at least three types, haemoglobin E I (x + y globulin chains), E II (alpha + y globulin chains) and E III (alpha + z globulin chains) produced during the yolk-sac phase of haemopoiesis (Fantoni et al. 1967). Allelic variants of the genes controlling the y polypeptide synthesis have been reported (Gilman and Smithies 1968). Synthesis of adult haemoglobin (alpha-2, beta-2) of either the diffuse or single variants (Ranney and Glueksohn-Waelsh 1955) begins in mouse foetal liver on the 10th day of gestation (Kovach et al. 1967).

Embryonic haemoglobin synthesis involves activation and suppression of the numerous loci initiating and regulating synthesis of the various globulin chains. Regulation of such events may be intrinsic to the developing erythroid cells with sequential programmed expression of the various genes or, alternatively, may be brought about by external control factors. In mice, the yolk-sac environment may inhibit the expression of adult haemoglobin production; certainly stem cells are present at the early stages of yolk-sac erythropoiesis, which can, on transfer to the environment of an irradiated adult, restore definitive erythropoiesis and produce adult haemoglobin (Moore, M. A. S., unpublished observations). Preliminary experiments have confirmed that donor-type adult haemoglobin can be produced in irradiated recipients following yolk-sac cell grafting (Barker 1968b). The critical experiment which has not yet been performed is to demonstrate that adult stem cells in a yolk-sac environment could produce foetal haemoglobin. An alternative approach has been to culture dispersed yolk-sac cells *in vitro* in the presence of embryonic liver tissue enclosed in a cell-impermeable diffusion chamber. This experiment has produced suggestive evidence of induction of adult haemoglobin production in yolk-sac cells (Barker 1968b).

The role of erythropoietin in yolk-sac erythropoiesis has been studied in the mouse by Cole and Paul (1966) and in the chick embryo by Malpoix (1967) with conflicting results. *In vitro* cultures of 8–9-day mouse embryos with yolk sacs did not show increased haem synthesis or earlier onset of synthesis in the presence of erythropoietin, which would suggest either that primitive generation erythropoiesis was not normally regulated by erythropoietin or that the system already was operating at maximum synthetic activity due to endogenous erythropoietin stimulation. In contrast, cultures of chick-embryo area vasculosa showed a 40% stimulation of haemoglobin synthesis and a 20% stimulation in RNA synthesis in the presence of erythropoietin.

In most vertebrates, yolk-sac haemopoiesis embraces both primitive and definitive erythropoiesis, granulopoiesis and megakaryocyte production. In birds, the avian equivalent of neutrophils develop at 3–4 days of incubation, and thrombocytes, the equivalent of megakaryocytes, shortly thereafter (Edmunds 1964, 1966). Lymphopoiesis does not occur in yolk sac, and the report of Sabin (1921) of small lymphocytes in yolk-sac vessels of the chick on the 4th day of incubation was undoubtedly an erroneous classification of the small mononuclear avian thrombocytes. Perhaps the most extreme restriction of haemopoietic activity is seen in the mouse yolk sac since primitive generation erythropoiesis is the only haemopoietic activity reported during the yolk-sac phase of haemopoiesis from 7–12 days of gestation. For this reason, studies of the potentialities of murine yolk-sac cells have been

particularly relevant, since in the theory to be elaborated in the following
section, the yolk sac is considered to be the precursor of all haemopoietic
populations, both lymphoid and myeloid, developing subsequently within
the embryo and in the adult animal.

CFU's were first detected on the 8th day of gestation in mouse yolk sac –
prior to their appearance in the body of the embryo. Numbers were very low
averaging 1.44 ± 0.69 per 10^6 cells on the 8th day and increasing in frequency to a maximum of 4.01 ± 0.89 per 10^6 on the 11th day before falling
to zero by the 13th day (Figure 4.6) (Moore and Metcalf 1970). CFU's in
yolk sac have not previously been reported, and Matioli et al. (1968) were
unable to detect such cells in C57BL yolk sac. The low incidence of CFU's
together with poor cell viability and the small numbers of cells in early yolk
sac undoubtedly increased the difficulty of detection. The possibility that the
spleen colonies developing after yolk-sac cell injection were of endogenous
origin was checked in chromosome marker experiments and all colonies
analysed were of yolk-sac donor type. The experimental design further
eliminated the possibility of maternal CFU contamination of the hybrid

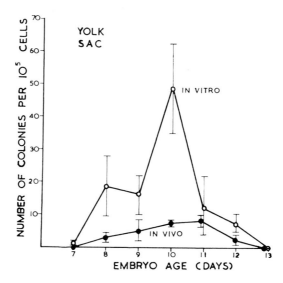

Fig. 4.6.   Numbers of *in vitro* CFC's and CFU's per 10^5 mouse yolk sac cells. Estimates
performed at daily intervals from 7 to 13 days' gestation on pooled yolk-sac cell suspensions.
Values are means of five estimates at each time point on pooled tissues from three to five
litters of (C57BL $\times$ CBA)F_1 embryos. Bars represent standard errors. CFU values adjusted
for seeding efficiency. (From Moore and Metcalf 1970, reproduced by permission of the
Brit. J. Haemat.)

yolk sac. Estimates of seeding efficiency using the 2-hour retransplantation assay disclosed a very low value of 0.05. If true seeding efficiency is similar to that of adult CFU's (0.04, see Chapter 3) a total of approximately 110 CFU's would be present on the 11th day of gestation within the yolk sac.

Yolk-sac cells formed both pure erythroid, megakaryocytic and granulocytic spleen colonies as well as mixed colonies. The proportion of 7–8-day colonies of these various types was not significantly different from that observed with CFU's of foetal liver and adult marrow origin (see Table 3.2, Chapter 3), but there was a trend to a higher percentage of mixed colonies than observed with adult marrow. Certain differences were detected when yolk sac-derived colonies were compared with those of adult marrow origin. Table 4.2 is a comparison of data on 10- and 12-day spleen colony cellularity and content of CFU's and *in vitro* CFC's. Yolk-sac-derived spleen colonies contained significantly more cells and at 12 days significantly more CFU's than did marrow-derived colonies. There were, however, significantly fewer *in vitro* CFC's in 10-day yolk-sac colonies than in the marrow colonies, but no difference was found at 12 days. These differences were most apparent when the ratio of CFU's to *in vitro* CFC's was considered, and a tenfold difference was evident both at 10 and 12 days, when yolk sac and marrow colonies were compared (Moore, M. A. S. and Metcalf, D., unpublished

TABLE 4.2

Comparison of 10- and 12-day spleen colonies produced by yolk-sac and marrow CFU's

	10 D colonies		12 D colonies	
	Bone marrow	Yolk sac	Bone marrow	Yolk sac
Total cells × 10^6	2.19± 1.17	3.80±1.21	6.07± 1.12	11.22±11.05
Total CFU's	16.28± 2.11	11.01±3.4	46.97±22.5	126.4 ±21.5
Total *in vitro* CFC's	151.4 ±133.4	3.63±1.85	58.88±16.41	57.54±21.43
$\frac{CFU}{CFC}$ratio	0.30± .22	3.03±3.52	0.28± .36	2.25± 3.75
CFU-CFC Correlation-Coefficient-R	0.484	0.361	0.174	0.019

observations). These differences may be related to an increased self-replicative capacity of the early embryonic CFU's with possible impaired differentiation into the progenitor (*in vitro* CFC) compartment at least in the early stages of colony development. In the experiments, to be discussed in detail in Chapter 8, the capacity of yolk-sac CFU's to sustain continuous proliferation in serial passage experiments is considerably greater than CFU's from adult or even neonatal sources.

In vitro CFC's were first detected in the mouse yolk sac of 7-day embryos at the presomite and early 1–4 somite stage, appearing in the blood islands at the earliest stages of haemopoietic development. From an initial level of 1.2 ± 0.1 per 10^5 cells *in vitro* CFC's attained a maximum of 49 ± 15 per 10^5 on day 10, representing a total of 300 per yolk sac. Thereafter the numbers fell to undetectable levels by the 13th day (Figures 4.6, 4.7). *In vitro* CFC's were not detected in the body of the embryo until the 9th day, after the circulation had been established. Thus *in vitro* CFC's were first detected 24

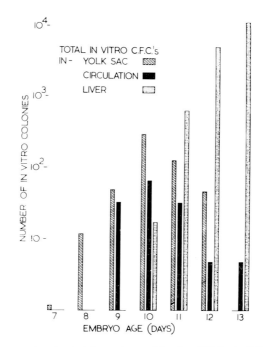

Fig. 4.7. Histogram showing total numbers of *in vitro* CFC's in (C57BL × CBA)F₁ mouse-embryo yolk sac, circulation and liver. Values are means of three to five estimates on one to five pooled litters at daily stages from 7 to 13 days' gestation. (From Moore and Metcalf 1970, reproduced by permission of the Brit. J. Haemat.)

hours earlier than CFU's could be demonstrated. It is probable that, as elsewhere, CFU's were the immediate precursors of the *in vitro* CFC's, but remained undetected at the earliest stages due to the low sensitivity of the *in vivo* assay.

In vitro colony formation by early embryonic cells exhibited the same absolute dependency on colony-stimulating factor, as has been shown for adult bone-marrow cells with the exception of yolk-sac cells plated at a high cell concentration (10^5 cells per plate) and early embryonic blood cells. In both cases some colony formation occurred in the absence of added colony stimulating factor. In the case of cultures of blood cells, colony formation was probably stimulated by colony-stimulating factor in the serum contaminating unwashed cell suspensions. Direct assay of 9-day mouse embryo serum showed high levels of colony-stimulating activity (350 colonies stimulated per 0.1 ml of 9-day foetal serum vs. 50 colonies stimulated per 0.1 ml of adult serum). The autonomous colony formation in certain yolk-sac cultures may likewise be due to the presence of small quantities of embryonic serum, but is more likely to have been due to production of colony-stimulating factor by yolk-sac cells themselves.

In vitro colonies formed by yolk-sac cells were in general smaller than colonies obtained from adult marrow (Figures 4.8a, b), but showed the same gross appearance as colonies formed by bone-marrow cells. In the first 3 days of development colonies contained granulocytic cells (Figure 4.9), but subsequently the colony population underwent transition, and by the 7th day of culture most colonies were composed of pure populations of macrophages

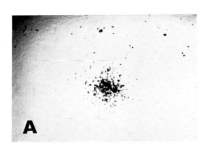 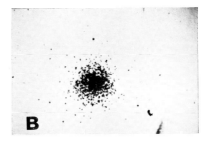

Fig. 4.8A.   View of unstained *in vitro* colony after 7 days' incubation of an 8-day yolk sac cell suspension, × 36.

Fig. 4.8B.   Unstained *in vitro* colony after 7 days' incubation of an 18-day foetal liver cell suspension. Note the greater size and cellularity than the colony in Fig. 4.8A, × 36. (Fig. A and B from Moore and Metcalf 1970, reproduced by permission of the Brit. J. Haemat.)

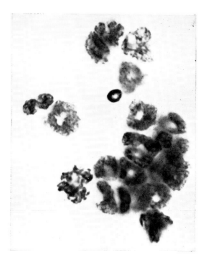

Fig. 4.9. Orcein stained preparation of a 3-day *in vitro* colony produced by 8-day yolk sac cells. The population is composed of meta-myelocytes and polymorphs, × 1200. (From Moore and Metcalf 1970, reproduced by permission of the Brit. J. Haemat.)

(Figure 4.10). The small size of the colonies apparently was due to inhibition by toxic cell breakdown products produced both by yolk-sac and early liver-cell suspensions. Colony formation by adult marrow cells was not inhibited by killed marrow cells but equivalent numbers of killed yolk sac or early liver cells reduced colony numbers by 75 %, and the colonies appearing were much smaller than normal and resembled in all respects those seen in yolk-sac cultures. The presence of this inhibitory material has probably resulted in an underestimation of the number of *in vitro* CFC's present in the yolk sac.

The developmental potentialities of haemopoietic cells in the yolk sac have been revealed in studies on the capacity of yolk-sac cells to repopulate the haemopoietic system of sublethally-irradiated chick embryos (Moore and Owen 1967a) and lethally-irradiated mice (Moore and Metcalf 1970). In both

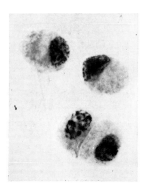

Fig. 4.10. Orcein stained preparation showing mono-nuclear cells present in 7-day *in vitro* colony produced by 8-day yolk sac cells, × 1200. (From Moore and Metcalf 1970, reproduced by permission of the Brit. J. Haemat.)

TABLE 4.3

Repopulation by yolk-sac-derived cells of the haemopoietic organs of irradiated recipients

	Mouse*	
Organ	Number of mitoses scored	% donor mitoses
Thymus	14, 28	100, 100
Spleen	100, 100	94, 92
Bone marrow	100, 100	92, 100
Peyer's patch	28, 15	72, 85
Mesenteric lymph node	62, 79	94, 89
	Chick**	
Thymus	50, 100, 50	24, 8, 36
Bursa of Fabricius	50, 100, 50	16, 20, 24
Bone marrow	100, 100, 100	12, 46, 32

* Recipient (C57BL × CBAT6T6)F_1 mice, irradiated 800 R and injected intravenously with 8 × 10^6 (C57BL × CBA)F_1 11-day yolk-sac cells. Organs examined at 30 days for T6 chromosome markers.
** Recipients 14-day chick embryos, irradiated 800 R and injected intravenously with 10^7 7-day yolk-sac cells from male donors. Recipients sampled 2 days after hatching for ZZ sex chromosome markers.

experimental designs the proliferation of donor cells in the recipient myeloid and lymphoid organs was detected using chromosome marker techniques. The results shown in Table 4.3 revealed that cells present in 11-day mouse yolk sac at a stage prior to any lymphoid development in the embryo had extensively repopulated the recipient thymus and secondary lymphoid organs, such as the mesenteric lymph node and Peyer's patches, in addition to promoting myeloid regeneration in spleen and marrow. Similar results were obtained in the sublethally-irradiated chick-embryo system, where 7-day yolk-sac cells partially repopulated the primary lymphoid tissue, thymus and the bursa of Fabricius and the myeloid tissue of bone marrow. Tyan (1968) and Tyan and Herzenberg (1968) have shown in irradiation reconstitution experiments that T6-marked yolk-sac cells from 7–14 day mouse embryos can repopulate the adult thymus, spleen and bone marrow. In these studies, placental cells were also stated to possess similar repopulating capacity.

However, the possibility of placental contamination by yolk sac may explain this observation.

Functional tests on reconstitution of immunological capacity following yolk-sac cell injection clearly demonstrated that precursors of immunologic-ally-competent cells are present in the early embryo yolk sac. Tyan (1968) established that precursors of cells capable of participating in a graft-vs.-host reaction were present in the mouse placenta as early as the 9th day of in-cubation and in embryonic liver by the 10th day, but not apparently in the yolk sac of 9–12-day embryos, despite the observation that yolk-sac cells repopulated the adult irradiated thymus. Yolk-sac cells were, however, capable of restoring immunoglobulin production to irradiated recipients, since donor allotypes of gamma G2A and gamma G1 immunoglobulins were detected even in thymectomised recipients (Tyan et al. 1968, 1969; Tyan and Herzenberg 1968). Yolk-sac-derived cells were also capable of producing specific antibody against sheep red cells (Tyan et al. 1969). Tyan has proposed that precursors of the immunoglobulin-producing cells arise independently in the yolk sac on the 9–10th day of gestation and constitute a different population from the precursors of cell-mediated immunity (Tyan 1968). Such early differentiation and dissociation of potentially immunolo-gically-competent cells would indeed be remarkable. It seems more likely that in the embryo, precursors of both the immunoglobulin-producing and graft-vs.-host reactive cells are multipotential stem cells, and that the apparent dissociation in the capacity of different embryo tissues to reconstitute either of these two systems may be due to quantitative rather than qualitative differences in the number of stem cells present in these early tissues. If availability of stem cells in the recipient is limited, competition may be established, and if, e.g. development of cell-mediated immunity requires a larger number of stem cells than regeneration of humoral immunity, severe impairment of recovery of this system may be observed even in the presence of donor immunoglobulin synthesis.

4.3 Dependence of intra-embryonic haemopoiesis on yolk-sac cell migration

One of the earliest theories of haemopoietic development proposed that haematogenous metastases from yolk sac initiated haemopoiesis in intra-embryonic tissues. Gotte (1867) believed that the splenic rudiment of the toad was composed of a mass of 'Dotterbildungszellen', or primitive blood cells derived from the yolk sac, which had entered the splenic mesenchyme from the circulation. The theory of haematogenous metastases is an attractive one but received little support from the majority of haematologists and embryologists who favoured an *in situ* mesenchymal and/or endothelial derivation of haemopoietic cells. The experimental evidence for the latter theory is slender, being largely circumstantial and based on the observation of apparent transitional stages between fixed elements and blood cells. Experiments in lower vertebrates have provided important evidence supporting the yolk-sac migration concept. Removal of blood islands from embryos of *Rana fusca* at the beginning of the tail bud stage resulted in some instances in the development of larvae completely devoid of erythrocytes (Frederici 1926). Similar results were obtained by Goss (1928) with embryos of *Amblystoma punctatum*. Complete suppression of haemopoiesis in liver, spleen and nephric tissue followed removal of yolk-sac blood islands at a stage when they were well localised structures not yet connected with the general vascular system. At a slightly later stage, removal resulted in a marked reduction in subsequent erythropoiesis but not complete suppression, since a few blood cells had drifted into the vitelline veins before operation.

Most previous work on embryonic haemopoiesis has been hampered by the difficulties of analysing dynamic cellular processes. Now, however, cell-marker techniques have provided satisfactory ways of tracing cells. An excellent marker is available in the chick embryo in which the sex chromosome differences between male and female cells can be used to investigate the interchange of cells between embryo pairs joined by a natural vascular union (in twins) or by an artificial yolk sac or chorioallantoic vascular anastomosis (produced by parabiosis) (see Chapter 2). Experiments of this design are reviewed in detail in subsequent sections and the results have indicated that, contrary to previous views, stem cells of marrow, spleen, thymus and bursa of Fabricius are blood-borne, migrating into the early organ rudiment from the circulation, and are not of intrinsic origin. Although similar experiments have not been performed in the mammalian embryo, natural vascular union has been followed by cellular chimaerism in haemopoietic organs of twin mammals (see Chapter 5). Stem-cell migration is likely therefore to play a similar and crucial role in mammalian haemopoietic development.

Since the yolk sac is the first site of embryonic haemopoiesis, circulating stem cells are probably derived from this source initially (Moore and Owen 1967b). In the preceding section, evidence was reviewed indicating that yolk-sac cells are capable of differentiating in both the myeloid and lymphoid series and in the latter case, can achieve full immunological competence.

Therefore, despite the extreme restriction in haemopoietic differentiation seen particularly in the mouse yolk sac, this tissue contains cells with the capability of producing all classes of haemopoietic cells when placed in the appropriate environment.

In the mouse embryo following the establishment of a circulation, all stages of haemopoietic differentiation seen in the yolk sac can also be seen in the blood. The frequency of circulating CFU's and *in vitro* CFC's in the blood on the 9th and 10th days of gestation is similar to their frequency in the yolk sac (Figure 4.7), and indeed the total population of circulating *in vitro* CFC's at this stage exceeds the total in the circulation of an adult mouse. The incidence of CFU's in the blood is also approximately 10-fold greater throughout the whole of gestation than in the adult. One of the primary postulates of the yolk-sac migration theory is that the colonising cells migrate through the circulation, hence the observation of considerable numbers of both stem cells and progenitor cells in the circulation throughout development and their probable initial origin from yolk sac constitute powerful support for the theory. Stem cells capable of repopulating lymphoid and myeloid tissue were also detected in considerable numbers in chick-embryo blood in irradiation reconstitution experiments (Moore and Owen 1967a).

The presence of considerable numbers of *in vitro* CFC's in both the yolk sac and circulation is notable because of the complete absence of granulopoiesis in these tissues at this early stage. Since *in vitro* CFC's are restricted to macrophage and granulocyte differentiation and *in vitro* produce cells of the latter type within 2–3 days, the yolk-sac environment must have the capacity to inhibit differentiation of *in vitro* CFC's. Recently Auerbach (Auerbach, R., personal communication) has obtained granulocytic differentiation in mouse yolk sacs cultured in the presence of a high serum concentration suggesting that this inhibition is not absolute. Such microenvironmental suppression must also be responsible for restriction of differentiation of multipotential CFU's. The accumulation and subsequent decline of the *in vitro* CFC's in the yolk sac may therefore represent the production and mass migration of this cell type into the circulation, with subsequent localisation within the foetal liver on the 10th day of gestation. The hepatic environment at this stage has the capacity to promote differentiation of *in vitro* CFC's and granulopoiesis is evident in this tissue by 11–12 days' gestation.

Direct proof of this migration was obtained in experiments where presomite and early 1–4 somite mouse embryos of 7-days' gestation (Figure 4.2) were cultured for 2–3 days on the surface of millipore filters in an *in vitro*

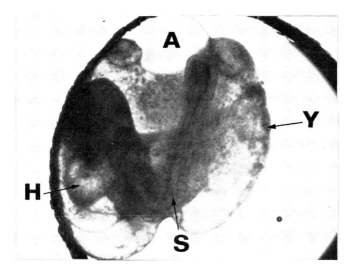

Fig. 4.11

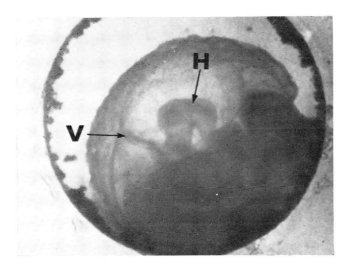

Fig. 4.12

Fig. 4.11. and Fig. 4.12. 7-day mouse embryo with yolk sac 2 days in organ culture. Numerous somites (S) can be seen together with extensive development of the heart (H) yolk sac (Y), amnion (A) and blood vessels (V). Living preparations *in situ* on millipore filter well, × 25. (From Moore and Metcalf 1970, reproduced by permission of the Brit. J. Haemat.)

organ-culture system. Presomite embryos with intact yolk sacs developed within 48 hours to a stage corresponding to that of an early 9-day embryo *in utero* with normal somite development, extensive haemopoiesis in yolk-sac blood islands, an actively-beating heart and circulating fluid containing primitive erythrocytes (Figures 4.11 and 4.12). In some embryos, evidence of early liver development was obtained. After more prolonged culture, the growth of the embryos became disorganised due to a breakdown in the normal pattern of development. Removal of the yolk sac from 7-day embryos prior to culture did not noticeably interfere with subsequent embryonic development *in vitro* and in a 2-day culture period, the isolated embryos grew to the 10–20 somite stage and developed actively-beating hearts (Figure 4.13). The most striking difference was that histologically there was no evidence of haemopoietic cells of any type either in vascular channels or in the region of the developing liver, and the circulating fluid in blood vessels appeared to be totally acellular. Isolated 7-day yolk sacs in culture underwent rapid growth and formed fluid-filled vesicles which adhered to the millipore filter surface. In a 48-hour culture period, extensive erythropoiesis was seen to develop in yolk-sac cultures. Histological studies revealed that blood islands developed normally and engaged in primitive generation erythropoiesis (Figure 4.14). Table 4.4 shows the number of *in vitro* CFC's

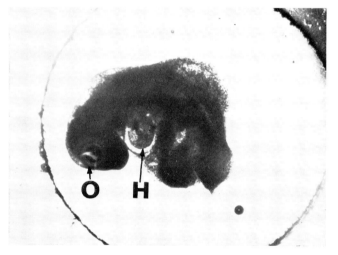

Fig. 4.13.   7-day mouse embryo with yolk sac removed. 2 days in culture. Note absence of extra-embryonic membranes but good development of the heart (H) and optic vesicles (O). Living preparation *in situ* on millipore filter well, × 25. (From Moore and Metcalf 1970, reproduced by permission of the Brit. J. Haemat.)

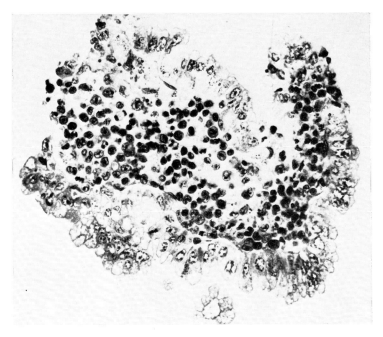

Fig. 4.14.   Extensive development of a blood island in 7-day yolk sac cultured by itself for 2 days *in vitro*. Note the accumulation of erythroid cells at all stages of development and the presence of mitoses, × 480. (From Moore and Metcalf 1970, reproduced by permission of the Brit. J. Haemat.)

detected in cultured embryos with intact yolk sacs after 2 days in culture. Within 48 hours, the number of *in vitro* CFC's appearing in such cultures compared favourably with the number observed in the normal 9-day embryos and yolk sacs. The majority of 7-day embryos cultured in the absence of yolk sac were completely devoid of *in vitro* CFC's even after 2–3 days in culture. The occasional embryo containing *in vitro* CFC's was consistent with failure to remove all of the yolk sac prior to culture, and contamination with less than 1 % of yolk sac would account for the number of *in vitro* CFC's observed. Isolated 7-day yolk sacs contained more *in vitro* CFC's after 2 days in culture than the total found in either the yolk sac cultured with an intact embryo or in the yolk sacs of normal 9-day embryos. The total approximated to the number of *in vitro* CFC's in yolk sac *and* embryo in these situations.

These experiments established that the development both of intraembryonic haemopoiesis and *in vitro* CFC populations required the presence of an

TABLE 4.4

Development of *in vitro* colony-forming cells in organ cultures of mouse embryos with or without yolk sacs. (From Moore and Metcalf 1970, by permission of British J. Haematology.)

Group	Tissue	*In vitro* CFC/ 10^5*	Total nos. of CFC per embryo and/ or yolk sac
7-day embryo + yolk sac without culture	Yolk sac	1.2 ± 0.9	0—1
	Embryo	0	0
	Total		0—1
7-day embryo + yolk sac 2 days in culture	Yolk sac	53.0 ± 21.0	45
	Embryo	10.1 ± 1.8	10
	Total		55
9-day embryo + yolk sac without culture	Yolk sac	16.0 ± 6.0	51
	Embryo	3.8 ± 2.1	12
	Total		63
7-day yolk sac alone – 2 days in culture	Yolk sac	92.1 ± 17.1	81
7-day embryo alone – 2 days in culture	Embryo	0.05 ± 0.01	0
	Total		81
7-day yolk sac alone – + colony-stim. factor** 2 days in culture	Yolk sac	100.7 ± 30.3	88
7-day embryo alone – + colony-stim. factor** 2 days in culture	Embryo	0	0
	Total	0	88

* Mean data from 7—12 experiments $\pm$ standard errors. In each experiment, *in vitro* CFC assays were performed on pooled embryos and/or yolk sacs from one litter.
** 10% of a human urine concentrate with high *in vitro* colony-stimulating activity.

intact yolk sac. This yolk-sac influence was not humoral, since yolk sacs separated from embryos by a cell-impermeable millipore filter, failed to induce intraembryonic haemopoiesis, and addition of exogenous colony-stimulating factor to embryo cultures was without effect in initiating *in vitro* CFC development (Table 4.4). A direct cellular migration from the yolk sac into the embryo is therefore indicated with intraembryonic haemopoiesis, particularly in foetal liver, dependent on an initial colonisation by yolk-sac-derived stem cells and progenitor cells (*in vitro* CFC's). Partial establishment of haemopoiesis and *in vitro* CFC's in embryos cultured after yolk-sac

TABLE 4.5

Incidence of *in vitro* colony-forming cells in mouse yolk sacs *in utero* or in organ culture.
(From Moore and Metcalf 1970, by permission of British J. Haematology.)

Yolk sac	Days of gestation:	10	11	12	13	14	15	16
In utero	CFC/10^5:	49.0$\pm$28.5*	13.0$\pm$9.3	8.0$\pm$2.3	0	0	0	0
10-day yolk sac	Days of culture:	0	1	2	3	4	5	6
In vitro	CFC/10^5:	49.0$\pm$28.5	24.0$\pm$12.0	16.8$\pm$7.3	11.2$\pm$6.1	8.1$\pm$3.0	0.9$\pm$0.8	0

* $\pm$ Standard error.

removal was obtained by addition of dissociated yolk-sac cells to embryos or by recombination of isolated yolk sacs and embryos. This reconstitution was never completely effective, however, since vascular union and circulatory exchange did not occur. Presumably the vascular architecture and pattern of blood circulation are important components in the process of yolk-sac cell migration into the embryo.

The loss of *in vitro* CFC's from normal yolk sac appears to be due to migration of these cells into the circulation and subsequent colonisation of the embryo. The large number of *in vitro* CFC's seen in yolk sacs cultured in the absence of the embryo pointed to accumulation in the absence of emigration. Furthermore, *in vitro* CFC's persisted in such cultures for considerably longer periods than observed *in vivo* (see Table 4.5) indicating that the total absence of such cells by 13-days' gestation *in vivo* was due to migration rather than differentiation or death.

4.4 Embryonic liver haemopoiesis

Conventional descriptions of liver histogenesis propose that the hepatic anlage arises from a number of interacting tissues. An endodermal diverticulum from the foregut penetrates the septum transversum, which comprises the vitelline veins with their surrounding mesenchyme between the endoderm of the yolk stalk, and the foregut on one side and the splanchnic mesoderm which forms the coelomic mesothelium on the other (Wilson et al. 1963). In the mouse the diverticulum appears on the 7th day and strands of cells of the diverticulum come into contact with the veins in the septum resulting in a mass composed of a spongework of parenchyma with the spaces occupied by a network of sinuses. The primary endodermal hepatic bud fails to develop in the absence of mesenchyme. A reciprocal interaction occurs between the two component tissues, endoderm and mesenchyme, altering the developmental course of both, leading to endodermal differentiation into hepatic cords and hepatocytes, and mesenchymal transformation into a connective tissue framework and the vascular endothelium (Croisille and Le Douarin 1965). By the 10th day in the mouse embryo, haemopoiesis is initiated in the liver, which becomes the major embryonic haemopoietic organ following the decline of yolk-sac haemopoiesis. In birds, the haemopoietic activity of the embryonic liver is far less than in mammals. It has been suggested that the intensity of foetal hepatic haemopoiesis can be correlated with the presence of an umbilical venous drainage in contrast to yolk-sac venous drainage through the avian liver (Danchakoff and Sharp 1917). Avian embryonic liver has been reported as a specific site of both erythropoiesis and granulopoiesis (Haff 1914; Karrer 1961), but it is probable that intravascular hepatic erythropoiesis reflects general intravascular erythropoiesis which occurs widely throughout the early embryo at any site where the circulation has slowed down (Romanoff 1960). Similarly, avian granulopoiesis is very widespread throughout the chick embryo and isolated foci of hepatic granulopoiesis assume no special significance (Moore, M. A. S., unpublished observations).

At the earliest stage of mammalian liver haemopoiesis, undifferentiated blast cells appear scattered throughout the liver cords and in the mouse erythropoiesis begins between 10–11-days' gestation with megakaryocytes and granulocytic cells appearing shortly thereafter. Hepatic haemopoiesis is predominantly extravascular and at the ultrastructural level, intimate contact is observed between haemopoietic cells and differentiating endoderm, with no intervening basement membrane (Grasso et al. 1962; Rifkind et al. 1968).

Historically, virtually every cell type in the developing liver has been proposed as the source of hepatic haemopoietic cells. Origins from hepatic endoderm, sinusoidal endothelium and mesenchyme of the septum transversum have been reported (see review by Bloom 1938). Indeed, in a histochemical study of megakaryocytic development in liver, these cells were claimed to be derived from undifferentiated mesenchyme, primitive reticulum and endothelium (Ackerman and Knouff 1960). However, the evidence reviewed in the preceding section leads to the conclusion that hepatic haemopoiesis is initiated by colonisation of the hepatic anlage by circulating haemopoietic precursor cells of yolk-sac origin. This haematogenous concept is not without precedent, and Van Der Stricht (1891) maintained that the haemopoietic primordia of the liver developed from circulating blood cells, while Danchakoff (1918) considered that the network of large hepatic sinusoids would slow the blood flow at a time when the circulation contained numerous haemocytoblasts and erythroblasts and would therefore produce conditions highly favourable for their localisation. Some experimental evidence was provided by Stockard (1915), who failed to observe any haemopoietic activity in embryonic fish liver when blood circulation was prevented; and though heavily criticised at that time, his conclusions from these experiments were probably valid.

Hepatic erythroid cells are similar to the cell type seen in bone marrow. The intermediate generation of erythrocytes produced by the mouse liver are non-nucleated and smaller (8μ) than the primitive generation of nucleated cells but larger than the adult erythrocytes (6μ diameter) (Russell and Bernstein 1966). The haemoglobin-containing cells of liver increase exponentially with a population doubling time of about 8 hours until $15\frac{1}{2}$ days when there is a sharp transition and doubling lengthens to about 2 days (Paul et al. 1969). Immature cells formed during the rapid phase of increase are poorly haemoglobinised and consequently, increase of haemoglobin lags behind that of erythroid cells. Of all cells in mouse embryonic liver 55–70% belong to the erythroid series (including reticulocytes and erythrocytes). The percentage of myelocytes and myeloblasts remains unchanged throughout embryogenesis (7–19%), while the more differentiated myeloid cells increase from the earliest times of observation with metamyelocytes finally amounting to about 50% of all haemopoietic cells 1 week after birth. The percentage of pro-erythroblasts falls after the 17th day followed by a drop in erythroblast count 3 days later (Silini et al. 1967). Liver haemopoietic activity subsides rapidly after birth, but the organ may contain haemopoietic foci even up to 1 week after birth (Borghese 1959).

It has been suggested that in the rat, foetal erythropoiesis is not erythropoietin-dependent (Stohlman et al. 1964), and suppression of maternal erythropoietin production in pregnant mice had no effect on foetal erythropoiesis (Jacobson et al. 1959). Cultures of liver cells from $10\frac{3}{4}$- to $14\frac{1}{2}$-day mouse foetuses and 12–13-day rat foetuses showed little haemoglobin synthesis *in vitro* but were markedly stimulated by erythropoietin. The response to erythropoietin in both mouse and rat liver was basically similar and can be divided into three phases. In the earliest phase the response to erythropoietin on a per cell basis was low, presumably reflecting the low frequency of erythropoietin-sensitive cells. This was followed by a phase of increased erythropoietin sensitivity and then a lack of any response to erythropoietin. This last phase occurred abruptly in the mouse and more gradually in the rat (Cole et al. 1968).

Baglioni (1963) has proposed that the switch from foetal to adult haemo-globin production results from an increase in the number of cell divisions in the erythroid series and that derepression of the foetal loci occurs earlier in the cell lineage than derepression of adult loci. On this theory, high erythro-poietin levels in the foetus stimulate rapid haemoglobin synthesis, which by limiting further cell division favours production of the foetal haemoglobin. This theory was not supported by observations that haemoglobin produced following erythropoietin stimulation of foetal cells was adult in type (Cole et al. 1968).

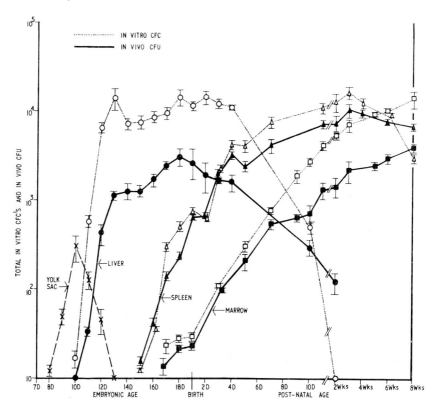

Fig. 4.15. Total numbers of *in vitro* CFC's and CFU's in (C57BL × CBA)F₁ mouse haemopoietic tissues from 7 days' gestation to 8 weeks of post natal life. Marrow values are totals per single femoral shaft. Means represent three to five estimates performed at each time point on two to ten animals. CFU values not adjusted for seeding efficiency.

Quantitation of CFU's in mouse embryonic liver has been performed with divergence of results, probably due to differences in the strains used and whether hybrid or inbred embryos were studied. There was general agreement that CFU's are most frequent (on a per cell basis) on the 12–14th days of gestation with reported values ranging from 2–13 per 10^5 (Silini et al. 1967; Barker et al. 1969; Matioli et al. 1968; Duplan 1968; Moore et al. 1970; Moore and Metcalf 1970). A second smaller rise in CFU concentrations is seen just before birth in some strains (Moore et al. 1970; Matioli et al. 1968; Silini et al. 1967), but in other strains a progressive fall is seen throughout embryonic development (Barker et al. 1969; Silini et al. 1967).

CFU's first appeared in the liver on the 10th day of gestation (Figures 4.15, 4.16) and the CFU population increased rapidly between 10–13 days with a doubling time of 7–8 hours. Since the CFU generation time is presumably considerably shorter than this population doubling time, a significant component of the early expansion of the hepatic CFU compartment must have been due to accumulation of CFU's migrating from the yolk sac. Total CFU's doubled again between 13 and 17 days reaching a maximum on the 18th day. CFU's persisted in the liver in the immediate postnatal period but were absent by the 8th day in the study of Barker et al. (1969). The liver contribution to total body CFU's in the first week after birth was not incon-

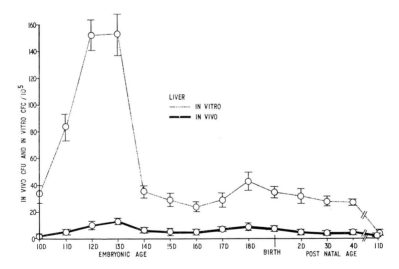

Fig. 4.16. Numbers of *in vitro* CFC's and CFU's per 10^5 liver cells from (C57BL × CBA)F_1 mice in the embryonic and early post natal stages. Values obtained on same material as results in Figure 4.15.

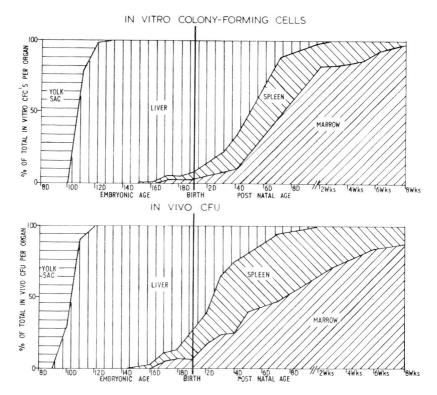

Fig. 4.17. Organ content of *in vitro* CFC's and CFU's expressed as a percentage of the total body population in (C57BL × CBA)F₁ mice during embryogenesis and postnatal life. Total marrow values estimated on the assumption that one femur is equivalent to 8% of the total marrow reserve. CFU values not adjusted for seeding efficiency.

siderable (Figure 4.17), and CFU's were still detectable 2 weeks after the birth (Moore, M. A. S., unpublished observation). In Swiss mice, many CFU's persisted in the liver in adult life (Silini et al. 1967).

The factors involved in the postnatal decline in hepatic haemopoiesis and loss of CFU's are not clearly understood. Possibly maturation of liver parenchymal cells and loss of haemopoietic-inducing capacity of the hepatic microenvironment forces stem-cell emigration to the more favourable environment of the developing marrow cavities.

In vitro CFC's have been demonstrated in mouse embryonic liver and appear to have a similar differentiating capacity and absolute dependence on colony-stimulating factor to those in adult haemopoietic tissue (Moore et al. 1970; Moore and Metcalf 1970). *In vitro* CFC's first appeared on the 10th day of gestation and the population increased rapidly to a peak on the 13th day with a population doubling time of 5–6 hours (Figures 4.7, 4.15). This early population-growth rate could not be sustained without a significant component of growth being due to migration of the *in vitro* CFC's from yolk sac to liver. This early rapid growth of *in vitro* CFC's is all the more remarkable, since it is occurring at the same time as the maximum growth rate of CFU population. Since there appears to be little evidence to suggest that *in vitro* CFC's are a self-maintaining population, much of the production of *in vitro* CFC's in the liver is sustained by CFU differentiation occurring simultaneously with the maximum rate of growth of the CFU compartment. By the 14th day, total *in vitro* CFC's drop abruptly to half the 13-day peak and this level is maintained until the 17th day (Figure 4.16). From the 18th day of gestation to the 4th day postnatally, the population increases again prior to a precipitous decline to undetectable levels 2 weeks after birth at a time when CFU's are still present.

Liver haemopoiesis can thus be divided into three phases, an initial phase of maximum growth rate between 10–13 day's gestation where *in vitro* CFC's outnumber CFU's by 12–17:1; an intermediate plateau phase between 13 days and birth with a more constant ratio of *in vitro* CFC's to CFU's (4–6:1); and a terminal postnatal decline phase where loss of CFU's initially occurs more rapidly than *in vitro* CFC's (Figures 4.15, 4.17, and 4.18).

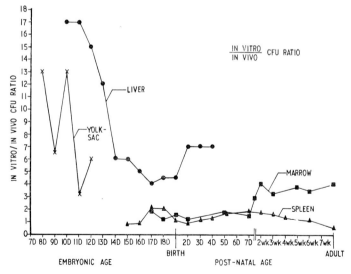

Fig. 4.18. Graph showing differences in the ratio of *in vitro* CFC's to CFU's in different organs and at different stages of development in (C57BL × CBA)F₁ mice.

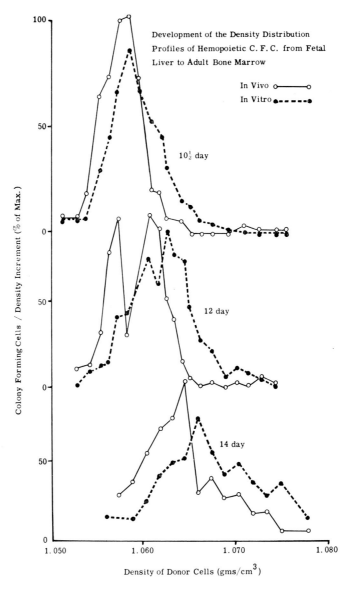

Fig. 4.19.   Density distribution profiles of CFU's and *in vitro* CFC's in 10.5-, 12- and 14-day mouse foetal liver. Profiles have been arbitrarily normalised to relate areas under the curves to the same value. (From Moore et al. 1970, reproduced by permission of J. Cell. Physiol.)

As discussed in Chapter 3, the population of CFU's and *in vitro* CFC's seen in adult bone marrow is heterogeneous with respect to both cell density (Haskill et al. 1970) and cell volume (Worton et al. 1969). It seemed possible that this heterogeneity would not be observed at the earlier stages of haemopoietic development, and consequently the density distribution profiles of CFU's and *in vitro* CFC's were investigated in developing mouse foetal liver using the BSA density gradient technique. At the earliest stage of liver haemopoiesis at $10\frac{1}{2}$ day's gestation, CFU's were confined to a narrow density region of the gradient with only one density population resolved in the region 1.057–1.059 (Figure 4.19). *In vitro* CFC's also showed a single major peak in

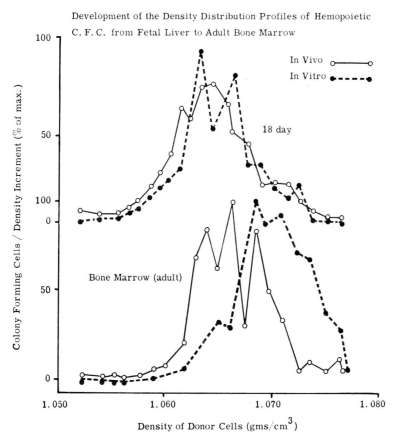

Fig. 4.20. Density distribution profiles of CFU's and *in vitro* CFC's in 18-day foetal liver and in adult marrow. The profiles have been arbitrarily normalised. (From Moore et al. 1970, reproduced by permission of J. Cell. Physiol.)

the density region 1.058–1.059. However, distortion of the distribution with a shoulder evident in the profile indicated the presence of an incompletely resolved subpopulation in the region 1.061–1.062 (Moore et al. 1970). The subsequent development of the liver was paralleled by the progressive acquisition of higher density subpopulations of CFU's and *in vitro* CFC's (Figures 4.19, 4.20) and by 18 day's gestation the density profile of these two cell types had acquired the heterogeneity and much of the density range seen in adult bone marrow. Comparison of the foetal liver and marrow density profiles revealed a progressive increase in the mean density of both CFU's and *in vitro* CFC's throughout the course of development and in general the mean density of *in vitro* CFC's exceeded that of the CFU population. The *in vitro* CFC profiles exhibited an 'out-of-phase' distribution when compared with the CFU's. This phase interrelationship may develop if CFU's in any particular density subpopulation had an equal chance of undergoing differentiation to produce *in vitro* CFC's. If this differentiation step involved a small incremental density increase which was similar in magnitude despite the initial density of the mother cell, an 'out-of-phase' density relationship would be observed.

In transfer experiments, the capacity of the lightest density population (less than 1.058) of CFU's and *in vitro* CFC's which comprise the bulk of these cells in $10\frac{1}{2}$ day foetal liver was tested for ability to generate CFU's occupying higher density regions. Figure 4.21 shows that this light density population produced in 7 days in the femoral marrow of adult irradiated hosts a population of CFU's and *in vitro* CFC's. The majority of both these cell populations occupied a higher density region than the original donor cells and were distributed throughout the entire density range occupied by these cell types in 18-day foetal liver.

In the regenerating marrow the peak of *in vitro* CFC activity appeared in a higher density region (1.066) than the CFU activity (1.062) and in the density region occupied by the original transfer fraction, *in vitro* activity was slight but considerable *in vivo* activity remained.

The homogeneous population of extremely light density stem cells observed at the earliest stages of liver haemopoiesis is most probably the product of migration from the yolk sac. As such they have the capacity not only to engage in liver haemopoiesis but also to eventually colonise the spleen and marrow, initiating haemopoiesis in these sites and establishing the adult stem-cell population. A small percentage of the CFU population of adult marrow overlaps the density region occupied by the early liver stem cells (1.0565–1.0585) and therefore may be of equivalent functional capacity.

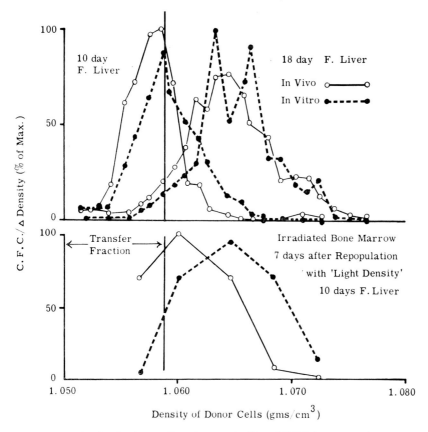

Fig. 4.21. Density distribution profiles of *in vitro* CFC's and CFU's in regenerating marrow, 7 days after transfer of 'light density' (< 1.058) fraction of 10.5-day foetal liver to adult irradiated recipients. Compare the regenerating profiles (lower graph) with normal 10.5- and 18-day foetal liver *in vitro* CFC and CFU profiles (upper graph). (From Moore et al. 1970, reproduced by permission of J. Cell. Physiol.)

If such were the case, there would be no necessity to postulate the existence of a uniquely embryonic form of stem cell and light density status might then reflect some functional activity of the cell such as a high rate of proliferation. There are, however, demonstrable differences between early embryonic and adult stem cells of the same density. Determinations of 2-hour spleen seeding efficiency of CFU's revealed a low f value of 0.05 for $10\frac{1}{2}$ day foetal liver CFU's, but a significantly higher value of 0.12 was found with adult marrow CFU's of the same density (Moore et al. 1970).

Further differences were found by Haskill and Moore (1970), who em-

ployed a two-dimensional cell-separation procedure. The first stage involved
density separation of CFU's and selection of adult marrow CFU's of the
same density as in $10\frac{1}{2}$ day foetal liver (1.0565–1.0585). The second stage
subjected these homogeneous density populations to velocity sedimentation
separation at unit gravity, a procedure which separates cells primarily on the
basis of their size or volume. The two-step procedure permits a high degree
of resolution of a complex mixture of cells varying in size and density. The
results shown in Figure 4.22 revealed that adult marrow CFU's of density
1.0565–0.0585 consisted of a major population of volume 260 μ^3 and a minor
population of 430 μ^3 (equivalent to spherical diameters of 7.9 and 9.3 μ).
In contrast, foetal liver CFU's of similar density revealed major populations
of volume 820 and 1000 μ^3 (equivalent to spherical diameters of 11.6 and
12.4 μ). It is difficult to relate spherical diameters to values measured on
smearing as smearing probably leads to overestimates of true cell diameters.
However, it is evident the early embryonic CFU must be much larger than
its adult equivalent.

The histological and autoradiographic studies of stem-cell morphology in
early embryonic haemopoietic tissue discussed in this chapter point to a large

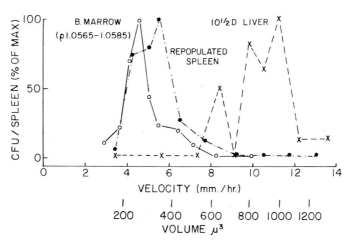

Fig. 4.22. Sedimentation velocity profiles of CFU's present in $10\frac{1}{2}$-day mouse embryo
liver (x- - -x) adult bone marrow (p. 1.0565–1.0585) (O———O) and from the spleen of
lethally irradiated recipients 7 days after injection of 2×10^5 adult marrow cells (●———●).
Cell loading in all experiments was less than 3×10^6 cells per ml (10 ml sample) for bone
marrow or spleen, and 2×10^6 cells per ml for embryonic liver. Cell volumes were determined on the pulse height analyser. (From Haskill and Moore 1970, reproduced by permission of Nature.)

basophilic blast-type cell, whose size corresponds to the spherical diameter of the CFU revealed by the two-dimensional separation procedure. In contrast, in adult marrow smaller cells of the small or medium lymphocyte (Cudkowicz et al. 1964) transitional cell (Moffat et al. 1967) or monocytoid types (Caffrey-Tyler and Everett 1966) have been implicated as haemopoietic stem cells. This perennial problem of stem cell morphology can therefore be resolved by compromise, since the CFU size heterogeneity seen in both adult and embryonic populations indicates that stem cells of the size of small and medium lymphocytes, transitional cells and blast cells can all exist, with small cells probably predominating in adult haemopoiesis and large in embryogenesis. We propose that stem cells may be able to modulate between these different sizes and morphological states depending on functional demand. E.g., small mononuclear cells may transform to transitional cells in adult marrow and embryonic basophilic blast cells may transform to small mononuclears in the course of development. It appears, however, that adult stem cells cannot produce the large embryonic stem cell type at least in the adult environment and therefore, the morphological change to the adult stem cell is probably irreversible. The differences in size of stem cells may be related to cell cycle status, with larger cells in more rapid cycle than smaller cells. In adults the majority of CFU's are not in cycle but rather in a G_0 state (see Chapter 3) and are smaller cells than CFU's in early foetal liver which are in very rapid cell cycle. To test the hypothesis that the difference between adult and embryonic stem cells is due to differences in proliferative activity, 2×10^5 adult marrow cells were passaged into lethally-irradiated recipients for 7 days (Haskill and Moore 1970). The spleens of these animals were then submitted to a sedimentation velocity separation. The results (Figure 4.22) clearly showed that adult marrow CFU's were incapable of reverting to the early embryonic type even under conditions of extreme proliferation though some size increase was evident.

A number of functional differences in proliferative capacity and regulation distinguish the embryonic liver stem cells from those of adult marrow. Micklem and Loutit (1966) injected equal quantities of bone marrow and foetal liver cells, each marked with a separate chromosome tag, into lethally-irradiated adult recipients. Two weeks after irradiation, the majority of dividing cells were derived from the injected marrow cells but by 4 weeks the proportion of foetal liver-derived cells increased and by 8–9 weeks, the latter had increased up to 100% of total dividing cells. In the host spleen, foetal liver-derived cells predominated as early as 2 weeks. The different pattern in proliferation between spleen and marrow may indicate different homing tendencies with foetal liver stem cells being less inclined to colonise bone marrow. The striking result of the study was, however, the capacity of the foetal liver stem cells, even though numerically considerably fewer than those in the bone-marrow inoculum, to sustain continuous proliferation for a longer period than those of marrow origin and in a competitive situation eventually outgrow the latter. Kubanek et al. (1969) compared erythroid regeneration in irradiated recipients given equal numbers of either foetal liver or adult marrow CFU's. Recipients of the foetal inoculum showed earlier onset of erythroid regeneration in both marrow and spleen and more extensive colonisation of marrow. These results suggest a number of possible explanations: (a) Since embryonic stem cells are actively proliferating, an earlier onset of regeneration might be anticipated. This would not explain the predominantly marrow-derived regeneration with delayed foetal liver-derived overgrowth in the experiments of Micklem and Loutit, nor the more extensive marrow colonisation reported by Kubanek et al. (b) Embryonic stem cells may sustain a more rapid rate of proliferation than those of the adult. This is unlikely in the first 2 weeks of proliferation since the cellularity and total CFU and *in vitro* CFC populations of individual spleen colonies of marrow or foetal liver origin were not significantly different between 9–14 days of development (Moore, M. A. S., unpublished observation). (c) A third alternative is that embryonic stem cells can sustain continuous proliferation over a longer period than those of adult origin, which would account for the eventual overgrowth of foetal-liver-derived cells in the competitive situation described by Micklem and Loutit. This possibility is supported by the observation that in serial spleen colony passaging experiments, the CFU content of second-passaged colonies of embryonic origin was not significantly less than in primary colonies and contrasted with the decline (to 1–100% of normal) in CFU content of second-passaged colonies of adult marrow origin (Moore, M. A. S. and Metcalf, D., unpublished observation). These results can be interpreted in terms of the number of divisions stem cells have undergone since their first appearance in the yolk sac (see Chapter 8). It appears that the more embryonic the stem cell the more population doublings it can sustain. An approximate calculation suggests that embryonic stem cells can undergo 20–80 more doublings than an equivalent stem cell in adult marrow. Two possible explanations for the difference in passaging capacity are apparent. Embryonic-derived stem cells may be less susceptible to population-size control and differentiation pressures and sustain self-replication at the expense of differentiation. Alternatively, if stem cells are programmed to undergo a fixed number of divisions or the number of mitoses is limited by accumulation of somatic mutations, stem cells in adult tissues will have utilised a greater proportion of their division potential than stem cells in the embryo. This latter point must be considered in the light of the yolk-sac migration theory of haemopoietic origin, which implies that adult stem cells are the progeny of cells that have engaged in continuous proliferation in the developing haemopoietic system since their first appearance in the yolk-sac blood islands.

Differences in regulation of embryonic stem cells are evident and this may be reflected in the greater proportion of spleen colonies of foetal-liver origin, which are histologically of mixed type when compared with colonies of adult origin (see Chapter 3). More direct evidence was provided in experiments where erythroid spleen-colony formation was assessed in polycythaemic recipients. With adult marrow stem cells 98–100% of erythroid spleen colonies were completely suppressed in polycythaemic mice. In contrast, foetal-liver-derived erythroid colonies were not completely suppressed in an equivalent situation, and only 44–69% reduction in erythroid colony numbers was observed (Feldman and Bleiberg 1967; Bleiberg and Feldman 1969). These results revealed that embryonic stem cells generated an erythroid progenitor cell population that could differentiate in the absence of erythropoietin or required only extremely low levels of this factor, since erythropoiesis occurred in animals whose endogenous erythropoietin production was almost completely suppressed. Further analysis of this situation (Haskill, J. S., personal communication) revealed that foetal liver CFU's were heterogeneous with respect to capacity to engage in erythroid colony formation in polycythaemic recipients. Two-dimensional density and velocity separation showed that in 17-day embryonic liver, CFU's with the characteristic large size and light density of the earliest embryonic CFU's were capable of forming erythroid colonies in the polycythaemic spleen, but that CFU's present in the liver with the density and size characteristic of adult marrow stem cells were unable to form erythroid colonies in a similar situation.

The studies of Vos et al. (1960) and Doria et al. (1962) showed that haemopoietic cells derived from injected foetal liver ultimately repopulated the lymphoid tissue and acquired immunological competence. Lymphoid repopulation was observed even if liver cells were used from embryos prior to the initiation of thymic lymphopoiesis (Taylor 1964). Tyan has also demonstrated that mouse foetal-liver cells can, on transfer to adult irradiated recipients, produce immunologically-competent lymphocytes, mediating cellular immunity and detectable by a graft-vs.-host assay. Foetal-liver cells also gave rise to cells producing gamma G2A immunoglobulin even in thymectomised irradiated recipients (Tyan et al. 1969, 1966; Tyan and Herzenberg 1968; Tyan and Cole 1963, 1964). Despite the presence of precursors of immunologically-competent cells, haemopoietic cells in the foetal liver do not produce a direct graft-vs.-host reaction (Bortin and Saltzstein 1968) or produce directly immunoglobulins (Van Furth et al. 1965; Moore, M. A. S. and Warner, N. L., unpublished observations). Using an *in vitro* assay of graft-vs.-host competence, Umiel et al. (1968) showed that embryonic liver cells did not have a capacity to induce splenomegaly directly, even after culture for 4–6 days. Capacity to induce splenomegaly was, however, acquired when liver explants were cultured in combination with thymus tissue. Experiments suggested that the competent cells were of liver origin maturing under the influence of thymus. We can conclude that the liver contains lymphoid precursor cells that achieve immunological competence only after migration out of liver and possibly residence in primary lymphoid tissue. It does not appear that local immunocyte differentiation occurs in the foetal liver under a humoral influence such as that of thymic factor. It is possible that in the early prenatal and immediate postnatal period when lymphoid precursor cells are present in the liver, a humoral influence has not as yet matured sufficiently to induce local immunological competence within the liver. Embryonic or neonatal liver cells injected together with thymus cells into irradiated adult recipients generated plaque-forming cells producing antibody against sheep red cells (Playfair 1968a). Plaque-forming cell precursors were most numerous in the liver at, or just before, birth and declined in numbers at a time when spleen PFC precursors were increasing. The PFC precursors in the newborn liver comprised 1 in 800 to 1 in 8,000 of all nucleated liver cells (Playfair 1968a) adjusted for seeding efficiency of 5–10 %. It may be that these precursors are identical with CFU's and certainly the incidence of the latter (adjusted for the same seeding efficiency) is 1 in 650 to 1 in 1300 liver cells at birth and therefore of similar frequency to PFC precursors. In a study of strain differences in the ontogeny of immunity, Playfair (1968b) showed that NZB mice developed PFC-forming capacity earlier and to a greater extent than C57BL mice. Also, irradiated NZB mice restored with syngeneic marrow recovered PFC responses earlier than other strains. Reconstitution of PFC responses in irradiated recipients following administration of mixtures of parental or F_1 hybrid newborn liver and thymus cells revealed that the high NZB PFC response to sheep red cells was a characteristic of the NZB liver cell population (PFC precursors) rather than the NZB thymus (Playfair 1968a). It was therefore argued that the liver precursor cells contained genetic information as regards antibody specificity.

4.5 Development of the spleen

The splenic primordium appears as a dense syncytial-like mesenchymal thickening in the dorsal mesogastrium. The extensive literature on spleen development has been reviewed by Bloom (1938) in mammals, De Laney and Ebert (1962) in birds and Klemperer (1938) in man. The earlier investigators believed the organ was of endodermal origin and recognised a close relationship between the developing spleen and the endodermal epithelium of the pancreatic diverticulum. Subsequent work refuted this view, recognising the mesodermal origin of the spleen, but opinion was divided on the role played by coelomic epithelium. Thiel and Downey (1921) in their definitive study of spleen development noted the close histological similarity of coelomic epithelium and mesenteric mesenchymal cells. In the stage prior to the development of the splenic rudiment, they observed a coelomic epithelial contribution to the mesenchymal cell population of the mesogastrium and in this sense the coelomic epithelium may be indirectly responsible for the development of the spleen but there appeared to be no participation once the rudiment had appeared.

An extension of the general theory of blood cell origin from fixed tissues derives the first splenic haemopoietic cells from undifferentiated mesenchymal cells of the splenic rudiment which separate, round up and develop an intense cytoplasmic basophilia (Bloom 1938; Danchakoff 1916; Klemperer 1938; Thiel and Downey 1921). An alternative view was that the haemopoietic cells developed by a process of budding from the endothelial lining of the developing splenic venous sinuses (Schmidt 1892; Schridde 1923; Jordan 1916). Historically, the earliest and least popular theory of splenic haemopoietic origin was the haematogenous theory of Gotte (1867). Thiel and Downey (1921) stated 'one cannot entirely disregard the possibility of an accompanying differentiation of elements brought in by the blood stream', particularly as they observed that the early system of vascularisation of the spleen provided ideal conditions of the development of a new haemopoietic organ by metastasis from another blood forming tissue.

In the chick embryo, the splenic anlage appears as a mesenchymal condensation interspersed with vascular spaces where the circulating blood comes into direct contact with mesenchymal reticulum cells. At the earliest stages of development, large immature cells characterised by intense cytoplasmic basophilia and prominent nucleoli are frequently observed both in the vascular spaces and perivascular mesenchyme of the spleen (Figures 4.23, 4.24). At later stages, they appear scattered throughout the mesenchymal

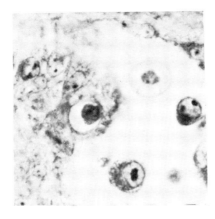

Fig. 4.23. 8-day chick-embryo spleen. Three basophilic cells are present in the vascular spaces. Giemsa × 1000.

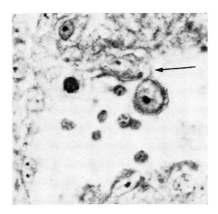

Fig. 4.24. 8-day chick-embryo spleen. A basophilic cell can be seen within a vascular space with a cytoplasmic process extending into perivascular mesenchyme (arrowed). Small nucleated cells in the vascular space are mature thrombocytes. Giemsa × 1000.

reticulum and are clearly distinguishable from the reticulum cells on the basis of both intensity of cytoplasmic staining and size and development of the nucleoli. Frequently the basophilic cells lie within sharply circumscribed vesicular spaces and often possess long tails of cytoplasm that extend between the reticulum cells for some distance from the main body of the cell (Figures 4.25, 4.26). By the 11th day of incubation, granulopoiesis is extensive in the spleen but foci of erythropoiesis are also present at this stage, particularly in sinusoids at the periphery of the spleen. On the 17th and subsequent days, regions of granulocyte depletion are observed throughout the organ corresponding to the reticulum cell sheaths around the splenic arterioles. By the end of incubation the spleen consists of numerous circumscribed reticulum sheaths that contrast with the densely-packed granulocyte population of the

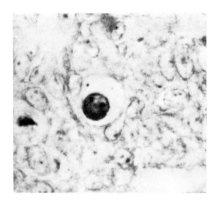

Fig. 4.25. 8-day chick-embryo spleen showing typical appearance of a basophilic cell in a sharply circumscribed vesicular space within the mesenchymal reticulum. Giemsa × 1000.

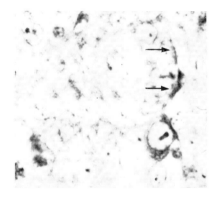

Fig. 4.26. 8-day chick-embryo spleen showing a basophilic cell within a vesicular space, and an extensive 'tail' of basophilic cytoplasm (arrowed) can be seen extending from another basophilic cell. Giemsa × 1000.

remainder of the tissue. These sheaths correspond to regions of early white-pulp development and consist of a central arteriole with a thickened endothelial lining separated by a distinct basement membrane from the whorls of reticulum cells which form a sheath 5–10 cells wide around it. A distinct demarcation exists between the outer margin of the sheath and the granulopoietic areas of the future red pulp region of the spleen. Small lymphocytes are observed in small numbers in the reticulum sheaths by the 19th day of incubation interspersed among the reticulum and frequently display highly irregular cell outlines. In the first week after hatching the reticulum sheaths become increasingly populated with lymphocytes and are in turn surrounded by collars of densely packed small lymphocytes populating the previously granulocytic areas of the spleen. Numerous capillaries and sinusoids are seen in the lymphoid collars and this region corresponds to the red-pulp region of the mammalian spleen. Granulopoietic activity diminishes in the days following hatching and the spleen becomes transformed into a predominantly lymphopoietic organ.

In mammals, e.g. the mouse, a similar developmental sequence is observed. The splenic anlage is detected by 13 days' gestation and has detectable erythropoietic activity by 15 days' but by 17 days granulopoiesis predominates (Borghese 1959). Small and medium lymphocytes first appear round the small follicular arteries at or shortly after birth. The spleen therefore is unique in that it is both a lymphoid and myeloid tissue and produces or contains during the course of its development, every cell type produced within the haemopoietic system.

The results of chromosome analysis of the spleens of twin and parabiosed chick embryos are presented in Table 4.6 (Moore, M. A. S. and Owen, J. J. T. 1965, and unpublished observations). In every embryo, high spleen chimaerism was observed and in embryos sampled between 12–20 days' incubation between 19–74% of the dividing cells were derived from the opposite partner.

TABLE 4.6

Sex chromosome analysis of the spleen of twin and parabiosed chick embryos*

Union	Age at parabiosis (days)	Age at sampling (days)	Percentage mitoses of opposite sex (% chimaerism)
Chorioallantoic membrane	8	15	36, 28, 26, 21
Chorioallantoic membrane	8	17	46, 38
Chorioallantoic membrane	8	19	28,
Chorioallantoic membrane	6	19	20, 26, 46, 19
Chorioallantoic membrane	11	19	48, 27
Chorioallantoic membrane	7	20	22,
Yolk sac	4	14	64, 57, 30
Yolk sac	4	15	34, 50
Yolk sac	5	16	74,
Twin embryo	—	12	27, 39
Twin embryo	—	13	40, 26

* 50—100 mitoses scored in each organ.

In three embryos, spleen chimaerism was greater than 50% and in these instances the embryo was considerably smaller than its partner, due to yolk-sac herniation through the parabiotic union. Histological studies revealed that the dominant cell type sampled was granulocytic but both erythroid and, at later stages (19–20 days), lymphoid cells formed a proportion of the dividing cell populations. These observations clearly indicate that circulating stem cells normally enter the splenic rudiment via the blood prior to the 12th day of incubation at the time of initiation of splenic haemopoiesis. However, stem-cell inflow is not confined to this early stage since in embryos where vascular anastomosis was established as late as the 12th day of incubation, the spleen was still highly chimaeric at the time of sampling 7 days later.

The haemopoietic development of embryonic spleens grafted to the chorio-allantoic membrane of host embryos was comparable with that of the host spleen (Moore, M. A. S., unpublished observations) and chromosome marker studies revealed host repopulation of the spleen by 4 days after grafting. Spleens from 14–16-day embryos sampled after 9 days on the chorioallantois (CAM) of 10-day host embryos showed considerable retardation of lymphoid development when compared with *in situ* spleens of comparable age. Small lymphocytes were observed in the periarteriolar sheaths scattered among the reticulum cells, but lymphoid development was never more advanced than in the host spleen. Similar observations were made by Danchakoff (1924) who failed to observe lymphoid development in embryonic spleen grafts on the CAM even after serial retransplantation to prolong the sojourn of the spleen in an embryonic environment. Two possible explanations may account for the failure of normal lymphoid development. It may be that the vascular architecture of the spleen in a graft situation is abnormal and this may be critical for the localisation of circulating lymphocytes or lymphoid precursors. Alternatively, and more probably, lymphoid development of the spleen is host-dependent and not an intrinsic property of the spleen occurring at a fixed stage of its development. In this context, external factors such as antigenic stimulation or at around the time of hatching and maturation of host thymus and bursa may determine the spleen lymphoid transition. There is considerable evidence that spleen lymphoid development is severely retarded, and in some cases completely inhibited, following neonatal thymectomy (Miller et al. 1965). Furthermore, the *in vitro* experiments of Auerbach (1966) showed that the mouse embryo spleen did not become lymphoid unless cultured with a lymphoid thymus. It would therefore appear that some thymic factor, either cellular or humoral, determines the time of initiation and magnitude of splenic lymphoid transformation.

The growth of embryonic spleen grafts was not significantly altered when the spleens were grafted singly or in multiples to the CAM of host embryos. This contrasts with the observations of Metcalf (1963, 1964) showing that the growth capacity of multiple spleen grafts in adult mice was restricted and that the total mass achievable by multiple spleen grafts in splenectomised animals approximated the normal spleen weight. Therefore either the growth regulation that limits total spleen mass operates only in the adult or serves mainly to regulate lymphoid development in the spleen and hence has less influence on embryonic pre-lymphoid development.

The capacity of the embryonic spleen at various stages to become populated by circulating stem cells was assayed 24 hours after the injection intravenously of myeloid and lymphoid cells (Moore, unpublished observation). Tritiated thymidine-labelled embryonic myeloid cells localised in considerable numbers in the avian embryo spleen at all stages observed (Figure 4.27). Maximum numbers per unit area of spleen were seen at the very early stages of spleen development at the time of initiation of splenic haemopoiesis on the 8th–9th day of incubation. The frequency of labelled cells was lower in embryos injected at 10–16 days of incubation, and injections at later stages of development attained a low but constant level. Between the 13th–16th day, the numbers of labelled thymic lymphocytes in the spleen following labelled

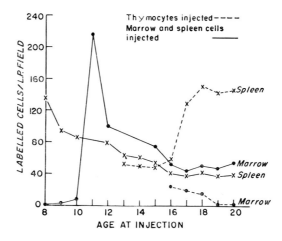

Fig. 4.27. The distribution of tritiated thymidine-labelled chick-embryo marrow and spleen cells or embryonic thymic lymphocytes 24 hours after intravenous injection into chick embryos. Each point represents the mean number of labelled cells per unit area (3 mm²) in host marrow or spleen. The number of cells injected was related to host body weight, and ranged from 2–40 × 10⁶. Ten embryos were used at each time point.

thymus cell injection were comparable with the numbers of labelled myeloid cells localising there. However, a considerable increase in localisation achievable using labelled thymic lymphocytes occurred by the 17th day and the numbers between 17–20 days were considerably in excess of the numbers of labelled cells following an injection of equivalent doses of myeloid cells. The labelled cells observed in the spleen in the early stages of its development following myeloid cell (embryonic marrow, spleen or yolk sac) injection were mainly large undifferentiated basophilic cells and myeloblasts. By 24–48 hours after injection, the majority of labelled cells were of the granulocytic series and all stages from the most immature myeloblast to the mature granulocyte were represented. The latter were frequently observed in clusters with similar grain counts. Although quantitative grain counts were not performed, the labelled mature granulocytes were always more lightly labelled than the more immature myeloblasts. Labelled mitotic figures were frequently observed in the labelled cell compartment of the spleen and in embryos injected at 12 and 13 days of incubation up to 6% of the labelled cell population in the spleen was in division. From this, it can be concluded that injected labelled myeloid cells not only localised within the spleen but also proliferated and underwent differentiation. The labelled thymocytes that could be located in considerable numbers in the spleen following injection of thymocytes at later stages of development were entirely small and medium lymphocytes and were confined to the regions surrounding developing foci of reticulum cells that form the sheaths around splenic arterioles. Labelled cells were observed only very rarely in these sheaths and the majority lay within the future splenic red-pulp regions where the collars of small lymphocytes that surround the sheaths develop after hatching. No evidence of labelled cell proliferation or differentiation was observed during the 48 hours after injection of thymus cells.

The differential uptake of thymic lymphocytes and myeloid cells suggests that the cell uptake mechanism of the spleen is selective and operates preferentially to abstract myeloid cells in the early stages of haemopoiesis. At later stages of spleen development, preferential uptake of lymphoid cells occurs in a period when the spleen is changing from a myeloid to a lymphoid organ. A similar accumulation of injected labelled thymic lymphocytes has been demonstrated in the mammalian spleen by Fichtelius (1960) and by Murray and Murray (1967).

More direct evidence that the first lymphocytes to appear in the spleen have migrated from the thymus was obtained by local *in situ* thymus labelling with tritiated thymidine followed by the observation that labelled small and medium lymphocytes appeared subsequently in the spleen (Nossal 1964; Linna 1968; Murray and Woods 1964; Moore, M. A. S., unpublished data; Weissman 1967). Both Weissman and Nossal observed that the highest rate of seeding from the thymus occurred in the very young animal. Evidence of migration of bursal lymphocytes to the spleen has also been obtained following local thymidine labelling of cells in the bursa of Fabricius (Woods and Linna 1965).

In the mouse embryo, initiation of splenic haemopoiesis on the 15th day of gestation is associated with the appearance of CFU's and *in vitro* CFC's within the splenic rudiment. The subsequent development of the stem cell and progenitor population is shown in Figures 4.15 and 4.28. CFU and *in vitro* CFC populations in the spleen doubled approximately every 24 hours up till birth and then every 34–38 hours in the first 1–2 weeks of postnatal life. This rate of expansion is considerably slower than seen in early stages of foetal liver development but more rapid than seen in marrow. Throughout embryonic and postnatal spleen development during the period of increase of these cells the total numbers of CFU's and *in vitro* CFC's are similar (ratio of CFU to *in vitro* CFC's 0.43–2.1, see Figure 4.18). The contribution of the spleen to the total body population of CFU's and *in vitro* CFC's is not

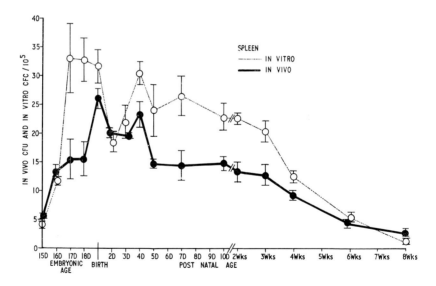

Fig. 4.28. Numbers of *in vitro* CFC's and CFU's per 10^5 spleen cells from (C57BL × CBA)F$_1$ mice in the embryonic and post natal period. CFU values not adjusted for seeding efficiency.

inconsiderable, indeed within 4 days after birth 50% of the total body population of CFU's and 30% of *in vitro* CFC's are present in the spleen (Figure
4.17). Maximum numbers of CFU's and *in vitro* CFC's are present in the
spleen by 3 weeks after birth and thereafter the two populations decline.
This transition is associated with an increasing contribution of lymphopoiesis
to total splenic haemopoietic activity. It is noteworthy that the *in vitro* CFC
(progenitor) population declines more than the CFU (stem-cell) population
with the result that the adult spleen is unique among embryonic and adult
haemopoietic tissues in having a permanent excess of CFU's relative to the
in vitro CFC population.

Erythropoietin-sensitive cells were not detected in the mouse embryo spleen
since no significant incorporation of ^{59}Fe into haem could be detected in
cultures derived from $16\frac{1}{2}$–18-day embryonic or neonatal spleens either
initially or after exposure to erythropoietin (Cole and Paul 1966). In rat
spleen, however, there was a clear response to erythropoietin in the 18-day
embryonic spleen and an even more marked response in the 19-day spleen,
but by 20 days spleen cells were no longer responsive to erythropoietin
(Cole et al. 1968).

It is possible then to define two phases of spleen development, the first
phase, occurring at 8–9 days' incubation in chick embryo and 15 days'
gestation in the mouse, is the colonisation of the mesenchymal splenic
rudiment by circulating stem cells which are probably morphologically the
large basophilic cells seen in the spleen at this stage. Functionally, these
immigrant cells are probably multipotential stem cells detected as CFU's in
the irradiated spleen. Since the embryonic spleen contains increasing numbers
of such cells and experiments in reconstitution of irradiated chick embryos,
and adult mice have revealed the capacity of the initial stem cell population
in the embryonic spleen to generate both lymphoid and myeloid cells, then
presumably these immigrant stem cells are undergoing self-replication in the
spleen environment. The origin of the first immigrant cells is probably the
yolk sac in the chick embryo since it is the only haemopoietic tissue with
proven spleen repopulating capacity present at the time of colonisation of
the splenic rudiment (Moore and Owen 1967a). In the mouse embryo at
15 days' gestation, the yolk sac is no longer a functioning haemopoietic
organ and only the foetal liver retains stem cells capable of repopulating the
irradiated spleen. Consequently a foetal liver to spleen migration of stem
cells is probable. The second phase of spleen development, occurring shortly
before birth or hatching, is that of lymphoid transition associated with
decline in haemopoietic activity. This phase is probably accomplished by

colonisation of the spleen by lymphoid cells or lymphoid progenitor cells (and not by stem cells as such) migrating from primary lymphoid tissue, the thymus and probably bursa of Fabricius or its equivalent in mammals. The subsequent spleen lymphoid development is augmented by antigen-induced lymphoid proliferation and the establishment of a recirculating pool of immunologically competent lymphocytes.

4.6 Development of bone marrow

The primordium of the bone-marrow cavity develops following penetration of perichondrial mesenchyme cells and blood vessels into the zone of calcified cartilage in the central region of the long bones. Following resorption of the cartilaginous matrix the developing marrow cavity appears as a network of connective tissue and a plexus of widely dilated veins (Bloom 1938; Sabin and Miller 1938; Hamilton 1952). Cartilage resorption is seen as early as 8–9 days' incubation in the chick embryo and the developing marrow cavities at this stage contain a loose network of mesenchymal cells. Marrow haemo-poietic activity is not initiated until 11–12 days and is preceded by the accumulation of large numbers of undifferentiated basophilic cells within the dilated marrow capillaries. Foci of erythropoiesis develop within the marrow sinusoids and reticulum cell spaces. The most immature erythroid cells are in contact with the walls of the vascular spaces but as these are discontinuous, erythropoietic cells frequently come into direct contact with the marrow reticulum. Marrow granulopoiesis appears to be entirely extravascular and the granulopoietic and erythropoietic areas are quite separate and distinct. In the mouse embryo at the 15th day of gestation, the femora are entirely cartilaginous with the exception of a collar of bone and perichondrial mesenchyme towards the middle of the shaft. Penetration and resorption of the shaft cartilage by mesenchymal buds from the surrounding mesenchyme results in the formation of the marrow cavity by the 17th day of gestation. By 17–18 days the marrow becomes populated by granulopoietic cells but erythropoiesis is not observed until after birth. The tail rudiment lags con-siderably behind the developing femur and marrow-cavity formation is not found until 1 week after birth (Petrakis et al. 1969). In the rat also, marrow erythropoiesis is not initiated until after birth (Lucarelli et al. 1967). In the human foetus, myelopoiesis was found at the 11th week of gestation in the femur and humerus (Rosenberg 1969).

Fifteen-day mouse embryo femurs in organ culture developed a marrow cavity although haemopoiesis was not observed unless erythropoietin or thyroxin was present in the culture medium (Petrakis et al. 1969). When the mesenchyme of the femoral rudiment was removed, penetration of the cartilaginous shaft and cavity formation did not occur and the rudiment degenerated. In reconstitution experiments with tritiated thymidine-labelled mesenchyme, a marrow cavity developed in the cartilaginous rudiment and mesenchymal cells migrated into the spaces (Petrakis et al. 1966, 1969). As colonisation of the marrow space by migration of mesenchymal cells immediately precedes the establishment of marrow haemopoiesis, it was natural to assume that haemopoietic colonising cells originated from periosteal mesenchyme (Bloom 1938). This traditional view was challenged by the observations on marrow development in chick embryos using a sex-chromosome marker system to analyse the migration of cells in the developing haemopoietic system (Moore and Owen 1965, 1967b). The results of sex-chromosome analysis of the dividing cell population of the bone marrow of

TABLE 4.7

Sex chromosome analysis of the bone marrow of twin and parabiosed chick embryos*

Union	Age at parabiosis (days)	Age at sampling (days)	Percentage mitoses of opposite sex (% chimaerism)
Chorioallantoic membrane	8	15	48, 14, 15, 17
Chorioallantoic membrane	8	17	42, 33
Chorioallantoic membrane	8	19	24,
Chorioallantoic membrane	6	19	24, 18, 18, 14
Chorioallantoic membrane	7	20	29
Yolk sac	4	13	40, 56
Yolk sac	4	14	52, 33
Yolk sac	4	15	48
Yolk sac	5	16	74
Twin embryo	—	11	2, 0
Twin embryo	—	12	4, 4
Twin embryo	—	13	44, 33

* 50—100 mitoses scored in each organ.

twin and parabiosed chick embryos of opposite sex united by a vascular anastomosis for 2–10 days are shown in Table 4.7. In embryos sampled between 13–20 days of incubation, 14–74% of the dividing cells in the marrow were derived from the opposite partner. In contrast, very low levels of chimaerism (0–4%) were observed at 11–12 days. Where separate estimates were performed on left and right femora of an embryo, the chimaeric levels were identical. Direct evidence of erythroid chimaerism was obtained in hatched chickens that had been parabiosed in combinations of known B blood group types. Erythrocyte chimaerism was demonstrated by use of specific agglutination antisera with no evidence of loss of chimaerism for up to 6 months after hatching (Moore, M. A. S., unpublished observation). The bone marrow of both parabiosed and twin embryos showed high reciprocal chimaerism in all embryos sampled between 13–19 days of incubation. The absence or low level of chimaerism in the marrow of 11- and 12-day embryos can be attributed to the absence of significant marrow haemopoiesis at this stage. In normal embryos the marrow is actively haemopoietic by the 12th day of incubation but in parabiosed and twin embryos, slight developmental retardation delayed the appearance of marrow haemopoiesis for up to 24 hours. The results indicate that high reciprocal chimaerism is present even at the earliest stages of marrow haemopoietic development. Chimaerism approached equilibrium levels of 50% in some pairs and this together with the observation of high chimaerism at all sampling stages throughout the remaining periods of embryonic haemopoiesis indicates that marrow haemopoietic tissue develops from a population of circulating stem cells that enter the marrow as early as the 12th–13th day of incubation. It can also be concluded that local production of haemopoietic cells from the fixed mesenchymal or endothelial cells of the marrow does not participate significantly, if at all, in normal marrow development.

The pattern of uptake of tritiated thymidine-labelled myeloid cells (embryonic marrow, spleen and yolk sac) in the developing marrow following intravenous injection into developing chick embryos was analysed 24 hours after injection to embryos of varying ages. The pattern of results was similar to that seen in embryonic spleen (Moore, M. A. S., unpublished observation). Occasional labelled cells were seen in the marrow cavity on the 8th–10th day of incubation but by the 11th day, maximum numbers of labelled cells per unit area were observed (Figure 4.27). It is noteworthy that between 11–12 days of incubation, haemopoietic development was initiated within the marrow cavity. In the later stages of marrow development considerable numbers of labelled cells were still observed but the trend was for an initial fall between 12–16 days followed by a period of relative constancy in frequency between 16 days and hatching despite a six-fold increase in the number of cells injected. The labelled cell population at 11 and 12 days of incubation consisted of large basophilic cells and more differentiated cells in the erythroid and granulocytic series. By 24–48 hours after injection, labelled mature granulocytes and polychromatic erythroblasts were seen. The labelled erythroid cells were confined to the sinusoidal regions of the marrow, while labelled granulocytes appeared only in the marrow parenchyma. This suggested either specific localisation of labelled erythroid and granulocytic cells in these two environments or differentiation of labelled undifferentiated stem cells determined by the environment in which they localised.

In mouse marrow, haemopoiesis is initiated in the femoral shafts on the 17th day of gestation and at this stage, both CFU's and *in vitro* CFC's can be detected (Figure 4.15) although the two populations did not increase until birth. In the first postnatal week the incidence of marrow CFU's and *in vitro* CFC's was similar (Figure 4.29) and the two populations doubled approximately every 34 hours. By the end of this period 50–60% of total body CFU's and 65–70% of total *in vitro* CFC's were localised in the bone marrow. The progressive expansion of marrow haemopoiesis in the first 2 months of postnatal life is associated with decline in liver haemopoiesis in the first week of life and decline in splenic myelopoiesis after the third week. After the period of most rapid expansion of marrow haemopoiesis in the first week, the frequency of *in vitro* CFC's is increased 2–5-fold to an average of 100 *in vitro*

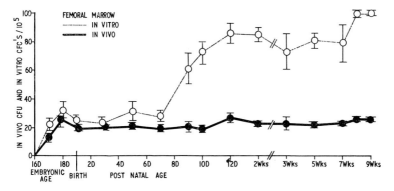

Fig. 4.29.   Numbers of *in vitro* CFC's and CFU's per 10^5 femoral marrow cells from (C57BL × CBA)F$_1$ mice in the late embryonic and post natal period. CFU values not adjusted for seeding efficiency.

CFC's per 10^5 marrow cells. However, the incidence of CFU's did not change in this period but remained at a plateau level of $22-26/10^5$ (Figures 4.18, 4.29).

It is apparent from the parabiosis data that the marrow cavity is colonised by circulating stem cells with the morphological appearance of large undifferentiated basophilic blast cells and that this inflow is initiated by the 12th day of incubation in the chick embryo and the 17th day of gestation in the mouse. Experiments of Petrakis et al. (1969) suggest that the stem cells may enter the periosteal mesenchyme as early as 15 days of gestation in the mouse and subsequently enter the marrow cavity at the time of mesenchymal invasion of the cartilaginous rudiment on the 17th day of gestation. The colonising population probably comprises both multipotential stem cells and progenitor cells since these are present in the marrow at the very earliest stages of haemopoiesis. This has been demonstrated both in the mouse where CFU's and *in vitro* CFC's are detected on the 17th day and in the chick embryo where early embryonic marrow has been shown to be capable of repopulating both the myeloid and lymphoid tissues of irradiated embryos (Moore and Owen 1967a). The source of the immigrant stem cells is most probably the foetal liver in the mouse and the spleen and possibly yolk sac in the chick embryo. It has been suggested that the decline in liver haemopoiesis shortly after birth in the mouse is brought about by mass migration of stem cells from the liver to colonise the spleen and the marrow (Barker et al. 1969). However, the number of stem cells colonising the developing marrow is not known and it is more probable that marrow development, once initiated by colonisation on the 17th and 18th days of gestation, is probably autonomous and proceeds by expansion of the initial stem cell population rather than by continuous and extensive recruitment of stem cells leaving the liver at, or shortly after, the time of birth.

4.7 Development of the thymus

The first account of the derivation of the thymic rudiment from the 3rd and 4th pharyngeal pouches is attributed to Verdun (1898). An additional contribution from the 2nd and 5th branchial clefts to the thymic anlage has been proposed (Marine 1932) but not substantiated by later studies. In experiments on chick embryos, Hammond (1954) surgically ablated or carbon-marked the early pharyngeal pouches and concluded that the thymus was a derivative of the branchial ectoderm of the dorsal part of the pharyngeal pouches 3 and 4 with no contribution from pouches 2 or 5 or branchial endoderm. Endoderm-ectoderm interaction was necessary, however, for the development of branchial ectoderm into the epithelium of the thymic anlage. In most mammals pouch 4 contribution to thymic development appears to be rudimentary and transitory and the relative contribution of pharyngeal ectoderm and endoderm is debated. In the absence of experimental investigations in mammals, the participation of either endoderm or ectoderm must remain an open question.

The subsequent lymphoid development of the thymus has been the subject of heated debate for the last 100 years, as illustrated by the comment of Badertscher (1915): 'There is perhaps no organ in the body whose mode of development has given rise to so bitterly contested and so widely divergent views as has that of the thymus. This is particularly true of its histogenesis.'

There have been four main theories of thymic lymphoid development, the earliest was the transformation theory of Kolliker (1879) and as initially formulated it considered that the thymus lymphocytes, Hassall's corpuscles and thymic reticulum originated in entirety by transformation of epithelial cells of the early anlage. Many of the pioneering studies on thymic development supported this theory (Prenant 1894; Beard 1899, 1902; Bell 1906; Dustin 1920; Stohr 1906; Cheval 1908; Baillif 1949). More recent histochemical, histological and electronmicroscopic studies have also claimed to demonstrate evidence of transitional forms between thymic epithelial and thymic lymphoid cells (Ackerman 1967a; Ackerman and Knouff 1964, 1965; King et al. 1964; Weakley et al. 1964; Sanel 1967), although Ackerman has recently reversed his position on thymic histogenesis and observed mesenchymal lymphoblastic infiltration of the epithelium of the rabbit thymic anlage (Ackerman and Hostetler 1970). The transformation theory was modified in some respects by Deanesly (1927), who considered that although thymic lymphocytes were of epithelial origin, the thymic reticulum was produced from mesenchymal cells that invaded the epithelial anlage. De Winiwarter (1924) initially supported the transformation theory but later adopted a compromise view, proposing a dual origin for thymic lymphocytes with an initial phase of epithelial transformation and a subsequent phase of invasion of the thymus by lymphocytes developing from perithymic mesenchyme.

The pseudomorphosis theory (His 1885) proposed that the thymic epithelial anlage was invaded by connective tissue and blood vessels from the surrounding mesenchyme. The original epithelium was destroyed except for scattered islands which formed Hassall's corpuscles and the mesenchymal reticulum thus formed became infiltrated by lymphocytes migrating into the thymus from connective tissue. This theory found no support in subsequent studies.

The substitution theory was initially formulated by Hammar (1905, 1908, 1910, 1911) following observations on thymic development in a number of species. Hammar proposed that thymic lymphocytes were derived exclusively from connective tissue lymphocytes which invaded the early epithelial anlage. The original epithelium formed the thymic reticulum cells and Hassall's corpuscles. The classic studies of Maximow (1909, 1912) supported Hammar's observations and indicated that the lymphocyte precursors originated from undifferentiated mesenchyme cells which differentiated into large lymphocytes or haemocytoblasts but then migrated into the thymic epithelium. These 'Wanderzellen' appeared generally as large amoeboid basophilic blast-type cells though Maximow's work disclosed both pleomorphism and clear species differences in the morphology of these cells. The substitution theory has found support in many subsequent studies in many species (Badertscher 1915 in pigs; Klapper 1946 and Gregoire 1932 in guinea pigs; Norris 1938 in humans; Danchakoff 1908, 1916; Venzke 1952 in birds). Kingsbury (1940) as a result of extensive studies on mammalian thymic development concluded with some foresight that '... there must lie some distinctive metabolic quality seemingly resident in the epithelial constituent inducing or determining the thymic differentiation. Whatever the nature of the factor or factors, one obvious effect is the liberation of a marked growth potential expressed in both of the interreacting tissues.'

Experimental studies of thymic development employing tissue culture and grafting techniques have provided conflicting results. Early *in vitro* culture studies of thymic epithelial rudiments failed to demonstrate lymphopoiesis (Pappenheimer 1913; Choi 1931; Emmart 1936), although Murray (1947) claimed to have observed lymphocyte transformation of epithelial cells from subcultures of an epithelial thymus outgrowth. No positive conclusions can be drawn from these early tissue culture studies, since failure of lymphoid development could be attributed to poor culture conditions. The more recent studies of Auerbach (1960, 1961) revived interest in thymic histogenesis, since he used improved culture techniques which permitted better growth and survival of the thymic cultures. In an initial study (Auerbach 1960) 12–12$\frac{1}{2}$-day mouse thymic anlagen were cultured in plasma clots but though the rudiments grew and lobulated, they remained predominantly epithelial. Trypsin-separation of the thymic mesenchyme from the epithelial rudiment resulted in failure of either component to grow and differentiate, but when recombined, growth and lobulation occurred. Mesenchyme from a wide variety of embryonic tissues was capable of inducing normal thymic epithelial morphogenesis and this effect could be mediated across a cell-impermeable millipore diffusion membrane. Using an improved filter well culture method Ball and Auerbach (1960) succeeded in obtaining lymphoid development in embryonic thymus cultures and the lymphoid development occurred within the epithelial portion of the rudiment but did not occur in the absence of mesenchymal induction (Auerbach 1961, 1964a). The capacity of the 12-day thymic rudiment to engage in lymphopoiesis appeared markedly radioresistant and was unaffected by 900 rads but was inhibited at 1200 rads (Auerbach 1963a, b). Urethan treatment *in vitro* inhibited thymic lymphopoiesis and the thymic rudiments lacked lymphoid organisation, remaining predominantly epithelial for up to 2 weeks in culture (Globerson and Auerbach 1965). The lymphoid potential of the rudiment was not lost, however, since lymphopoiesis was restored by addition of bone marrow, an effect which was mediated across a cell-impermeable filter. A similar inductive influence on thymic development was noted in combined embryonic spleen and thymus cultures (Auerbach 1964b, 1966).

Early grafting experiments using the prelymphoid thymic anlage were performed by Gregoire (1935, 1958). In these studies grafts to the anterior eye chamber failed to show normal lymphoid development and complete failure of lymphoid development was noted with mammalian thymic grafts to the chick embryo chorioallantoic membrane or, in adult animals if grafts were enclosed in cell-impermeable membranes. In contrast, Auerbach (1960, 1961) obtained normal lymphoid development of the mouse thymic rudiment when grafted to the anterior eye chamber although both thymic epithelial and mesenchymal components were necessary. Since chick and mouse lymphocytes can be distinguished morphologically both in interphase and mitosis, Auerbach (1960, 1961) grafted chimaeric combinations of prelymphoid mouse thymic epithelium and chick mesenchyme and concluded that the epithelial component produced lymphocytes and the mesenchyme produced connective tissue and glandular stroma. Similar results were obtained when 12-day mouse embryo thymus was grafted to the chick chorioallantoic membrane, and the lymphocytes developing were all of mouse type (Auerbach 1961; Moore and Owen 1967c). Auerbach interpreted his observations as evidence that thymic epithelial cells transform into lymphocytes. The experiments of Auerbach appear to provide powerful support for the transformation theory of the epithelial origin of thymic lymphocytes. The crucial issue on which the interpretation of these experiments hinged, was that of the purity or otherwise of the epithelial anlage of the $12–12\frac{1}{2}$-day mouse embryo.

Auerbach considered that at this stage of development, only epithelial cells were present (though not excluding invasion of mesenchymal cells that had assumed an epithelial morphology). This view is untenable, however, since a number of studies conclusively demonstrated the presence as early as 11 days' gestation in the mouse embryo thymus of cells characterised by intensely basophilic cytoplasm and prominent nucleoli which were quite distinct from the epithelial population (Maximow 1909; Smith 1965; Moore and Owen 1967c; Owen and Ritter 1969; Hoshino et al. 1969). Consequently, Auerbach's experiments demonstrate that lymphoid precursor cells were present in significant numbers by the 12th day of gestation, but since these could have migrated into the epithelium prior to this stage, the origin of thymic lymphocytes remained unsolved.

The morphological development of the thymus in animals as diverse as the chick and mouse embryo showed remarkable similarity (Moore and Owen

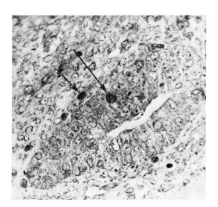

Fig. 4.30. Thymic rudiment of 11-day mouse embryo. Two heavily basophilic cells are arrowed, one is just within the rudiment, the other in the surrounding mesenchyme, and the central pharyngeal pouch lumen is evident. (Giemsa × 450.) (From Moore and Owen 1967c, reproduced by permission of J. Exp. Med.)

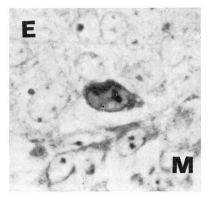

Fig. 4.31. High magnification of 11-day mouse thymic rudiment. A basophilic cell lies just within the pale-staining epithelial cells of the rudiment (E). Note the surrounding mesenchyme (M). (Giemsa × 1500.) (From Moore and Owen 1967c, reproduced by permission of J. Exp. Med.)

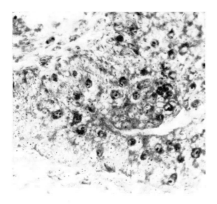

Fig. 4.32. Thymic rudiment of 12-day mouse embryo. By this stage there are large numbers of basophilic cells within it. The pharyngeal pouch lumen is still present at this stage. (Giemsa × 450.) (From Moore and Owen 1967c, reproduced by permission of J. Exp. Med.)

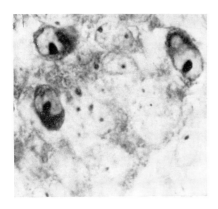

Fig. 4.33. High-power view of basophilic cells within 12-day thymic rudiment showing their finely granular cytoplasm. In some cells a prominent juxtanuclear vacuole is present (probably the Golgi structure). (Giemsa × 1500.) (From Moore and Owen 1967c, reproduced by permission of J. Exp. Med.)

1967c). In the mouse embryo, on the 10th day of gestation, the thymic rudiment appears at an early pharyngeal pouch stage predominantly composed of third pharyngeal pouch epithelium. At this early stage, the thymic rudiment comprises only two cell types – pharyngeal epithelium separated by a basement membrane from surrounding mesenchyme. By the late third pouch stage on the 11th day of gestation, the thymic rudiments appear as masses of pale-staining epithelial cells surrounding a central lumen in the pharyngeal region in close relation to the third branchial arch artery and ganglion nodosum. At this stage, a few isolated basophilic cells can be first observed, lying both within the epithelium and in the surrounding mesenchyme and blood vessels (Figures 4.30, 4.31). The basophilic cells possess deeply-staining granular cytoplasm, prominent nucleoli and in certain preparations, a well-developed Golgi apparatus. By the 12th day, the thymic anlage contains large numbers of these cells (Figures 4.32, 4.33) and migrates into an anterior

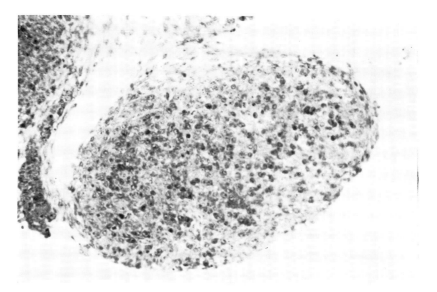

Fig. 4.34. 13-day mouse-embryo thymus. By this stage, numerous lymphoid cells are present and the thymus appears as an encapsulated organ almost completely separated from the surrounding connective tissue. Giemsa × 450.

mediastinal position where on the 13th–14th day it appears as a paired vascularised and capsulated organ engaged in active lymphopoiesis (Figure 4.34).

The thymic anlage in the chick embryo is first visible at the 5th day of incubation and forms an epithelial cord extending along the jugular vein and by $5\frac{1}{2}$ days is entirely closed off from the pharyngeal pouches. By the 6th day the thymic rudiment consists of a cord of pale-staining epithelial cells separated from the surrounding mesenchyme by a distinct basement membrane and is at a corresponding stage to that of the 10-day mouse embryo. Between the 7th–8th days of incubation a second population of cells appears in the more cranial region of the thymic rudiment as well as in the surrounding mesenchyme. These cells appearing singly or in clusters (Figures 4.35, 4.36, and 4.37) are similar to those seen in the 11th–12th day mouse thymus with granulated cytoplasm and prominent nucleoli. A characteristic feature of the basophilic cells is the irregularity of their nuclear and cytoplasmic outlines with the frequent presence of tails of cytoplasm extending for some distance from the body of the cell and sometimes traversing the epithelial basement membrane. By the 9th day, the number of basophilic cells within the epithelium is considerably increased and foci of pyknotic and degenerating cells

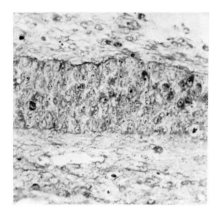

Fig. 4.35. Section of the thymic rudiment of a normal 8-day chick embryo. The rudiment is separated from the surrounding mesenchyme by a distinct basement membrane. There are cells with basophilic cytoplasm within the rudiment and in the surrounding mesenchyme. (Giemsa × 450.) (From Moore and Owen 1967c, reproduced by permission of J. Exp. Med.)

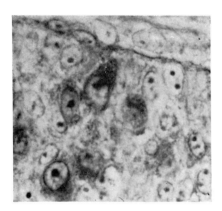

Fig. 4.36. High-power view of basophilic cells with the 8-day chick-embryo thymic rudiment. A well-defined basement membrane can be seen. (Giemsa × 1500.) (From Moore and Owen 1967c, reproduced by permission of J. Exp. Med.)

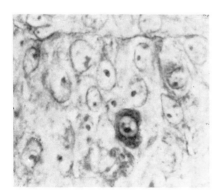

Fig. 4.37. Basophilic cell within epithelium of an 8-day chick-embryo thymic rudiment. Note similarity in morphology with basophilic cells in the mouse thymus in Figures 4.31 and 4.33. (Giemsa × 1500.) (From Moore and Owen 1967c, reproduced by permission of J. Exp. Med.)

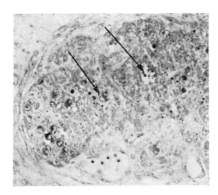

Fig. 4.38. 9-day chick-embryo thymus. Cells with deeply stained cytoplasm are present throughout the rudiment. Regions of cell degeneration can be seen (arrowed). (Giemsa × 450.)

are seen at this stage (Figure 4.38). This necrosis appears to be a normal developmental process associated with remodelling of the reticular epithelial cell framework of the thymus. Between 10–12 days' incubation (correspond- ing to 13–14 days in the mouse) the avian thymus becomes predominantly lymphoid and vascularised.

The basophilic cells appear in the mesenchyme surrounding the thymus prior to their appearance within the epithelium. However, their development within the epithelium precedes vascularisation, hence if they have migrated into the epithelium from surrounding tissues, they could have done so only by traversing the basement membrane and migrating between the closely- packed epithelial cells.

Of the three theories of thymic lymphocyte origin reviewed so far, the most recent histological observations appear to support the substitution theory but definite conclusions cannot be made on this evidence since cell tracer tech- niques were not employed. However, when chromosome marker and tritiated thymidine labelling methods were applied, very different conclusions con- cerning the origin of thymic lymphocytes were reached.

The first investigation employing a cell-marker system to study embryonic aspects of thymic lymphopoiesis was performed by Moore and Owen (1967c). Their experiments utilised a sex-chromosome marker system in pairs of chick embryos united by a vascular anastomosis of chorioallantoic or yolk- sac blood vessels produced either artificially by parabiosis or occurring naturally in dizygotic twin embryos. The results of chromosome analysis of the thymus of twin and parabiosed embryos are presented in Table 4.8. Following chorioallantoic (CAM) vascular anastomosis in embryos para- biosed between the 6th to 8th days of incubation, low levels of chimaerism were observed in two embryos and no chimaerism in the majority of cases.

TABLE 4.8

Sex-chromosome analysis of the thymus of twin and parabiosed chick embryos (From
Moore and Owen 1967c, by permission of J. Exp. Med.)

Union	Time of onset of vascular anasto-mosis (days)	Age at sampling (days)	Percentage mitoses of opposite sex (% chimaerism)
Chorioallantoic membrane	10 days	15	0, 0, 0, 0
Chorioallantoic membrane		17	0
Chorioallantoic membrane		19	0, 3, 0, 0
Chorioallantoic membrane		20	12,
Twin embryos	9—10 days	11	8, 2
Twin embryos		12	1, 4
Twin embryos		13	4, 1
Yolk sac	6— 8 days	14	44, 58, 8
Yolk sac		15	6,
Yolk sac		16	70

However, chimaerism was observed in other organs, such as marrow, spleen
and bursa (Moore and Owen 1965) and vascular union in every instance was
established after the initiation of thymic lymphopoiesis. An earlier vascular
union was established in twin embryos (by 9–10 days incubation) but this
was still subsequent to initiation of thymic lymphopoiesis and only low levels
of thymic chimaerism (1–8%) were found. Following parabiosis at 4–5 days,
a vascular yolk-sac anastomosis was established considerably earlier than
chorioallantoic union and prior to, or at the time of, initiation of thymic
lymphopoiesis (by 8 days of incubation). Thymic chimaerism was found in
all these embryos and in three instances very high levels were noted (44–70%).
The correlation between the time of establishment of vascular anastomosis
and the extent of thymic chimaerism suggested that blood-borne lymphoid
precursor cells were entering the avian thymic rudiment in the early stages
of its development probably by the 7th–9th days of incubation. This initial
immigrant population is probably responsible for the majority of dividing
lymphoid cells sampled throughout the remainder of incubation. The
possibility of a continued inflow of cells into the thymus at later stages of
development cannot be ruled out, particularly if this subsequent inflow

contributes only a small percentage of the total dividing cells sampled in the short time interval studied. The variability of chimaerism observed within the thymus is marked and led to the suggestion that perhaps very few immigrant cells were responsible for the initial colonisation of the thymus (Auerbach 1967). A more probable cause of this variability is the dominant situation observed following yolk-sac anastomosis. Frequently the yolk sac of one embryo herniates through the parabiotic union, resulting in stunting of growth and some developmental retardation of the partner. Invariably the smaller partner had a higher level of chimaerism than the dominant partner, suggesting the latter contributed more extensively to the circulating pool of cells that were equilibrating across the vascular anastomosis.

The haematogenous theory of thymic lymphocyte origin was developed to explain the results in chimaeric chick embryos. It extends the substitution theory since it recognises the colonisation of the epithelial anlage by cells present in the surrounding mesenchyme but considers these cells to have in turn migrated into the mesenchyme from the circulation and not therefore to have developed locally by mesenchymal transformation. It suggests that it should be possible to define a phase of thymic development prior to entry of circulating stem cells when an isolated thymic anlage would possess no lymphopoietic capacity and a phase of colonisation when the extent of lymphopoiesis occurring in an isolated organ would be proportional to the number of precursor cells that have entered the rudiment prior to removal.

These proposals were tested in two experimental systems. In the first (Moore and Owen 1967c) the thymic rudiment was removed from chick embryos at different stages of development from 8–15 days of incubation and grafted to the chorioallantoic membrane (CAM) of 10-day host embryos. Where donor and recipient were of opposite sex, chromosome analysis of the thymic grafts was carried out on the 4th–9th day after grafting. The results shown in Figure 4.39 define three phases of thymic development. The first phase seen with the 8-day chick thymus grafts was associated with almost complete population of the grafted rudiment by host cells at all stages of graft development studied. The second stage seen with the 9-day thymus grafts was that of considerable variation in the percentage of host-type mitoses when examined 4–5-days after grafting. The third phase, seen with 10–15-day thymus grafts exhibited more extensive donor proliferation with 94–98 % of mitoses of donor type 4 days after grafting. Host-type dividing cells increased progressively in the following 5 days, and by the 9th day on the CAM, the dividing population was uniformly 100 % host type. The difference in contribution of host mitoses in 8-, 9- and 10–15-day thymus grafts, was most

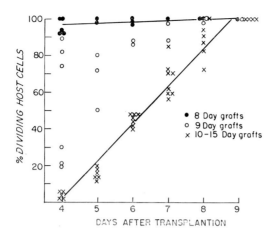

Fig. 4.39. Graph showing the proportion of dividing host cells in chick embryo thymic grafts to the embryo chorioallantoic membrane. Each point represents a chromosome analysis of a single graft. Note that 8-day grafts are almost entirely populated by dividing host cells 4 days after transplantation, whereas at this time 10–15-day grafts are still almost entirely donor in type. The rate of host cell repopulation of 9-day grafts is very variable.
(From Moore and Owen 1967c, reproduced by permission of J. Exp. Med.)

pronounced after 4 days on the CAM. At one extreme the 8-day grafts had a mean of 96% host mitoses, while the 10–15-day grafts had a mean of 4% host mitoses, and 9-day grafts a mean of 53% host mitoses.

The repopulation of thymic grafts from 12–15-day old embryos may be considered unphysiological, since necrosis was noted with 24–48 hours after grafting. Thymic grafts from 8–10-day old embryos showed no evidence of necrosis at any stage after grafting (Figure 4.40) and therefore, repopulation may be interpreted as a demonstration of a normal cell migration pathway. The lymphopoiesis in a grafted 8-day thymic rudiment containing few or no immigrant cells at the time of grafting was therefore dependent on population by circulating lymphoid precursor cells of the host. By 9 days of incubation variable numbers of immigrant cells had entered the rudiment prior to grafting and hence the capacity of the graft to engage in donor-type lymphopoiesis was variable and dependent on the number of immigrant cells in the rudiment at 9 days. By the 10th day of incubation, sufficient lymphoid precursor cells were present in the rudiment to sustain extensive lymphopoiesis. During the first 4–5 days, these latter grafts exhibited a ten-fold weight increase entirely due to donor proliferation.

Mouse thymic graft development on the avian CAM demonstrated the

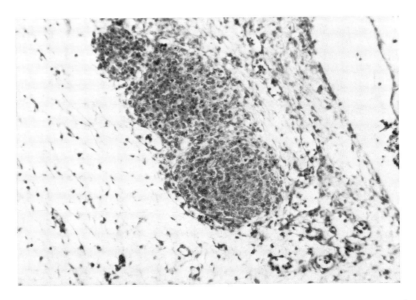

Fig. 4.40.   Chick thymic rudiment (removed from a 10-day embryo) after 48 hours on the chorioallantois. Note the absence of necrosis and presence of lymphoid differentiation in the graft. Haematoxylin and Trichrome × 450.

apparent species specificity of the thymic repopulating cell. The majority of 12–12½-day mouse thymic rudiments recovered after 5 days on the avian embryo CAM showed excellent lymphoid development (Figure 4.41) and grafts increased considerably in size during this period. By 7 days a distinct cortex and medulla were observed and the grafts were densely populated with small lymphocytes. Graft lymphopoiesis was entirely mouse in type as assessed by characteristic mouse lymphocyte morphology and mouse-type mitoses.

A second approach to the analysis of the role of immigrant cells in thymic lymphopoiesis was that of Owen and Ritter (1969). In this study, embryonic mouse and chick thymic rudiments at different stages of development were cultured in cell-impermeable diffusion chambers on the chicken chorio-allantois. In this situation the supply of blood-borne precursor cells was cut off. Ten-day mouse and 7-day chick thymic rudiments failed to become lymphoid in this situation and remained as epithelial anlagen. Older rudiments sustained lymphopoiesis in this situation but the extent of lymphoid development correlated with the numbers of basophilic cells, presumably the immigrant lymphoid precursor cells present in the rudiment prior to culture.

Cells with the capacity to repopulate the irradiated thymus have been

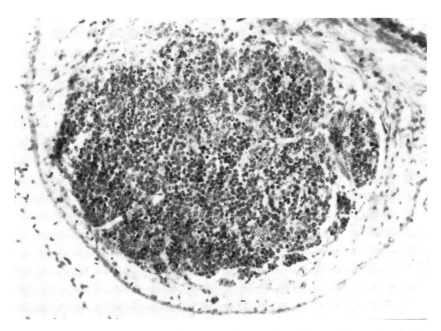

Fig. 4.41. 12-day mouse-embryo thymus rudiment 5 days after grafting to the chorio-allantois of a 10-day chick embryo. The graft is well incorporated into the membrane and is densely populated with small lymphocytes of mouse origin. Haematoxylin and Trichrome × 450.

detected in avian embryo blood, spleen, marrow and yolk sac (Moore and Owen 1967a), in mammalian yolk sac (Moore and Metcalf 1970; Tyan 1968; Tyan and Herzenberg 1968) and in foetal liver (Taylor 1964) and as well as in mouse embryonic spleen, blood, and marrow (Moore, M. A. S., unpublished observations). At the time of entry of the first immigrant cells into the thymic rudiment (7–8 days of incubation in the chick, 11 days of gestation in the mouse) the only tissues containing lymphoid precursor cells are the yolk sac and foetal liver in the mouse and the yolk sac and spleen in the bird. At this early stage, both the mouse liver and avian spleen are rudimentary and are themselves in the process of being populated by immigrant cells and therefore unlikely to be making a significant contribution to the circulating stem cell pool. For this reason it can be concluded that the first lymphoid precursor cells populating the thymus are predominantly of yolk-sac origin and enter the circulating pool prior to localisation in the thymic rudiment.

The assumption that the lymphoid precursor cell is the large basophilic cell seen in the thymic rudiment is based on the correlation between the appear-

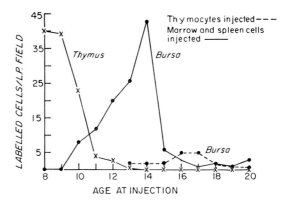

Fig. 4.42. The distribution of tritiated thymidine labelled chick embryo marrow and spleen cells or thymic lymphocytes 24 hours after intravenous injection into chick embryos. Each point represents the mean number of labelled cells per unit area (3 mm²) in host thymus and bursa of Fabricius. The number of cells injected at each time point was related to host body weight and ranged from 2–40 × 10⁶. Ten embryos were used at each time point.

ance and number of these cells in the thymus at the time of cell inflow and the capacity of the rudiment to engage in lymphopoiesis. More direct evidence was obtained in experiments where tritiated thymidine-labelled embryonic haemopoietic cells were injected intravenously into developing chick embryos and the localisation and subsequent fate of the labelled cells in the thymus was investigated (Moore, M. A. S., unpublished observations). Maximum numbers of labelled myeloid cells (embryonic, marrow, spleen and yolk sac) were observed in the 8–9-day chick-embryo thymus (Figures 4.42, 4.43). At this stage in the first 12–24 hours following cell injection, numerous labelled cells were seen in blood vessels and connective tissue sur-

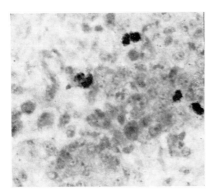

Fig. 4.43. Labelled cells in the chick-embryo thymus 24 hours after injection of 18-day embryonic marrow cells into an 8-day embryo. Haematoxylin and Eosin, auto-radiograph exposed 6 weeks, × 450.

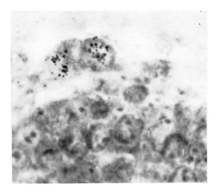

Fig. 4.44. As in Figure 4.43. A pair of labelled cells with basophilic cytoplasm and prominent nucleoli are in contact with the epithelial thymic rudiment and are probably the division products of a more heavily labelled immigrant cell. Giemsa, autoradiograph exposed 7 days, × 1500.

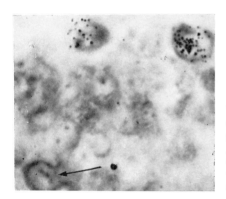

Fig. 4.45. As in Figure 4.43. Two labelled cells are present within the thymic epithelial rudiment. The labelled cells are morphologically similar to the unlabelled basophilic cell (arrowed) present at this stage in the thymus of uninjected embryos. Giemsa, autoradiograph exposed 7 days, × 1500.

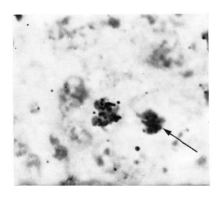

Fig. 4.46. As in Figure 4.43. A labelled mitotic figure in the thymic rudiment. Note the unlabelled mitosis which is also present (arrowed). Haematoxylin and Eosin, autoradiograph exposed 14 days, × 1500.

rounding the thymic rudiment and in many instances, labelled cells were in contact with the basement membrane of the thymic epithelium (Figure 4.44). Morphologically, the labelled cells were large and undifferentiated with deeply basophilic cytoplasm and prominent nucleoli (Figures 4.44, 4.45). The labelled cells were observed within the thymus in considerable numbers, and entered prior to vascularisation of the rudiment. These must therefore have migrated from the blood vessels into the surrounding mesenchyme and then penetrated the basement membrane and entered the thymic epithelium. By 24–48 hours after injection smaller labelled cells were seen within the thymus and were identified on nuclear/cytoplasmic ratios and nuclear morphology as large and medium thymic lymphocytes. Since no labelled lymphoid cells were observed in the initial inoculum nor indeed in the labelled cell population in and around the thymus in the early stages after injection, it appeared likely that such cells originated from large labelled basophilic cells. In addition, labelled dividing cells were observed within the thymus (Figure 4.46). Localisation of labelled myeloid cells was no longer observed after the 13th day of incubation, despite a 20-fold increase in the number of cells injected at later stages of development (Figure 4.42). Labelled thymus cells likewise failed to localise in the embryonic thymus at any stage of its development.

It is generally assumed that the thymus does not participate directly in immune reactions but is of vital importance in development and maturation of cell-mediated immune responses in peripheral lymphoid tissue. There are, however, reports that a small percentage of thymic lymphocytes undergo blastoid transformation in response to phytohaemagglutinin (Claman 1966; Weber 1966) or when genetically dissimilar thymic lymphocytes are present in mixed culture (Schwarz 1966). The genesis of phytohaemagglutinin responsiveness in the human thymus takes place on the 14th–16th week of gestation and coincides with the phase of thymic development where cortex and medulla become clearly demarcated and when the earliest Hassall's corpuscles appear (Kay et al. 1970). Mouse-thymus cells from newborn or adult donors are capable of producing a graft-vs.-host reaction in an allogeneic recipient (Billingham 1958; Cohen et al. 1963; Miller 1960). Parental strain thymus cells can also induce a graft-vs.-host reaction after inoculation into sublethally irradiated adult hybrid mice (Kaplan and Rosston 1959). Chicken thymus also contains cells capable of producing a graft-vs.-host reaction detected by capacity to form pocks on the chorioallantoic membrane of chick embryos (Warner 1964) and such competent cells are probably present in the thymus at the time of hatching (Owen et al. 1964). It is apparent that a few cells capable of producing graft-vs.-host reaction appear in the thymus at the time of or indeed preceding the appearance of similar cells in peripheral lymphoid tissue. The number of such cells in the thymus is always low and thymus cells are considerably less effective in producing a graft-vs.-host reaction than an equivalent number of spleen or lymph node lympho-cytes. A further parameter of immunological maturation of thymus cells is their capacity to restore plaque-forming cell responses and haemagglutinin titres in adult irradiated thymectomised mice in the presence of injected marrow cells. Newborn mouse thymus cells were as effective in this regard as equivalent numbers of thymus cells from 4 week old or 1 year old mice. Late-term embryonic thymus cells were, however, considerably less effective and 20×10^6 foetal thymocytes produced a restoration equivalent only to that of 5×10^6 neonatal thymus cells (MacGillivray et al. 1970).

Antigen-binding cells have been detected in both adult and foetal thymus and are presumed to be antigen-reactive cells bearing immunoglobulin receptor sites specific for the bound antigen (see Chapter 3). Using radioio-dinated flagellin as a labelled antigen, Dwyer and Mackay (1970) found 1 cell in 50 showed some degree of labelling in the thymus of a 20–22-week human foetus. Labelled cells were detected in the thymus as early as 12–13 weeks of gestation and were present in higher frequency in thymus than in foetal blood. Since the frequency of flagellin-binding cells was much lower in the adult human thymus (1 in 2×10^3 cells) and flagellin is known to give an excellent humoral antibody response but not a delayed hypersensitivity reaction in man, it was suggested that the human thymus may function in a bursal-equivalent capacity in foetal life (Dwyer and Mackay 1970).

Flagellin-binding cells were infrequent in the mouse thymus, both em-bryonic and adult, though considerable numbers of haemocyanin-binding cells were present in the 17-day embryonic thymus (Dwyer, J. 1970, un-published observations). In this context, flagellin is highly immunogenic in humans but less so in mice. It would seem probable that genetic differences, possibly associated with histocompatibility antigen status, may influence the incidence of cells binding specific antigens in the developing thymus. Further-more, the high frequency of antigen-binding cells for a particular antigen in the foetal thymus suggests that the antibody patterns arise independently of antigenic stimulation and this favours the role of genetic programming for development of antibody patterns (Dwyer and Mackay 1970). It may be that the thymus functions to introduce somatic diversification on a repertoire of genetically-programmed antibody responses.

Preliminary data has suggested that true antigen-binding cells may exist in the foetal liver at early stages of development (Dwyer, J., personal communication, 1970). The significance of this requires further investigation, in particular to determine whether these binding cells are coated with cytophilic antibody, and if not, to discover whether their development precedes the appearance of similar cells in the thymus.

It might have been postulated that cells do not achieve full immunological competence within the thymus and that cells capable of producing graft-vs.-host reaction are either contaminant lymphocytes or have re-entered the thymus after maturation at the periphery. This possibility can be excluded since thymus rudiments developing *in vitro* or in diffusion chambers on the chorioallantois undergo lymphopoiesis and produce cells capable of inducing a graft-vs.-host reaction. Indeed the embryonic thymus after a period in culture contains more cells capable of inducing graft-vs.-host reaction than the thymus of equivalent age *in vivo* (Ritter, M. A. and Owen, J. J. T., personal communication). It is possible that competent cells generated within the thymus normally migrate rapidly out of this organ, whereas in culture when cell migration is prevented, accumulation of these cells occurs. Evidence of lymphocyte migration from thymus to spleen and lymph nodes was obtained in experiments where the thymus was labelled *in situ* by local tritiated thymidine injection and this migration was most active in the neonatal period (see Section 4.5 on Spleen Development).

The number of lymphoid precursor cells required to populate the embryonic thymus has not been established but some approximate calculations can be made. The 12-day mouse thymic rudiment contains 100–200 large basophilic cells within the epithelium and 90–100 in the perithymic mesenchyme. In organ culture, such a rudiment can develop $1–2 \times 10^5$ small lymphocytes and in the more favourable chorioallantoic graft situation (with no contribution by host cells) the same rudiment can contain 2×10^6 small lymphocytes. If all basophilic cells in the 12-day rudiment are lymphoid precursors, then each cell has the capacity to produce up to 10,000 small lymphocytes as a result of 13–14 divisions in the graft situation. Even *in vitro* in the organ culture system, each cell may produce approximately 1000 small lymphocytes requiring 10 cell divisions.

4.8 Development of the bursa of Fabricius

The bursa of Fabricius is a cloacal lymphoid organ that has been considered unique to the class *Aves* though a similar organ has been reported in the turtle (Sidky and Auerbach 1969). In the chick embryo the bursal primor-

dium appears by 4–5 days of incubation as an epithelial thickening at the margin of the urodaeal membrane. Early investigators claimed that the anlage appears as a result of proliferation of entodermal cells at the dorsocaudal margin of the urodaeal membrane, in close association with the ectodermal lining of the proctodaeum (Jolly 1915; Boyden 1924). More recent work has demonstrated an origin from the ventrocaudal contact of the cloaca with external ectodermal epithelium and the resulting bursal epithelium may be endodermal, ectodermal or a combination of the both (Ruth 1960; Ruth et al. 1964). As both bursal and thymic anlagen develop at sites of endodermal-ectodermal interaction, this origin may be of some fundamental importance in the early induction of primary lymphoid organs. By the 6th day of incubation the epithelial anlage appears as a slightly rounded protuberance of the cloaca and begins to vacuolate as a result of epithelial cell breakdown. The vacuolated spaces coalesce to form a bursal lumen communicating with the proctodaeal sinus by a bursal duct and by the 10th–11th day longitudinal folds of lining epithelium develop and project into the lumen. At this stage the bursa comprises a thin outer layer of serosa and muscle, an inner epithelial lining of several layers of columnar or cuboidal epithelium raised into folds or plicae, and between these two layers the mesodermal tunica propria develops as a loose vascular network of mesenchyme cells (see Figure 4.47). On the 12th–13th day groups of primitive undifferentiated epithelial cells in the intermediate or basal layer of epithelium lining the plicae enlarge and

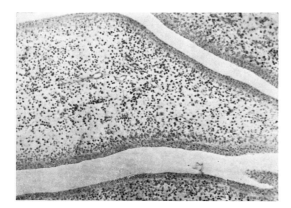

Fig. 4.47.   Bursa of Fabricius of a 12-day chick embryo. Extensive folding or plication of the lining epithelium has occurred by this stage but epithelial budding has not yet commenced. Blood vessels are present within the connective tissue in the centre of the plicae. Numerous granulocytes are present, scattered throughout the tunica propria. Haematoxylin and Trichrome × 150.

proliferate forming epithelial buds that project into the underlying tunica propria. Mesenchymal cells around the developing buds retract from their firm attachment to the basement membrane and are compressed to form a mesenchymal sheath around the developing bud (Jolly 1915; Ackerman and Knouff 1959; Ackerman 1962; Warner and Szenberg 1964). Associated with the formation of epithelial buds is an increased vascularisation of the sub-jacent mesenchyme and development of loops of capillaries surrounding, but not penetrating, the bud. Ackerman and Knouff (1963) demonstrated relati-vely intense alkaline phosphatase activity in the subjacent compact mesen-chyme during the phase of bud formation which subsequently declines as the follicle matures. This metabolic change may reflect an epithelial-mesen-chymal inductive interaction involved in epithelial bud formation.

By the 14th day of incubation bursal lymphopoiesis is initiated within the epithelial buds. At this stage, numbers of large morphologically undifferen-

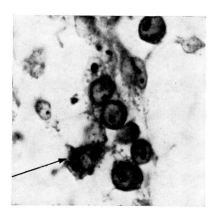

Fig. 4.48. A cluster of basophilic cells in a blood vessel and in mesenchyme of the tunica propria of a 14-day embryonic bursa. Note the irregular cytoplasmic outline of the cell apparently traversing the endothelial lining (arrowed). Giemsa × 1000.

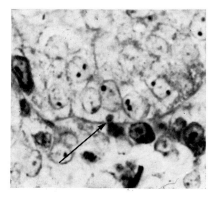

Fig. 4.49. Basophilic cells in and around and developing epithelial bud in a 14-day embryonic bursa. Note a basophilic cyto-plasmic process extending across the epithelial basement membrane from a cell whose body lies outside the plane of section (arrowed). Giemsa × 1000.

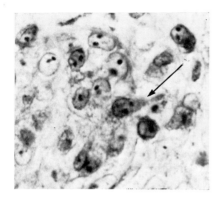

Fig. 4.50. 14-day bursal epithelial bud. A cell can be seen with a cytoplasmic extension passing through the basement membrane into the surrounding mesenchyme (arrowed). Giemsa × 1000.

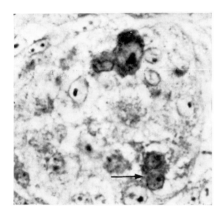

Fig. 4.51. 14-day bursal follicle. The circumscribed epithelial bud is detached from the lining epithelium. A large basophilic cell and a pair of much smaller basophilic cells (arrowed) possibly division products of a larger cell are present in this early stage of follicular development and contrast with the pale stained epithelial cells. Giemsa × 1000.

tiated cells are observed in blood vessels of the bursal mesenchyme (Figure 4.48). With Giemsa staining these cells possess intensely basophilic cytoplasm and prominent nucleoli, resembling in every detail the basophilic cells described in early thymic development. Basophilic cells are observed throughout the tunica propria but particularly in the mesenchyme around the developing epithelial buds (Figure 4.49 and 4.50). Similar cells also appear within the epithelium of the buds and are readily observed in this site since the intensity of their nucleolar and cytoplasmic staining contrasts with the pale-staining epithelial cells (Figure 4.51). Frequently cells are observed with tails of basophilic cytoplasm extending across the epithelial basement membrane (Figure 4.49, 4.50). By the 15th–16th days, both medium and small bursal lymphocytes appear in the epithelial buds. The buds completely detach from the lining epithelium and lie within the tunica propria as sharply circumscribed lymphoid follicles. At this stage very few lymphocytes are

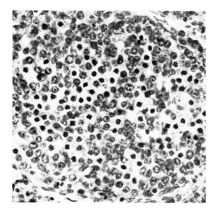

Fig. 4.52. Bursal lymphoid follicle of a 20-day chick embryo. The follicle is filled with small lymphocytes but a distinct cortex and medulla has not yet developed. Note the very high mitotic activity demonstrated by the numbers of blocked metaphase figures which have resulted from colchicine treatment of the embryo 3 hours previously. Haematoxylin and Trichrome × 450.

present outside the follicles which remain separated from the surrounding mesenchyme and capillary network by a distinct basement membrane. The mitotic activity of the bursal lymphoid population is intense and expansion of the lymphoid follicles at later stages of development is due to accumulation of small lymphocytes (Figure 4.52). Foci of granulopoiesis appear in bursal mesenchyme in juxtaposition to the blood vessels of the tunica propria, particularly prior to the establishment of lymphopoiesis. The extent of bursal granulopoiesis is highly variable however and subsides later in development as the lymphoid folllicles expand and the mesenchyme condenses. After hatching, the lymphoid follicles develop a distinct cortex and medulla. The latter comprises the network of epithelial cells diffusely populated by lymphocytes contrasting with the densely packed small lymphocyte population of the cortical region.

The classical and extensive observations of Jolly (1915) on bursal development laid the foundation for the theory of mesenchymal origin of bursal lymphocytes. So definitive did this work seem that there was subsequently little further investigation of bursal development until recent years. Jolly recognised that the large basophilic cells which he termed 'lymphoid haemocytoblasts' appeared in the bursal mesenchyme prior to their appearance in the epithelial buds. These cells apparently developed by a transformation of the stellate mesenchyme cells in the tunica propria and subsequently migrated into the epithelial buds between 14–18 days of incubation. The proliferation and lymphoid differentiation of this cell within the bursal epithelium was thought by Jolly to be due either to a mechanical compressive effect, i.e. contact-mediated differentiation or to the activity of exuded interstitial fluid i.e., a possible diffusible inductive factor. Ortega et al. (1965)

also considered that bursal lymphopoiesis was initiated by migration of cells of mesenchymal origin into the epithelial bud.

Early studies proposed that bursal epithelial cells transformed into lymphocytes (Retterer 1885) and this concept was revived by Ackerman (Ackerman and Knouff 1959; Ackerman 1962). In extensive histological, histochemical and ultrastructural studies of bursal development, Ackerman reported apparent transitional cells with a morphology intermediate between an undifferentiated epithelial cell and a lymphoblast. Bursal medullary lymphocytes were claimed to have a solely epithelial origin whereas cortical lymphocytes, as well as developing from epithelial cells that had migrated into the mesenchyme, could also develop by transformation of fixed stellate mesenchymal cells.

Both the epithelial and mesenchymal transformation theories assume that bursal lymphopoiesis is a potential of cells intrinsic to the bursa. Since the techniques employed were not able to trace the migration of cells, a third

TABLE 4.9

Sex-chromosome analysis of the bursa of Fabricius of twin and parabiosed chick embryos*

Union	Age at parabiosis (days)	Age at sampling (days)	Percentage mitoses of opposite sex (% chimaerism)
Chorioallantoic membrane	8	15	50, 0, 4, 8,
Chorioallantoic membrane	8	17	29, 32,
Chorioallantoic membrane	6	19	37, 27, 26, 50
Chorioallantoic membrane	8	19	38,
Chorioallantoic membrane	11	19	47, 49
Chorioallantoic membrane	7	20	42,
Yolk sac	4	14	25, 10, 3,
Yolk sac	5	16	44
Twin embryo	—	11	0, 0,
Twin embryo	—	12	0, 0,
Twin embryo	—	13	4, 2,

* 50—300 mitoses scored in each organ.

developmental origin of bursal lymphocytes from circulating cells extrinsic to the bursa could not be eliminated. Moore and Owen (1965, 1966) employed a sex-chromosome marker system to trace cell migration in the developing haemopoietic system of chick embryos united by anastomoses of yolk sac or chorioallantoic blood vessels. The anastomoses and resultant exchange of circulating cells was produced artificially by parabiosis or occurred naturally in dizygotic twin embryos. Chromosome analysis of bursal tissue of paired embryos of opposite sex revealed that up to 50% of the dividing cells in the bursa between 15–19 days of development were of the sex-chromosome constitution of the opposite partner (Table 4.9). Furthermore, this chimaerism was observed in both embryos, e.g. in one pair the female embryo had 47% dividing male cells in the bursa while the male partner had 49% dividing female cells. Where the bursa was sampled prior to lymphoid differentiation between 11–13 days' incubation little or no chimaerism was evident (0–4%). In the critical period of lymphoid transition between 14–15 days, chimaerism was highly variable (0–50%) and the extent of chimaerism correlated with the degree of lymphopoiesis in the bursa at the time of sampling. As soon as lymphopoiesis was initiated in bursal follicles, chimaerism was obtained and since in some instances chimaerism approached the theoretical equilibrium of 50% in both partners, it was concluded that the circulating cells equilibrating across the vascular anastomosis colonised the bursa and were responsible for all subsequent bursal lymphopoiesis.

The circulatory origin of bursal lymphoid precursors was confirmed in grafting experiments (Moore and Owen 1966). Embryonic bursas between 10–14 days of development were grafted to the chorioallantoic membranes of 10–12-day chick embryos. Histological examination of grafts removed at various intervals showed that the 10-day bursal rudiments usually became vascularised within 24–48-hours of transplantation, with no evidence of necrosis at any stage. Excellent follicular lymphoid development occurred in such grafts paralleling that of the host bursa. Twelve- and 14-day bursal transplants vascularised less rapidly and most underwent partial necrosis within 2 days of transplantation. This was followed by a period of rapid regeneration and ultimately follicular formation equivalent to that of the host bursa. Chromosome analysis of bursal grafts of opposite sex to the host revealed that 10-day bursal rudiments, after 7 days on the chorioallantoic membrane, contained 80–83% host metaphases and 86–94% by 9 days (Table 4.10). Similar results were obtained with 12-day bursal rudiments but 13- and 14-day grafts showed a more variable host component after 9 days on the CAM (48–92%). Analysis of the distribution of colchicine-blocked

TABLE 4.10

Sex-chromosome analysis of bursal grafts to the chorioallantoic membrane*

Age of bursa at grafting (days)	Duration of graft on CAM (days)	% Host mitoses in graft
10	7	83, 80, 82, 82
12	7	76, 88,
10	9	94, 86
12	9	92, 72, 88,
13	9	88, 48, 92
14	9	64

* Hosts 10—12-day chick embryos. Counts were made on 50 mitoses in each case.

mitoses in representative areas of biopsies of bursal grafts sampled for chromosome analysis revealed that 5–31 % were in non-lymphoid structural tissues (epithelium and mesenchyme). This would account for the 6–20 % of donor metaphases detected in the grafts of 10–12-day bursas but not for the more extensive donor proliferation seen with older bursal grafts. It was concluded from this study that lymphoid precursor cells were not present in the bursa at 10–12 days' incubation hence graft lymphopoiesis was dependent on inflow of circulating host cells. However, by 13–14 days, numbers of precursor cells had entered the bursa prior to grafting and hence donor lymphoid proliferation participated in the growth of these older bursal grafts in addition to the contribution from immigrant host cells.

The unlikely possibility that the circulating precursor cells were indeed initially formed within the bursa and had entered a circulating phase prior to re-entering the organ, was eliminated by evidence that bursal grafts were repopulated by host cells even when host bursal development was completely inhibited by testosterone (Moore and Owen 1966). Furthermore, intravenously-injected bursal cells did not repopulate the bursa of an irradiated embryo.

The chromosome-marker system has demonstrated bursal chimaerism following haemopoietic cell injection into irradiated embryos (Moore and Owen 1967a). The results of chromosome-marker analysis of irradiated embryos injected with 10^7 embryonic marrow, spleen, yolk sac or thymus cells or with 0.1 ml of embryonic blood are presented in Table 4.11. The radiation dose (800 rad) was sublethal and uninjected embryos in many cases survived through hatching and for up to 6 weeks thereafter. Histologically, the regeneration of bursal lymphoid tissue was very variable. In some birds the bursa remained atrophic with failure of lymphoid regeneration while in others, extensive regeneration was apparent. Chromosome marker analysis showed that embryonic marrow, spleen and yolk sac contained cells capable of repopulating the bursa and such cells were also present in the circulation. In two out of three birds studied, thymus cells did not appear to proliferate within the bursa, though one bird showed a small percentage (6 %) of dividing thymus-derived cells within its bursa. It has not been possible to quantitate the numbers of cells in the various tissues that are capable of bursal repopulation but it is evident that marrow and yolk-sac cells are approximately equally as effective in repopulating, while 14-day embryonic spleen cells were most effective in this regard and embryonic thymic cells had little repopulating capacity. In this latter case, the single example of chimaerism observed may well have been due to contamination of the thymus inoculum by repopulating cells present in the blood. The repopulating cells present in the various haemopoietic tissues may be multipotential stem cells or alternatively progenitor cells limited to bursal lymphoid differentiation. The observation that they are present in the yolk sac at least 1 week prior to initiation of bursal lymphopoiesis suggests it is unlikely that they are specifically committed to lymphoid differentiation. At the time of entry of circulating cells into the bursa on the 13th–14th day of incubation, both yolk sac and spleen are actively engaged in haemopoiesis and have bursal-repopulating capacity, hence these organs are the most likely candidates to act as the

TABLE 4.11

Chromosome-marker analysis of the bursa of Fabricius of chicks irradiated at 13 days' incubation (800 R) and injected at 14 days with chick embryonic haemopoietic cells*

Donor cells	Age of donor (days incubation)	Host age at sampling (days)	% Donor mitoses in bursa
Bone marrow	16	20 D (embryo)	25, 16
Bone marrow	18	2 D (post hatch)	8, 12
Bone marrow	18	7 D (post hatch)	23
Spleen	14	2 D (post hatch)	98
Yolk sac	7	2 D (post hatch)	16, 20, 24
Thymus	14	2 D (post hatch)	0, 0
Thymus	18	2 D (post hatch)	6
Whole Blood	13	2 D (post hatch)	32

* 50—100 mitoses counted from each bursa. 10^7 cells injected or 0.1 ml of whole blood.

normal source of cells populating the bursa. The marrow is only poorly developed at this stage but later possesses bursal repopulating capacity. It is extremely unlikely that it is the source of the initial population of bursal lymphoid precursors.

Morphological characterisation of the circulating lymphoid precursor cells was undertaken in experiments where embryonic haemopoietic cells labelled with tritiated thymidine were injected intravenously into embryos at different stages of development (Moore, M. A. S., unpublished observations). The

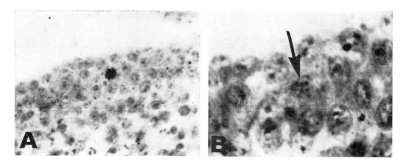

Fig. 4.53A.   Labelled cell in bursal epithelium at a site of early bud formation 24 hours after injection of 14-day embryonic spleen cells into a 14-day chick embryo. Haematoxylin and Eosin, autoradiograph exposed 28 days, × 500.

Fig. 4.53B.   Higher magnification of A after grain removal. The labelled cell (arrowed) is difficult to distinguish from the epithelial cells with this stain. Haematoxylin and Eosin × 1000.

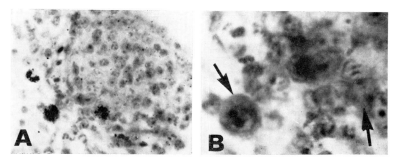

Fig. 4.54A.   Three labelled cells in and around a bursal follicle 24 hours after injection of 14-day embryo spleen cells into a 14-day embryo. One of the labelled cells is a mature granulocyte. Haematoxylin and Eosin, autoradiograph exposed 28 days, × 500.

Fig. 4.54B.   Higher magnification of A after grain removal. Arrows point to the two large labelled cells. Note their undifferentiated appearance and prominent nucleoli. Haematoxylin and Eosin × 1000.

number of cells injected ($2–40 \times 10^6$) was adjusted to the body weight of the developing embryo and the number of labelled cells per unit area of the bursa was determined 24 hours after cell injection. The results are shown in Figure 4.42. No labelled cells localised in the bursa between 8 and 9 days of development but between 10 and 14 days, the number of labelled myeloid cells (marrow and spleen inocula) per unit area increased progressively to reach a peak on the 14th day. During this period, bursal weight increased six-fold, which was only partially compensated for by a three-fold increase in

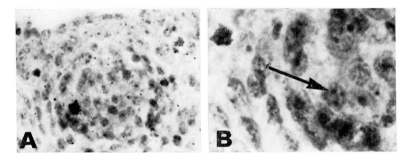

Fig. 4.55A.   Labelled cell in a bursal follicle 24 hours after injection of 13-day embryonic blood cells (buffy coat) into a 14-day embryo. Haematoxylin and Eosin, autoradiograph exposed 28 days, $\times$ 500.

Fig. 4.55B.   Higher magnification of A after grain removal. Arrow points to labelled cell in bursal follicle. Haematoxylin and Eosin, autoradiograph exposed 28 days, $\times$ 1000.

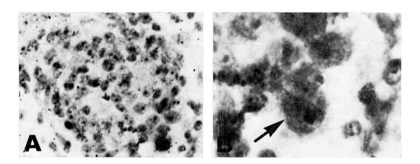

Fig. 4.56A.   Bursal follicle with labelled cell at its periphery 24 hours after injection of 11-day embryonic yolk-sac cells into a 14-day embryo. Haematoxylin and Eosin, autoradiograph exposed 28 days, $\times$ 500.

Fig. 4.56B.   Higher magnification of A after grain removal. The labelled yolk-sac cell (arrowed) has a prominent nucleolus and irregular nuclear and cytoplasmic outlines and is probably migrating into the follicle. Haematoxylin and Eosin $\times$ 1000.

the number of cells injected. It may be argued that this period of increasing uptake of labelled cells per unit area represented an even more dramatic absolute uptake of injected cells. Between 15–20 days, the numbers of labelled cells in the bursa showed an abrupt and highly significant reduction to very low levels despite a three-fold increase in the number of cells injected over this period. It is of significance therefore that considerable numbers of labelled cells localised in the prelymphoid bursa and that the greatest number were observed at the time of initiation of bursal lymphopoiesis. In the experiments where comparable numbers of labelled embryonic thymus cells were injected, very few labelled cells were found in the bursa between 13 and 15 days. The capacity of the bursa for uptake of labelled myeloid cells therefore considerably exceeds its capacity for uptake of injected thymocytes.

In the first few hours after myeloid cell injection on the 14th day of incubation, the majority of labelled cells were confined to the bursal blood vessels and adjacent mesenchyme. Morphologically the labelled cells were

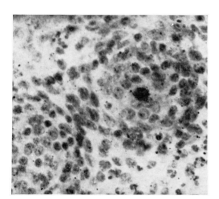

Fig. 4.57. Labelled cell in bursal follicle 24 hours after injection of 18-day embryonic bone marrow into a 14-day embryo. Haematoxylin and Eosin, autoradiograph exposed 28 days, × 500.

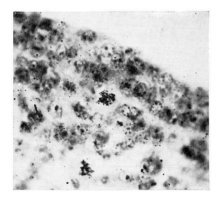

Fig. 4.58. A labelled mitosis can be seen within a bursal follicle 48 hours after injection of 18-day embryonic bone marrow into a 14-day embryo. Focus is on the cell and not the grains. Note the unlabelled mitosis in the mesenchyme. Haematoxylin and Eosin, autoradiograph exposed for 28 days × 500.

large and immature with basophilic cytoplasm and prominent nucleoli. Many labelled cells in the mesenchyme underwent mitosis in the first 24 hours and labelled myeloblasts and, at later stages, more mature labelled granulocytes were evident. The majority of the undifferentiated labelled cells accumulated in relation to the epithelium and developing epithelial buds (Figures 4.53–4.57) and by 24 hours after injection up to 10 % of the labelled cells in the bursa were within the follicles. Labelled cells were associated with epithelial buds at the very earliest stages of follicular development (Figure 4.53). The labelled cells first appearing in the bursal epithelium and originating from the injected spleen, marrow, buffy coat or yolk-sac inocula were large immature, basophilic cells identical to the basophilic cells seen in normal embryos at this stage of bursal development. By 48 hours after injection, the follicles were considerably enlarged, and although at 24 hours, it was rare to find more than one or two labelled cells in a section through a follicle, by 48 hours, 4–5 labelled cells were seen in a similar region (Figure 4.59). The majority of intrafollicular labelled cells in the later stages following injection were smaller than the labelled basophilic cells that initially entered the follicles and were identified as bursal lymphocytes on the basis of both size and nuclear morphology (Figure 4.59a, b). The fact that these smaller labelled cells were found in clusters showing similar grain counts and morphology together with the presence of labelled mitotic figures (Figure 4.58)

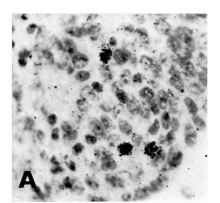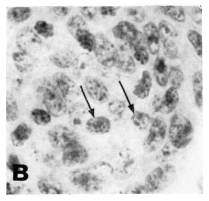

Fig. 4.59A. Three labelled cells within a bursal follicle 48 hours after injection of 14-day embryonic spleen cells into a 14-day embryo. Haematoxylin and Eosin, autoradiograph exposed for 6 weeks, × 500.

Fig. 4.59B. Higher magnification of A after grain removal. Arrows point to the pair of labelled cells. Their small size, coarse nuclear chromatin and nucleoli indicate that these are early bursal lymphocytes. Haematoxylin and Eosin × 1000.

strongly suggest that they were the progeny of large labelled basophilic cells. The few labelled thymocytes entering the bursa at this stage did not appear within the follicles but only in the mesenchyme around the blood vessels and there was no evidence of thymocyte proliferation in the bursa and the labelled cells were frequently pyknotic.

From these studies utilising cell tracer techniques it is now possible to delineate with some accuracy the development of bursal lymphocytes. Large, morphologically-undifferentiated, cells with prominent cytoplasmic baso-philia migrate from the spleen and yolk sac to enter a circulating pool of cells. The cells then migrate into the bursal mesenchyme from capillaries and sinusoids in the tunica propria on the 13th–14th day and then migrate into intimate relationship to the epithelial basement membrane. As a result of an inductive interaction between mesenchyme and epithelium, epithelial buds develop and it is in this environment that the immigrant cells finally localise after traversing the basement membrane. Within the epithelial buds a second interaction occurs between epithelial reticular cells and the immi-grant cells leading either to lymphoid commitment of an otherwise multi-potential stem cell or impartment of a proliferative stimulus to a precom-mitted lymphoid progenitor cell. The subsequent proliferation and maturation of this cell results in the establishment of a population of bursal small lymphocytes.

4.8.1 Hormonal modification of bursal development

The observation that the bursa involutes at sexual maturity led to the sugges-tion that this organ was under hormonal control, and attempts were made to induce involution by administration of gonadal hormones (Glick 1957). Treatment of chick embryos with testosterone early in development produced complete inhibition of bursal development in both male and female embryos (Meyer et al. 1959; Papermaster et al. 1962; Glick 1964). The bursal primor-dium fails to vacuolate and remains as a short convoluted duct without a bursal vesicle. When testosterone is administered in larger doses at 11–12 days of incubation, the bursa remains as an epithelial sac with no bud formation or lymphoid development (Rao et al. 1962; Warner and Burnet 1961). If hormone administration is delayed until after the initiation of bursal lymphopoiesis, the developing lymphoid follicles revert into cyst-like or crypt-like structures lined with epithelium (Warner and Burnet 1961). The complete suppression of lymphopoiesis in the bursa at the time of hatching following testosterone treatment at day 9 is illustrated in Figure 4.60. The

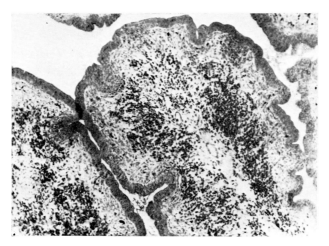

Fig. 4.60. Bursa of Fabricius of a 19-day chick embryo injected with 1 mg of testosterone on the 9th day of incubation. Complete failure of lymphoid follicular development is evident and intensive granulopoiesis is present in the tunica propria. Haematoxylin and Trichrome × 150.

epithelium shows no evidence of either budding or follicle formation but there has been considerable epithelial and mesenchymal proliferation in the 10 days following treatment. The epithelial cells of treated bursas are considerably elongated and hypertrophied and cystic spaces containing mucoid secretion are present in the lining epithelium (Figure 4.61). Granulo-poietic activity is intense in the mesenchyme of treated bursas and immature

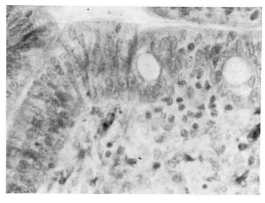

Fig. 4.61. Higher magnification of Figure 4.60. The bursal lining epithelial cells are hypertrophied and cystic spaces can be seen. Haematoxylin and Trichrome × 1000.

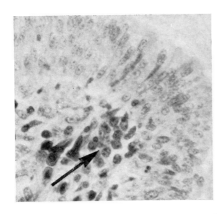

Fig. 4.62. Higher magnification of Figure 4.60. Note the accumulation of mononuclear cells, possibly lymphocytes, beneath the lining epithelium (arrowed). Haematoxylin and Trichrome × 1000.

cells and occasional small lymphocytes are observed in some preparations both in the subepithelial mesenchyme and in intimate relationship with the lining epithelium (Figure 4.62) (Moore and Owen 1966).

Rao et al. (1962) proposed that the testosterone inhibition was due to mitotic arrest of proliferating bursal epithelial cells induced by interference with endogenous metabolism or nucleic acid synthesis. The permanent inhibition of lymphoid development long after the androgen had lost its biological activity was explained by mitotic arrest occurring at a critical period of bursal development after which the epithelium loses its power of proliferation. The mitotic arrest theory is unlikely, since intense epithelial proliferation has been observed following androgen treatment (Warner and Burnet 1961).

In a series of grafting experiments, Moore and Owen (1966) showed that 12-day embryonic bursal transplants made to testosterone-treated host embryos showed a wide range of histological development when sampled 9 days later. In all cases, the host bursa had completely failed to develop, but whereas some of the transplants were extremely retarded in development, some had reached a stage of follicular formation, similar to that found in 12-day bursas grafted to normal embryos. Chromosome-marker analysis of grafts showing good follicular development revealed that the dividing lymphoid cells were host in type. Twelve-day bursas removed from testosterone treated embryos and transplanted to normal hosts also showed good follicular development, but by way of contrast, treated bursas transplanted to treated hosts completely failed to develop. These findings indicated that the bursal lymphoid precursor cells are available in the hormone-treated embryo. It is also apparent that these cells must originate from a source other than the host bursa. The inhibitory effect of testosterone seems therefore to be an indirect one on the differentiation rather than on the availability of lymphoid precursor cells. Inhibition of alkaline phosphatase activity has been demonstrated in bursal mesenchymal cells of testosterone-treated embryos (Ackerman and Knouff 1963). Thus, the action of the hormone may be on mesenchymal cell function with a secondary failure of the epithelial environment. In this context, it is of interest to note that mesenchymal activity has been shown to be necessary for induction of lymphoid transformation in the thymus (Auerbach 1961).

4.8.2 *Functional development of the bursa of Fabricius*

The first indication that the bursa was concerned in immune reactions came from the chance finding of Glick et al. (1956) that hens surgically bursectomised within 12 days of hatching were very susceptible to infection and did not produce detectable antibody. These original observations initiated considerable work on the immune response of birds, either surgically bursectomised, with or without irradiation, or in hormonally bursectomised birds. Bursectomy, particularly hormonal bursectomy, abrogates humoral antibody-forming capacity to undetectable levels (Warner et al. 1962; Cooper et al. 1966) and may even result in total agammaglobulinaemia in some birds (Warner et al. 1969). The expression of cellular immunity (homograft rejection, delayed hypersensitivity and graft-vs.-host reactivity) is not affected in bursectomised birds (Warner 1967; Cooper et al. 1966) and these are ontogenetically thymic-dependent reactions (Warner and Szenberg 1962; Jankovic and Isvaneski 1963). Following bursectomy, particularly with irradiation, there is a profound deficiency of plasma cells in the spleen and peripheral lymphoid tissue and a failure of development of the sharply circumscribed lymphoid nodules or germinal centres of the spleen. The small lymphocyte population of white pulp and the circulation remains unimpaired (Jankovic and Isakovic 1964; Warner and Szenberg 1962; Good et al. 1966). These observations have led to the concept of the dissociation of the immune system into a bursal-dependent system with the bursa as a central or primary lymphoid organ for the development of humoral immunity controlling immunoglobulin production, specific antibody formation and secondary or peripheral populations of cells comprising the germinal centres and plasma cells. The thymus-dependent system has the thymus as the central or primary organ for the differentiation of cells capable of expressing cellular immunity such as homograft rejection, delayed hypersensitivity and graft-vs.-host reactivity and residing in a peripheral lymphoid population of lymphocytes in the thymus-dependent areas of the spleen and lymph nodes in mammals.

Despite the importance of the bursa for specific antibody formation, the organ is not a major site of antibody formation after specific antigen stimulation and it has been suggested that the immunologically-competent cells are not present in the bursa (Thorbecke and Keuning 1953; Dent and Good 1965). In germfree birds, lack of exposure to intestinal flora only slightly affects the size of the bursa (Thorbecke et al. 1957) but profoundly depresses other gut-associated lymphoid tissue.

In a study of the formation of immunoglobulins *in vitro* by bursal tissue, incorporation of ^{14}C-labelled amino acids into IgM and IgG immunoglobulin was demonstrated by means of radioimmunoelectrophoresis, and the results were correlated with observations on tissue sections stained for the presence of immunoglobulin with fluorescein-labelled antisera (Thorbecke et al. 1968). The bursa was shown to be the first site of immunoglobulin production, synthesising IgM as early as the 18th day of embryonic development and IgG by the time of birth. Spleen synthesis of these immunoglobulins was not detected until 1 week after hatching. Fluorescein studies confirmed that immunoglobulin synthesis was initially limited to the medullary portion of the bursal follicles and was seen by the 18th day of incubation but not earlier. Kincade and Cooper (1970) and Cooper et al. (1970) have detected IgM production as early as 14 days of incubation in bursal medullary lymphocytes, within 24 hours of stem-cell entry into the organ. These studies have raised most important questions concerning the ontogeny of antibody formation. Is this early immunoglobulin synthesis antigen-dependent? The failure to demonstrate specific antibody formation by bursas following antigen administration may be due to inability of antigen to localise in, or be processed by, the bursa. It is unlikely that the immunoglobulin could be directed against bacterial antigens in the gut since no difference between conventional and germfree chickens in early bursal IgM synthesis was detected (Thorbecke et al. 1968), although stimulation by viral antigens present in the egg cannot be excluded.

Preliminary studies in the chick embryo have shown that the bursa contains considerable numbers of antigen-binding cells that specifically bind radio-iodinated flagellin (Dwyer and Warner 1971). Embryonic bursal cells bound flagellin as early as 14 days of incubation and the frequency of such antigen-binding cells was considerably higher in bursa than in either spleen or thymus throughout embryogenesis. This binding may be due to specific IgM receptors on bursal lymphocytes or alternatively may be due to coating of the cells by cytophilic antibody of maternal origin. In this context, up to 18 % of bursal lymphocytes from 17-day embryos were antigen binding after treatment with serum from chickens immunised with flagellin (Dwyer and Warner 1971).

Since the lymphoid precursor cells enter the bursa only 1–2 days prior to the detection of bursal lymphocytes producing IgM, the immunoglobulin genes must be activated in the lymphocytes after a maximum of only 4–8 divisions (assuming a minimum cell generation time of 6 hours). The clonal selection theory of Burnet (1959) recognises that antibody diversity is due to a somatic mutational mechanism with associated clonal selection. Antibody variability is recognised in the variability of the amino-acid composition of the 107 positions at the amino end of both the heavy and light chains. This variability has been attributed to somatic modification of the genes controlling the variable regions. If a somatic mutational frequency of 10^{-5} per cistron per generation is operating, there will be little opportunity for diversity generation in the immunoglobulin genes in the short period in the bursa between entry of the precursor cells and appearance of immunoglobulin synthesis. If, however, large numbers of lymphoid precursor cells were colonising this organ, then somatic mutations accumulating in this population prior to seeding in the bursa would be an important component of the diversity generation within the bursal lymphocytes (since somatic mutation would accumulate in the immunoglobulin genes from the first post-fertilisation division). From studies of labelled cell localisation and morphological characterisation of immigrant cells, the initial cell inflow to the bursa is unlikely to be less than 10^2 or more than 10^3 precursor cells. Therefore unless the bursa can specifically preselect lymphoid precursor cells carrying mutant V genes, little or no diversification can be anticipated prior to proliferation of these immigrant cells within the bursa. For the above reasons it might be anticipated that the bursal immunoglobulin would prove to be relatively homogeneous and possibly monoclonal. Jerne (1971) has proposed an hypothesis linking generation of diversity with the establishment of tolerance to self antigens. He postulates that antibody genes present in the germ line are structural genes for antibodies specifically directed against histocompatibility antigens and that the suppression of non-mutant cells of proliferating clones generates self-tolerance and results in selective survival of a diversity of mutant cells. It will be particularly relevant therefore to investigate the possibility that this early bursal immunoglobulin was directed against avian histocompatibility antigens, particularly those of the B-blood group locus.

The precise mechanism by which the bursa controls the development of the bursal-dependent lymphoid tissue and specific antibody formation is not clearly understood. One proposal considers that a bursal hormone influences or confers immunological competence on the secondary lymphoid tissue and partial reconstitution of antibody-forming capacity and immunoglobulin synthesis has been reported in bursectomised birds bearing bursal tissue in cell-impermeable diffusion chambers (St. Pierre and Ackerman 1965). The specificity of this reconstitution by hypothetical bursal hormone is questionable, since an equivalent degree of reconstitution has been demonstrated using endotoxin. Direct migration of cells already expressing immunoglobulin genes from the bursa to the peripheral lymphoid tissue is more probable. Woods and Linna (1965) utilising a technique of direct intrabursal tritiated thymidine labelling found evidence of bursal cell migration to the spleen.

4.9 Lymph-node development

Lymph-node anlagen develop as a plexus of anastomosing lymphatic vessels and condensations of mesenchymal cells that exhibit intense alkaline phosphatase reactivity (Hostetler and Ackerman 1966; 1969). Small and medium lymphocytes appear 1–2 days after mesenchymal condensation, by 18–19 days of gestation in the rabbit embryo, but lymphocytes do not increase rapidly until the 25th day with lymphatic nodular organisation evident 2–3 days before birth. The initial small and medium lymphocytes are probably immigrant cells from the circulation and can be seen at an early stage of lymph-node histogenesis within the capillaries and in transit across vascular endothelium (Hostetler and Ackerman 1969). Lymphoblasts are not seen until late foetal life and germinal centres do not develop until 2–3 weeks in the rabbit. A thymic origin for the lymph node small and medium lymphocyte population is suggested by the observation that tritiated thymidine-labelled thymic lymphocytes migrate to the lymph nodes in neonatal rats and constitute a considerable proportion of the total lymphocyte population of the nodes (Weissman 1967). However, in the cat foetus an extrathymic source has been proposed since small and medium lymphocytes were first seen in lymph nodes at 30 days' gestation at a stage when lymphocytes of an equivalent stage of development had not yet appeared in the thymus (Ackerman 1967b). A direct demonstration of the role of thymus-derived cells in lymph node ontogeny has been made possible using a thymic theta antigen marker in mice (Owen, J. J. T., personal communication).

4.10 Intestinal lymphoid development

In the mammalian gut, lymphoid tissue is diffusely present with small lymphocytes within the gut epithelium and plasma cells and lymphocytes in the
submucosal connective tissue. Specific aggregates of lymphoid tissue appear
in the tonsils, appendix and Peyer's patches. Lymphoid development of the
rabbit appendix has been most extensively studied and is preceded by the
development of subepithelial condensations of the mesenchyme in the
lamina propria which form dome-like elevations at the proximal third of
each villus. At this stage (28–29 days' gestation) the mesenchymal cells
display intense alkaline phosphatase activity (Hostetler and Ackerman 1966).
The first appendicial lymphocytes appear prior to birth in the lamina propria
rather than the epithelium of the crypt and are smaller than medium lymphocytes. The initial appearance of such cells in the vascular spaces of the
lamina propria indicates a vascular origin for appendicial lymphocytes.
There is some variation in reports of the first appearance of lymphocytes in
the rabbit appendix although in general the rabbit gut appears to lack
lymphocytes until shortly before birth (Stramignoni and Mollo 1968;
Archer et al. 1964; Ackerman 1967a). The number of lymphocytes in the
appendix increases rapidly in the immediate postnatal period and the
lymphoid tissue develops into nodules in the subepithelial mesenchyme or
even within the crypt epithelium but lymphocytes are always more numerous
in the deeper connective tissue layers (Stramignoni and Mollo 1968).
Lymphoblasts are not observed until after birth and immunoglobulin
synthesis commences in the rabbit appendix consistently by the first week of
age.

The histogenesis of Peyer's patches is similar to that of appendicial lymphoid aggregates. Lymphoid development is preceded by mesenchymal or
reticular cell aggregation in the submucosa with subsequent infiltration of
small and medium lymphocytes. Lymphoid nodule development in the
submucosal layer precedes lymphocytic infiltration of the epithelium
(Gyllensten 1950). In the human foetus accumulations of lymphocytes are
seen by 12–13 weeks in the terminal ileum and lymphatic vessels are evident
in the Peyer's patch anlage and are full of small lymphocytes (Yoffey 1968).
In fully developed Peyer's patches, lymphocytes are seen infiltrating between
epithelial cells but the epithelium is frequently seen to be separated from the
underlying lymphoid tissue by a thin but continuous reticulum cell layer
which is not evident on the mesenteric side of the Peyer's patch (Chin et al.
1968). As in lymph node and appendix, lymphoblasts appear after small and

medium lymphocytes, and germinal centre development is not evident until later (usually in the postnatal stages of development). In the rabbit the appendix develops prior to the Peyer's patches (Cooper et al. 1968). Early studies favoured an epithelial or local mesenchymal origin of Peyer's patch lymphocytes (Latta 1921) though more recent studies indicate an origin from circulating lymphocytes (Ackerman and Knouff 1966). The possible role of gut-associated lymphoid tissue as a mammalian equivalent to the avian bursa is discussed in Chapter 6 and experimental observations on the gut origin of lymphoid cells are reported.

4.11 Conclusions

The evidence reviewed in this chapter has demonstrated the existence and importance of migration streams of haemopoietic cells passing via the circulation between different tissues in the course of ontogeny of the haemopoietic system. The dependence of haemopoietic differentiation in intra-embryonic lymphoid and myeloid tissues on immigrant stem cells has led to the proposal that the development of stem cells within the yolk-sac blood islands at early stages of development is a unique process, since this is the only stage when haemopoietic tissue develops from a more undifferentiated precursor population not itself possessing stem cell capacity in the various assay systems used. All other sites of haemopoiesis are dependent on colonisation by circulating stem cells originating in the yolk-sac blood islands.

The yolk-sac migration concept is shown schematically in Figure 4.63 with the yolk-sac-derived stem cells entering the circulation and initially colonising foetal liver and primary lymphoid tissue. At later stages following decline in yolk-sac haemopoiesis, the expanding stem cell population in foetal liver contributes to the circulating stem-cell pool and leads to colonisation of spleen and marrow, while continuing to supply the stem-cell inflow requirements of primary lymphoid tissue. After decline in hepatic haemopoiesis in the early postnatal stages, expanding marrow function replaces the liver as a source of circulating stem cells with exchange of stem cells between spleen and marrow and continuing migration to primary lymphoid tissue. The migration pathways probably involve progenitor cells (e.g. *in vitro* CFC's) as well as stem cells, but, since the proliferative and self-maintenance capacity of progenitor cells is not extensive, their contribution to the establishment and maintenance of haemopoiesis within a colonised organ cannot be of major importance. The important embryonic colonising cell (stem cell)

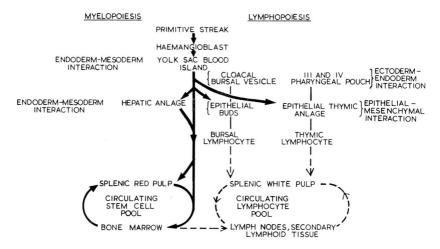

Fig. 4.63. Scheme of haemopoietic cell-migration streams in embryonic and early post natal life compiled from studies on the mouse and chick embryos. The black arrows show the migration of haemopoietic stem cells via the circulation from the yolk sac to the liver, thymus and bursa and subsequently to spleen and marrow. The nature of the inductive interactions occurring in the course of development of the haemopoietic and primary lymphoid microenvironments are shown. Dotted lines represent the migration streams of lymphoid progenitor cells from primary to secondary lymphoid tissue, and the establishment of a recirculating lymphocyte pool.

appears to be a large morphologically-undifferentiated cell with basophilic cytoplasm and prominent nucleoli as observed both in developing primary lymphoid and myeloid tissues. There is, however, little information on the functional homogeneity of this population. In mouse development, stem cells detected in the CFU assay are the most likely candidates for the stem-cell population migrating between different components of the myeloid system. No comparable evidence exists that such cells populate the thymus apart from the observation that CFU's are detected in low numbers in embryonic thymus and are present as early as at 12 days' gestation in the mouse thymic rudiment (prior to its vascularisation) (Moore, M. A. S. and Metcalf, D., unpublished observations). Alternatively, a specialised lymphoid stem cell may be responsible for colonisation or a more primitive and infrequent cell which antecedes the CFU and possesses both lymphoid and myeloid potentialities. The latter cell which would produce colony-forming cells among its progeny must surely be detected among the population of spleen CFU's. The concept of a specialised lymphoid stem cell implies that dissociation into the lymphoid and myeloid stem cells must antecede by a considerable period the appearance of distinct lymphoid tissues, since in the early stages of yolk-sac haemopoiesis the population contains cells capable of repopulating primary lymphoid and myeloid tissues of irradiated recipients. This problem of potentiality of colonising stem cells is discussed in more detail in the context of adult haemopoiesis in Chapter 5. However, the application of Ockham's razor to embryonic haemopoiesis leads us to conclude that in the absence of information on the existence of an embryonic, unipotent lymphoid stem cell or a stem cell more primitive than the multipotential CFU, that the latter remains the most likely candidate for the circulating cell responsible for the initiation of both myelopoiesis and primary lymphopoiesis.

Migration streams of more highly differentiated cell populations are also evident at later stages of development and are implicated in the development of secondary lymphoid tissue and the acquisition of immunological competence. Though vital for the initiation of peripheral lymphopoiesis as revealed in thymectomy and bursectomy experiments, such migration streams may be of lesser importance in postnatal life (see Section 6).

The control of entry and exit of stem cells is a major unsolved problem. At the present time we favour a vascular trapping mechanism and establishment of an equilibrium between circulating cells and the stem-cell compartment within the tissues. Deficiency of the latter seen in the initial establishment and growth phase produces a negative balance with trapping of circulating stem cells, whereas in the equilibrium phase, a positive balance is established and stem cells re-enter the circulation. Such a process is of course a very simplified point of view of what are undoubtedly a series of complex cell recognition and interaction processes. The diversity of haemopoietic differentiation seen throughout development appears to be an organotypic characteristic determined by the nature of the environment presented to the immigrant stem cells. The haemopoietic microenvironment appears to attain its characteristics as a result of inductive interactions between endoderm and mesoderm in the yolk sac and foetal liver, and between endoderm and ectoderm followed by epithelial-mesenchymal induction in the bursal and thymic environment (see Figure 4.63). Further, more complex, developmental interactions can be postulated with the development of the haemopoietic environments of spleen and marrow where a complex of vascular and mesenchymal networks appears to constitute a microenvironmental mosaic (see Chapter 6).

The final interactions occur between stem cells and epithelial or mesenchymal reticulum in the various tissues. Such interactions determining probabilities of stem cell renewal or differentiation along the various haemopoietic maturation sequences, remain the *terra incognita* of experimental haematology. Hopefully, the problems can be resolved by a further understanding of the interacting cell populations, the nature of the differentiation process and the role of the cell-membrane receptor sites. The problems are no less complex than those presented by other embryonic systems. An understanding of the nature of the development of the haemopoietic and immune systems may provide a model, however complex, that will allow a general insight into the mechanisms of embryogenesis.

References

Ackerman, G. A., 1962, J. Cell. Biol. *13*, 127.

Ackerman, G. A., 1964, Anat. Rec. *148*, 253.

Ackerman, G. A., 1967a, The lymphocyte: Its morphology and embryological origin. In: The lymphocyte in immunology and haemopoiesis, edited by J. M. Yoffey. London, Edward Arnold Ltd., p. 11.

Ackerman, G. A., 1967b, Anat. Rec. *158*, 387.

Ackerman, G. A. and J. R. Hostetler, 1970, Anat. Rec. *166*, 27.

Ackerman, G. A. and R. A. Knouff, 1959, Am. J. Anat. *104*, 163.

Ackerman, G. A. and R. A. Knouff, 1960, Blood *15*, 267.

Ackerman, G. A. and R. A. Knouff, 1963, Anat. Rec. *146*, 23.

Ackerman, G. A. and R. A. Knouff, 1964, Anat. Rec. *149*, 191.

Ackerman, G. A. and R. A. Knouff, 1965, Anat. Rec. *152*, 35.

Ackerman, G. A. and R. A. Knouff, 1966, Anat. Rec. *154*, 21.

Archer, O. K., D. E. R. Sutherland, and R. A. Good, 1964, Lab. Invest. *13*, 259.

Auerbach, R., 1960, Devel. Biol. *2*, 271.

Auerbach, R., 1961, Devel. Biol. *3*, 336.

Auerbach, R., 1963a, J. Natl. Cancer Inst. *11*, 23.

Auerbach, R., 1963b, Science *139*, 1061.

Auerbach, R., 1964a, On the function of the embryonic thymus. In: The thymus. Wistar Institute Symposium Monograph No. 2, edited by V. Defendi and D. Metcalf, Philadelphia, Wistar Inst. Press, p. 1.

Auerbach, R., 1964b, Experimental analysis of mouse thymus and spleen morphogenesis. In: 'The thymus in immunobiology', edited by R. A. Good and A. E. Gabrielsen. New York, Hoeber, p. 95.

Auerbach, R., 1966, Embryogenesis of immune systems. In: CIBA Symposium on The thymus: experimental and clinical studies, edited by G. E. W. Wolstenholme, and R. Porter. London, J. and A. Churchill, p. 39.

Auerbach, R., 1967, Dev. Biol. Suppl. *1*, p. 254.

Auerbach, R., 1970, In: Developmental aspects of antibody formation and structure, edited by J. Sterzyl. Prague (in press).

Badertscher, J. A., 1915, Am. J. Anat. *17*, 437.

Baglioni, C., 1963, Correlations between genetics and chemistry of human hemoglobins. In: Molecular genetics, pt. 1, edited by J. H. Taylor. New York, Acad. Press, p. 405.

Baillif, R. N., 1949, Am. J. Anat. *84*, 457.

Ball, W. D. and R. Auerbach, 1960, Exp. Cell. Res. *20*, 245.

Barker, J. E., 1968a, Dev. Biol. *18*, 14.

Barker, J. E., 1968b, quoted by Auerbach, R. In: Epithelial-mesenchymal interactions, edited by D. Fleishmeyer. Baltimore, Williams and Wilkins.

Barker, J. E., M. A. Keenan, and L. Raphals, 1969, J. Cell. Physiol. *74*, 51.

Beard, T., 1899, Lancet *1*, 144.

Beard, T., 1902, Zool. Jahrb. *17*, 403.

Bell, E. T., 1906, Am. J. Anat. *5*, 29.

Billingham, R. E., 1958, Ann. N.Y. Acad. Sci. *73*, 782.

Bleiberg, I. and M. Feldman, 1969, Dev. Biol. *19*, 566.

Bloom, W., 1938, Embryogenesis of mammalian blood. In: Handbook of hematology, Vol. II, edited by H. Downey. New York, Hoeber, p. 863.

Bloom, W., and G. W. Bartelmez, 1940, Am. J. Anat. *67*, 21.

Borghese, E., 1959, Acta Anat. *36*, 185.

Bortin, M. M. and E. C. Saltzstein, 1968, J. Immunol. *100*, 1215.

Boyden, E. A., 1924, J. Exp. Zool. *40*, 437.

Burnet, F. M., 1959, The clonal selection theory of acquired immunity. Cambridge, University Press.

Caffrey-Tyler, R. W. and N. B. Everett, 1966, Blood *28*, 873.

Cheval, T., 1908, Bibliograph. Anat. *17*.

Chin, K. N., G. Hudson, and J. M. Yoffey, 1968, J. Anat. *102*, 584.

Choi, M. H., 1931, Folia Anat. Jap. *9*, 495.

Claman, H. N., 1966, Proc. Soc. Exp. Biol. Med. *121*, 236.

Cohen, M. W., G. T. Thorbecke, G. M. Hochwald, and E. B. Jacobson, 1963, Proc. Soc. Exp. Biol. Med. *114*, 242.

Cole, R. J. and J. Paul, 1966, J. Embryol. Exp. Morphol. *15*, 245.

Cole, R. J., J. Hunter, and J. Paul. 1968, Brit. J. Haemat. *14*, 477.

Cooper, M. D., R. D. A. Peterson, M. A. South, and R. A. Good, 1966, J. Exp. Med. *123*, 75.

Cooper, M. D., D. Y. Perey, A. E. Gabrielsen, D. E. R. Sutherland, M. F. McKneally, and R. A. Good, 1968, Internat. Arch. Allergy *33*, 65.

Cooper, M. D., P. W. Kincade, A. R. Lawton, and D. E. Bochman, 1970, Fed. Proc. *29*, 492 (Abs.).

Craig, M. L. and E. L. Russell, 1964, Dev. Biol. *10*, 191.

Croisille, Y. and N. M. Le Douarin, 1965, Development and regeneration of the liver. In: Organogenesis, edited by R. L. De Haan, and H. Ursprung. New York, Holt. Rinehard and Winston.

Cudkowicz, G., M. Bennett, and G. M. Shearer, 1964, Science *144*, 866.

Danchakoff, V., 1908, Arch. of mikr. Anat. *73*, 117.

Danchakoff, V., 1916, J. Exp. Med. *24*, 87.

Danchakoff, V., 1918, Am. J. Anat. *24*, 1.

Danchakoff, V., 1924, Anat. Rec. *27*, 201.

Danchakoff, V. and C. Sharp, 1917, Anat. Rec. *11*, 347.

Deanesly, R., 1927, Quart. J. Micr. Sci. *71*, 113.

De Lanney, L. E. and J. D. Ebert, 1962, Contrib. to Embryol. (Carnegie Inst., Washington) *37*, 57.

Dent, P. B. and R. A. Good, 1965, Nature *207*, 491.

De Winiwarter, H., 1924, Bull. Histol. *1*, 11.

Doria, G., J. W. Goodman, N. Gengozian, and C. C. Congdon, 1962, J. Immunol. *88* 20.

Duplan, J. F., 1968, Nouv. Rev. Franç. d'Hématol. *8*, 445.

Dustin, A. P., 1920, Arch. Biol. *30*, 601.

Dwyer, J. M. and I. R. Mackay, 1970, Lancet *1*, 1199.

Dwyer, J. M. and N. L. Warner, 1971, Nature *229*, 210.

Edmonds, R. H., 1964, J. Ultrastruct. Res. *11*, 577.

Edmonds, R. H., 1966, Anat. Rec. *154*, 785.

Emmart, E. W., 1936, Anat. Rec. *66*, 59.

Fantoni, A., A. Bank, and P. A. Marks, 1967, Science *157*, 1327.

Federici, H., 1926, Arch. Biol. *36*, 466.

Feldman, M. and I. Bleiberg, 1967, Studies on the feedback regulation of haemopoiesis. In: CIBA Symposium on Cell Differentiation, edited by A. V. S. De Reuck and J. Knight. London, Churchill, p. 79.

Fichtelius, K. E., 1960, On the destination of thymus lymphocytes. In: CIBA Symposium on Haemopoiesis, edited by G. E. W. Wolstenholme and M. O'Connor. Boston, Little, p. 204.

Finnegan, C. V., 1953, J. Exptl. Zool. *123*, 371.

Gilman, J. G. and O. Smithies, 1968, Science *160*, 885.

Glick, B., 1957, Poultry Sci. *36*, 18.

Glick, B., 1964, The bursa of Fabricius and the development of immunologic competence. In: The thymus in immunobiology, edited by R. A. Good and A. E. Gabrielsen. New York, Hoeber, p. 348.

Glick, B., T. S. Chang, and R. G. Jaap, 1956, Poultry Sci. *35*, 224.

Globerson, A. and R. Auerbach, 1965, In Vitro studies on thymus and lung differentiation following urethan treatment. In: Wistar Inst. Symp. Monograph No. 4 on Methodological approaches to the study of leukemia, edited by V. Defendi. Philadelphia, Wistar Inst. Press, p. 3.

Good, R. A., A. E. Gabrielsen, R. D. A. Peterson, J. Finstad, and M. D. Cooper, 1966, The development of the central and peripheral lymphoid tissue: ontogenetic and phylogenetic considerations. In: CIBA Symposium on The thymus: Experimental and clinical studies, edited by G. E. W. Wolstenholme and R. Porter. London, J. A. Churchill, p. 181.

Goss, C. M., 1928, J. Exp. Zool. *52*, 45.

Gotte, G., 1867, Quoted by G. A. Thiel and H. Downey, 1921, Am. J. Anat. *28*, 278.

Grasso, J. R., H. Swift, and G. A. Ackerman, 1962, J. Cell. Biol. *14*, 235.

Gregoire, C., 1932. Arch. Internat. Med. Exper. *7*, 513.

Gregoire, C., 1935, Arch. Biol. *46*, 717.

Gregoire, C., 1958, Quart. J. Micro. Sci. *99*, 511.

Gyllensten, L., 1950, Acta Anat. *10*, 130.

Haff, T., 1914, Arch. Mikr. Anat. u. Entwicklungsmech. *84*, 321.

Hamilton, H. L., 1952, Lillie's development of the chick. New York, Henry Holt.

Hammar, J. A., 1905, Anat. Anz. *27*, 23.

Hammar, J. A., 1908, Arch. f. mikr. Anat. *73*, 1.

Hammar, J. A., 1910, Ergebn. d. Anat. u. Entwickl. *19*, 1.

Hammar, J. A., 1911, Anat. Hefte *43*, 201.

Hammond, W. S., 1954, J. Morphol. *95*, 501.

Haskill, J. S. and M. A. S. Moore, 1970, Nature *226*, 853.

Haskill, J. S., T. A. McNeill, and M. A. S. Moore, 1970, J. Cell. Physiol. *75*, 167.

His, W., 1885, Anatomie der menschlichen Embryonen. Leipzig.

Hoshino, T., M. Takeda, K. Abe, and T. Ito, 1969, Anat. Rec. *164*, 47.

Hostetler, J. R. and G. A. Ackerman, 1966, Anat. Rec. *156*, 191.

Hostetler, J. R. and G. A. Ackerman, 1969, Am. J. Anat. *124*, 57.

Houser, J. W., G. A. Ackerman, and R. A. Knouff, 1961, Anat. Rec. *140*, 29.

Huehns, E. R. and E. M. Shooter, 1965, J. Med. Gen. *2*, 48.

Jacobson, L. O., E. K. Marks, and E. O. Gaston, 1959, Blood *14*, 644.

Jankovic, B. D. and K. Isakovic, 1964, Int. Arch. Allergy *24*, 278.

Jankovic, B. D. and M. Isvaneski, 1963, Int. Arch. Allergy *23*, 188.

Jerne, N. K., 1971, European J. Immunol. *1*, 1.

Jolly, J., 1915, Arch. d'Anat. micr. *16*, 363.

Jordan, H. E., 1916, Am. J. Anat. *19*, 227.

Kaplan, H. S. and B. M. Rosston, 1959, Stanford Med. Bull. *17*, 77.

Karrer, H. E., 1961, J. Ultrastr. Res. *5*, 116.

Kay, H. E. M., J. Doe, and A. Hockley, 1970, Immunol. *18*, 393.

Kincade, P. W. and M. D. Cooper, 1970, Fed. Proc. *29*, 503 (Abs.).

King, J., G. A. Ackerman, and R. A. Knouff, 1964, Anat. Rec. *148*, 300.

Kingsbury, B. F., 1940, Am. J. Anat. *67*, 343.

Klapper, C. E., 1946, Am. J. Anat. *78*, 139.

Klemperer, P., 1938, The Spleen. Downey's Handbook of haematology, vol. III, edited by H. Downey. New York, Hoeber, p. 1587.

Kolliker, A., 1879, Entwicklungsgeschichte des Menschen und der höheren Tiere. 2nd edition. Leipzig.

Kovach, J. S., P. A. Marks, E. S. Russell, and H. Epler, 1967, J. Mol. Biol. *25*, 131.

Kubanek, B., N. Rencricca, A. Porcellini, D. Howard, and F. Stohlman, 1969, Proc. Soc. Exp. Biol. Med. *131*, 831.

Latta, J. S., 1921, Am. J. Anat. *29*, 159.

Linna, T. J., 1968, Blood *31*, 727.

Lucarelli, G., L. Ferrari, A. Porcellini, C. Carnevali, V. Rizzoli, and F. Stohlman, 1967, Exp. Hemat. *14*, 7.

MacGillivray, M. H., B. Mayhew, and N. R. Rose, 1970, Proc. Soc. Exp. Biol. Med. *133*, 688.

Malpoix, P., 1967, Biochem. Biophys. Acta *145*, 181.

Marine, D., 1932, The thyroid, parathyroids and thymus. In: Special Cytology, vol. II, edited by E. V. Cowdry. New York, Hafner, p. 797.

Matioli, G. T., H. Niewisch, and H. Vogel, 1968, Fed. Proc. *27*, 672 (Abs.).

Mato, M., E. Aikawa, and K. Kishi, 1964, Exp. Cell. Res. *35*, 426.

Maximow, A., 1909, Arch. f. mikr. Anat. *74*, 525.

Maximow, A., 1912, Arch. f. mikr. Anat. *79*, 560.

Metcalf, D., 1963, Aust. J. exp. Biol. Med. *41*, 51.

Metcalf, D., 1964, Transp. *2*, 387.

Meyer, R. K., M. A. Rao, and R. L. Aspinall, 1959, Endocrinol. *64*, 890.

Micklem, H. S. and J. F. Loutit, 1966, Tissue grafting and radiation. New York, Academic Press.

Miller, J. F. A. P., 1960, Brit. J. Cancer *14*, 244.

Miller, J. F. A. P., M. Block, D. T. Rowlands, and P. Kind, 1965, Proc. Soc. Exp. Biol. Med. *118*, 916.

Miura, Y. and F. H. Wilt, 1969, Dev. Biol. *19*, 201.

Miura, Y. and F. H. Wilt, 1970, Exp. Cell. Res. *59*, 217.

Moffatt, D. J., C. Rosse, and J. M. Yoffey, 1967, Lancet *2*, 547.

Moore, M. A. S. and D. Metcalf, 1970, Brit. J. Haemat. *18*, 279.

Moore, M. A. S. and J. J. T. Owen, 1965, Nature *208*, 956.

Moore, M. A. S. and J. J. T. Owen, 1966, Dev. Biol. *14*, 40.

Moore, M. A. S. and J. J. T. Owen, 1967a, Nature *215*, 1081.

Moore, M. A. S. and J. J. T. Owen, 1967b, Lancet *1*, 658.

Moore, M. A. S. and J. J. T. Owen, 1967c, J. Exp. Med. *126*, 715.

Moore, M. A. S., T. A. McNeill, and J. S. Haskill, 1970, J. Cell. Physiol. *75*, 181.

Mueller, A. P., H. R. Wolfe, and R. K. Meyer, 1960, J. Immunol. *85*, 172.

Murray, P. D. F., 1932, Proc. Roy. Soc. (B) London *111*, 497.

Murray, R. G., 1947, Amer. J. Anat. *81*, 369.

Murray, R. G. and A. Murray, 1967, Migration and transformation of lymphoid cells. In: The lymphocyte in immunology and haemopoiesis, edited by J. M. Yoffey. London, Arnold, p. 160.

Murray, R. G. and P. A. Woods, 1964, Anat. Rec. *150*, 113.

Norris, E., 1938, Contrib. to Embryol. (Carnegie Inst., Washington) *27*, 191.

Nossal, G. J. V., 1964, Ann. N.Y. Acad. Sci. *120*, 171.

Ortega, L. G., A. A. Kattine, and B. O. Spurlock, 1965, Fed. Proc. *24*, 160 (Abs.).

Owen, J. J. T. and M. A. Ritter, 1969, J. Exp. Med. *129*, 431.

Owen, J. J. T., A. R. Mawdsley, and G. A. Harrison, 1964, Transp. *2*, 503.

Papermaster, B. W., D. I. Friedman, and R. A. Good, 1962, Proc. Soc. Exp. Biol. Med. *110*, 62.

Pappenheimer, A., 1913, Arch. f. exp. Zellforsch. *4*, 395.

Paul, J., D. Conkie, and R. I. Freshney, 1969, Cell Tissue Kinet. *2*, 283.

Petrakis, N. L., S. Pons, and R. E. Lee, 1966, Exp. Hematol. *9*, 15.

Petrakis, N. L., S. Pons, and R. E. Lee, 1969, An experimental analysis of factors affecting the localisation of embryonic bone marrow. In: Hemic cells in vitro, edited by P. Farnes. Baltimore, Williams and Wilkins, p. 3.

Playfair, J. H. L., 1968a, Immunol. *15*, 815.

Playfair, J. H. L., 1968b, Immunol. *15*, 35.

Prenant, A., 1894, Cellule *10*, 85.

Ramney, H. M. and S. Glueksohn-Waelsh, 1955, Ann. Hum. Genet. *19*, 269.

Rao, M. A., R. L. Aspinall, and R. K. Meyer, 1962, Endocrinol. *70*, 159.

Retterer, E. J., 1885, J. Anat. Physiol. *21*, 369.

Rifkind, R. A., D. Chui, and M. Djaldetti, 1968, Fed. Proc. *27*, 724.

Romanoff, A. L., 1960, The avian embryo. New York, Macmillan.

Rosenberg, M., 1969, Blood *33*, 66.

Rosenquist, G. C., 1966, Contrib. Embryol. (Carnegie Inst. Washington) *38*, 71.

Rudnick, D., 1938, Anat. Rec. *70*, 351.

Russell, E. S. and S. E. Bernstein, 1966, Blood and blood formation. In: Biology of the laboratory mouse, edited by E. L. Green. New York, McGraw-Hill, p. 351.

Ruth, R. F., 1960, Fed. Proc. *19*, 579 (Abs.).

Ruth, R. F., C. P. Allen, and H. R. Wolfe, 1964, The effect of thymus on lymphoid tissue. In: The thymus in immunobiology, edited by R. A. Good, and A. E. Gabrielsen. New York, Hoeber, p. 183.

Sabin, F. R., 1921, Johns Hopkins Hosp. Bull. *32*, 314.

Sabin, F. R. and F. R. Miller, 1938, Normal bone marrow. In: Handbook of haematology, vol. III, edited by H. Downey. New York, Hoeber, p. 1791.

Sanel, F. T., 1967, Z. Zellforsch. *83*, 8.

Schmidt, M. B., 1892, Beitr. z. path. Anat. u. Path. *11*, 199.

Schriddie, H., 1923, In: Pathologische Anatomie, edited by L. Aschoff. Jena, Fisher, p. 102.

Schwarz, M. R., 1966, Immunol. *10*, 281.

Settle, G. W., 1954, Contributions to Embryology (Carnegie Inst., Washington) *241*, 223.

Shepherd, M. K., D. J. Weatherall, and C. L. Conley, 1962, Bull. Johns Hopkins Hosp. *110*, 293.

Sidky, Y. A. E. and R. Auerbach, 1968, J. Exp. Zool. *167*, 187.

Silini, G., L. V. Pozzi, and S. Pons, 1967, J. Embryol. Exp. Morphol. *17*, 303.

Smith, C., 1965, Am. J. Anat. *116*, 611.

Spratt, N. T., Jr. and H. Haas, 1965, J. Exptl. Zool. *158*, 9.

Stockard, C., 1915, Am. J. Anat. *18*, 525.

Stohlman, F. Jr., G. Lucarelli, D. Howard, B. Morse, and B. Leventhal, 1964, Medicine (Baltimore) *43*, 651.

Stohr, P., 1906, Anat. Hefte *31*, 409.

St. Pierre, R. L. and G. A. Ackerman, 1965, Science *147*, 1307.

Stramignoni, A. and F. Mollo, 1968, Acta Anat. *70*, 202.

Taylor, R. B., 1964, Brit. J. Exp. Path. *46*, 376.

Thiel, G. A. and H. Downey, 1921, Am. J. Anat. *28*, 279.

Thorbecke, G. J. and F. J. Keuning, 1953, J. Immunol. *70*, 129.

Thorbecke, G. J., H. A. Gordon, B. S. Wostmann, M. Wagner, and J. A. Reyniers, 1957, J. Infect. Dis. *101*, 237.

Thorbecke, G. J., N. L. Warner, G. M. Hochwald, and S. H. Ohanian, 1968, Immunol. *15*, 123.

Tyan, M. L., 1968, J. Immunol. *100*, 535.

Tyan, M. L. and L. J. Cole, 1963, Transplantation *1*, 347.

Tyan, M. L. and L. J. Cole, 1964, Transplantation *2*, 241.

Tyan, M. L. and L. A. Herzenberg, 1968, Proc. Soc. Exp. Biol. Med. *128*, 952.

Tyan, M. L., L. J. Cole, and P. C. Nowell. 1966, Transp. *4*, 79.

Tyan, M. L., Cole, L. J., and L. A. Herzenberg, 1968, Fetal liver cells: A source of specific immunoglobulin production in radiation chimeras. In: Advances in transplantation. Proc. 1st Internat. Cong. Transp. Soc., edited by J. Dausset, J. Hamburger, and G. Mathe. Copenhagen, Munksgaard, p. 87.

Tyan, M. L., L. A. Herzenberg, and P. R. Gibbs, 1969, J. Immunol. *103*, 1283.

Umiel, T., A. Globerson, and R. Auerbach, 1968, Proc. Soc. Exp. Biol. Med. *129*, 598.

Van der Stricht, O., 1891, Arch. Biol. (Liège) *12*, 199.

Van Furth, R., H. R. E. Schuit, and W. Hijmans, 1965, J. Exp. Med. *122*, 1173.

Venzke, W. G., 1952, Am. J. Vet. Res. *13*, 395.

Verdun, P., 1898, Comp. Red. Soc. Biol. *5*, 243.

Vos, O., J. W. Goodman, and C. C. Congdon, 1960, Transp. Bull. *25*, 408.

Warner, N. L., 1964, Aust. J. Exp. Biol. Med. Sci. *42*, 401.

Warner, N. L., 1967, Folia Biol. (Praha) *13*, 1.

Warner, N. L. and F. M. Burnet, 1961, Aust. J. Biol. Sci. *14*, 580.

Warner, N. L. and A. Szenberg, 1962, Nature *196*, 784.

Warner, N. L. and A. Szenberg, 1964, Ann. Rev. Microbiol. *18*, 253.

Warner, N. L., A. Szenberg, and F. M. Burnet, 1962, Aust. J. Exp. Biol. Med. Sci. *40*, 373.

Warner, N. L., J. W. Uhr, G. J. Thorbecke, and Z. Ovary, 1969, J. Immunol. *103*, 1317.

Weakley, B. S., D. J. Patt, and S. Shepro, 1964, J. Morphol. *115*, 319.

Weber, W. T., 1966, J. Cell. Physiol. *67*, 285.

Weissman, I. L., 1967, J. Exp. Med. *126*, 291.

Wilson, V. W., C. S. Groat, and E. H. Leduc, 1963, Ann. N.Y. Acad. Sci. *111*, 8.

Wilt, F. H., 1965, Science *147*, 1588.

Wilt, F. H., 1967, The control of embryonic hemoglobin synthesis. In: Advances in morphogenesis, vol. 6, edited by M. Abercrombie and J. Brachet. New York, Academic Press, p. 89.

Woods, R. and J. Linna, 1965, Acta Path. Microbiol. Scand. *64*, 470.

Worton, R. G., E. A. McCulloch, and J. E. Till, 1969, J. Cell. Physiol. *74*, 171.

Yoffey, J. M., 1968, J. Anat. *102*, 584.

CHAPTER 5

Haemopoietic cell migration streams in adult life

In this chapter evidence will be presented that the migration of haemopoietic stem cells and progenitor cells which occurs during embryonic development persists in the form of migration streams throughout adult life. The existence of such migration streams disproves older concepts of the origin of haemopoietic cells from fixed cells in haemopoietic organs in adult life and indicates the highly dynamic state of adult haemopoietic organs.

Evidence for the existence of migration streams in adult life has been obtained from studies on radiation chimaeras, parabiotic animals and animals grafted with haemopoietic organs.

5.1 Radiation chimaeras

A considerable body of evidence has now accumulated to show that lethally irradiated animals may be saved from death by infusion of bone marrow, spleen or foetal liver cells (see review by Micklem and Loutit 1966), with recovery due to repopulation of the host's aplastic myeloid and lymphoid tissues by proliferating donor cells (Ford et al. 1956). Although suspensions of myeloid cells can save irradiated animals, lymphoid cells from lymph nodes, thymus or thoracic duct lymph cannot, despite their capacity to proliferate in the host's lymph nodes (Micklem and Ford 1960). The fate of injected lymphoid and myeloid cells has been extensively analysed using the T6 chromosome-marker technique, which has permitted a simultaneous analysis of proliferation of injected lymphoid (lymph node or thymic) cells and marrow cells, together with host-cell proliferation in radiation chimaeras (see Chapter 2). Donor marrow cells were found to rapidly and completely replace host cells in recipient marrow within 7 days. Marrow repopulation of the thymus was more delayed with dividing host cells predominating in the first 2 weeks after irradiation followed by almost complete repopulation by donor cells shortly thereafter (Micklem and Loutit 1966). Injected lymph node and thymic lymphocytes behaved identically as regards homing and proliferation in irradiated mice, proliferating extensively in host lymph nodes within 3 days of injection. By 10 days, donor lymphoid cells comprised 80–90% of the total lymph node mitoses but then numbers fell progressively to low levels due to replacement by marrow-derived cells. Donor lymphoid mitoses never disappeared entirely and still comprised up to 10% of lymph node mitoses 400 days after injection. Donor lymphoid cells proliferated in the first few days in the spleen, constituting up to 50% of the total dividing cells within 2 days, but by 7 days very few lymphoid donor mitoses were seen and donor lymphoid proliferation disappeared almost entirely, with the marrow-derived cells constituting 95–98% of total dividing cells in the spleen after this time (Micklem and Loutit 1966).

The observation that lymphoid donor mitoses could comprise from 10–20% of total lymph-node mitoses in irradiation chimaeras even after many months (Ford et al. 1968) has been cited in support of the existence of a lymphoid stem cell. If many donor lymphoid cells entered the recirculating lymphocyte pool and existed in an undividing state for prolonged periods, this pool might continue to supply memory cells which could proliferate extensively in the host lymphoid tissue in response to antigenic stimulation. This situation of continuous replenishment of lymph-node populations by cells from a long-lived recirculating pool would account for persistent proliferation of donor lymphoid cells in lymph nodes. If donor lymphoid cells underwent clonal expansion in response to specific antigenic challenge prior to re-entering the circulating memory cell pool, they would indeed behave in a manner analogous to stem cells. However, for reasons discussed in Chapter 3.6 it is probably more accurate to regard such cells as lymphoid progenitor cells.

Marrow cells can repopulate the irradiated thymus but lose their capacity to home to this organ after a period of residence in the thymus. Ford (1966) studied the homing characteristics in irradiated secondary recipients of thymic cells from radiation chimaeras repopulated with marrow cells 16–30 days earlier. Marrow cells that repopulated the thymus had lost their capacity to home to the thymus of the secondary recipient within 16 days of residence in the primary host thymus and by 23 days had acquired the characteristic of thymic lymphocytes to home to, and proliferate in, lymph nodes, a capacity that was even more strongly expressed after 30 days of residence in the thymus. Order and Waksman (1969) utilised an indirect fluorescence technique to detect cells bearing donor histocompatibility antigens following repopulation of irradiated rats with donor marrow. Influx of marrow-derived cells was evident in the host thymus by 4–5 days after radiation with the appearance of large and medium lymphocytes. By 2 weeks, most of the cells in lymph nodes were of marrow origin. Cells from the recipient thymus 6 days after marrow injection retained the capacity to home to irradiated marrow (8–22% of femoral marrow cells were positive for donor antigen) but by 7–9 days the marrow-homing capacity of the thymic repopulating cells was markedly diminished. Cells in the early stages of thymus regeneration that retained marrow-homing characteristics were apparently restricted to lymphoid differentiation forming large and medium lymphocytes in the recipient marrow with no evidence of granulocytic or erythroid differentiation. It is possible that the thymic repopulating cells are themselves restricted to lymphoid differentiation prior to entry into the thymus or, alternatively restriction may rapidly develop upon localisation in the thymic environment and may precede loss of thymic-homing capacity.

Experiments with lymph nodes from chimaeras showed that by 16 days, cells from the original marrow donor that had proliferated in the lymph nodes had lost their capacity for regenerating myeloid tissue but had developed the capacity to home to, and proliferate, in lymph nodes. Evidently myeloid cells developed lymphoid functional properties earlier in lymph nodes than in thymus (Ford 1966). This may indicate intrinsic lymphoid differentiation from marrow stem cells within lymph nodes rather than secondary repopulation of lymph nodes by marrow cells originally seeding in the thymus. Alternatively, myeloid cells acquiring lymphoid-homing properties in the thymus immediately migrate out of this organ to repopulate the peripheral lymphoid tissue and consequently do not accumulate in significant numbers in the early stages of thymic regeneration. Evidence on this point was presented by Barnes et al. (1967) in a comparison of lymph-node lymphocyte and marrow proliferation in lymph nodes of intact and thymecto-mised irradiated mice. No significant difference was observed in lymph-node repopulation between the two groups, with decline in lymphoid-donor proliferation with time and similar replacement by marrow-donor cells in both groups. Thus repopulation of lymph nodes by marrow-derived cells can occur whether the thymus is present or not. The progressive replacement of lymphoid donor mitoses by the marrow donor shows that the lymphoid population is not self-sustaining and since the replenishing cells do not require maturation in the thymus, a direct cell migration from marrow to lymph nodes appears probable. Foetal liver cells were also capable of repopulating the lymph nodes of irradiated thymectomised recipients but not to the same degree as seen with marrow, since lymph node-type mitoses persisted in higher numbers (32–52 %) over a prolonged period (Barnes et al. 1967). This experiment was complicated by the use of C57BL foetal liver and (C57-BL × CBA)F$_1$ lymphoid cells and it is possible that hybrid resistance on the part of the initial population of (C57BL × CBA)F$_1$ lymphoid cells might have inhibited the proliferation of the C57BL liver cells.

In part-body irradiation experiments, the upper part of the body was shielded and the animals subsequently injected with chromosomally-marked lymphoid and marrow cells. The irradiated femur and spleen were extensively repopulated by marrow cells within 1 week but the unirradiated humerus showed no tendency to equilibrate and even after 2 years the humerus contained only 8 % of dividing donor marrow cells while the irradiated femur contained 40–50 % (Ford et al. 1966). This is further confirmation of the parabiosis data, which suggest that in the adult the bulk of marrow stem cells do not enter a circulatory phase which would lead to equilibration between irradiated and unirradiated bone marrows. Within the lymphoid tissues of these irradiated mice, the unirradiated thymus showed no donor proliferation for up to 9 weeks, but thereafter 48–51 % of the dividing cells were of donor-marrow origin. This need not imply that immigrant cells were failing to enter the unirradiated thymus during this period since it is probable that in the regenerating marrow, myeloid differentiation was establishing a demand for donor-marrow stem cells and that these were not initially available for entering the circulating pool and were not yet able to compete with stem-cell migration from unirradiated host marrow. Lymphoid donor cells proliferated in the lymph nodes as early as 1 week after injection and marrow-donor cells proliferated in lymph nodes after 3 weeks. Chimaerism in irradiated lymph nodes was more extensive and of earlier onset than in unirradiated thymus and marrow and again indicated the dependence of lymph-node lymphopoiesis on lymphocyte recirculation occurring between unirradiated and irradiated lymph nodes and spleen. The extent of thymic chimaerism in these experiments was slightly influenced by immunological stimulation. Some increase in the proportion of donor-marrow cells was observed in the organ following skin allografting or xenografting (rat), though antigenic stimulation with large doses of pertussis was without effect (Ford et al. 1966).

5.2 Natural chimaeras

In mammals erythrocyte chimaerism has been demonstrated in dizygotic twins where synchorial placental vascular anastomosis had developed during embryogenesis (Woodruff et al. 1962 – in humans; Owen et al. 1945 – in cattle). Embryonic circulatory interchange due to chorioallantoic vascular anastomosis also leads to erythrocyte chimaerism in twin chick embryos (Billingham et al. 1956; Moore, M. A. S. and Owen, J. J. T., 1966 – unpublished observations).

Since erythrocyte chimaerism persists in adult life, and the donor component may remain unchanged for up to 11 years in freemartin cattle (Stone et al. 1964), it is apparent that the initial population of erythroid precursor cells that enters the marrow cavity in embryogenesis is not replaced to any significant degree by further immigration in adult life. Furthermore stem cells cannot be developing locally by transformation of 'fixed' components of marrow such as vascular endothelium or mesenchyme. The immigrant cells entering the embryonic marrow must provide a pool of stem cells whose capacity for proliferation and erythroid differentiation is sufficient for a considerable period of adult life, indeed probably sufficient for the life span of the animal.

High levels of marrow chimaerism have been demonstrated, using sex-chromosome markers, in marmosets and freemartin cattle (Gengozian et al. 1964; Benirschke and Brownhill 1962; Ford 1966). In both species synchorial twinning and embryonic interchange of blood is of frequent occurrence. High levels of thymic chimaerism have also been reported in these species (Ford 1966) but since the analysis was performed on the post-embryonic thymus, this does not constitute evidence for a cell migration stream into the embryonic thymus since the results could equally be explained by an inflow of cells after birth from a chimaeric tissue such as marrow.

Basrur and Kanagawa (1969) performed sex-chromosome marker studies on a large number of heterosexual cattle twins and observed that the degree of chimaerism of peripheral blood lymphocytes was uninfluenced by phenotypic sex. However, Gengozian et al. (1969) reported that cells of male karyotype predominated in both marmoset and cattle chimaeras. This selectivity for male cells may reflect the operation of a dominance situation *in utero* similar to that observed in parabiosed chick embryos (see Chapter 4) with, in this instance, the male foetus making a greater contribution to the circulating stem-cell pool.

Levels of chimaerism in bone marrow and peripheral blood lymphocytes were similar in cattle chimaeras (Kanagawa et al. 1967; Muramoto et al. 1965) and in marmosets over a chimaeric range of 2–9% (Gengozian et al. 1969), though in twin sheep no correlation was found between erythrocyte chimaerism and leukocyte chimaerism (Dain and Tucker 1970).

5.3 Parabiotic chimaeras

The natural twin chimaeras and embryonic parabiotic chimaeras have demonstrated active cell migration occurring during the embryonic stages of haemopoiesis. Although the evidence from radiation chimaeras indicated that adult haemopoietic organs could be repopulated by injected cells, this type of experiment involved the abnormal situation of organ regeneration and gave no indication of the situation in normal adult life. The use of parabiosis in normal young adult mice was an extremely simple procedure which led to the fundamental observation that migration streams occur between different components of the haemopoietic system in normal adult life.

Pairs of CBA mice, differing with respect to the presence of the T6 marker chromosome, were parabiosed at 4–5 weeks of age and 4–5 weeks later significant numbers of dividing cells with the chromosome complement of the opposite partner were observed in the marrow, lymph nodes, spleen and thymus of both members of the pair (Harris et al. 1964). Chimaerism approached 40–50% in the lymph nodes and a somewhat lower level in the spleen after 8 weeks of parabiosis with the greatest exchange occurring in the first 4 weeks. Thymus and marrow chimaerism did not attain such high levels, thymus chimaerism reaching 15–18% after 8 weeks of parabiosis with no further rise even up to 30 weeks after union.

Marrow chimaerism remained at 5–10% throughout the period of parabiosis (Ford 1966). The low marrow chimaerism contrasts with much higher values reported in parabiosed chick embryos and in twin mammals. It is consistent with the proposal that the colonising stem cells that initially populate the embryonic marrow form a largely self-sustaining population in adult life which does not depend on an intake of new stem cells from the circulation. Furthermore, most marrow stem cells do not appear to enter a circulating phase during the normal life span of the animal. However, a proportion probably 10–20% of the total stem-cell reserve of the adult animal does circulate and can be equated with the circulating population of CFU's found in the blood, and the readily mobilised stem-cell compartment detected in irradiation experiments with marrow shielding (see Chapter 3). Using bone-marrow cells from parabiotic mice (containing 10 % of immigrant dividing cells) to repopulate lethally irradiated recipients, Ford (1966) obtained evidence of a distinct compartment of lymph node-homing cells in the marrow. The irradiated recipients showed donor repopulation of the marrow with a similar proportion of migrant cells to that observed in the initial marrow inoculum. The marrow repopulating ability of the migrating stem cells was therefore no different from the more fixed population of marrow stem cells. However, analysis of the cells in the recipient lymph nodes showed, in contrast, considerably enhanced proliferation of the 'migrant' component of the donor inoculum (a maximum of 160-fold enhanced proliferation of the 'migrant' component of marrow compared with the 'fixed' component of the inoculum). These results indicated a distinct compartment of the haemopoietic population of the marrow characterised by capacity to migrate from one parabiont into the marrow of the other and a propensity to seed and multiply in lymphoid tissue. Several alternative explanations can be advanced to account for these observations. In the initial homing of stem cells to spleen and marrow only the migrant population persists in the circulation or is capable of rapidly re-entering the circulation in significant numbers and repopulating the lymphoid compartment. On the other hand, migrant stem cells may form a greater proportion of the stem-cell compartment than analysis of the total dividing cell population would indicate and if their probability of differentiation was less than the more immobile stem cells, then their contribution to the differentiating compartment of the marrow would also be less but the contribution to the circulating stem-cell pool proportionately greater. Alternatively a specific lymphoid progenitor cell may be responsible for marrow lymphopoiesis and also be capable of colonising the lymph nodes.

Although the thymus of some parabiotic mice on occasions showed up to 50 % of mitotic cells derived from the partner, the majority showed only 15 % implying that 70 % or more of the thymic lymphoid precursor cells must be self-generating over prolonged periods. Furthermore, parabiosis involves considerable stress with resulting involution of the thymus and regeneration, making it even more likely that in the normal thymus the lymphoid precursor cells must be largely self-generating and able to persist for long periods in the thymus, despite the massive degree of generation of lymphoid cells. If self-replication does occur in the thymus, this population of 'lymphoid stem cells' must differ from the immigrant cell, since thymus cells have no capacity to home to, or populate, the irradiated thymus.

Though stress factors complicate the interpretation of the parabiosis data, it must be remembered that stress is a normal component of existence in mice as much as in man. Chimaerism has been demonstrated in situations where irradiation or parabiotic stress factors have been avoided (Micklem et al. 1968). In this situation 2×10^7 chromosomally-marked marrow cells were injected into normal adult mice and proliferated in all haemopoietic tissues, with up to 1.6% of mitoses in the thymus and 3.45% in the lymph nodes being of donor type. Studies on W/W^v and W^v/W^v mice which have genetically determined deficiencies in stem cells revealed an even greater dependence of the thymus on repopulating cells than was observed in CBA mice. Normal marrow or foetal liver cells injected into neonatal W/W^v and W^v/W^v mice resulted in almost complete donor repopulation of the thymus 9–18 months later (Seller 1970). This study disclosed that in these mice the initial thymic colonising cells entering the thymic rudiment in embryogenesis must undergo total replacement in postnatal life (within a maximum period of 9 months) and supports the view that the thymus, unlike the bone marrow, has a continuous requirement for a certain amount of cell inflow in adult life.

The high parabiotic chimaerism in spleen and lymph nodes implies that lymphopoiesis in these tissues is dependent on a constant inflow of circulating cells. This is not surprising in view of the importance of lymphocyte recirculation for these organs. E.g., in the rat, half the recirculating pool of lymphocytes migrates into the spleen every 18 hours (Ford and Gowans 1969). Active migration of new cells from marrow and thymus to the spleen and lymph nodes contributes to this high chimaerism. Direct migration of cells from the marrow to the lymph nodes was discussed in an earlier section. The thymic contribution was revealed in experiments where thymectomised mice were parabiosed with a non-thymectomised partner. The lymph nodes of the thymectomised mouse contained significantly more dividing cells from the partner than seen in the non-thymectomised animal suggesting that the one thymus had contributed large numbers of cells to the lymph nodes of both partners (Ford 1966).

Thus, with the lymph nodes and spleen of parabiotic mice two sources of repopulating cells exist: (a) recirculating lymphoid cells, and (b) cells newly generated in the bone marrow and thymus. A further extension of the parabiotic experiments indicated that newly-generated cells were the main repopulating cells. When parabiotic mice were separated, the proportion of cells from the other partner fell sharply in the lymph nodes, thymus and spleen indicating that repopulating cells which had earlier crossed into the animal from the partner were not themselves capable of indefinite proliferation.

Although the spleen contains CFU's and progenitor cells, the high levels of chimaerism seen in the spleen of parabiotic mice indicates that these populations are not capable of sustained self-maintenance and are replaced regularly by new cells, presumably of bone-marrow origin. Thus the parabiotic experiments clearly indicate that the spleen is subordinate to the marrow as a source of haemopoietic stem cells.

5.4 Organ-graft studies

Analysis of cell populations in haemopoietic organs grafted subcutaneously in the anterior eye chamber or under the renal capsule has revealed the existence of graft repopulation by circulating cells of the host and has emphasised the importance of circulating cells in normal haemopoietic development. Neonatal mouse thymus tissue grafted either subcutaneously or under the renal capsule of adult mice underwent massive central necrosis in the first 24–48 hours due to inadequate vascularisation. Regeneration proceeded from a peripheral rim of surviving lymphocytes and normal thymic architecture was restored within 1 week (Dukor et al. 1965). Chromosome-marker studies showed that the initial regeneration was due to donor-cell proliferation, but after the first 5–10 days progressively more of the dividing cells were found to be of host origin, and by 20–30 days the dividing population (lymphoid) was completely replaced by host cells (Harris and Ford 1964; Metcalf and Wakonig-Vaartaja 1964a; Metcalf et al. 1965; Miller and Osoba 1967). If the thymic graft was irradiated prior to grafting only host cells participated in graft regeneration (Dukor et al. 1965). The repopulation of thymic lymphoid populations in grafts by host cells suggests a more rapid and complete turnover of existing cell populations than was seen in parabiotic studies and is similar to that seen in the regenerating thymus after irradiation. It is likely that the parabiotic studies give a more accurate picture of the situation in the normal thymus (a slow and possibly incomplete repopulation) because of anoxic or irradiation damage sustained by surviving thymic lymphoid cells in the other two situations. In this regard, donor proliferative activity persists for a longer interval in renal subcapsular grafts where there is a better blood supply than in subcutaneous grafts (Metcalf et al. 1965).

In addition to migration of host cells into thymic grafts, there is evidence

of donor-cell migration from the grafts into the recipient. Analysis of neonatally thymectomised mice bearing thymic grafts showed that up to 38% of
dividing cells in lymph nodes were of donor type within 3–4 weeks after
grafting but that at later stages these fell to very low levels at a time when the
thymic graft was completely repopulated by host cells (Ford 1966). In this
study, very few donor mitoses were detected in the spleen, though Miller
(1964) observed considerably more thymus-derived mitoses in this organ.
Antigenic factors were probably responsible for this discrepancy, since the
proportion of thymic donor-type cells increased significantly in host lymphoid
tissue after antigenic stimulation (Davies et al. 1966) and a small histocompatibility difference existing between the graft donor and the recipient further
stimulated donor thymic cell proliferation (Leuchars et al. 1966). The
eventual disappearance of thymus-donor dividing cells in host lymph nodes
and spleen is presumably due to repopulation of the thymic graft by host
cells and though the graft may continue to export cells, these are progressively
more and more of host type. Harris and Ford (1964) confirmed this in
retransplantation experiments in which primary thymic grafts were re-
grafted to secondary recipients after a period of 3–18 weeks and cells from
the primary host were found in the lymph nodes of all the secondary recipients, proving that cells entering the primary graft had acquired the
characteristic lymph node-homing properties of thymic lymphocytes.

The full extent of persistence of thymic graft-derived cells in the host
cannot be determined by chromosome-marker analysis of the dividing
population of host lymphoid tissue since many cells may have entered a non-
proliferative phase. By using phytohaemagglutinin stimulation of mouse
peripheral blood lymphocytes it was possible to perform chromosome analyses on this population of predominantly long-lived lymphocytes. In
thymectomised irradiated mice, bearing chromosomally-marked thymus
grafts and injected with syngeneic marrow, 77–89% of PHA-transformed
blood lymphocytes were found to be of thymic graft origin 50 days after
grafting (Davies et al. 1968). In this situation the graft by this stage would
have been completely repopulated by host cells but had nevertheless contributed in a major degree to the reconstitution of the circulating lymphocyte
pool. In a similar experimental design (Barnes et al. 1967) injected irradiated
mice with marrow and lymph node or thymic lymphocytes and 4–18 weeks
later performed chromosome analysis on PHA-transformed peripheral
blood cultures. The great majority of cells observed were from the marrow
donor though considerable numbers of host cells were also present but almost no lymphoid donor mitoses. Why, in the graft situation, the circulating

PHA-transforming cells were of thymic donor origin but, in the thymus cell-injection experiments, they were of marrow origin is puzzling. Barnes et al. (1967) antigenically-stimulated animals with pertussis vaccine 7 days prior to peripheral blood culture and so may have been analysing a population of cells not normally present in large numbers in the circulation but released as a result of antigenic stimulation and therefore differing from the population analysed by Davies et al. (1968).

The characteristics of the immigrant cells which colonise the adult thymus have been studied in repopulation experiments using irradiated thymic grafts (Dukor et al. 1965). Small lymphocyte-like cells were seen in the medulla of the irradiated graft between 4–8 days post grafting and progressively increased in number and dispersed throughout the graft. A host origin for these cells seems probable, since they were not observed in grafts to lethally-irradiated hosts. These lymphocyte-like cells differed from typical lymphocytes and possessed relatively large multiple nucleoli, high concentrations of ribosomes, numerous microvesicles and a well-developed Golgi apparatus (Dukor et al. 1965). In the irradiated thymus *in situ* a monocytoid cell has been implicated as the colonising cell (Everett and Tyler 1969). It is evident that the small lymphocyte-like cells or monocytoid cells are morphologically very different from the large basophilic cells that populate the embryonic thymus, but evidence was reviewed in Chapter 4 to show that the embryonic and adult stem-cell populations are very different with respect to both size and density, despite similarity of functional capacity. It is therefore to be expected that morphological differences exist between the adult and embryonic thymus-colonising cells.

Host repopulation of grafts in adult animals is not restricted to the thymus since rapid and complete repopulation of spleen grafts by 30–40 days has been demonstrated (Metcalf and Wakonig-Vaartaja 1964b). In contrast to the rapid and complete repopulation of thymic and spleen grafts by host cells, haemopoietic populations in bone-marrow grafts become replaced by host cells much more slowly. Grafts of neonatal mouse bone develop marrow cavities in subcutaneous or renal subcapsular locations and chromosome analysis revealed delayed host repopulation of the marrow cavity. Haemopoietic cells were predominantly of donor type nearly 2 months after grafting (Moore, M. A. S. and Holmes, M., unpublished observations). In grafts of long standing (14 months) both differentiating haemopoietic cells and stem cells in the graft were of host type, but the osteogenic precursor cells and bone tissue of the transplant remained donor type (Freidenstein et al. 1968).

5.5 *Evidence for a common lymphoid and myeloid stem cell*

This controversial issue has occupied the time and effort and taxed the ingenuity of generations of haematologists. The personalisation of the issue unfortunately banished a certain degree of objectivity, and it is only recently that approaches to the solution of this problem have become possible using the newer techniques outlined in Chapter 2.

In an earlier chapter the evidence was reviewed for the existence of stem cells (CFU's) which can generate colonies of erythroid, granulocytic and megakaryocytic cells in the spleen of irradiated animals. The evidence was also reviewed that other cells in these colonies can repopulate the thymus and lymphoid organs of irradiated mice or of the genetically-defective W/W^v and W^v/W^v mice. These experiments provided clear evidence that many multi-potent haemopoietic stem cells exist which can generate both myeloid and lymphoid tissues.

This section will review further evidence for the existence of such cells and will also discuss the possibility that subordinate stem cells might exist with the potentiality only to generate myeloid or lymphoid cells.

Further support for the existence of a multipotential stem cell was obtained in situations of late recovery and regeneration of host haemopoietic cells following near-lethal irradiation. In such animals a single clone of cells with characteristic chromosomal abnormalities was described as predominating in marrow, spleen, thymus and lymph nodes (Barnes et al. 1959; Ford 1964). The striking individuality of the chromosome rearrangement made it virtually impossible that the cells proliferating in both lymphoid and myeloid tissue might have been derived from more than one stem cell (Micklem and Loutit 1966). Further, more indirect, evidence was presented by Bryant and Cole (1967) when they observed an inverse relationship between lymph-node regeneration and erythropoietic demand in irradiated mice restored with marrow cells. Such a situation may be expected if both myelo- and lympho-poietic potentiality was present in a common stem cell whose functional capacity to feed into the differentiating cell compartment is influenced by differentiation pressure towards erythropoiesis. Urso and Congdon (1957) injected marrow cells in a wide range of doses and found that the smaller doses induced disproportionately less lymphoid than myeloid regeneration. This is compatible with a common stem cell if it is assumed that in the irradiated recipient, the demand for myeloid cells is such that the stem cells can be diverted along a myeloid rather than a lymphoid pathway when only a limited number of stem cells is present.

An original approach to this problem was provided by Gandini and Gartler (1969). The basic premise of this study was that mosaic cell populations resulting from mammalian X chromosome inactivation reproduced true to type throughout somatic growth and thus formed a natural system of cell markers for use in developmental studies. The sex-linked marker chosen was glucose-6-phosphate dehydrogenase variants where X chromosome inactivation leads to a mosaic population of cells in individuals heterozygous for this sex-linked gene. The distribution of electrophoretic variants of this enzyme was studied in different tissues and the mosaic composition of the skin and hair follicles differed from the composition of haemopoietic cells. However, a positive correlation was observed between the mosaic composition of erythrocytes, granulocytes and lymphocytes in G6PD heterozygotes which was fully compatible with the concept of a multipotential stem cell.

In chimaeric mice, produced artificially by egg fusion of two unrelated mouse strains (allophenic or tetraparental mice) (see Chapter 2), the erythroid cells constitute a chimaeric population as tested by haemagglutination and absorption tests for specific H_2 antigens. This indicates that the erythroid population must normally be multicellular in origin rather than unicellular and must be derived from at least two genetically-determined cells (Mintz and Palm 1969). Furthermore, erythrocyte phenotypes and gamma-globulin allotypes showed considerably more concordance than between erythrocytes and adult liver or heart tissue, which again supports the concept of a common precursor for the myeloid and lymphoid lines. It is noteworthy that the adult liver often consisted entirely, or largely, of a cellular genotype absent or only present in low frequency in the circulating population of erythrocytes. Wegman and Gilman (1970) also observed a correlation between immunoglobulin allotypic chimaerism and haemoglobin chimaerism in tetraparental mice, suggesting a common stem-cell origin for both the erythrocytes and immunoglobulin-secreting cell series. However, in one animal the haemoglobin ratio changed without a noticeable change in the allotype ratio. This is not incompatible with the concept of a common stem cell since the potentially long-lived immunologically-competent cells and immunoglobulin-secreting cell populations would be slower to reflect a change in the composition of the stem-cell compartment than would the relatively short-lived erythrocyte population.

One piece of evidence which appears to argue strongly for the existence of lymphoid stem cells which are distinct from stem cells for other haemopoietic populations is the situation in patients with chronic granulocytic leukaemia. In these patients an abnormal chromosome, the Philadelphia chromosome has been observed in granulocytic, erythroid and megakaryocytic cells but not in PHA-stimulated cultures of lymphocytes (Nowell and Hungerford 1960, 1961; Whang et al. 1963). One possible explanation of these observations again relates to the long-lived nature of the PHA-transformable lymphocytes in the peripheral blood, particularly in humans (Buckton et al. 1967). If the Philadelphia chromosome develops as a somatic mutation in the stem-cell compartment, then it is possible that insufficient time has elapsed in the average patient for significant replacement of the long-lived lymphocyte pool by newly-formed lymphocytes bearing the Philadelphia chromosome. Alternatively, the presence of the Philadelphia abnormality may be incompatible with normal lymphoid differentiation.

Recently, compelling evidence for the existence of multipotential stem cells has been obtained in the adult rat given near-lethal doses of irradiation to produce haemopoietic cell clones marked by radiation-induced chromosomal abnormalities. Chromosome-marker analysis revealed that in several instances cells of an erythroid spleen colony, and a proportion of peripheral blood lymphocytes reacting in a mixed lymphocyte reaction, were progeny of the same stem cell. Furthermore, lymphocytes of the same radiation-marked clone proliferated in response to several different histo-compatibility isoantigens suggesting that immunological specificity was determined during lymphoid differentiation subsequent to the stem-cell stage (Nowell et al. 1970).

5.6 Function of bone-marrow lymphocytes and cell migration from the marrow

The dominant role played by the bone marrow as the source of haemopoietic stem cells in adult life has naturally led to much speculation regarding the morphology of these stem cells in the bone marrow. Since it seems improbable that differentiating cells of the erythropoietic or granulopoietic populations could serve as stem cells, interest has centered either on the population of blast cells and other more primitive cells or on the population of small lymphocyte-like cells (up to 25% of all bone-marrow cells in the mouse). It has been argued that a cell such as a small lymphocyte, having little morphological evidence of specialised function, might well represent an undifferentiated stem cell in which most of the genetic information is in a repressed state.

From the evidence discussed in Chapter 3 on some of the physical properties of CFU's in adult animals it is obvious that the morphology of stem cells must be quite heterogeneous, and for this reason alone the proposition that *all* stem cells have the morphology of small lymphocytes is untenable. However, the lymphocytes of the bone marrow are enigmatic cells and since there is lymphocyte traffic to and from the bone marrow, some discussion of this population is warranted at this point.

The work of Yoffey and co-workers on the nature and function of the small mononuclear cells of marrow revived interest in the possible role of lymphocytes in haemopoiesis (see review by Yoffey 1960). Working mainly with the guinea pig, Yoffey maintained that the marrow small mononuclear cells were indistinguishable from lymphocytes elsewhere, even at the ultra-structural level (Yoffey et al. 1965). Furthermore, these cells exhibited similar responses to radiation (Harris 1958) and to corticosteroids and radiomimetic drugs (Harris 1961). Measurements of cell kinetics showed that marrow small lymphocytes are short-lived cells, unlike the majority of circulating lymphocytes. Although most of these cells do not incorporate thymidine and are therefore non-dividing, the entire marrow small lymphocyte population is renewed in 3 days or less (Osmond and Everett 1964; Craddock 1965). Thus the kinetics of marrow small lymphocyte production are essentially similar to those of small lymphocyte production in the thymus (Metcalf and Wiadrowski 1966). The assumption that marrow lymphocytes are a mor-phologically uniform population was questioned by Harris et al. (1963) in a study of regenerating marrow. Two populations of small mononuclear cells were distinguished on the basis of stain reactions. The major population appeared to be typically small lymphocytic with pachychromatic nuclear chromatin, but there was an additional minority population of small mono-nuclear cells with leptochromatic nuclei corresponding to the micro-myeloblasts of the early haematologists. Transitional cells are frequently included in the marrow lymphocyte population and are intermediate in morphology between typical small lymphocytes and blast cells, possessing more extensive basophilic cytoplasm than the former and having leptochro-matic nuclei (Harris and Burke 1957; Hulse 1963; Yoffey 1966). Since transitional cells are frequently included in counts on the marrow lymphocyte population, this must invalidate much of the quantitative work on marrow based on the enumeration of the relative numbers of lymphocytes to pro-erythroblasts and myeloblasts, since classification of a continuous transition-al sequence of morphological types must of necessity be arbitrary. This may explain why some reports claim a low incidence of mitoses in transitional cells (Yoffey 1966) while others observe a high mitotic index (Harris and Kugler 1967).

A circulatory origin for some marrow small lymphocytes was indicated by the observation that the absolute increase in the marrow lymphocyte population following antigenic stimulation was too rapid to be accounted for by local proliferation (Yoffey 1960). Perfusion experiments using the isolated rat femur (Gordon et al. 1964) clearly showed that large numbers of circulating lymphocytes could seed in the bone marrow in replacement of granulocytes following the administration of the leucocytosis-inducing factor. Contradictory evidence has been obtained in different species regarding the extent of local marrow formation of lymphocytes. In the guinea pig, comparison of marrow lymphocyte labelling kinetics in an *in vivo* system involving occlusion of the circulation to one limb in conjunction with tritiated thymidine administration to the rest of the circulation demonstrated that a significant influx of circulating lymphocytes to the marrow was not occurring but rather that local production of lymphocytes, probably from transitional cells, occurred (Osmond and Everett 1964). On the other hand, Keiser et al. (1967) used a similar limb occlusion technique in dogs and concluded that some marrow lymphocytes entered from the circulation. Everett and Caffrey (1967) concluded in rats that only 3% of marrow lymphocytes had an extrinsic origin. Since limb occlusions and marrow aspiration techniques involve marrow trauma, it is possible that abnormal influx of circulating lymphocytes may have occurred in some experimental situations.

Marrow lymphocytes were not depleted in shielded marrow following lethal irradiation (Harris and Kugler 1965) and no reduction was seen in thymectomised rats (Bierring 1960). However, Hays (1967) reported a reduction in marrow lymphocytes in neonatally thymectomised mice from 33% in the neonatal period to zero by 12 weeks with restoration of marrow lymphocytes following thymus grafting. This effect of thymectomy may be indirect as neonatally thymectomised animals become wasted and stressed and both wasting and cortisone deplete the bone marrow population of small lymphocytes.

In primary hypoxia, marrow lymphocytes were depleted in guinea-pig marrow and on return to normal atmosphere, rebound was seen with the animals becoming polycythaemic and marrow lymphocytes returning to normal values. Secondary hypoxic stimuli increased erythropoiesis and this was associated with a marked increase in the marrow lymphocytes (Yoffey 1964, 1966). A general proportionality between marrow small lymphocytes and CFU's has been reported in the post-hypoxic rebound phase (Hurst et al. 1969). In contrast, Shadduck et al. (1969) observed that the lymphocyte rise on the 7th post-hypoxic day in the rebound phase *followed*, rather than preceded or paralleled, the CFU rebound. In the early stages of regeneration following sublethal irradiation, guinea-pig marrow consisted predominantly of small lymphocytes and transitional cells (Yoffey 1966), although in rats no relation between haemopoietic regeneration and lymphoid accumulation was seen (Hulse 1963). The use of regenerating marrow to restore lethally-irradiated recipients has implicated the transitional cell population as the repopulating cell (Harris and Kugler 1967) although in marrow regeneration following nitrogen-mustard treatment, haemocytoblasts were indicated as the repopulating stem cells and no evidence of transition from small lymphocytes to haemocytoblasts was seen (Thomas et al. 1965; Fliedner et al. 1965).

Glass filtration of marrow can selectively enrich for small lymphocytes and the concentration of small lymphocytes was correlated with capacity to restore haemopoiesis in irradiated recipients (Cudkowicz et al. 1964a, b). Decline in haemopoietic restorative ability on serial passage was also correlated with a progressive reduction in marrow-lymphocyte content (Cudkowicz 1964c). In subsequent studies, Bennett and Cudkowicz (1967) tested the capacity of filtered marrow to produce CFU's and stimulate[59] Fe and IUdR uptake in spleens of irradiated recipients. These three assays of haemopoietic proliferative capacity correlated with the small lymphocyte (and transitional cell) content of the donor marrow, although in polycythaemic recipients, where non-erythroid regeneration could be separately assessed, no correlation was observed. This result led to the proposal that marrow lymphocytes were in fact erythroid stem cells or progenitor cells with limited developmental capacity. The erythropoietin-sensitive population of progenitor cells may indeed belong to the marrow lymphocyte population, but there is no conclusive evidence that such cells are capable of extensive proliferation in irradiated recipients.

Different techniques for enriching or depleting the marrow lymphocyte population have not supported an exclusively lymphocytic morphology for haemopoietic stem cells or progenitor cells in marrow. Mel and Schooley (1965) used a horizontal-flow, layered, system which separated cells according to differences in sedimentation rate and found that the marrow fraction with the highest percentage of small lymphocytes contained the lowest incidence of CFU's. In Rabinowitz column-separated marrow the fractions enriched for lymphocytes were depleted of *in vitro* CFC's, and enriched for CFU's, whereas fractions most depleted in lymphocytes were most enriched in *in vitro* CFC's and only slightly depleted for CFU's (Moore, M. A. S., Metcalf, D., and Shortman, K., unpublished observations).

In Chapter 3, evidence was reviewed to indicate that the marrow CFU and *in vitro* CFC populations are heterogeneous with respect to cell size and density. A proportion of this stem cell and progenitor cell population appears to be of similar size and density to the marrow small lymphocytes, but it is equally clear that other stem cells and progenitors cannot have the morphology of small lymphocytes.

While some small lymphocytes could be stem cells, the great majority of marrow lymphocytes probably are not. Cortisol depletes marrow small lymphocytes to one-third of normal but does not affect CFU content (Bennett and Shearer 1965) though depleting the *in vitro* CFC population (Metcalf 1969). Furthermore, marrow of radiation chimaeras suffering from wasting and secondary disease showed severe depletion of both small and transitional lymphocytes but no deficit in CFU content (Barnes et al. 1967). In mouse marrow, stem cells constitute approximately 0.5–1 % of the total population of haemopoietic cells. *In vitro* progenitor cells approximate 1–2 % and a similar incidence of erythropoietin-sensitive cells can be considered. Since marrow lymphocytes constitute up to 25 % of total marrow cells, even if all stem cells and progenitor cells were small lymphocytes, they would constitute only about 10 % of the total small lymphocyte population of the marrow. Of the remaining 90 % a proportion may be macrophage precursors and a small proportion may belong to the recirculating lymphocyte pool (approximately 3 %) but the majority have no ascribed function. The demonstration that marrow-derived cells act as precursors of antibody-forming cells (see Chapter 3), and preliminary evidence that such cells are predetermined with respect to immunoglobulin class (Shearer and Cudkowicz 1969) lead us to postulate that most marrow lymphocytes may be responsible for generating antibody-forming cells. In this context, the high turnover rate of this population, the absence of direct immunological competence on the part of the marrow lymphocytes and their probable activity as antibody-forming cell precursors suggest a comparable situation to that seen in the avian bursa of Fabricius. The absence of a direct epithelial inductive influence on marrow lymphoid proliferation does not invalidate this proposal, since such an influence may operate at a distance via the mediation of a humoral factor originally produced by gut epithelium.

The fate of the rapidly turning over marrow lymphocytes may be that of death, differentiation or emigration, with probably all three processes occurring. Evidence for emigration has been obtained in local marrow thymidine labelling experiments where discharge of marrow small lymphocytes into the circulation and their localisation in spleen and lymph nodes has been described in guinea pigs (Osmond 1965; 1967; Everett and Caffrey 1965). Following local labelling of marrow in an occluded limb, the occlusion was removed and cold thymidine given to suppress tritiated thymidine uptake by reutilisation. With this experimental design up to 45% of marrow small lymphocytes became labelled in the occluded limb and labelled lymphocytes appeared subsequently in the circulation, in the spleen and in the unoccluded marrow (Everett and Caffrey 1967). Circulating lymphocyte production was studied in animals with major masses of organised lymphoid tissue removed and the results here suggested that a considerable number of the newly-formed small lymphocytes in the circulation orginated in the marrow (Everett and Caffrey 1967). Electronmicroscopic studies have indicated that lymphocytes migrate out of the marrow into the circulation by passing between the sinusoidal endothelial cells (Hudson and Yoffey 1966). The main migration of marrow lymphocytes appears to be to the spleen, and Linna and Liden (1969) observed that locally-labelled marrow cells localised in the spleen lymphoid follicles but not in Peyer's patches, mesenteric lymph node or thymus.

In the adult animal, the marrow is the source of stem cells migrating throughout the life of the animal to spleen and thymus and possibly of cells migrating directly to lymph nodes. Marrow is also the origin of the migrating precursors of macrophages appearing in inflammatory exudates (see later). The number of precursors involved in the migration stream from marrow is unknown, but even if some have the morphology of lymphocytes this is unlikely to account for all the lymphocytes that migrate from the bone marrow. It may be that, as with the movement of lymphocytes from thymus to spleen, many of the marrow lymphocytes are destined to seed in the spleen and lymph nodes. Here many may die but some may achieve immunological competence as a result of interaction with appropriate antigens or with thymus-derived antigen-reactive cells and persist as antibody-forming cells.

5.7 Origin and migration of mononuclear phagocytes

The population of mononuclear phagocytes can be divided into two classes of cells, differing in both function and morphology. The first group comprises the blood monocytes while the second includes both the fixed and wandering macrophage components of the reticuloendothelial system. Metchnikoff (1905) was first to recognise the phagocytic properties of these cells dividing them into two groups, the histogenous macrophages of local origin and the haematogenous macrophages which he considered to be of lymphocytic origin. The protagonists of the monophyletic theory of haemopoiesis proposed a lymphocytic origin for monocytes and macrophages (Bloom 1938), while the polyphyletic theory of dualism recognised separate myeloid and lymphoid lines deriving monocytes from the former (Naegeli 1931). The trialist theory of haemopoiesis recognised the reticuloendothelial system as a third source of haemopoietic cells and as the origin of monocytes and macrophages (Cunningham et al. 1925). Local production of inflammatory phagocytes also received consideration and an origin from vascular endothelium, serosal mesothelium, fibroblasts and adventitial cells, etc., was reported (Bloom 1938; Ebert 1965; Kojima and Imai 1964). Recent autoradiographic, chromosomal-marker and tissue-culture data have revived interest in the origin of mononuclear phagocytes and have allowed some definitive conclusions concerning the origin and life history of these cells.

It is generally accepted that blood monocytes of mammals do not incorporate tritiated thymidine *in vitro* (Cohn 1968), which contrasts with the extensive labelling of monocytes seen *in vivo* within 36 hours of tritiated thymidine labelling (25–35% labelled) (Fliedner et al. 1961; Volkman and Gowans 1965a; Matsuyama et al. 1966; Van Furth and Cohn 1968). These results led to the conclusion that monocytes are the progeny of rapidly-dividing precursors and have a short turnover time in the circulation. Estimates of the half life of circulating monocytes range from 40–72 hours in the rat (Whitelaw 1966; Volkman 1967) to as short as 22 hours in the mouse (Van Furth and Cohn 1968). The generation time of monocyte precursors has been estimated at 21–24 hours with 3–4 generations between the early precursor and the mature monocyte (Whitelaw et al. 1968; Whitelaw 1966). The mature macrophage in, e.g., peritoneal exudates, is a rarely dividing cell with a slow turnover rate estimated at about 40 days by Van Furth and Cohn (1968). Recent studies have shown that macrophages can have potentially a very long life span, and 100 days has been reported by Spector and Ryan (1969).

The early tissue culture studies of blood leucocytes showed the production of macrophages followed degeneration of polymorphs and lymphocytes (Lewis 1925; Carrell and Ebeling 1926) and it can now be assumed that these cells developed from blood monocytes. Direct observation *in vivo* in amphibians provided further evidence of monocyte to macrophage transformation (Clark and Clark 1930). A similar observation of such transformation in inflammatory tissue within a rabbit ear chamber was reported by Ebert and Florey (1939). More recently Bennett and Cohn (1966) observed macrophage maturation of isolated blood monocytes accompanied by an increased phagocytic ability and elevated intracellular levels of lysosomal enzyme. An electronmicroscopic study of the ultrastructural features of the monocyte to macrophage maturation confirmed the formation of lysosomal organelles during the course of maturation (Sutton and Weiss 1966). Macrophages appearing in inflammatory exudates have also been shown, by the use of tritiated thymidine and colloidal carbon labelling, to be predominantly of circulating monocyte origin (Spector et al. 1965; Spector and Coote 1965). Despite this evidence, the concept of a lymphocyte origin for macrophages has retained support, and direct lymphocyte to macrophage transformation has been reported *in vitro* (Rebuck et al. 1958; Klein 1959; Petrakis et al. 1961), although Schooley and Berman (1960) found only a few monocytoid cells developing in cultures of thoracic duct lymph and no evidence of small lymphocyte transformation. Serial analysis of the cell populations in inflammatory exudates has been performed using the skin-window technique of Rebuck and Crowley (1955) and Rebuck et al. (1964). Rebuck interpreted the initial small lymphocyte infiltration and subsequent macrophage development as evidence of a lymphocytic origin for macrophages. Volkman and Gowans (1965a) combined tritiated thymidine labelling with the skin-window technique and found no correlation between the percentage of labelled small lymphocytes and the labelling of the inflammatory macrophages. They concluded that macrophages originated from a rapidly dividing precursor population and the immediate blood-borne antecedant was most probably the blood monocyte. Histochemical studies have been performed with divergent results. Rebuck et al (1958) obtained histochemical evidence for lymphocyte to macrophage transformation, whereas Leder (1967) found histochemical similarity only between blood monocytes and exudate macrophages.

The origin of circulating macrophage precursors has been extensively investigated in radiation chimaeras, and peritoneal and alveolar macrophages appearing in such reconstituted animals were shown to be derived from donor inoculae of bone marrow, foetal liver, peripheral blood leucocyte and peritoneal exudate origin (Balner 1963; Goodman 1964; Pinkett et al. 1966). Volkman and Gowans (1965b) established that bone marrow, and to a lesser extent spleen, in the rat were the sources of macrophage precursors. Macrophage production in skin windows was not affected by thymectomy, thoracic duct drainage or sublethal irradiation. Lethal irradiation inhibited macrophage production but not if a region of bone marrow was shielded. Infusion of tritiated thymidine-labelled lymphoid or myeloid cells into recipients revealed that only bone marrow or spleen cells could produce labelled macrophages. Chromosome-marker analysis of dividing macrophage outgrowths from cultures of peritoneal and pulmonary exudates, spleen, marrow, lymph node and thymus also established the bone-marrow or spleen origin of these cells (Virolainen 1968). Analysis of host and donor cells in a passively-transferred delayed hypersensitivity reaction in allogeneic rat chimaeras also demonstrated that most of the infiltrating cells were of bone-marrow origin (Lubaroff and Waksman 1967, 1968).

A lymphocyte origin for hepatic macrophages (Kuppfer cells) has been reported in situations of intense reticuloendothelial stimulation (Howard et al. 1967, 1966; Boak et al. 1968, 1969). In the graft-vs.-host reaction produced by parental spleen cell inoculation into hybrid recipients, there was an obvious increase in the size and number of macrophages in the hepatic sinusoids and 83 % of mitoses in the macrophages were of spleen donor type. Donor proliferation in the hepatic macrophage population was even more pronounced when parental thoracic duct lymphocytes were used to produce a graft-vs.-host reaction. Of cells in mitosis 97–98 % were found to be of donor origin and the phagocytic ability of the dividing cells was confirmed by double labelling with colloidal carbon and tritiated thymidine. Depletion of the thoracic-duct lymphocyte population of the large lymphocyte fraction did not reduce the capacity of the thoracic-duct lymphocytes to produce hepatic macrophages, and enrichment for large lymphocytes did not increase the proportion of donor mitoses (Howard et al. 1967; Boak et al. 1968). These results implied that some cells in thoracic-duct lymph, probably small lymphocytes, can settle in the liver sinusoids during a graft-vs.-host reaction and acquire, at least superficially, the properties of mononuclear phagocytes.

The origin of hepatic macrophages was also studied in radiation chimaeras restored with chromosomally-marked marrow and thoracic-duct lymphocytes or glass wool-filtered lymph-node lymphocytes. Six to 21 days after irradiation, *Corynebacterium parvum* was given to stimulate hepatic macrophage proliferation, and 60–70 % of dividing macrophages were found to be of lymphocyte type and 16–34 % of marrow type (Howard et al. 1966; Boak et al. 1968). Though only one-third of the mitotic macrophages were of marrow type, it must be noted that the ratio of thoracic-duct lymphocytes to marrow donor cells was between 20 and 35:1. Dividing cells in liver macrophage preparations isolated at various intervals after partial hepatectomy were found to be derived almost entirely from marrow and evidence for a lymphocyte precursor in this regenerating situation was minimal (Howard et al. 1967).

It appears that hepatic macrophages can originate from two different extra-hepatic sources during the course of various experimental conditions. Bone-marrow precursors are the major source of normal macrophages, but lymphocyte precursors can, during the course of intense reticuloendothelial stimulation, produce hepatic, alveolar and peritoneal macrophages (Boak et al. 1969).

Mononuclear phagocytes show pronounced functional heterogeneity, and these dissimilarities may extend to differences in the origin of the various populations of these cells. Because of this the quest for a single precursor of all macrophage types may be doomed from the outset (Howard et al. 1967).

An indirect origin from lymphocytes for the macrophages appearing in inflammatory skin windows has recently been claimed (Vernon-Roberts 1969). In this study, the peritoneal cavity was thought to act as an extravascular 'culture chamber' where lymphocytes transformed to macrophages before mobilisation to distant inflammatory sites. Estrogen stimulated the accumulation of peritoneal lymphocytes and cultures of almost pure peritoneal lymphocytes transformed into macrophages, but only if viable polymorphs were present. Injected carbon-marked peritoneal macrophages appeared in skin windows within 24–48 hours after injection, thus demonstrating the capacity of functional macrophages to migrate in this situation.

Chen and Schooley (1970) have investigated the kinetics of macrophage precursors available for tritiated thymidine labelling and quantitatively harvestable as labelled macrophages in glycogen-induced peritoneal exudates. Macrophage precursors were reduced to 4% of control values after the administration of 80 μg of vinblastine and were radiosensitive with a D_0 of 120 R. The vinblastine and radiation sensitivities were characteristic of a population of macrophage precursors in a state of rapid turnover with an approximate generation time of 8.5 hours. The population of macrophage precursors recovering after vinblastine treatment increased exponentially after 24 hours with an approximate 16 hours doubling time and attained supranormal values by day 5. After recovery, the population showed overshoot and subsequent oscillations. More rapid recovery was evident following 200 R with recovery complete within 2 days.

The possibility of a common precursor for granulocytes and macrophages was first proposed by Naegeli (1931) on the basis of similar oxidative properties of myeloblasts and monocytes. This concept was revived by Leder (1967), who demonstrated a histochemical similarity between promyelocytes and monocytes and concluded that 'promyelocytes can be considered as common progenitors of neutrophils and monocytes'. A common origin of monocytes and granulocytes was further indicated by similarities in their cortisol sensitivity (Craddock et al. 1967) and recovery kinetics after drug or antineutrophil serum-induced agranulocytosis (Lawrence et al. 1967). Furthermore, analysis of a myelomonocytic leukaemia in mice (Warner et al. 1969; Metcalf et al. 1969, see Chapter 9) demonstrated the existence of neoplasia of a common progenitor cell for granulocytes and monocytes. The concept has received strong support from the demonstration that *in vitro* colony-forming cells can produce mixed colonies of granulocytes and macrophages (see Chapter 3) and the cell involved appears to be a progenitor cell limited to these two lines of differentiation. Transplantation of single cells from early *in vitro* granulocytic clusters has shown that some granulocytic cells can transform and produce macrophages (Metcalf 1971a) although some of the cells form only granulocyte clusters and do not undergo macrophage transformation (Metcalf 1971a).

In mice, the population of *in vitro* CFC's is augmented in spleen, marrow and peritoneal exudate during chronic inflammatory reactions and following antigenic stimulation, and this increase is accompanied by an increased level of granulopoiesis and macrophage production (McNeill 1970; Metcalf 1971b). Virolainen and Defendi (1968) showed a positive correlation existed between the granulocyte content of individual spleen colonies and the capacity of the colony to form macrophages in culture. A similar correlation exists between spleen colony contents of granulocytes and *in vitro* CFC's (Moore, M. A. S. and Metcalf, D. 1970, unpublished observations). The pattern of recovery of *in vitro* CFC's in mice following vinblastine treatment was similar to the recovery of tritiated thymidine-labelled peritoneal macrophages (Chen and Schooley 1970). On the basis of these observations, the population of *in vitro* CFC's must be considered as a source of macrophages and monocytes *in vivo*, but at this stage it is not possible to conclude that such progenitor cells are the only source of the phagocytic mononuclears.

5.8 *Lymphocyte recirculation*

The output of lymphocytes from the thoracic duct is sufficient to replace the total circulating lymphocyte population of the blood several times daily. Studies in the rat provided the first experimental demonstration of a massive recirculation of small lymphocytes (Gowans 1957, 1959; Gowans and Knight 1964). Recirculating lymphocytes migrate across the endothelium of specialised post-capillary venules in lymph nodes and Peyer's patches. Electronmicroscopic studies revealed that the lymphocytes actively penetrate the cytoplasm of the cuboidal endothelial cells in their migration out of the post-capillary venules (Marchesi and Gowans 1964). Post-capillary venules are confined to the deep and mid-zones of the lymph-node cortex, and from here the lymphocytes presumably migrate through the nodes to the medullary sinuses and leave via the efferent lymphatics. Labelled thoracic-duct lymphocytes localise in the periarteriolar lymphoid follicles of the spleen and the main route of recirculation in the spleen is via the marginal zone and sinuses of the lymphoid follicles. Very few labelled cells are seen in the first few hours after injection in the spleen red pulp, marginal zone and follicles. As post-capillary venules are not present in the spleen, recirculating lymphocytes leave the circulation by migrating between the flattened endothelial cells of the marginal sinuses which envelop the lymphoid follicles and separate them from the marginal zone (Goldschneider and McGregor 1968a).

The extent of lymphocyte recirculation through lymph nodes was revealed in experiments where tritiated thymidine was infused into the afferent lymphatics of popliteal lymph nodes in sheep. Less than 4% of the small lymphocytes in the efferent lymph were shown to be actually produced within the lymph node, the rest were blood migrants (Hall and Morris 1965). It has been estimated that half the recirculating pool of lymphocytes migrates into the rat spleen every 18 hours (Ford and Gowans 1969). The small percentage of large lymphocytes in thoracic duct lymph can be accounted for on the basis of production of new cells in the nodes. The life span of these larger lymphocytes is of the order of a few days (Caffrey et al. 1962) and they probably do not recirculate but tend to migrate into the walls of the gut where they may develop into immature plasma cells (Gowans and Knight 1964).

The population of lymphocytes that recirculates through the lymphatics is not the only component of the total circulating lymphocyte population and 10–20% of blood small lymphocytes appear not to take part in recirculation (Ford and Gowans 1969). Segregation of lymphocyte populations through differential migration has been demonstrated (Lance and Taub 1969) by tracing the distribution of chromium-labelled lymphocytes, from various sources, in the haemopoietic tissues of normal syngeneic recipients. Thoracic-duct lymphocytes localised in about equal numbers in spleen and lymph nodes (20% of total injected cells in each organ). Approximately 10% of lymph-node lymphocytes migrated to lymph nodes and a somewhat larger proportion to liver and spleen. Labelled thymus cells went largely to spleen and liver with only 1–2% in lymph nodes and only a minute fraction in thymus. In retransplantation experiments, cells which localised in the lymph nodes of the first host showed a marked tendency to localise in the lymph nodes of secondary recipients, behaving in a manner similar to thoracic-duct lymphocytes. The proportion of thymus cells localising in lymph nodes after secondary transfer from the primary lymph node was 7–14-fold greater than that characteristic of the first transfer. The property of migrating to lymph nodes is therefore possessed in different degrees by different lymphocyte populations and probably characterises a population of readily mobilisable lymphocytes. The thymus cells recovered after localising to lymph nodes had cell-for-cell a much greater graft-vs.-host inducing capacity than the original population, revealing that a functionally distinct population of lymphocytes was selected by the lymph nodes, on the basis of homing capacity. Further evidence of selectivity of migration was the demonstration that about 1 in 10 small lymphocytes in blood perfusing the sheep popliteal lymph node migrated across post-capillary venules (Hall and Morris 1965), whereas the spleen cleared approximately one in every five blood lymphocytes (Ford and Gowans 1969).

Recent studies (Griscelli et al. 1969) have suggested that recirculating lymphoid cells do not settle at random. Thus labelled large lymphocytes from the mesenteric lymph node of rats, on injection into syngeneic recipients, homed selectively to gut-associated lymphoid tissue, whereas cells from subcutaneous nodes homed to subcutaneous lymph nodes. Small lymphocytes, on the other hand, showed no such selective localisation. Labelled lymphocytes from donors primed with a particular antigen homed selectively, or were selectively trapped, in the lymph nodes draining a site of local injection of that antigen as compared with localisation of similar cells in the contralateral lymph node.

The majority of recirculating lymphocytes has a long life span measured in the order of months in rodents (Robinson et al. 1965) and years in man (Buckton et al. 1967). The latter conclusion was based on the observation that small lymphocytes from peripheral blood of patients who, many years previously, had received therapeutic X-irradiation, when stimulated to divide by phytohaemagglutinin, displayed unstable chromosome abnormalities. These lymphocytes were undoubtedly entering their first division since irradiation, which in some instances was 10 years previously.

The migratory properties of lymphocytes recirculating through the spleen has been investigated by Ford (1969) using isolated rat spleens perfused with labelled blood lymphocytes. Labelled cells traversed the splenic white pulp and reappeared in the blood with an average delay of 5–6 hours. Cells were also released from the spleen and these were mainly small lymphocytes whose rate of release was independent of the prevailing lymphocyte concentration in the perfusate. The release of lymphocytes from the spleen was at the expense of the lymphocyte population of the lymphoid follicles, and it appeared probable that these constituted a component of the recirculating lymphocyte pool. This was supported by the observation that small lymphocytes released from perfused spleens recirculated when injected into syngeneic recipients, and conversely, that perfused spleens released thoracic duct small lymphocytes which had been administered to spleen donors 24 hours previously.

5.9 Origin of thoracic duct lymphocytes

The circulating pool of small lymphocytes is a class of cells whose development is dependent on a normally functioning thymus. The thoracic-duct small lymphocyte output of neonatally thymectomised mice is only 3% of normal, and this deficiency is associated with lymphocyte depletion in the periarteriolar regions of the splenic lymphoid follicles and in the deep cortex of lymph nodes (Metcalf 1960; Metcalf and Brumby 1966; Parrott et al. 1966; Miller et al. 1967; Miller and Osoba 1967). Impaired thoracic-duct lymphocyte output is also found after adult thymectomy with a slow progressive fall in circulating lymphocytes to 30–40% below normal (Metcalf 1960; Miller et al. 1963). The deficiency following neonatal thymectomy in rats was shown to be in the long-lived small lymphocyte population of the recirculating pool (Rieke and Schwartz 1967). There is evidence from local thymus labelling experiments and experiments involving injected thymic cells (Weissman 1967; Parrott et al. 1966) that thymus-derived lymphocytes localise exclusively in peripheral lymphoid areas involved in recirculation. Extrapolation from the data of Weissman suggested that the number of cells leaving the thymus was sufficient to renew the entire circulating lymphocyte pool within 2–3 months. Ernstrom and Larsson (1969) cannulated the thymic vein in guinea pigs and calculated that, at 3 days after local thymus labelling, 500 lymphocytes per mm^3 of blood perfusing the thymus were being produced by the thymus and entering the circulating pool. Injected labelled thymocytes appeared in the thoracic duct lymph and recirculated for at least 14 days (Everett et al. 1964; Goldschneider and McGregor 1968b). Both long-lived and short-lived small lymphocytes in rat thoracic duct lymph are phytohaemagglutinin-responsive (Rieke and Schwartz 1967) and phytohaemagglutinin-responsive cells were shown to be of thymus-graft origin in peripheral blood (Davies et al. 1968). Despite this evidence for an initial thymic origin for many recirculating small lymphocytes there is little doubt that a portion of the recirculating pool is normally produced locally in peripheral lymphoid tissue as a result of continual antigenic challenge. The reduced population of recirculating small lymphocytes in specific pathogen-free rats (Schooley and Kelly 1964) and in germfree mice (Dukor et al. 1968) supports this view. Migrating cells from marrow such as the rapidly-labelled small lymphocytes, may enter the recirculating pool in small numbers, although transfusion studies suggest that the splenic red pulp is the main destination of the rapidly-labelled small lymphocytes of marrow origin and the majority may not recirculate (Parrott 1967).

5.10 Functional capacity of circulating lymphocytes

Circulating lymphocytes in thoracic duct lymph and blood are capable of mediating transplantation immunity and both populations of lymphocytes are highly effective in producing a graft-vs.-host reaction in allogeneic or semi-allogeneic recipients (Gowans et al. 1961; Hildemann 1964). Blood lymphocytes of adult chickens, e.g., produce local graft-vs.-host reactions on the chorioallantoic membrane of histoincompatible chick embryos. This reaction is detected by the development of foci or pocks on the membrane and each pock may represent a local reaction on the part of a single immunologically competent cell (Coppleson and Michie 1966). Purified small lymphocytes are capable of producing pocks but density distribution profiles of fowl-blood lymphocytes showed that graft-vs.-host activity resides within a small subpopulation distinct from the bulk of blood lymphocytes, and activity could not be attributed exclusively either to the total population of large or small lymphocytes (Shortman et al. 1967). As few as 50–100 lymphocytes have been shown to elicit a detectable graft-vs.-host reaction in chickens (Nisbet et al. 1969).

In the course of a graft-vs.-host reaction, small lymphocytes transform into large pyroninophilic cells in the spleen white pulp within 48 hours of transfer, proliferate and differentiate into a family of lymphoid cells of progressively decreasing size (Gowans et al. 1962; W. L. Ford et al. 1966). The progeny of the large pyroninophilic cells are effector cells mediating the reaction and also constitute memory cells that re-enter the circulating pool. Small lymphocytes released into the circulating pool by perfused rat spleen were shown to be capable of evoking a graft-vs.-host reaction (Ford 1969). Parental strain thoracic-duct lymphocytes from donors rendered tolerant to histocompatibility antigens of the other parental component of the hybrid recipient were unable to evoke a graft-vs.-host reaction though retaining the capacity to react against histocompatibility antigens of a different recipient (McCullagh and Gowans 1967).

The recirculating small lymphocytes play an important role in the primary response of rats to skin homografts. Prolonged thoracic-duct drainage extends skin homograft survival time, although depletion of lymphocytes of sensitised animals did not impair secondary reactions, suggesting that immunological memory cells resided in a fixed lymphocyte pool (McGregor and Gowans 1964). The primary immune response to skin homografts would appear to be initiated by interaction with certain recirculating long-lived lymphocytes which become established in regional draining lymph nodes. The transformation of these cells to large pyroninophilic cells and the subsequent proliferation of these cells produces small lymphocytes which are the effector cells mediating graft rejection. Evidence for the peripheral sensitisation of circulating lymphocytes within homografts was obtained by perfusion of F_1 hybrid rat kidneys *in vitro* with parental thoracic duct lymphocytes (Strober and Gowans 1965). Perfusing lymphocytes were returned to parental hosts and transfer of sensitisation to F_1 hybrid skin grafts was demonstrated. Therefore, circulating lymphocytes were able to be primed by antigens very rapidly and sensitisation was evident with lymphocytes that had perfused the kidney for only 1 hour.

Transformation of circulating lymphocytes into blast or pyroninophilic cells has been extensively studied *in vitro*, since the demonstration that phytohaemagglutinin extracted from the bean *Phaseolus vulgaris* induced blast transformation and mitoses in peripheral blood leucocytes (Nowell 1960). The mechanism of PHA-induced blastogenesis and mitosis of cultured lymphocytes is highly controversial despite a large number of studies (see Elves 1966; Ling 1968; Naspitz and Richter 1968 for reviews). With improved culture conditions a very high percentage of total blood lymphocytes undergoes transformation and a striking increase in the total number of lymphoid cells in culture over a 6-day period has been demonstrated (Owen and Harrison 1967). A well-marked sequence of morphological changes paralleled this increase, with peak mitotic activity and numbers of blast cells appearing at 48–72 hours of incubation and a progressive size reduction thereafter so that by 6 days of culture the majority of cells were no larger than blood lymphocytes. Other non-specific lymphocytic mitogenic factors such as pokeweed mitogen and streptolysin S have been described. More typical immune reactions *in vitro* associated with lymphocyte transformation are seen with lymphocytes from tuberculin-sensitive individuals cultured in the presence of tuberculin antigen. This transformation induced by a classic antigen was of far smaller magnitude and exhibited different kinetics from that of the PHA reaction. A most interesting *in vitro* model of lymphocyte involvement in cell-mediated immune reactions is the mixed lymphocyte reaction, where blast transformation is seen in mixed cultures of lymphocytes from two genetically-distinct individuals (Bain et al. 1964; Elves and Israels 1965). Studies with inbred rats clearly demonstrated that this reaction occurs only when two leucocyte populations in culture differ for antigens of the major histocompatibility systems (Wilson et al. 1967; Elves 1968). Evidence has been obtained in two systems to show that the mixed lymphocyte reaction is a complete *in vitro* model for allograft rejection. Parental strain rat leucocytes cultured in the presence of hybrid leucocytes produced a greater degree of graft-vs.-host reaction when transferred to 7-day hybrid hosts than did parental cells cultured alone. Parental cells became sensitised to allogeneic transplantation antigens in a process requiring 24 hours (Elves 1969). Mouse peripheral blood lymphocytes sensitised *in vitro* by culturing with allogeneic lymphocytes produced immunospecific destruction of target cells measured by release of ^{51}Cr (Hayry and Defendi 1970). Thus *in vitro* the sensitisation, blast transformation and effector phases of a cell-mediated immune response have all been demonstrated.

In vitro systems have been described where target cell destruction by lymphoid cells from immunised donors is seen (Friedman 1964; Hellstrom 1967; Brunner et al. 1968). Target-cell destruction was also demonstrated with non-sensitised allogeneic lymphocytes in the presence of phytohaemagglutinin (Holm et al. 1964). Culture of mouse embryo cell monolayers with rat lymph-node cells resulted in lymphocyte transformation into large pyroninophilic cells within 4–6 days and lysis of the mouse cells. Transfer of the transformed cells to new monolayers caused destruction of the target cells within 24–48 hours if they possessed the same H_2 antigens as the priming monolayer (Ginsburg 1968). Despite the development of such *in vitro* systems, the precise mechanism of target-cell destruction is unknown. Evidently recognition by the effector cell of target-cell membrane antigens and intimate cell contact are required. Specificity of recognition may in turn be associated with release of non-specific pharmacological factors or possibly lysosomal enzymes which mediate the cytopathogenic effect of the effector cells. The recognition process may involve antibody on the surface of the lymphocyte. Cells may synthesise antibody, which is only released upon intimate contact with the target cell, or alternatively, cells may carry on their surface cytophilic antibody produced elsewhere. However, cytophilic antibody is unlikely to be involved, since immune sera do not impart destructive activity to normal lymphoid cells. Other alternatives are that antibodies are not involved in recognition or that the lymphocytes carry a special type of antibody, IgX, not present in the normal circulating immunoglobulin pool. The involvement of immunoglobulin-like molecules present in, or on, lymphocytes mediating target-cell destruction is supported by the observation that antisera directed against immunoglobulins or immunoglobulin allotype determinants will induce blast transformation of lymphocytes *in vitro* (for a review, see Sell and Asofsky 1968). Direct evidence has recently been obtained that graft-vs.-host reactivity of parental spleen cells in young hybrid recipients can be blocked by treatment of donor cells with antiserum directed against light chains but not heavy chain components of immunoglobulins (Mason and Warner 1970). It seems probable that the recognition process in cell-mediated immunity is carried out by immunoglobulins that are either buried in the membrane so that only certain regions of the molecule are exposed or that incomplete immunoglobulins are present.

Animals depleted of lymphocytes by thoracic-duct drainage also have impaired capacity to undertake humoral immune responses as well as cellular responses (McGregor and Gowans 1963). Immunological capacity can be restored by inoculation of thoracic-duct small lymphocytes or by small lymphocytes released from isolated perfused spleen (Ford 1969). Haemolysin responses may be restored in irradiated rats by glass-bead column-purified thoracic-duct small lymphocytes, though these are less effective than fresh thoracic-duct lymphocytes in transferring primary and secondary anti-*Salmonella adelaide* flagellin responsiveness (Nossal et al. 1967). Antibody responses to sheep red-cell antigens were also restored to irradiated rats and to rats tolerant to sheep red cells by infusing thoracic-duct lymphocytes, but lymphocytes from tolerant donors were unable to correct the unresponsiveness of irradiated recipients (McGregor et al. 1967). Adoptive transfer of secondary antibody responsiveness to bacteriophage (Gowans and Uhr 1966) and tetanus toxoid (Ellis et al. 1967) has been performed with thoracic duct small lymphocytes, showing that many committed small lymphocytes do recirculate. However, since secondary responses to sheep red cells and tetanus toxoid are not depressed by chronic thoracic duct drainage, many memory cells must remain fixed in lymphoid tissues (W. L. Ford et al. 1966).

In a further analysis of the adoptive secondary response, thoracic duct lymphocytes from pre-sensitised donors, when administered to irradiated rats together with antigen, localised in periarteriolar lymphoid follicles of the spleen and transformed into large pyroninophilic cells. Cells containing specific antibody were first detected in lymphoid follicles and later migrated into red pulp as evidenced by massive plasma cell reaction (Ellis et al. 1969). Isoantisera directed against the thoracic duct lymphocyte donor component showed the plasma cells to be of donor origin in this system. To initiate maximum antibody responses a traffic of lymphoid cells must pass through the spleen at the time of antigenic stimulation (W. L. Ford et al. 1966). Antigenic stimulation of regional lymph nodes of the sheep leads to the appearance of large numbers of large lymphocytes in the efferent lymph (Hall and Morris 1963), some of which are cells synthesising specific antibody (Cunningham et al. 1966). Direct evidence of recirculating antibody-forming cells was obtained from the demonstration that sheep red-cell stimulation of rats led to the appearance of haemolytic plaque-forming cells (PFC) in the lymph as early as 4 days after stimulation, with maximum numbers of PFC's being of the same order of magnitude as in the spleen at this time (Haskill et al. 1969). Density distribution profiles of 19S haemolytic PFC's in the rat spleen showed marked heterogeneity. PFC's in the blood and lymph gave quite different density distribution profiles from fixed tissue cells, showing less heterogeneity and only three main density regions of PFC activity, which corresponded to certain density peaks in the lymph node profile (Haskill et al. 1969; Shortman et al. 1967). There appears therefore to be a restriction on the entry of certain subpopulations of antibody-forming cells into the circulating compartment. Immunoglobulin-secreting cells can also be demonstrated in thoracic-duct lymph by radioimmunoelectrophoresis and immunofluorescence. Van Furth (1969) showed appreciable synthesis of IgA, IgM and IgG by human thoracic-duct lymphocytes, and of IgG and IgA synthesis by peripheral blood lymphocytes. Fluorescent studies revealed appreciable numbers of immunoglobulin-containing large lymphocytes and plasma cells in thoracic-duct lymph. Any simple interpretation of the role of recirculating lymphocytes in humoral or cell-mediated immunity is complicated by the existence of cellular interactions between marrow and thymus-derived cells in the genesis of antibody formation (Claman et al. 1966; Miller and Mitchell 1967) (see Chapter 3).

5.11 Conclusion

The evidence reviewed in this chapter indicates that in adult animals the circulation contains multipotent haemopoietic stem cells and at least some of the progenitor cells of the various blood cell classes. Furthermore a variety of evidence from parabiotic animals, irradiation chimaeras and organ grafts indicates that the haemopoietic populations in the spleen, lymph nodes and to a lesser degree the thymus are continually replaced in adult life by an inflow of circulating stem cells, and progenitor cells (see Figure 5.1). The bone marrow represents the only organ in adult life in which haemopoiesis is genuinely self-sustaining and not dependent on an inflow of stem cells.

The existence of stem-cell migration in adult life is presumably the price to be paid for homeostasis and flexibility of haemopoietic response in the face of fluctuating demands. Excessive differentiation pressure may produce local exhaustion of the stem-cell populations which can only be circumvented by migration of additional stem cells into the region. Furthermore, adaptation to situations of chronic demand for haemopoiesis involves the colonisation by circulating stem cells of potential haemopoietic microenvironments existing in the fatty marrow spaces, the spleen and, to a lesser extent, the liver. One may also speculate that, as haemopoiesis places a continuous proliferative demand on the stem-cell population, safeguards are required to avoid excessive proliferation of stem-cell clones since their reproductive integrity may be impaired by known limitations on the division capacity of

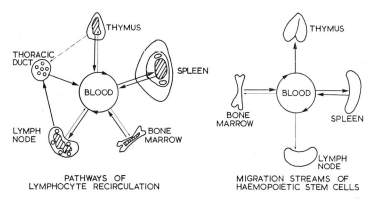

Fig. 5.1.   Schematic diagram showing pathways of lymphocyte migration and recirculation with areas of lymphoid organs involved in recirculation indicated by hatched areas. Shown in adjacent diagram are the migration streams of haemopoietic stem cells from bone marrow to other organs.

somatic cells (see Chapter 8). Stem-cell circulation and equilibration may therefore ensure equalization of proliferative pressure throughout the entire stem-cell population.

In the case of the lymph nodes and spleen, repopulation is complicated by the fact that lymphocytes recirculate in massive numbers between the various lymphoid organs via the lymph and blood (see Figure 5.1). Many of these cells are lymphoid progenitor cells which can become activated by the appropriate antigen and generate clones of lymphoid and plasma cells which add to the lymphoid population. The migrating lymphocytes, both recirculating from blood to lymph and drifting throughout the connective tissue particularly beneath exposed epithelial surfaces are engaged in a continuous mission of immunological surveillance. Lymphocyte recirculation permits contact of a large proportion of total body lymphocytes with localised antigen and increases the probability of interaction with the appropriate, though infrequent, antigen-reactive cells. The requirement of cell collaboration in antibody formation presents additional conceptual problems, particularly the probability of interaction of two rare cells. These problems are partially overcome by the existence of lymphocyte recirculation since the probability of cell interaction is increased both by more thorough equilibration of the total lymphocyte population, and more particularly by the channelling of recirculating cells through lymphocyte populations concentrated in limited compartments. The macrophage populations in various organs are also capable of a limited degree of relocation and are in most cases continually replaced by new populations of cells originating in bone marrow and migrating into other tissues via the blood. Macrophage infiltration, e.g. in regions of local inflammation or necrosis, is evidently more efficiently supported by mobilisation of macrophage precursors from a central reserve with vascular dissemination, rather than diffuse distribution of macrophages and their precursors throughout the tissues of the body.

Thus the haemopoietic organs of the adult animal are highly dynamic tissues dependent for their existence on migration streams of stem cells and progenitor cells. This is a highly unusual situation, in which organ function throughout adult life depends on a continuation of the ontological process responsible for the origin of the organs during embryogenesis.

References

Bain, B., M. Vas, and L. Lowenstein, 1964, Blood *23*, 108.

Balner, H., 1963, Transp. *1*, 217.

Barnes, D. W. H., C. E. Ford, S. M. Gray, and J. F. Loutit, 1959, Spontaneous and induced changes in cell populations in heavily irradiated mice. In: Progr. Nucl. Energy Ser. VI, *2*, 1.

Barnes, D. W. H., G. Breckon, C. E. Ford, H. S. Micklem, and D. A. Ogden, 1967, Fate of lymphoid cells injected into lethally irradiated mice: Further experiments. In: The lymphocyte in immunology and haemopoiesis, edited by J. M. Yoffey. London, E. Arnold, p. 207.

Basrur, P. K. and H. Kanagawa, 1969, Genetics *63*, 419.

Benirschke, K. and L. E. Brownhill, 1962, Cytogenetics *1*, 245.

Bennett, M. and G. Cudkowicz, 1967, Functional and morphological characterization of stem cells: The unipotential role of 'lymphocytes' of mouse marrow. In: The lymphocyte in immunology and haemopoiesis, edited by J. M. Yoffey. London, E. Arnold, p. 183.

Bennett, M. and G. M. Shearer, 1965, Fed. Proc. *24*, 240 (Abs.).

Bennett, W. E. and Z. Cohn, 1966, J. Exp. Med. *123*, 145.

Bierring, F., 1960, Quantitative investigations on the lymphomyeloid system in thymectomised rats. In: CIBA Symposium on Haemopoiesis, edited by G. E. W. Wolstenholme and M. O'Connor. London, Churchill, p. 185.

Billingham, R. E., L. Brent, and P. B. Medawar, 1956, Phil. Trans. Roy. Soc. (London) B, *239*, 357.

Bloom, W., 1928, Folia Haemat. *37*, 1.

Bloom, W., 1938, Lymphocytes and monocytes: theories of hematopoiesis. In: Handbook of hematology, Vol. I, edited by H. Downey. New York, Hoeber, p. 375.

Boak, J. L., G. H. Christie, W. L. Ford, and J. G. Howard, 1968, Proc. Roy. Soc. B, *169*, 307.

Boak, J. L., G. H. Christie, J. Elson, W. L. Ford, and J. G. Howard, 1969, Brit. J. Surg. *56*, 699.

Brunner, K. T., J. Mauel, C. Cerottini, and B. Chapuis, 1968, Immunol. *14*, 181.

Bryant, B. J. and L. J. Cole, 1967, Evidence for pluripotentiality of marrow stem cells: modification of tissue distribution of *in vivo* [125] I-UdR labelled transplanted marrow. In: The lymphocyte in immunology and haemopoiesis, edited by J. M. Yoffey. London, E. Arnold, p. 170.

Buckton, K. E., W. M. Court-Brown, and P. G. Smith, 1967, Nature *214*, 470.

Caffrey, R. W., W. O. Rieke, and N. B. Everett, 1962, Acta Haematol. *28*, 145.

Carrell, A. and A. H. Ebeling, 1926, J. Exp. Med. *44*, 285.

Chen, M. G. and J. C. Schooley, 1970, Rad. Res. *41*, 623.

Claman, H. N., E. A. Chaperon, and R. F. Triplett, 1966, J. Immunol. *97*, 828.

Clark, E. R. and E. L. Clark, 1930, Am. J. Anat. *46*, 149.

Cohn, Z. A., 1968, Adv. in Immunol. *9*, 163.

Coppleson, L. W. and D. Michie, 1966, Proc. Roy. Soc. Lond. B, *163*, 555.

Craddock, C. G., 1965, Acta Haematol. *33*, 19.

Craddock, C. G., A. Winkelstein, Y. Matsuyuki, and J. S. Lawrence, 1967, J. Exp. Med. *125*, 11.

Cudkowicz, G., A. C. Upton, L. H. Smith, D. G. Gosslee, and W. L. Hughes, 1964a, Ann. N.Y. Acad. Sci. *114*, 571.

Cudkowicz, G., M. Bennett, and G. M. Shearer, 1964b, Science *144*, 866.

Cudkowicz, G., A. C. Upton, G. M. Shearer and W. L. Hughes, 1964c, Nature *201*, 165.

Cunningham, A. J., J. B. Smith, and E. H. Mercer, 1966, J. Exp. Med. *124*, 701.

Cunningham, R. S., F. R. Sabin, and C. A. Doan, 1925, Contrib. to Embryol. (Carnegie Inst., Washington) *16*, 227.

Dain, A. R. and E. M. Tucker, 1970, Proc. Roy. Soc. B, *175*, 183.

Davies, A. J. S., E. Leuchars, V. Wallis, and P. C. Koller, 1966, Transp. *4*, 438.

Davies, A. J. S., H. Festenstein, E. Leuchars, V. J. Wallis, and M. J. Doenhoff, 1968, Lancet *1*, 183.

Dukor, P., J. F. A. P. Miller, and E. Sacquet, 1968, Clin. exp. Immunol. *3*, 191.

Dukor, P., J. F. A. P. Miller, W. House, and V. Allman, 1965, Transp. *3*, 639.

Ebert, R. H., 1965, The experimental approach to inflammation. In: The inflammatory process, edited by B. W. Zweifach, L. Grant, and R. T. McCloskey. New York, Academic Press, p. 1.

Ebert, R. H. and H. W. Florey, 1939, Brit. J. Exp. Path. *20*, 342.

Ellis, S. T., J. L. Gowans, and J. C. Howard, 1967, Cold Spring Harbor Symp. Quant. Biol. *32*, 395.

Ellis, S. T., J. L. Gowans, and J. C. Howard, 1969, Antibiotica et Chaemotheropia *15*, 40.

Elves, M. W., 1966, The lymphocyte. London, (Lloyd-Luke).

Elves, M. W., 1968, Transp. *6*, 363.

Elves, M. W., 1969, Transp. *8*, 44.

Elves, M. W. and M. C. G. Israels, 1965, Lancet *1*, 1184.

Ernstrom, U. and B. Larsson, 1969, Nature *222*, 279.

Everett, N. B. and R. W. Caffrey, 1965, Anat. Rec. *151*, 347.

Everett, N. B. and R. W. Caffrey, 1967, Radioautographic studies of bone marrow small lymphocytes. In: The lymphocyte in immunology and haemopoiesis, edited by J. M. Yoffey. London, E. Arnold, p. 108.

Everett, N. B. and R. W. Tyler, 1969, Cell Tissue Kinet. *2*, 347.

Everett, N. B., R. W. Caffrey, and W. O. Rieke, 1964, Ann. N. Y. Acad. Sci. *113*, 887.

Fliedner, T. M., E. P. Cronkite, and V. P. Bond, 1961, Paper No. 62, In: Proc. 8th Congress European Soc. Haematol., Vienna. New York-Basel, Karger.

Fliedner, T. M., E. D. Thomas, I. Fache, D. Thomas, and E. P. Cronkite, 1965, Pattern of regeneration of nitrogen-mustard treated marrow after transfusion into lethally irradiated homologous recipients. In: La greffe des cellules hématopoiétiques allogéniques. Colloques Internationaux du Centre National de la Recherche Scientifique *147*, 45.

Ford, C. E., 1964, Selection pressure in mammalian cell populations. In: Sym. Internat. Soc. Cell. Biol. New York, Academic Press, *3*, 27.

Ford, C. E., 1966, Traffic of lymphoid cells in the body. In: CIBA Symposium on the thymus, edited by G. E. W. Wolstenholme and R. Porter. London, Churchill, p. 131.

Ford, C. E., J. L. Hamerton, D. W. H. Barnes, and J. F. Loutit, 1956, Nature *177*, 452.

Ford, C. E., H. S. Micklem, E. P. Evans, J. G. Gray, and D. A. Ogden, 1966, Ann. N.Y. Acad. Sci. *129*, 283.

Ford, C. E., H. S. Micklem, and D. A. Ogden, 1968, Lancet *1*, 621.

Ford, W. L., 1969, Brit. J. Exp. Path. *50*, 257.

Ford, W. L. and J. L. Gowans, 1969, Seminars in Hematology *6*, 67.

Ford, W. L., J. L. Gowans, and P. J. McCullagh, 1966, The origin and function of lymphocytes. In: CIBA Symposium on the thymus, edited by G. E. W. Wolstenholme and R. Porter. London, Churchill, p. 58.

Friedenstein, A. J., K. V. Petrakova, A. I. Kurolesova, and G. P. Frolova, 1968, Transp. *6*, 230.

Friedman, H., 1964, Science *145*, 607.

Gandini, E. and S. M. Gartler, 1969, Nature *224*, 599.

Gengozian, N., J. S. Batson, and P. Eide, 1964, Cytogenetics *3*, 384.

Gengozian, N., J. S. Batson, C. T. Greene, and D. G. Gosslee, 1969, Transp. *8*, 636.
Ginsburg, H., 1968, Immunol. *14*, 621.
Goldschneider, I. and D. D. McGregor, 1968a, J. Exp. Med. *127*, 155.
Goldschneider, I. and D. D. McGregor, 1968b, Lab. Invest. *18*, 397.
Goodman, J. W., 1964, Blood *23*, 18.
Gordon, A. S., E. S. Handler, C. D. Siegel, B. S. Dornfest, and J. LoBue, 1964, Annals N. Y. Acad. Sci. *113*, 766.
Gowans, J. L., 1957, Brit. J. Exp. Path. *38*, 67.
Gowans, J. L., 1959, J. Physiol. *146*, 54.
Gowans, J. L. and E. J. Knight, 1964, Proc. Roy. Soc. B *159*, 257.
Gowans, J. L. and J. W. Uhr, 1966, J. Exp. Med. *124*, 1017.
Gowans, J. L., B. M. Gesner, and D. D. McGregor, 1961, The immunological activity of lymphocytes. In: Biological activity of the leucocyte. CIBA Foundation Study Group No. 10, edited by G. E. W. Wolstenholme and M. O'Connor. London, Churchill, p. 32.
Gowans, J. L., D. D. McGregor, D. M. Cowen, and C. E. Ford, 1962, Nature *196*, 651.
Griscelli, C., P. Vassalli, and R. T. McClusky, 1969, J. Exp. Med. *130*, 1427.
Hall, J. G. and B. Morris, 1963, Quart. J. Exp. Physiol. *48*, 235.
Hall, J. G. and B. Morris, 1965, J. Exp. Med. *121*, 901.
Harris, C., 1961, Blood *18*, 691.
Harris, C. and W. T. Burke, 1957, Am. J. Path. *33*, 931.
Harris, J. E., D. W. H. Barnes, C. E. Ford, and E. P. Evans, 1964, Nature *201*, 886.
Harris, P. F., 1958, Brit. J. Exp. Path. *39*, 557.
Harris, P. F. and J. H. Kugler, 1965, Acta Haemat. *33*, 351.
Harris, P. F. and J. H. Kugler, 1967, Transfusion of regenerating bone marrow into irradiated guinea pigs. In: The lymphocyte in immunology and haemopoiesis, edited by J. M. Yoffey. London, Arnold, p. 135.
Harris, P. F., G. Haigh, and J. H. Kugler, 1963, Brit. J. Haemat. *9*, 385.
Haskill, J. S., D. G. Legge, and K. Shortman, 1969, J. Immunol. *102*, 703.
Hayry, P. and V. Defendi, 1970, Science *168*, 133.
Hays, E. F., 1967, Blood *29*, 29.
Hellstrom, I., 1967, Int. J. Cancer *2*, 65.
Hildemann, W. H., 1964, Transp. *2*, 38.
Holm, G., P. Perlmann, and B. Werner, 1964, Nature *203*, 841.
Howard, J. G., J. L. Boak, and G. H. Christie, 1966, Ann. N.Y. Acad. Sci. *129*, 327.
Howard, J. G., J. L. Boak, and G. H. Christie, 1967, Macrophage-type cells in the liver derived from thoracic duct cells during graft-versus-host reactions. In: The lymphocyte in immunology and haemopoiesis, edited by J. M. Yoffey. London, Arnold, p. 216.
Hudson, G. and J. M. Yoffey, 1966, Proc. Roy. Soc. (London) B *165*, 486.
Hulse, E. V., 1963, Brit. J. Haemat. *9*, 376.
Hurst, J. M., M. S. Turner, J. M. Yoffey, and L. G. Lajtha, 1969, Blood *33*, 859.
Kanagawa, H., K. Kawata, T. Ishikawa, and T. Inoue, 1967, Jap. J. Vet. Res. *15*, 31.
Keiser, G., H. Cottier, B. J. Bryant, and V. P. Bond, 1967, Origin and fate of bone marrow lymphoid cells of dog. In: The lymphocyte in immunology and haemopoiesis, edited by J. M. Yoffey. London, E. Arnold, p. 149.
Klein, R., 1959, C. R. Soc. Biol. (Paris) *153*, 545.
Kojima, M. and Y. Imai, 1964, In: Reticuloendothelial system. Organising Committee IVth Internat. Sympos. on RES, Kyoto, Japan. Kyoto, Nissha Printing Co., p. 17.
Lance, E. M. and R. N. Taub, 1969, Nature *221*, 841.
Lawrence, J. S., C. G. Craddock, and T. N. Campbell, 1967, J. Lab. Clin. Med. *69*, 88.
Leder, L. D., 1967, Blut *16*, 86.
Leuchars, E., A. J. S. Davies, V. Wallis, and P. C. Koller, 1966, Ann. N.Y. Acad. Sci. *129*, 274.

Lewis, M. R., 1925, Am. J. Path. *1*, 91.

Ling, N. R., 1968, Lymphocyte stimulation. Amsterdam, North Holland Publ. Co.

Linna, T. J. and S. Liden, 1969, Int. Arch. All. *35*, 35.

Lubaroff, D. M. and B. H. Waksman, 1967, Science *157*, 322.

Lubaroff, D. M. and B. H. Waksman, 1968, J. Exp. Med. *128*, 1437.

Marchesi, V. T. and J. L. Gowans, 1964, Proc. Roy. Soc. B *159*, 283.

Mason, S. and N. L. Warner, 1970, J. Immunol. *104*, 762.

Matsuyama, M., M. N. Wiadrowski, and D. Metcalf, 1966, J. Exp. Med. *123*, 559.

McCullagh, P. J. and J. L. Gowans, 1967, Immunologically tolerant lymphocytes. In: The lymphocyte in immunology and haemopoiesis, edited by J. M. Yoffey. London, E. Arnold, p. 234.

McGregor, D. D. and J. L. Gowans, 1963, J. Exp. Med. *117*, 303.

McGregor, D. D. and J. L. Gowans, 1964, Lancet *1*, 629.

McGregor, D. D., P. J. McCullagh, and J. L. Gowans, 1967, Proc. Roy. Soc. B *168*, 229.

McNeill, T. A., 1970, Immunology *18*, 61.

Mel, H. C. and J. C. Schooley, 1965, Stable-flow free boundary fractionation of spleen colony forming cells from mouse bone marrow. In: La greffe des cellules hémato-poiétiques allogéniques. Centre National de la Recherche Scientifique, Paris, edited by G. Mathe, J. L. Amiel, and L. Schwarzenberg, p. 221.

Metcalf, D., 1960, Brit. J. Haematol. *6*, 324.

Metcalf, D., 1969, Proc. Soc. Exp. Biol. Med. *132*, 391.

Metcalf, D., 1971a, J. Cell. Physiol. *77*, 277.

Metcalf, D., 1971b, Immunology (in press).

Metcalf, D. and M. Brumby, 1966, J. Cell. Physiol. Suppl. 1, *67*, 149.

Metcalf, D. and R. Wakonig-Vaartaja, 1964a, Proc. Soc. Exp. Biol. Med. *115*, 731.

Metcalf, D. and R. Wakonig-Vaartaja, 1964b, Lancet *1*, 1012.

Metcalf, D. and M. Wiadrowski, 1966, Cancer Res. *26*, 483.

Metcalf, D., R. Wakonig-Vaartaja, and R. Bradley, 1965, Aust. J. Exp. Biol. Med. Sci. *43*, 17.

Metcalf, D., M. A. S. Moore, and N. L. Warner, 1969, J. Nat. Cancer Inst. *43*, 983.

Metchnikoff, E., 1905, Immunity in infective diseases. Transl. by F. G. Binnie. London-New York, Cambridge Univ. Press.

Micklem, H. S. and C. E. Ford, 1960, Transp. Bull. *26*, 436.

Micklem, H. S. and J. F. Loutit, 1966, Tissue grafting and radiation. New York, Academic Press.

Micklem, H. S., C. M. Clarke, E. P. Evans, and C. E. Ford, 1968, Transp. *6*, 299.

Miller, J. F. A. P., 1964, Effect of thymic ablation and replacement. In: The thymus in immunobiology, edited by R. A. Good and A. E. Gabrielsen. New York, Hoeber-Harper, p. 436.

Miller, J. F. A. P. and G. F. Mitchell, 1967, Nature *216*, 659.

Miller, J. F. A. P. and G. F. Mitchell, 1968, J. Exp. Med. *128*, 901.

Miller, J. F. A. P. and D. Osoba, 1967, Physiol. Rev. *47*, 437.

Miller, J. F. A. P., S. M. A. Doak, and A. M. Cross, 1963, Proc. Soc. Exp. Biol. Med. *112*, 785.

Miller, J. F. A. P., G. F. Mitchell, and N. S. Weiss, 1967, Nature *214*, 992.

Mintz, B. and J. Palm, 1969, J. Exp. Med. *129*, 1013.

Muramoto, J., T. Ishikawa, and T. Kanagawa, 1965, Nucleus *8*, 25.

Naegeli, O., 1931, Blutkrankheiten und Blutdiagnostik, Fünfte Aufl. Berlin, Springer Verlag, p. 137.

Naspitz, C. K. and M. Richter, 1968, Prog. in Allergy *12*, 1.

Nisbet, N. W., M. Simonsen, and M. Zaleski, 1969, J. Exp. Med. *129*, 459.

Nossal, G. J. V., K. D. Shortman, J. F. A. P. Miller, G. F. Mitchell, and J. S. Haskill, 1967, Cold Spring Harbor Symp. Quant. Biol. *32*, 369.

Nowell, P. C., 1960, Cancer Res. *20*, 462.

Nowell, P. C. and D. A. Hungerford, 1960, J. Natl. Cancer Instit. *25*, 85.

Nowell, P. C. and D. A. Hungerford, 1961, J. Natl. Cancer Instit. *27*, 1013.

Nowell, P. C., B. E. Hirsch, D. H. Fox, and D. B. Wilson, 1970, J. Cell. Physiol. *75*, 151.

Order, S. E. and B. H. Waksman, 1969, Transp. *8*, 783.

Osmond, D. G., 1965, Radioautographic studies of blood-borne cells and lymphocyte turnover in the bone marrow of anaemic guinea pigs. In: Proc. 8th Int. Cong. Anat. p. 90.

Osmond, D. G., 1967, Lymphocyte production in the bone marrow: radioautographic studies in polycythaemic guinea pigs. In: The lymphocyte in immunology and haemopoiesis, edited by J. M. Yoffey. London, E. Arnold, p. 120.

Osmond, D. G. and N. B. Everett, 1964, Blood *23*, 1.

Owen, J. J. T. and G. A. Harrison, 1967, Transp. *5*, 643.

Owen, R. D., H. P. Davis, and R. F. Morgan, 1945, J. Hered. *37*, 290.

Parrott, D. M. V., 1967, The integrity of the germinal center: An investigation of the differential localization of labeled cells in lymphoid organs. In: Germinal centers in immune responses, edited by H. Cottier, N. Odartchenko, R. Schindler, and C. C. Congdon. Berlin, Springer-Verlag, p. 168.

Parrott, D. M. V., M. A. B. de Sousa, and J. East, 1966, J. Exp. Med. *123*, 191.

Petrakis, N. C., M. Davis, and S. P. Lucia, 1961, Blood *17*, 109.

Pinkett, M. O., D. R. Cowdrey, and P. C. Nowell, 1966, Am. J. Path. *48*, 859.

Rebuck, J. W. and J. H. Crowley, 1955, Ann. N.Y. Acad. Sci. *59*, 757.

Rebuck, J. W., R. W. Monto, E. A. Monaghan, and J. M. Riddle, 1958, Ann. N.Y. Acad. Sci. *73*, 8.

Rebuck, J. W., H. I. Coffman, G. B. Bluhm, and C. L. Barth, 1964, Ann. N.Y. Acad. Sci. *113*, 595.

Rieke, W. O. and M. R. Schwartz, 1967, Acta Haemat. *38*, 121.

Robinson, S. H., G. Brecher, S. I. Lourie, and J. E. Haley, 1965, Blood *26*, 281.

Schooley, J. C. and I. Berman, 1960, Blood *16*, 1133.

Schooley, J. C. and L. S. Kelly, 1964, Influence of the thymus on the output of thoracic-duct lymphocytes. In: The thymus in immunobiology, edited by R. A. Good and A. E. Gabrielsen. New York, Harper and Row, p. 236.

Sell, S. and R. Asofsky, 1968, Prog. in Allergy *12*, 86.

Seller, M. J., 1970, Transp. *9*, 303.

Shadduck, R. K., B. Kubanek, A. Porcellini, L. Ferrari, W. S. Tyler, D. Howard, and F. Stohlman, Jr., 1969, Blood *34*, 477.

Shearer, G. M. and G. Cudkowicz, 1969, J. Exp. Med. *129*, 935.

Shortman, K., J. S. Haskill, A. Szenberg, and D. G. Legge, 1967, Nature *216*, 1227.

Simons, M. J. and R. Fowler, 1966, Nature *209*, 588.

Spector, W. G. and E. Coote, 1965, J. Path. Bact. *90*, 589.

Spector, W. G. and G. B. Ryan, 1969, Nature *221*, 860.

Spector, W. G., M. N. I. Walters, and D. A. Willoughby, 1965, J. Path. Bact. *90*, 181.

Stone, W. H., S. Friedman, and A. Fregin, 1964, Proc. Nat. Acad. Sci. U.S. *51*, 1036.

Strober, S. and J. L. Gowans, 1965, J. Exp. Med. *122*, 347.

Sutton, J. S. and L. Weiss, 1966, J. Cell. Biol. *28*, 303.

Thomas, E. D., T. M. Fliedner, D. Thomas, and E. P. Cronkite, 1965, J. Lab. Clin. Med. *65*, 794.

Urso, P. and C. C. Congdon, 1957, Blood *12*, 251.

Van Furth, R., 1969, Seminars in Hematol. *6*, 84.

Van Furth, R. and Z. A. Cohn, 1968, J. Exp. Med. *128*, 415.

Vernon-Roberts, B., 1969, Nature *222*, 1287.

Virolainen, M., 1968, J. Exp. Med. *127*, 943.

Virolainen, M. and V. Defendi, 1968, Nature *217*, 1069.

Volkman, A., 1967, Haematol. Lat. *10*, 61.

Volkman, A. and J. L. Gowans, 1965a, Brit. J. Exp. Path. *76*, 50.

Volkman, A. and J. L. Gowans, 1965b, Brit. J. Exp. Path. *76*, 62.

Warner, N. L., M. A. S. Moore, and D. Metcalf, 1969, J. Nat. Cancer Inst. *43*, 963.

Wegman, T. G. and J. G. Gilman, 1970, Dev. Biol. *21*, 281.

Weissman, I. L., 1967, J. Exp. Med. *126*, 291.

Whang, J., E. Frei, J. H. Tjio, P. P. Carbone, and G. Brecher, 1963, Blood *22*, 664.

Whitelaw, D. M., 1966, Blood *28*, 455.

Whitelaw, D. M., M. F. Bell, and M. F. Batho, 1968, J. Cell. Physiol. *72*, 65.

Wilson, D. W., W. K. Silvers, and P. C. Nowell, 1967, J. Exp. Med. *126*, 655.

Woodruff, M. F. A., M. Fox, K. A. Buckton, and P. A. Jacobs, 1962, Lancet *1*, 192.

Yoffey, J. M., 1960, The lymphomyeloid complex. In: CIBA Symposium on haemopoiesis, edited by G. E. W. Wolstenholme and M. O'Connor. London, Churchill, p. 1.

Yoffey, J. M., 1964, Ann. N.Y. Acad. Sci. *113*, 867.

Yoffey, J. M., 1966, Bone marrow reactions. London, Arnold.

Yoffey, J. M., G. Hudson, and D. G. Osmond, 1965, J. Anat. *99*, 841.

CHAPTER 6

Microenvironmental regulation of haemopoiesis

The initial concepts of haemopoiesis envisaged that the different haemopoietic organs contained sessile populations of cells which proliferated, forming mature cells which were then released to the circulation. The role of the non-haemopoietic cells in these organs was considered to be two-fold: (a) they served as a simple framework for the organ, and (b) some of these framework cells served as the ancestors of the various haemopoietic cell populations. The more recent experimental analysis of haemopoiesis described in the preceding chapters has shown these initial concepts to be wrong. The haemopoietic populations are *not* renewed by the proliferation of stromal cells, and in all organs except the bone marrow the haemopoietic populations are regularly replaced by the progeny of stem and progenitor cells entering the organs via the blood.

These facts necessitate a reassessment of the role of the stromal cells in the various haemopoietic organs. If stem and progenitor cells are present in the blood and humoral regulators exist which can act on these cells then, theoretically, haemopoiesis should be able to occur in any organ in which such cells accidentally lodge. In fact, however, haemopoiesis does not occur diffusely throughout the body, but only in certain restricted organs. Furthermore, within these organs there is clear evidence of specialisation, e.g. in the lymph nodes, only lymphopoiesis occurs. These general considerations make it evident that the stromal cells of haemopoietic organs must play a highly specialised role in haemopoiesis by creating special local conditions ('microenvironments') sustaining and directing the proliferation of immigrant haemopoietic stem cells.

In the context of this present discussion the term 'microenvironment' denotes a specialised region in part or all of a haemopoietic organ which differs from adjacent areas in the organ and from other organs. The term 'microenvironment' may be a little misleading in that the region concerned may embrace anything from a few cells to the tens of millions of cells in an entire organ. In the latter case, however, it will be shown that the organ is usually broken down into replicate compartments of microscopic dimensions, containing relatively small numbers of cells. In some of the examples to be discussed it is apparent that a microenvironment is delineated by a meshwork or solid barrier of cells, which could influence haemopoietic cells on a contact basis, but in other examples no such cellular barriers have yet been identified, and the possibility exists that a functional microenvironment of limited volume may be created by the diffusion of short-range humoral factors which are only in effective concentration a short distance from their source.

It is not wished to imply here that haemopoietic organs are the only organs in the body in which specialised microenvironments are to be found. It is entirely probable even in a relatively homogeneous organ such as the liver that the fluids bathing the liver parenchymal cells vary significantly from one part of the organ to another. Inevitably there must be gradients of metabolites and cell products extending from arterial to venous vascular channels and from vascular to lymphatic channels, which will produce fluc-tuating states of heterogeneity in the composition of tissue fluids bathing liver cells. Such intraorgan variability can be assumed to be a feature of all tissues in the body. Over and above this fundamental variability there must also be specialised microenvironmental differences which give the different tissues their distinctive characteristics. E.g., there must be in the liver, local factors which determine that this organ is the only location in which a cell can express its genetic potential to function as a specialised liver cell and which can be loosely characterised as a 'liver microenvironment'. It is in this sense that the term 'haemopoietic microenvironment' is used. The added complexity with haemopoietic cell populations is that a number of widely different classes of specialised cells are involved and that these often occupy the same general tissue space, e.g. the bone marrow or spleen.

In the case of haemopoietic cells, certain specific questions can be raised concerning the nature and function of haemopoietic organ microenviron-ments: (a) why do circulating stem and progenitor cells seed in such micro-environments and what happens when an 'unsuitable' cell seeds in a tissue, e.g. when a progenitor cell already committed to granulopoiesis lodges in the thymus or the lymph node?; (b) when an uncommitted stem cell seeds in a microenvironment, what commits this cell to a specific pathway of differen-tiation – the microenvironment, or humoral regulators, or both?; (c) does the organ microenvironment provide proliferative stimuli for haemopoietic cells or merely allow or sustain the expression of an inherent capacity of the cells to proliferate?; (d) how can the same microenvironment apparently sustain simultaneously two different types of haemopoiesis (e.g. where proliferating erythroid and granulocytic cells can exist literally side by side as in the bone marrow or the spleen)?; (e) how is release of mature cells regulated from such microenvironments?

While the above general considerations make it evident that specialised microenvironments exist with in haemopoietic organs, and while these are often plainly visible on examination of microscopic sections of such organs, it must be admitted that the study of this aspect of haemopoiesis is only in its earliest crudest phase. At the present time many of the questions posed can only be discussed in general terms using as illustrations the few examples for which some data exist.

6.1 *The thymus microenvironment*

In some ways the microenvironment of the thymus cortex appears to offer the least complex example of the specialised haemopoietic microenviron-ments. In the adult thymus cortex, with the exception of a few incidental granulocytes, eosinophils and plasma cells, the only blood cells present are lymphoid cells. Certainly the only proliferating blood cells are lymphoid. We discussed earlier the fact that the proliferating thymic lymphoid popula-tion is not completely self-sustaining and that it is slowly replaced by new cells derived from immigrant stem cells which are probably multipotent. The first problem raised therefore is, do these immigrant stem cells replicate themselves within the thymus? Assays of thymic cell populations have consistently failed to reveal significant numbers of multipotent stem cells (CFU's). Cells can be demonstrated which will seed and proliferate in the lymph nodes and spleen, but such cells appear to be able only to generate lymphoid cells and not erythroid or granulocytic cells. Rare multipotent stem cells have been found in the thymus, but these are in sufficiently low numbers to be compatible with the interpretation that they represent occasion-al stem cells in blood trapped in thymic vessels.

Three alternative conclusions can be drawn from these observations: (a) if multipotent stem cells seed in the thymus, they may rapidly be committed to a restricted lymphoid pathway of differentiation; (b) multipotent stem cells may never seed in the interior of the thymus cortex, the only stem cells able to seed being already pre-committed along a general lymphoid pathway of differentiation; or (c) multipotent stem cells may seed in the thymus cortex together with progenitor cells pre-committed to various pathways of differentiation, but of these only multipotent cells or those pre-committed to a lymphoid pathway remain, the others rapidly dying or re-entering the circulation. Little evidence exists regarding the presence of a specialised vascular barrier which would permit only the entry of lymphoid stem cells into the adult thymus. Furthermore lymphoid cell populations are unable to seed in the thymus. Although assays of cell suspensions from the adult thymus have consistently failed to reveal progenitor cells of the granulocytic series (*in vitro* CFC's), such cells have been found in the 12-day embryonic thymus (Metcalf, D. and Moore, M. A. S., unpublished data). At least in the thymus at this stage, no barrier appears to exist to the localisation of 'inappropriate' precursor cells. Assays of later embryonic thymuses have failed to reveal *in vitro* CFC's, but the fate of those cells which did seed initially is unknown. It is not impossible that these inappropriate cells may die in the thymus or transform into macrophages, but it is perhaps more reasonable to suppose that they re-enter the circulation, seeking a more favourable environment, e.g. the liver or the developing spleen and bone marrow.

Evidence will be presented later that microenvironments probably exert an inductive influence in determining specific pathways of differentiation in immigrant stem cells, at least for erythropoietic and granulopoietic cells. However, in the case of the thymus, it is uncertain whether the thymic microenvironment exerts an inductive influence on immigrant cells or merely selects pre-committed stem cells. Since thymic cortical lymphocytes are of a highly specialised nature with unique size and antigenic charac- teristics, it seems basically unlikely that such specific predeterminations are imprinted on stem cells whilst still in the bone marrow. However, some intermediate type of commitment, e.g. to a general lymphoid pathway rather than an erythroid or granulocytic pathway, might conceivably be initiated in the bone marrow before the stem cells enter the circul- ation.

Three pieces of evidence indicate the existence and operation of an in- ductive influence in the thymus microenvironment:

(a) Bone-marrow stem cells can repopulate the thymus of an irradiated recipient, and these thymic cells can then repopulate the lymph nodes of irradiated secondary recipients. However, these thymic cells cannot repopu- ate the thymus of an irradiated secondary recipient (Ford 1966). Clearly, if selection of suitable thymus-homing migrants was the only mechanism involved in the seeding of stem cells in the thymus, such cells should be equally able to seed in the thymus of a secondary recipient. Failure to observe this implies a qualitative change in the immigrant stem cells follow-ing their entry into the thymic microenvironment.

(b) When mixtures of chromosomally-marked bone marrow and thymic or lymph-node cells were injected into lethally irradiated syngeneic mice, thymic and lymph-node-derived cells were found to preferentially repopulate the lymph nodes, at least in the initial post-irradiation period (Ford 1966). This demonstrates that thymic and lymph-node cells have lymph-node 'homing' characteristics. When bone-marrow cells were injected into lethally irradiated recipients, approximately 80–90% of the mitoses in the thymus were found to be of donor bone-marrow origin by 16 days after injection. However, tests on cell suspensions from such thymuses showed that these cells, when injected into irradiated secondary recipients, had lost the capacity to behave as bone-marrow stem cells but did not yet possess lymph-node 'homing' properties. This latter property began to appear in cell suspensions from repopulated thymuses by 23 days after irradiation and was well established by 30 days after irradiation (Ford 1966). This interval of 16–30 days between the entry of bone-marrow stem cells into the thymic micro-environment and the development of distinctive 'thymic' behaviour of the cells in the thymus might well represent the time needed for an inductive influence of the thymus microenvironment on previously uncommitted stem cells. The long inductive period demonstrated by these experiments may be longer than in the normal thymus, as it is quite possible that the lethal doses of whole-body irradiation used in the experimental design may have damaged the non-lymphoid inductive cells of the thymus.

(c) Thymic lymphoid cells in some strains of mice have been found to exhibit a distinctive antigen – the TL antigen – on their cell surface. An analysis of the repopulation of C57BL (TL-negative) thymus grafts in TL-positive $(A \times C57BL)F_1$ mice, studying the serological type of the re-populating cells as well as their content of TL-antigen revealed that some grafts were fully repopulated by host cells by 13 days, whereas TL-positive cells only began to appear after 15 days (Schlesinger and Hurvitz 1968a, b). This suggests that it may take several days for immigrant cells and their immediate progeny to be induced to form the characteristic antigens of cells in the thymic microenvironment. The difficulty with an antigen marker approach is that stem cells are rare in a cell population, and there can be no positive evidence of the modification of the original stem cells to exhibit this antigen. It may equally well be that only the more differentiated progeny (large, medium and small lymphocytes) are capable of exhibiting this antigen. In the mouse embryo the theta alloantigen is apparently induced to appear on thymic lymphocytes 3–4 days after stem cells seed in the epithelial environment (Owen, J. J. T. and M. Raff, personal communication). Schlesinger (1970) reached a similar conclusion from an analysis of the repopulation of thymus grafts in adult mice by theta-negative cells, presumably of bone-marrow origin.

From this data it seems likely that stem cells entering the thymus are either entirely uncommitted or are at most minimally committed along a general lymphoid pathway, and that the thymus microenvironment modifies or commits these stem cells to be precursors of thymic lymphoid cells.

The thymic microenvironment appears to differ significantly from the lymph-node microenvironment, although both support lymphoid populations. These differences will be discussed in more detail in discussing the lymph-node microenvironment, but one major difference concerns the capacity of lymphoid stem cells for self replication in the two sites. As discussed in the previous chapter, studies on mice united in parabiosis showed that most dividing cells in lymph nodes are not capable of sustained self-replication and are continually replaced by new cells entering from the circulation. In the thymus, the situation appears to be almost the opposite of that in the lymph nodes. Following parabiotic union, although occasional thymus glands showed up to 50% of mitotic cells derived from the partner, the majority of thymuses showed only about 15% of cells derived from the partner, implying that 70% of more thymic stem cells must be self-generating over long intervals.

While the early steps in the initiation of thymic-type lymphopoiesis remain uncertain, there is better evidence on the manner in which proliferative activity of the progeny of these cells is regulated by the thymic microenvironment. Histological studies have demonstrated a marked regional concentration in the cortex of primitive (large and medium) thymic lymphocytes adjacent to the subcapsular epithelial sheath and along the epithelial sheaths lining the radial vessels (Metcalf 1964a). Since only large and medium lymphocytes exhibit the capacity to divide in the thymus, mitotic activity is also concentrated in these zones. Scattered mitoses do occur throughout the remaining regions of the cortex but these are non-random in distribution (Metcalf 1964b), and electronmicroscopic studies have shown most of these mitotic cells also to be in intimate contact with epithelial cells – in this case, the epithelial cells forming a loose meshwork between adjacent epithelial sheaths surrounding radial vessels (Mandel 1969). Thus there is clear morphological evidence that a close association between thymic epithelial and lymphoid cells in the cortex could be the critical element in determining mitotic activity in the lymphoid cells.

Studies on established thymus grafts in which the organ is a chimaeric mixture of donor epithelial cells and host lymphoid cells have indicated that the thymic epithelial cells also determine strain, sex, and age-related differences in proliferative activity of thymic lymphoid cells (Metcalf et al. 1961; Metcalf 1962, 1963a). Grafts of thymic fragments exhibited thymic-type lymphopoiesis only if portions of medullary epithelial tissue were also present in the fragment, and grafts of purely cortical tissue uniformly failed to survive as recognisable thymic tissue (Metcalf 1963a). Furthermore, a striking constancy was observed in the proportion of cortical to medullary tissue in thymus fragment grafts, regardless of the absolute size of such fragments.

AKR thymic tissue exhibits a higher proportion of large and medium lymphocytes than does C3H thymic tissue and the lymphoid cells in the AKR thymus exhibit higher mitotic indices (Nakamura and Metcalf 1961). When grafts of such thymuses were made to (AKR × C3H)F$_1$ recipients, the AKR thymus grafts grew to a larger size, exhibited a higher percentage of large and medium lymphocytes and a higher overall mitotic activity than did C3H grafts, despite the fact that both types of graft were resident in the same F$_1$ environment and both were repopulated completely by F$_1$ hybrid lymphoid cells (Metcalf 1962). Similarly, the female thymus in AKR mice is larger and has a higher incidence of large and medium lymphocytes and mitotic cells than the male thymus. These differences also persisted in reciprocal thymus grafts between male and female mice. Finally, the pronounced age-related changes in thymus size and content of large, medium and mitotic cells have been shown to be determined by the age of the epithelial cells of the thymus. Grafts of neonatal C3H thymus tissue to post-involutional recipients were found to first increase in weight, then plateau in size and finally lose weight with exactly the same timing as is seen with the normal C3H thymus (Metcalf 1966). The timing of age involution was thus related entirely to the age of the graft and not to the age of the host. This age involution sequence of weight changes in thymus grafts is a dramatic demonstration of the existence of built-in biological time clocks in cells associated with, and influencing, haemopoietic cells and can be assumed to have parallels in other haemopoietic organs.

The histological evidence and the data from the analysis of thymus graft behaviour make it clear that the epithelial cells and possibly other cell types in the thymus cortex (Ishidate and Metcalf 1963) regulate the pattern of differentiation and the mitotic activity of lymphoid cells in the thymus cortex. A further question arises as to whether this influence is generally diffused throughout the cortex in some integrated fashion or whether it operates on a strictly local basis, each region being independent of the others in the cortex.

One of the highly unusual properties of the thymus is its failure to regenerate after partial removal of the organ (Metcalf 1964; Borum 1969). The portion remaining exhibits no enlargement and no compensatory rise in its content of large and medium cells or in the mitotic activity of these cells. Similarly, the proliferative activity of thymus fragments (provided they contain medullary tissue) proceeds at a normal rate regardless of the total size of the fragment. On the other hand, when the epithelial framework of the cortex is made to collapse inwards by destruction of the thymic lymphocytes (e.g. by cortisone or X-rays) regeneration promptly occurs with the usual development of higher than normal percentages of large and medium lymphocytes and a higher than normal mitotic activity until the normal size of the organ is restored (Smith and Kieffer 1957; Ito and Hoshino 1961; Ishidate and Metcalf 1963).

These observations clearly suggest that thymic lymphopoiesis is not regulated on an organ-wide basis but on the basis of much smaller subunits. These subunits are at least as small as the wedge-shaped cortical regions between radial vessels and possibly are as small as the epithelial 'packets' – the meshwork of cortical epithelial cells with their enclosed aggregates of lymphoid cells. There appears to be no overall feedback mechanism operating between adjacent subunits which might maintain some uniformity in the level of lymphopoiesis in all subunits. This was seen clearly in the thymus regenerating after X-irradiation or cortisone treatment (Ishidate and Metcalf 1963) and in regenerating thymus grafts (Dukor et al. 1965). In all three situations areas of well-developed cortical lymphopoiesis were seen adjacent to cortical areas in which minimal, or no, lymphoid regeneration had yet occurred.

This autonomy of thymus subunits was even more evident when an analysis was made of the growth patterns of thymus grafts. Thymus grafts achieved the same size and mitotic activity in thymectomised as in sham-operated recipients, and when as many as 50 thymus grafts were placed in a single recipient, each graft achieved the same size it would have if grafted alone to a normal or thymectomised recipient (Metcalf 1963a). This behaviour appears to be unique amongst haemopoietic organs. E.g., spleen-graft growth and proliferation was much greater in splenectomised recipients than in normal mice (Metcalf 1963b), and when multiple spleen grafts were placed in the same recipient, the total graft mass achievable reached a plateau corresponding roughly to the size of a normal spleen (Metcalf 1964c).

It seems clear that no specific feedback mechanism exists in the body which can restrict the total amount of proliferating thymic lymphoid cells – an observation which reinforces the conclusion that thymic lymphopoiesis is dependent on, and regulated by, the non-lymphoid elements of the thymus operating strictly on the basis of autonomous subunits. The precise mechanisms operating within a thymus subunit are unknown. Morphological evidence suggests strongly that direct cell contact between epithelial cells, reticuloendothelial cells and target lymphoid cells is the primary mechanism for regulation, but cell membranes are never as sharply delineated as might be imagined from fixed material and the difference between contact of adjacent attenuated cytoplasmic margins, and short-range diffusible factors with an effective range of a few microns would not be apparent from morphological studies.

The general biological nature of such interactions can only be speculated upon. Essentially all such a regulating influence need do is to maintain a preponderance of parental-type progeny in dividing large and medium lymphocytes, i.e. delay or postpone differentiation to the non-dividing small lymphocyte. This would have the joint effect of maintaining a high incidence of such cells and a comparatively high overall incidence of mitotic activity in the cell population. Although thymic lymphoid populations are characterised by their uniquely highly mitotic activity (Nakamura and Metcalf 1961) and by their short cell-cycle times (Metcalf and Wiadrowski 1966) the regulating influence of the thymic microenvironment need not actually stimulate mitotic activity. Here of course the distinction between 'permitting' and 'stimulating' mitotic activity may approach meaningless semantics.

Some uncertainty remains concerning the relation of medullary to cortical epithelial cells. Electronmicroscopic evidence suggests that many of the epithelial cells of the medulla have a morphology, and possibly a function, similar to those in the cortex. However, Clark (1966) produced morphological and functional evidence suggesting that some medullary epithelial cells may differ from those in the cortex. Most epithelial cells show morphological structures compatible with the possibility that they have a secretory function (Arnesen 1958; Clark 1966). The nature of the secretory product is unknown but it may be the thymic humoral factor (see later). We discussed above the possibility that the regulation of lymphoid differentiation and proliferation in the cortex could be mediated by short-range humoral factors. If such factors exist, these could also be secretory products of thymic epithelial cells.

One puzzling aspect regarding the structural organisation of the thymus is why there is so little lymphopoiesis in the medulla despite the fact that it does contain lymphoid cells scattered among the masses of epithelial cells. Two possibilities may explain this lack of lymphopoiesis: (a) the epithelial cells of the medulla may indeed differ functionally from those in the cortex and may not be involved in stimulating thymic-type lymphopoiesis, or (b) the lymphoid cells in the medulla may differ from cortical lymphocytes and not be susceptible to stimulation or regulation by the thymic microenvironment. Most studies on thymic lymphoid cells have demonstrated a small subpopulation, which differs from the majority of lymphoid cells, e.g. in radiation sensitivity (Trowell 1961), cortisone sensitivity (Ishidate and Metcalf 1963), antigenic content (Cerottini and Brunner 1967; Schlesinger 1970), and cell kinetics (Metcalf and Wiadrowski 1966); and autoradiographic and histological studies indicate that medullary lymphoid cells resemble lymph node-type lymphocytes in size, morphology and labelling patterns with tritiated thymidine. Furthermore the thymus medulla has been shown to be one of the sites of lymphocyte recirculation (Brumby and Metcalf 1967). It seems likely therefore that many of the lymphoid cells of the thymus medulla may be long-lived recirculating lymphocytes which differ from cortical lymphocytes in not being susceptible to the special influence of the thymus microenvironment.

The mechanisms regulating cell death within the thymus or release of lymphocytes from the thymus cortex are not understood. Indirect evidence indicates that these processes are profoundly influenced by physiological levels of cortisol (Dougherty et al. 1964), and this hormone may exert an overall regulatory influence on the processes either by direct action on lymphoid cells or, less likely, by modifying the function of the non-lymphoid cells of the cortex. Cell crowding in the tissue spaces between the epithelial meshwork might also influence the fate of the lymphoid cells. The labelling data indicate that the first small lymphocytes formed are the first to die or leave the organ (Metcalf and Wiadrowski 1966), but little else is known of the nature of the process determining the fate of thymic small lymphocytes.

Several lines of evidence indicate that in the adult thymus the majority of small lymphocytes formed never leave the organ but die locally after a mean intrathymic life span of 3–4 days. Although direct labelling studies of thymic lymphocytes indicate that many migrate, the total numbers involved in this migration are small in the adult animal (Murray and Woods 1964; Nossal 1964). Total labelled thymidine levels in DNA in the thymus remained constant for more than 3 days following pulse labelling (Craddock et al. 1964) and similar data were obtained from an analysis of grain counts over autoradiographs of thymic lymphoid cells (Matsuyama et al. 1966). Furthermore, in animals grafted with up to 50 thymus glands no autoradiographic evidence was noted for increased cell migration from labelled thymus tissue to lymphoid organs in the remainder of the body (Matsuyama et al. 1966). Although most lymphocytes generated in the adult thymus appear to die locally after a short life span, as discussed earlier, those which do leave the organ serve as an important source of recirculating cells for the peripheral lymphoid organs. Migration of cells from the thymus appears to be much more extensive in the neonatal than in the adult thymus (Weissman 1967).

The curious combination of extensive cell birth and death within the adult thymus has led to speculation as to the possible purpose of this process in terms of the general immune defence system. One suggestion has been (Burnet 1962) that the high mitotic activity of the thymic lymphoid cells is needed to generate by random genetic mutation the large number of variant lymphoid cells needed to respond by proliferation to all possible antigenic determinants. Direct studies on thymic lymphoid cells have indeed indicated that there is a pre-determined diversity in the responsiveness of thymic lymphoid cells to antigens (Shearer and Cudkowicz 1969; Mitchell and Miller 1968; Dwyer and Mackay 1970).

One basic problem in the general schemes for generating antigenic diversity is how to eliminate 'undesirable' lymphoid cells. In this context an undesirable lymphocyte is one which by random mutation has acquired the capacity to respond to self-antigens. Such cells need to be suppressed or eliminated otherwise they might cause damage or disease by reacting to antigens on the normal cells of the body. It has been postulated that the large-scale death of thymic lymphocytes may represent this process of elimination of undesirable, or autoreactive, lymphoid cells (Burnet 1962). On this proposition, the thymic microenvironment would need to play a role quite different from those so far discussed. It would need to be so designed as to present 'self-antigens' to the self-reacting lymphocytes in such a way that contact with the antigen results in cell death rather than blast transformation and proliferation. This proposal leaves unanswered the question of how such contact between antigen and antigen-responsive cells might differ fundamentally from similar contacts occurring in the peripheral lymphoid organs, where contact usually leads to a wave of proliferation in the responding cells.

The above discussion concerning the possible generation and death of self-reactive cells in the thymus is entirely speculative. Its one virtue is that it offers a plausible explanation for the massive local death of thymic lymphocytes occurring within the normal cortex. However, it is possible to advance other explanations for the biological usefulness of this unusual process, e.g. the provision of nuclear building blocks for use by other body cells, and the real reason for this process remains to be firmly established. It is sufficient at present to point out that this process must basically be the result of certain unique features of the thymic microenvironment.

6.1.1 Summary

The functions characterised for the thymic microenvironment can be summarised as follows:

(1) To trap stem cells.

(2) To select those stem cells with predetermined lymphoid potentiality or, more likely, to induce this differentiation in uncommitted stem cells.

(3) To provide by cell contact processes with epithelial and other cells an environment in which a high proportion of lymphoid cells remains capable of division, thus allowing a sustained high level of proliferation in the lymphoid cells.

(4) To support a high degree of self-generation by dividing lymphoid progenitor cells and their immediate progeny, the large and medium lymphocytes.

(5) To induce lymphocytes to differentiate as cells having a characteristic size, morphology and antigenic content.

(6) To induce a high turnover in thymic small lymphocytes in part by cell release but mainly by causing cell death after a life span of 3–4 days.

(7) To allow the generation of cells (ARC) capable of responding specifically to a diversity of antigenic determinants by virtue of immunoglobulins located on their surfaces.

6.2 Microenvironment of the bursa of Fabricius

The avian bursa of Fabricius shares with the thymus the status of a primary lymphoid organ, since it is required for the development of humoral immune responses and immunoglobulin synthesising capacity, but is not itself a site of local immune responses (see Warner 1967 for review). Very close parallels in development and function of the bursal and thymus microenvironment are evident. In both sites lymphopoiesis is initiated within an epithelial environment which develops as a result of an initial ectoderm-endoderm inductive interaction, followed by epithelial-mesenchymal induction. In both sites the epithelial environment induces lymphoid differentiation in immigrant stem cells of yolk-sac origin in the embryo or bone-marrow origin in the adult, and lymphopoiesis is evident at early stages of development. Bursal lymphopoiesis also exhibits cortico-medullary organisation, very high mitotic activity which is antigen-independent, a high incidence of local cell death, and susceptibility to stress, and age-related involution. The bursal epithelial environment is not a site of local immunological reactions or of antigen localisation but fosters the development of lymphocytes which can adoptively transfer humoral antibody responses to irradiated recipients (Gilmour et al. 1970). The bursa exerts a vital influence on the development of immunological capacity, and this influence is most dramatically revealed in the defective immunological maturation, with agammaglobulinaemia and absence of antibody formation, which results from bursal removal or ablation prior to, or at the time of hatching. This defect in humoral immunity parallels the defect in cell-mediated immunity (and thymus-dependent humoral responses) seen following neonatal thymectomy, and in both cases probably results from removal of primary lymphoid tissue at a stage prior to peripheralisation of lymphoid progenitor cells from their site of production to their site of function in the secondary, or peripheral, lymphoid tissue.

Much of the discussion on the thymic epithelial microenvironment is also applicable to the bursa but there are certain differences which must be emphasised. The bursal epithelial microenvironment induces stem cells to differentiate into a line of immunoglobulin-secreting cells which function as antibody-forming cell precursors. This environmental influence, leading to the expression of immunoglobulin receptors on bursal lymphocytes may involve an antigen-independent somatic diversification of the genome leading to the generation of a number of clones of cells with different antigen-recognition sites. Immunoglobulin class expression may also be irreversibly determined within the bursal environment. The observation that IgM production by bursal lymphocytes precedes IgG production by some days during the course of embryonic development suggests that the capacity to induce (or derepress) the IgM loci develops earlier than the capacity to induce IgG. This difference may reflect qualitative changes in the nature of the epithelial environment during ontogeny or may simply be due to quantitative differences in the induction process. Bursal restriction of immunoglobulin class expression was further revealed in hormonal bursectomy experiments, where some birds may have normal IgM levels and absence of

IgG. This dysgammaglobulinaemia may be due to the escape of some pro-genitors of IgM antibody-forming cells from the bursal environment prior to hormonal treatment and prior to the genesis of IgG-producing cells. Alter-natively, the testosterone treatment which interferes with the epithelial-mesenchymal induction step required for production of a suitable epithelial environment may produce a partial epithelial defect which allows the bursa to induce IgM-producing cells but blocks IgG induction.

6.3 The mammalian equivalent of the bursa of Fabricius

The equivalent of the bursa in mammals has not yet been unequivocally identified; yet some dissociation of immunological responsiveness has clearly been demonstrated in mammals. Various gut-associated lymphoid tissues which have been proposed as the mammalian bursal equivalent are the appendix (Archer et al. 1964; Sutherland et al. 1964) the tonsils (Peterson et al. 1965) and the Peyer's patches (Cooper et al. 1966; Perey et al. 1968). Evidence for such tissues having a primary lymphoid role and behaving as the mammalian bursal homologue has mainly been the apparent develop-mental similarity, the association of the lymphopoiesis with gut epithelium, and the defects in antibody formation following their surgical removal. In a more generalised hypothesis, Fichtelius (1968) has proposed that the entire gut epithelium and its population of rapidly proliferating theliolymphocytes may act as a first-level lymphoid organ, and more recently has extended this to include the scattered lymphocytes in the germinal layers of the skin (Fichtelius et al. 1970). The developmental homology between these tissues and the bursa is more apparent than real. In the bursa, lymphopoiesis is initiated within epithelial follicles following immigration of large basophilic stem cells from yolk sac and marrow, whereas in the mammalian gut, lymphopoiesis is first evident as accumulations of small and medium lym-phocytes in a subepithelial mesenchymal environment. Furthermore, the cells colonizing the gut lymphoid tissue are progenitor cells of lymphoid origin rather than myeloid stem cells, since many display theta antigen on their surface (Owen, J. J. T., personal communication) and in radiation chimaeras repopulation of Peyer's patches by thymus and lymph-node cells has been detected using chromosome-marker techniques (Micklem 1967; Evans et al. 1967). The bursal characteristics of antigen-independent lym-phopoiesis and absence of antigen localisation are not revealed in gut-associated lymphoid tissue, though the evidence is conflicting. It has been suggested that in Peyer's patches follicular development in ungulates (Carlens 1928) and in humans (Cornes 1965) occurs *in utero* long before bacterial or antigenic stimulation. In rabbits, lymphoid cells were detected in gut-associated lymphoid tissue before birth and in some animals follicular formation was evident (Perey et al. 1968; Perey and Good 1968). In contrast, lymphoid follicular formation in the gut of foetal lambs occurred long after the first manifestations of foetal capacity to form antibodies and complete *in utero* removal of the intestinal tract prior to gut lymphoid organisation did not alter this immunological maturation (Silverstein et al. 1970). Furthermore, precocious development of gut-lymphoid tissue could be induced by introduction of antigen into the gut lumen of foetal lambs showing that lymphopoiesis at this site was influenced by antigenic stimulation. It has been maintained that Peyer's patches develop in normal numbers in germfree mice (Perey and Good 1968). However, Peyer's patches were few in number, poorly developed and deficient in follicular organisation in germfree guinea pigs (Miyakawa 1959). Furthermore, conventionalisation of germfree mice results in enlargement of Peyer's patches with the appearance of germinal centres (Pollard 1970).

Peyer's patches in rats were shown to be most efficient in trapping large particulate antigens such as sheep red cells, and unlike primary lymphoid tissue, were capable of showing very active primary and secondary immune responses with production of large quantities of antibody (Cooper and Turner 1967; Stoner and Hale 1955). The Peyer's patches also share with other peripheral lymphoid tissues the capacity to localise thymus cells following local thymus labelling with tritiated thymidine (Iorio et al. 1970) and though the degree of labelling of the immigrant cells was less than seen in other tissues, this could have been produced by more rapid proliferation of cells in Peyer's patches. Lymphocytes also recirculate through gut-associated lymphoid tissue, accumulate in Peyer's patches with a pattern similar to that seen in regional lymph nodes and apparently employ the same route of migration through post-capillary venules (Gowans and Knight 1964).

Studies of tritiated thymidine labelling indices in mammalian gut-lymphoid tissue revealed that cell proliferation in the lymphoid follicles of Peyer's patches, sacculus rotundus and appendix was more intense than in any other lymphoid tissue (Meuwissen et al. 1969). Extremely intense lymphoid proliferation is also seen in the bursa, where it is antigen-independent, but it is more probable that local antigenic stimulation of gut-lymphoid tissue is responsible for the intense proliferation in these sites.

In other respects the bursa differs from gut-lymphoid tissue of mammals:

the bursal lymphocytes are unresponsive to phytohaemagglutinin (PHA) (Weber 1967), whereas lymphocytes of tonsil and appendix show a high degree of PHA transformation (Schwarz 1967; Oettgen et al. 1966). Secondly, the precocious initiation of immunoglobulin synthesis in the bursa is not seen in Peyer's patches where immunoglobulin synthesis was not detected until after initiation of immunoglobulin synthesis in spleen and mesenteric lymph nodes (Thorbecke 1967; Moore, M. A. S. and Warner, N. L., unpublished observations).

It has been reported that mammalian intestinal lymphoid tissue shares with the primary lymphoid tissue of bursa and thymus the capacity to involute at the beginning of puberty (Cooper et al. 1968). However, no reduction in the numbers of Peyer's patches was reported in old guinea pigs (Miyakawa 1959) and in ageing mice their numbers were normal and individual patches appeared in many instances to be hypertrophied (Moore, M. A. S., unpublished observations).

It is apparent that gut-lymphoid tissue shares many of the characteristics of typical secondary lymphoid tissues which are discussed in the following section, and there are few, if any, points of similarity with the avian bursa. Some alternative explanation must be sought for the observation that neonatal removal of the sacculus rotundus, appendix and Peyer's patches in rabbits produces selective antibody deficiency characterised by depression of specific antibody responsiveness to the antigen used, decreased IgM levels and significant lymphopenia (Cooper et al. 1968). It may be that in some species removal of a considerable mass of gut-lymphoid tissue with subsequent depression of humoral immunity, reflects the importance of this tissue as a normal site of antibody formation with a greater preoccupation in humoral immune responses than other peripheral lymphoid tissue. The gut-lymphoid tissue may possess a greater proportion of thymus-independent microenvironments than e.g. lymph nodes, reflecting a greater degree of specialisation towards humoral antibody formation as a predominant response to antigenic stimulation from the gut. The absence of Peyer's patches in humans with primary agammaglobulinaemia (see Chapter 10) may likewise reflect the greater depletion of a lymphoid tissue predominantly colonised by 'B'-type lymphoid progenitor cells than e.g. in peripheral lymph nodes where the 'T'-cell series would predominate. Thus absence of Peyer's patches would be the consequence of the defect, rather than the cause.

The possibility cannot be excluded that the gut-lymphoid microenvironment is more specialised than in spleen and lymph nodes and fulfils a dual role both as a primary and a secondary lymphoid microenvironment. The epithelium associated with the developing lymphoid aggregates may induce differentiation of lymphoid stem cells which subsequently move into the mesenchymal environment of the lymphoid follicles which then functions as a secondary site of lymphoid differentiation. The microenvironment may have this dual capacity only in the early stages of development or may have dual capacity throughout life but with the secondary microenvironment predominating. A third possibility is that the gut epithelium related to lymphoid aggregates is a site of production of a diffusible maturation factor which may act on stem cells to induce their differentiation into the 'B'-cell series. This hypothetical factor may act locally on stem cells entering the subepithelial mesenchyme, or may act at a distance on target cells situated in spleen, mesenteric lymph node or in the bone marrow where antibody-forming cell progenitors can be detected.

The necessity of postulating a gut epithelial influence in the ontogeny of the mammalian 'B'-cell series is only indirectly supported by the evidence of the vital role of the bursal epithelial microenvironment in the induction of differentiation in immigrant stem cells. In birds this requires intimate contact between epithelium and stem cells in the bursal microenvironment but evolution of this system may have led in the mammal to separation of the inducing cell from the target cell, and it has even been proposed that the mammalian thymus may have incorporated an inducing function of bursal type at early stages of foetal life (Dwyer and Mackay 1970).

6.4 The lymph node and spleen lymphoid microenvironment

Many aspects of organ microenvironments discussed for the thymus and bursa apply equally to the peripheral lymphoid organs – the lymph nodes, splenic white pulp and gut-associated lymphoid tissue. Studies on parabiotic animals or radiation chimaeras have shown that most of the peripheral lymphoid compartment is not self-sustaining but is regularly replaced by immigrant cells. Evidence reviewed in Chapter 5 has demonstrated the highly dynamic flux of recirculating lymphocytes and lymphoid progenitor cells in these organs. It is consequently the purpose of this chapter to establish that these cells, when involved in immune responses, have certain microenvironmental requirements that must be met if they are to perform their function with maximum efficiency.

The basic units of the peripheral lymphoid tissue are cells of the lymphocyte series, pyroninophilic blast cells, plasma cells and macrophages organised in a reticulo-endothelial environment. The intricate microscopic organisation, and regional specialisation of this tissue, particularly after immunological activation, justifies the conclusion that peripheral lymphoid tissue contains highly specialised microenvironments.

The lymph nodes are composed of a thymus-independent region of primary follicles, whose organisation is uninfluenced by neonatal thymectomy. These follicular organisations of lymphocytes are separated from the marginal sinus by a layer of phagocytic cells and from each other by a loose inter-follicular area rich in macrophages and with relatively few lymphocytes. Within the follicles the germinal centres, or secondary lymphoid nodules, are found. These are normally absent from lymphatic tissue at birth but appear early in post-natal life, increase in size and number during the course of antigenic stimulation, and are few in number in germfree animals and in patients with agammaglobulinaemia. Germinal centres have a characteristic histological appearance comprising aggregations of large pale-staining cells which contrast with the surrounding marginal zone or corona of loosely packed small and medium lymphocytes. The microenvironment of the germinal centre comprises a network of dendritic reticulum cells whose processes are in intimate contact with the proliferating population of pri-mitive lymphoid cells (germinoblasts). In this sense the organisation can be envisaged as corresponding in structure to the thymic cortex but with a mesenchymal, rather than an epithelial, reticulum. Further parallels between the primary lymphoid organs and germinal centres are the high mitotic activity and often extensive local cell death. Local cell death in germinal centres accounts for the presence of macrophages with ingested pyknotic nuclear debris – the so-called 'tingible bodies'.

The paracortical region (or loose cortex) of the lymph node lies below, and to some extent between, the lymphoid follicles and consists largely of re-circulating, thymus-dependent lymphocytes, though blast cells and mitotic figures are not uncommon. This region occupies a considerable area of the lymph node and is extensively depleted following neonatal thymectomy, extracorporeal irradiation or chronic thoracic duct drainage (Parrott et al. 1966; McGregor and Gowans 1963; Cronkite et al. 1964). Recirculating lymphocytes enter this region from the blood after traversing the specialised endothelium of the post-capillary venules located below and on each side of the follicles and in the interfollicular areas (see Chapter 5). The recirculating cells, together with lymph draining through the afferent lymphatics and marginal sinus, traverse the cortical areas and enter the medullary sinuses which are one of the main exit pathways from the paracortex. In unstimulated lymph nodes the medullary sinuses contain many macrophages but relatively few small lymphocytes, plasma cells and blast cells, though the picture changes rapidly following antigenic stimulation. Following a delayed hyper-sensitivity response, the sinuses of the draining lymph node become distended and possibly occluded by tightly packed small lymphocytes which may temporarily block the drainage of the medullary sinuses (De Petris et al. 1966).

This commitment of specific lymph node zones to different types of immunological function is probably related to the nature of the lymph-node reticulum. Three patterns of reticulin arrangements have been reported in the mouse lymph node: an outer cortical pattern with little reticulin with the exception of a layer deliniating the germinal centres; an open reticulin net-work enclosing groups of 9–12 cells in the mid-cortex; and a cortico-medul-lary and medullary pattern of a closed network of reticulin surrounding individual cells (De Sousa 1968).

The white pulp areas of the spleen are analogous to the cortex and para-cortex of the lymph nodes, but a relatively larger area of the splenic lymphoid follicles is thymus-independent. Germinal centres are present in this region and are morphologically similar to those in the lymph nodes. The splenic equivalent of the lymph-node marginal sinuses are the sinuses of the red pulp, present at the periphery of the thymus-independent areas of white pulp. The thymus-dependent periarteriolar areas of the lymphoid follicle surround a central arteriole and consist of tightly packed small lymphocytes, which may be replaced by blast cells or even plasma cells in an immune response. Recirculating lymphocytes enter the thymus-dependent areas through the perifollicular marginal sinuses and may exit through vascular channels lined by flattened endothelium which run parallel with the central artery (a lymphatic drainage route for splenic lymphocytes apparently does not exist) (Goldschneider and McGregor 1968; W. H. O. Technical report series No. 448, 1970). The exit vessel is usually collapsed and empty, but after antigenic stimulation it may become distended with small lymphocytes. The red pulp appears to be the splenic equivalent of the lymph-node medulla and is rich in macrophages, blast cells and plasma cells with moderate numbers of small lymphocytes.

The recirculation of lymphocytes through the spleen and lymph nodes permits the channelling of cells through circumscribed areas, or compart-ments, of lymphocytes and macrophage-rich zones and increases the prob-ability of cell interactions both with other cells as in thymus-bone marrow collaboration, or with antigen trapped or presented on the surface of macrophages and reticulum cells. In this sense the peripheral lymphoid environment has a specific role to play both in selecting recirculating cells, retaining some and permitting others to pass through, and in antigen presentation. The apparent selective trapping of recirculating lymphocytes can be prevented by pretreatment of lymphocytes with enzymes such as galactosidase (Gesner and Ginsburg 1964) which suggests the role of stereospecific saccharide structures on lymphocyte cell membranes, which may serve physiologically as recognition sites. Preincubation with trypsin inhibited the entry of lymphocytes into lymph nodes but not into the spleen indicating that different membrane recognition sites are involved in the post-capillary venule migration in lymph node and the marginal sinus migration route in spleen (Woodruff and Gesner 1968).

Recent studies (Griscelli et al. 1969) have suggested that recirculating lymphoid cells do not settle at random in various lymphoid organs. Thus labelled large lymphocytes from mesenteric nodes of rats injected into the blood of syngeneic recipients homed selectively to gut-associated lymphoid tissue, whereas cells from subcutaneous lymph nodes homed to subcutaneous lymph nodes. Small lymphocytes, on the other hand, showed no such selective localisation. The observed selective organ localisation for large lymphocytes suggests that the microenvironment in different lymphoid organs may have subtle differences, which may selectively affect the seeding out of certain lymphocytes in these organs. Further experiments have provided a more likely basis for these observations. It was observed by the same workers that labelled lymphocytes from a donor primed with a particular antigen homed selectively to (or were selectively trapped in) lymph nodes draining a local injection of that antigen as compared with the localisation of similar cells in the contralateral lymph nodes. This might explain the apparent homing of cells to organs of their origin since various regional lymph nodes can be expected to normally trap antigens characteristically present in these regions and thus to be able to selectively trap cells already reactive to those antigens. This function of selective trapping requires further study to determine the exact mechanisms involved but it represents a further function of the lymph-node microenvironment as an extension of its capacity to trap antigens. This capacity to concentrate or select out those lymphocytes specifically reactive to the antigen trapped in the lymph node obviously represents a process which can magnify the efficiency of bringing antigen into contact with specifically preprogrammed cells reactive to that antigen.

6.4.1 Antigen localisation

The primary factor determining the character of the peripheral lymphoid micro-environment is the necessity for antigen to trigger the proliferation of the lymphoid cells. Antigen presumably determines the location and magnitude of lymphopoiesis and to some extent the fate of the lymphoid progeny generated by the mitotic activity. Stated in its broadest terms, the environment is one in which antigens are captured, retained and presented to reactive lymphoid cells in such a way as to elicit a proliferative response by these cells. Antigens can come into contact with pre-programmed lymphoid cells by one of three mechanisms: (a) antigen held on specific patches on the surface of reticular cells, (b) antigen held on the surface of carrier cells, e.g. the thymus-derived ARC's, and (c) antigen coming into direct contact with receptor sites on antigen-binding lymphocytes. The nature of the antigen, its mode of presentation and whether the stimulus is primary or secondary all affect the relative importance of the three modes of antigen presentation.

The localisation of antigens on reticular cells in lymphoid follicles and germinal centres is a complex process, which has been discussed at length in a number of reviews (Ada et al. 1967; Ada and Nossal 1971). However, because antigen trapping and processing is a function of the peripheral lymphoid microenvironment, a brief discussion of the process must be made.

Much of the antigenic material of large physical size which enters the lymph node is trapped by the cells lining the marginal sinuses and by the medullary macrophages (Ada et al. 1967). This material rapidly becomes incorporated in phagolysosomes within the cytoplasm of these cells. Shortly after these events, particulate antigens diffuse into the cortical regions of the lymph node where they become concentrated in discrete patches on the membranes of reticular cells of the primary lymphoid follicles or germinal centres. Soluble antigens are initially more diffusely spread throughout the cell populations in the lymph node before they again eventually become localised on reticular cell membranes in primary lymphoid follicles and germinal centres (Ada et al. 1967). Antigens are characteristically *not* localised on, or in, the plasma cells in the medullary cords of lymph nodes which are responding to antigenic stimulation.

The speed and extensiveness of localisation of antigens on reticular cells is dependent on the existence of pre-formed antibody (either of immune origin or natural antibody) to the antigen concerned (Ada 1967). Experimental analysis of this phenomenon suggests that antigen becomes associated with the reticular cells of the follicles because of the localisation of antibody molecules on the dendritic processes of these cells or because of local antigen-antibody complexing occurring in regions adjacent to these cells (Balfour and Humphrey 1967; Lang and Ada 1967). One of the significant features of antigen localisation on the surface of reticular cells in primary follicles and germinal centres is the persistence of antigen in this location. Antigen retained in these specialised regions of the lymph node is therefore potentially available over long time periods for stimulating the proliferation of responsive lymphoid cells or their precursors.

6.4.2   Cellular changes following antigenic stimulation

Detectable alteration in the organisation of peripheral lymphoid tissue is seen following antigenic stimulation, but the nature of the antigen, route of administration and previous history of antigen exposure greatly influence the morphological picture. Primary antigenic stimulation, eliciting a humoral antibody response, induces a limited degree of blast-cell production and proliferation in thymus-dependent areas and some initial lymphocyte depletion. Antibody-forming cells appear within 4–5 days in the medullary zone of lymph nodes and in the outer part of the perifollicular areas of the spleen, with nests of plasma cells appearing between the perifollicular areas and the red pulp. At later stages germinal centres become involved in the response as evidenced by antigen trapping and hypertrophy. With secondary stimulation, antigen trapping is more rapid and extensive in lymph nodes and germinal centre involvement appears earlier. In the spleen, blast cell production in the periarteriolar sheaths is more intense with more rapid appearance of antibody-forming cells and clusters of plasma cells in perifollicular areas and red pulp.

Direct studies on the location of specific antibody in the spleen following sheep erythrocyte antigenic stimulation showed localisation over periarteriolar lymphoid follicles and in the area surrounding the marginal zone where pyroninophilic blast cells appear. Later in the response or following further antigenic stimulation, haemolysins were detected in some germinal centres (Fitch et al. 1968). With endotoxin as an antigen, focal areas of antibody in spleen sections corresponded histologically with lymphoid follicles and in general with germinal centre development (Young et al. 1968).

Antigenic stimulation influences the number and type of cells leaving lymph nodes via the efferent lymphatics showing that cells of the lymph-node microenvironment have a certain capacity to regulate the magnitude and type of cells leaving the region. Monitoring of efferent lymphatic vessels revealed that immediately after antigenic stimulation there was a cessation of cell exit from the lymph nodes (Hall and Morris 1965). The basis for this phenomenon is unknown but it would appear to be unselective in that many of the cells which normally would have left the organ during that period would have been reactive to antigens other than the one injected. Possibly tissue oedema resulting from entry of large amounts of antigen may have occluded the efferent lymphatics, or lymphocytes may have accumulated and blocked the medullary sinuses. Subsequent to the initial reduction in cell outflow from lymph nodes a period of increased cell output was seen during which the lymph contained a high proportion of cells which were more primitive than the usual recirculating small lymphocytes and most were making antibody to the antigen concerned. This effect may be due to population crowding brought about by increased proliferation of clones of responding cells, or may depend on more subtle events.

The response of regional draining nodes to local immunisation with contact-sensitising agents is seen as early as 4–5 days after contact and is manifest as a remarkable proliferation of pyroninophilic blast cells in the thymus-dependent areas (De Sousa and Parrott 1967). Blast-cell numbers subsequently declined as the cells transformed into medium and small lymphocytes which migrated out of the draining node. Germinal centres do not appear to participate in this cell-mediated immune response. Local administration of pneumococcus polysaccharide antigen, which elicited a humoral antibody response, did stimulate germinal centre development in the draining lymph node but did not produce blast cell transformation in the thymus-dependent areas (De Sousa and Parrott 1967).

Germinal centres evidently play a central role in humoral immune responses but our present knowledge of their development, function and fate is still incomplete. The localisation of antigen on dendritic reticulum cells in intimate contact with rapidly proliferating germinal centre cells has suggested two alternative, though not necessarily mutually exclusive, functions for the centres. One theory proposes that germinal centres are sites of production of plasma-cell precursors (Hanna 1965), whereas the second considers them to be sites of production of memory cells (Wakefield and Thorbecke 1968).

Immunoglobulins and specific antibody have consistently been detected in germinal centres and both local synthesis, and the presence of cytophilic antibody must be considered. Pernis et al. (1965) have shown that some intercellular antibody in germinal centres originates from circulating immunoglobulin which becomes fixed in germinal centres. However, recent studies using primary stimulation with horseradish peroxidase as an antigen detected intracellular antibody in germinal centre cells at an early stage with subsequent appearance of intercellular antibody localised between the dendritic reticulum cells and lymphoid cells (Sordat et al. 1970). Furthermore, some germinal centres were positive for antibody and some negative suggesting monospecificity of individual centres for particular antigens, with locally produced antibody initiating, or enhancing, antigen trapping.

Germinal centres are further implicated in antibody formation since they are absent in patients with Bruton-type sex-linked hypogammaglobulinaemia (see Chapter 10) and in hormonally bursectomised chickens with no antibody-forming capacity but normal cell-mediated immunity. Antilymphocyte serum produced severe depletion of the thymus-dependent areas of lymph nodes and spleen but had no influence on plasma cell formation or germinal centres, also indicating that the latter system was comprised of thymus-independent cells of the 'B'-cell series (Turk and Oort 1968). There is also good evidence to indicate that labelled thymic cells fail to localise in germinal centres (Parrott 1967) but labelled bursal cells apparently do in the chicken (Theis et al. 1968).

Germinal centre formation is not mandatory for antibody formation and phylogenetic studies have revealed that species lacking germinal centres can synthesise 19S antibody and possess plasma cells, though germinal centres may be necessary for 7S antibody formation (Pollara et al. 1968). Furthermore chickens bursectomised *in ovo* produced abundant IgM and plasma cells though lacking IgG and germinal centres (Cain et al. 1969) and detailed studies of the events following antigenic stimulation showed that plasma-cell formation begins prior to the formation of germinal centres (Movat and Fernando 1965).

Histological and autoradiographic studies suggest that germinal centres in normal animals are in a steady state with respect to cell entry and exit. Antigenic stimulation alters this state, causing increased mitotic activity in the centres and cell migration from the centres into the surrounding cortex or red and white pulp (Hanna et al. 1966). This germinal centre dissociation results in temporary atrophy of the centres in the first 24 hours after antigen injection and is antigen-dose-dependent, with a direct relationship between the duration of germinal centre atrophy and increasing antigen dose. At later stages recovery and hyperplasia of the centre were seen. In tonsil labelling studies, evidence also was obtained for a migration of germinal centre cells out into sub-epithelial and inter-epithelial sites with transformation into small lymphocytes (Koburg 1967). Sequential studies on location of antibody-forming cells to SRBC in the spleen during an immune response have clearly demonstrated an orderly migration of such cells from their initial location in the lymphoid follicles to the red pulp and in lymph node from germinal centres to the medullary region (Fitch et al. 1968; Ellis et al. 1967).

The evidence that germinal centre formation follows the first appearance of antibody-forming cells and is a more prominent component of a secondary response has implicated the germinal centres in immunological memory in humoral immunity. Secondary immune responses may be adoptively transferred by cells from spleen white pulp containing germinal centres, and tritiated thymidine-labelled germinal centre cells transformed into small lymphocytes on transfer and in the absence of further antigenic stimulation probably entered a long-lived recirculating lymphocyte pool (McGregor and Gowans 1963; Wakefield and Thorbecke 1968). While some memory is thus present in the recirculating population with cells capable of renewed proliferation on contact with antigen, at least some memory cells remain fixed in lymphoid tissue (McGregor and Gowans 1963). Primed cells were found to concentrate in lymphoid tissue draining a site of antigen injection and may only slowly be released into the circulation to be distributed to the remaining lymphoid tissue (Jacobson and Thorbecke 1969).

It is important to discover whether the proliferation of cells associated with germinal centres is due to a specific stimulus exerted by the specifically oriented reticulum cell microenvironment of the lymphoid progenitor cells or whether the environment simply provides a passive supportive framework for cell proliferation. The fact that the germinal centre reticulum framework can still be recognised as a discrete morphological entity following irradiation- or actinomycin-D-induced germinal centre involution indicates a more specific function of the microenvironment (Swartzendruber 1966). The appearance of germinal centres in sites other than peripheral lymphoid tissue in chronic inflammatory situations or autoimmune disorders implies that undifferentiated mesenchymal cells throughout the body can, under certain circumstances, differentiate to produce an environment suitable for germinal centre formation.

Antigen presentation to lymphocytes in peripheral lymphoid tissue may lead to active immune responses as have been described, but antigens may also induce specific tolerance which may involve deletion or repression of progenitor cells for either humoral or cell-mediated immunity. The mechanisms involved in tolerance induction are not well characterised but appear to involve the same antigen interaction with thymus-derived and marrow-derived cells as occurs in an active immune response. The cells altered in tolerant animals are lymphocytes, as has been shown in adoptive transfer experiments. The tolerisation of thymus-derived ARC's has been described by Miller and Mitchell (1970) and here the turnover of ARC's may be the factor normally limiting the rate of recovery of immunological responsiveness to the tolerated antigen. With sheep erythrocytes, no evidence was obtained for tolerance induction at the level of the lymphocyte population of the thymus itself (Miller and Mitchell 1970). Recent studies using bovine serum albumin as an antigen suggested that tolerance could be achieved at the level of the thymus lymphocyte population (Taylor 1969). It is possible that the difference between the two antigens in terms of the site of tolerance induction may be related to differences in antigen localisation, with sheep erythrocytes failing to diffuse readily into the thymus.

There is preliminary evidence to suggest specificity in the marrow-derived AFC-P population and its capacity to be rendered tolerant (Playfair 1969; Chiller et al. 1970; Singhal and Wigzell 1970). The simplest explanation of the tolerogenic situation may involve presentation of antigen to ARC's or AFC-P's in doses either too low or too high to elicit a wave of proliferation in the cells. It is uncertain whether cell death follows this type of tolerogenic contact and to what extent the efficiency of tolerance induction is influenced by the activity of the non-lymphoid cells of the peripheral lymphoid environment.

At this point it should be made clear that both specific immune responses and specific tolerance can be produced *in vitro* by adding antigens to dispersed cell cultures of lymphoid organs, e.g. from spleen or lymph nodes. Furthermore, lymphoid cells can be shown to selectively bind antigen *in vitro* and the responsiveness of such cells to antigenic stimulation either *in vitro* or *in vivo* can be destroyed by incorporating lethal amounts of isotope into the antigen binding on the reactive cell (see Chapter 3, Section 3.6). At first sight such *in vitro* experiments might suggest that the function of the lymph-node microenvironment is at best a method for collecting together the reacting populations of lymphoid cells or their precursors and that essentially most of the events in lymphopoiesis or plasma-cell production do not require the operation of a fixed population of cells creating a special microenvironment. This conclusion is probably correct, as has been shown in the discussion on granulocyte formation *in vitro*. Provided one can start with a cell population in which specific progenitor cells are already committed, e.g. to become antibody-forming cells, subsequent cell proliferation and differentiation can be achieved *in vitro* using the correct stimulus (antigen in the present case) in the absence of any formal microenvironmental structure. It should be realised, however, that in cell-culture systems where immune responses are obtained, a considerable degree of cell aggregation occurs and this may be necessary in order to reconstitute a microenvironment *in vitro* in which the response may occur. The special properties of the peripheral lymphoid environment cannot be completely reconstituted *in vitro* since the *in vivo* immune response is more efficient in terms of the number of progeny generated per progenitor cell or per unit of antigen. Furthermore, *in vitro* immune responses cannot readily be achieved using bone-marrow and thymus cells alone suggesting that the *in vivo* efficiency of such cell populations in reconstituting immune responses involves some sort of specific function of the peripheral lymphoid microenvironment in initiating the activation of uncommitted progenitor cells into the differentiating, immunologically competent, cell population.

At this stage some speculation on the actual organisation of the lymphoid progenitor cells (described in Chapter 3) and the influence of the micro-environment on their proliferation and subsequent fate is warranted. Such synthesis is of necessity speculative since most immunological studies *in vivo* and *in vitro* have involved a 'black box' approach where the input and output have been carefully monitored but the intermediate events (and the location of these events) have not.

As previously discussed in Chapter 3, Section 3.6, both antigen-reactive cells (ARC's) and antibody-forming cell progenitors (AFC-P's) are gener-ated in the absence of antigenic stimulation, are capable of recognising antigen and can be rendered tolerant or unresponsive prior to their entry into the peripheral lymphoid microenvironment. The microenvironmental in-fluence is directed therefore mainly towards the subsequent proliferative and differentiative events involving these two progenitor cell populations. The process of 'education' of ARC's, initiated by antigen recognition, occurs in the thymus-dependent areas of peripheral lymphoid tissue and involves the transformation of antigen-reactive lymphocytes into pyroninophilic blast cells which subsequently proliferate and differentiate into small and medium lymphocytes which may re-enter the recirculating lymphocyte pool (Miller and Mitchell 1969). This education step may simply involve clonal expansion of ARC's in the lymphoid environment or may involve a more specific step in differentiation with selection of cells with higher affinity receptors and production of long-lived memory cells. The actual site of collaboration between 'B'- and 'T'-cells may therefore be the region where thymus-derived cells undergo blast-cell transformation in the vicinity of marginal sinuses and periarteriolar lymphoid follicles, and it is in these regions that the first antibody-forming cells appear (Fitch et al. 1969). Intimate contact between appropriate 'B'- and 'T'-cells may be facilitated in this region since a flux of recirculating lymphocytes exists in the presence of antigen and an appropriate reticular microenvironment. An alternative possibility is that 'T'-cells actually export their immunoglobulin receptor sites for short distances and these may be trapped on the surface of macrophage or reticulum cells of the microenvironment and be available for activation of the appropriate 'B'-cells. In this context a synergistic immune response to foreign erythrocytes may be induced in heavily irradiated mice injected with marrow cells and an antigen-specific factor, possibly some form of antibody, released from immunised peritoneal exudate cells (probably from an ARC subpopulation) (Kennedy et al. 1970). The subsequent fate of the AFC-P's following interaction with antigen or collaboration with ARC's is presumably blast-cell transformation followed by proliferation and differentiation into antibody-forming cells or memory cells. In the early stages of a primary immune response, involving a predominantly IgM antibody production, the proliferating AFC-P's undergo differentiation into antibody-forming cells (AFC's) which appear in the vicinity of the marginal sinuses and periarteriolar lymphoid follicles. The subsequent fate of differentiating antibody-forming cells involves migration into the medullary regions of lymph nodes and red-pulp areas of the spleen in addition to probable dissemination via the efferent lymphatic drainage route. The majority of AFC-P's may undergo differentiation into AFC's in the early stages of an immune response, but at later stages some cells avoid differentiation and, following antigen-induced proliferation, may enter a prolonged latent phase and join the recirculating population of memory cells. The appearance of germinal centres late in the primary response and early in the secondary response may signify the continuous and possibly clonal expansion of certain AFC-P's that had migrated into the follicular regions following an earlier phase of antigen-induced 'education'. The function of the germinal centres may then be to clonally expand AFC-P's under the influence of antigen presented on the surface of reticular cells. The amount or nature of the antigen may alter the proliferation of AFC-P's and influence their tendency to differentiate further, either into antibody-forming plasma cells which may migrate out into the red pulp or medulla, or into B-type memory cells which may accumulate in the small lymphocyte population of the follicle or enter a recirculating phase. It has been suggested that stimulation of cells in germinal centres by antigen-antibody complexes, particularly in the presence of complement could play an inducing role different from antigen alone and could possibly be responsible for AFC-P proliferation in germinal centres without associated maturation into antibody-forming cells (Gajl et al. 1969). The proliferation of germinal centre cells may then function as an amplifying mechanism superimposed on the earlier and more restricted wave of AFC-P proliferation and differentiation seen early in the primary response and revealed in studies of haemolytic focus formation (see Chapter 3, Section 3.6). Such amplification may be necessary for the establishment of good immunological memory. Alternatively, or perhaps in addition, the centres may act as sites where clones of lymphoid progenitor cells undergo further somatic diversification and selection for cells capable of producing antibodies of progressively higher affinity under the influence of protracted or repeated stimulation by antigen held on the surface of reticular cells. In this context, the high mitotic activity and incidence of local cell death in germinal centres may reflect the operation of some selection process which differentially influences cell survival. A third possibility is that germinal centres may preselect for AFC-P's committed to IgG production or may influence the immunoglobulin class expression of uncommitted progenitor cells, or of cells capable of modulating their class expression.

The peripheral lymphoid environment therefore receives 'virgin' ARC's and AFC-P's from thymus and marrow. It may also be capable of some degree of production of such progenitor cells from more undifferentiated stem cells. The environment is also continually traversed by recirculating 'memory' cells of both the 'T'- and 'B'-cell series. These cells differ from the virgin population in that they have previously encountered antigen and undergone proliferation within peripheral lymphoid tissue. The differences between 'virgin' and 'educated' cells in terms of survival, proliferative ability and differentiation capacity may reflect real differences in levels of differentiation or more simply be due to changes in affinity of receptor sites due to selection processes.

6.4.3 Summary

The prime function of the peripheral lymphoid environment is to selectively localise, present and possibly process antigen and facilitate the interaction of antigen with appropriate lymphoid progenitor cells. The environment also shows regional specialisation in the handling of thymus-dependent, cell-mediated, immune responses and thymus-independent humoral-antibody responses. It has in addition the capacity to facilitate the interaction of these two limbs of the immune system by increasing the probability of interaction of appropriate 'B'- and 'T'-cells in thymus-dependent antibody responses. The microenvironment may also influence the differentiation of more primitive stem cells into the progenitor cell population and may function as an additional site of diversity generation and selection for ARC's and AFC-P's. The peripheral lymphoid tissue does not act simply as a passive filter for recirculating cells but can actively select and retain appropriate cells and can regulate the exit of cells proliferating locally under the influence of antigenic stimulation. Finally, the microenvironment serves to amplify the populations of reactive cells and regulate the balance between progenitor cell proliferation, differentiation or entry into a long-lived memory pool, and in the latter case can regulate the balance between 'fixed' immunological memory due to cell retention, and recirculating memory due to exit of cells from the peripheral lymphoid tissues.

6.5 Spleen microenvironment

In the mouse, the spleen is possibly the most complex haemopoietic organ, containing stem cells and generating populations of erythroid, granulocytic, megakaryocytic, lymphoid and antibody-forming cells. We have already discussed the lymphoid follicles of the spleen and the role such structures play in the generation of clones of antigen-reactive and antibody-forming cells. There is clear morphological evidence in the spleen of segregation of the various haemopoietic populations. Granulopoiesis is concentrated under the spleen capsule and along the subcapsular ends of the spleen trabeculae, whereas erythropoiesis is more diffusely scattered throughout the red pulp. This morphological evidence of segregation strongly suggests that different microenvironments exist within the spleen, each favouring the proliferation of distinct cell populations.

As was discussed in earlier chapters, the spleen contains multipotent stem cells (CFU's), but their incidence is lower than in the bone marrow. More importantly, the evidence from parabiotic animals indicated that the dividing cells in the spleen are regularly replaced by new cells probably of bone-marrow and thymic origin. While much of this replacement involves progenitor cells of the lymphoid series which can be presumed only to have a limited capacity for self-generation, the stem cells also appear to be regularly replaced otherwise their persistence would be detectable in the dividing erythroid and granulocytic cells.

The basis for this difference in stem-cell behaviour in the spleen and bone marrow remains obscure. Three possibilities are: (a) that spleen stem cells differ intrinsically from marrow stem cells in having only a limited capacity for self-replication, (b) that the spleen microenvironment does not favour extended stem cell self-replication, or (c) that haemopoiesis is more labile in the spleen and that fluctuating demands on the few stem cells in the spleen soon exhaust their capacity for self-replication.

As was discussed in Chapter 3, stem cells from the marrow can undergo extensive self-renewal in spleen colonies in irradiated recipients, but there is evidence (see Chapter 8) that stem cells are only capable of a finite number of self-replicative divisions. These facts coupled with the evidence that the spleen is more responsive to stresses such as antigenic stimulation and pregnancy suggest that alternative (c) is the most likely explanation for the apparently limited survival of stem cells in the spleen.

The production by stem cells (CFU's) of colonies of haemopoietic cells in the irradiated spleen has allowed some conclusions to be drawn regarding the role played by the microenvironment in this process. The relevant observations are that:

(a) more erythroid colonies form in the spleen than granulocytic or megakaryocytic colonies;

(b) colonies are initially pure populations of one haemopoietic class but on continued growth develop mixed populations;

(c) when mixed populations develop in colonies, the second population occurs at the edge of the colony and such mixed colonies are usually still single clones derived from the original colony-forming cell;

(d) colonies usually contain stem cells and regardless of the morphological type of colony, such stem cells can generate a full range of morphological types of colonies in secondary recipients.

These key observations allow the conclusion that stem cells initiating colonies are not precommitted to a particular pathway of differentiation but that this commitment is an inductive influence exerted by the microenvironment in which the stem cell lodges. It is clear that the microenvironments in the spleen are heterogeneous, each type being specialised to induce one type of differentiation. Further, these microenvironments are discrete physical entities showing characteristic patterns of distribution in the organ. Thus erythropoietic microenvironments are more numerous than granulocytic ones and are scattered diffusely through the red pulp, whereas the granulocytic microenvironments are restricted predominantly to the subcapsular region. Mixed colonies appear to develop when an expanding colony overlaps from one microenvironment to another of different type and presumably one or more stem cells in the colony is then induced to differentiate along the other pathway of differentiation (Wolf and Trentin 1968).

Because multipotent stem cells can be demonstrated in most spleen colonies it must be concluded that the spleen microenvironments are unable to induce a total commitment of all stem cells within the microenvironment. It may be that stem-cell commitment only occurs when a precise cell contact is established between a stem cell and an adjacent cell of the microenvironment, e.g. between two specific receptor sites, and not all progeny of the original stem cell might make such a contact. Alternatively, since stem cells are heterogeneous and may or may not be in active cell cycle, only stem cells in a particular phase of the cell cycle may be susceptible to the inductive influence of the microenvironment.

The role played by humoral regulators in the induction of differentiation in stem cells is uncertain. To date no regulators have been detected with an action on stem cells, and the known regulators e.g. erythropoietin and CSF appear to operate at the progenitor cell level. The case of CSF is of interest since it has been shown that spleen cells can produce or release CSF in liquid cultures, which raises the question of whether CSF, by itself, can commit a stem cell to differentiate to a granulocytic progenitor cell and generate a clone of granulocytic cells. In experiments using marrow cells from vinblastine-treated mice, Haskill et al. (1970) observed that some density-separated fractions contained no *in vitro* CFC's but did contain CFU's which could generate spleen colonies containing *in vitro* CFC's. The inability to grow colonies *in vitro* from these original bone-marrow suspensions, even in the presence of CSF suggests that CSF alone cannot induce the transformation of CFU's to *in vitro* CFC's. Even the addition of dispersed spleen cell suspensions to such cultures failed to result in colony formation (Metcalf, D. and Moore, M. A. S., unpublished data) and it would appear that this transformation requires a more sophisticated type of cell-cell interaction occurring within spleen microenvironments. On the other hand, once the *in vitro* CFC (granulocyte progenitor) stage is reached, the *in vitro* evidence would suggest that the subsequent generation of a colony of differentiating granulocytes is a simple process, requiring CSF but no special microenvironment.

Any attempt to understand the nature of the haemopoietic microenvironments in the spleen must consider the structural arrangement of the cells constituting these areas. The vascular organisation of these tissues is complex and is still not clearly defined. The theory of closed circulation proposes that arterioles communicate directly with the lumen of venous sinuses which in turn empty into veins (Kinsley 1936; Simon and Pictet 1964). The opposing open-circulation theory recognises that arterioles open into extravascular spaces, the pulp cords or 'spaces of Billroth' in splenic red pulp, whence

blood filters back into the vascular bed through gaps in the sinus wall
(Weiss 1963; Thomas 1967). Pictet et al. (1969a) favour the closed theory but
recognise that hydrostatic pressure may drive some cells from inside the
sinuses into the spaces of Billroth and recognise that this extravasation may
be intrinsically regulated by contractile lining cells. In addition to such bulk
blood flow, certain circulating cells may more specifically migrate out of the
sinuses either between or through the reticulo-endothelial lining cells.

The reticulo-endothelial system is intimately involved in the structure of
haemopoietic tissue yet it remains an ill-defined system even though it is in
all probability the basis of the haemopoietic microenvironment.

The absence of a standardised definition of the R-E system has made
analysis difficult. Historically the original reticulo-endothelial concept
grouped endothelial cells (or at least cells in an endothelial location) of
certain blood vessels in spleen, marrow, lymph nodes, liver, adrenals and
pituitary together with reticulum cells in haemopoietic tissue, sharing a
common capacity to phagocytose and lay down reticulin fibres (Aschoff
1924). This grouping was subsequently broadened by inclusion of the histio-
cytic or macrophage system. A later classification included R-E cells
together with many other types and was based on a common histochemical
property. This 'metalophil' system grouped all cells sharing a common
affinity for silver staining (Marshall 1956). Much of the difficulty in accepting
the Aschoff concept is the status of the phagocytic endothelial cell component.
Since true endothelia are not normally phagocytic then the sinusoidal lining
cells such as Kupffer cells of liver and littoral cells of marrow and spleen must
either be a unique form of activated endothelial cell or a quite different type
of cell in an endothelial location. Fresen (1960) defined a 'retothelial system'
which excluded the sinus-lining cells of pituitary and adrenals and considered
reticular cells in endothelial positions in haemopoietic tissue were not
endothelial in origin. Azazaki (1962) restricted the system still further to
reticulum cells and histiocytes only.

The supporting framework of the spleen consists of a first-order skeleton
consisting of fibroblasts, smooth muscle cells and collagen and elastin fibres
and a second order network of cells intimately associated with reticulin and
collagen and distinguished from fibroblasts by the presence of numerous
fingerlike cytoplasmic processes (Pictet et al. 1969a). Metallic impregnation
of this network of fixed reticulum cells has shown its organisation into
follicular, sinusoidal, interstitial and perivascular reticulum with apparently
well-defined differences in distribution, structure and probably function
(Ravens 1968).

In Figure 6.1 the relationship of the sinus-lining cells to the reticulum of the cords of Billroth is shown. Sinus-lining cells are frequently indistinguishable from typical macrophages but are in intimate contact with a discontinuous basement membrane. On the outer aspect of the sinus membrane branched reticular cells impinge on the membrane forming a ramified network constituting the cords or spaces of Billroth. These adventitial cells are morphologically similar to lining cells and their diffuse, abundant cytoplasm forms a complex reticular cell structure binding haemopoietic cells.

The free macrophages present in the spaces of Billroth are involved in a further degree of organisation which characterises haemopoiesis in spleen, marrow and embryonic liver and yolk sac. This organisation involves aggregation of erythroblasts around a central macrophage (see Figure 6.1) and these were interpreted by Bessis and Breton-Gorius (1962) as erythroblastic islets for transfer of ferritin from the central macrophage or 'nurse cell' to the developing erythroblasts. Evidence was obtained for ferritin transfer by rhephocytosis, a form of pinocytosis. Tanaka et al. (1966) observed both rhephocytosis and ferritin accumulation on specific areas of the erythroblast plasma membrane, but specific iron transfer was not indicated since there was no correlation between intercellular iron accumulation and macrophage iron content. Indeed ferritin accumulations may be incidental to general micropinocytosis and ferritin may be transferred in the reverse direction from erythroblast to nurse cell (Berman 1967). A very close asso-

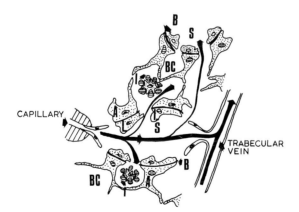

Fig. 6.1. Schematic diagram of sinuses and Billroth cords in splenic red pulp, indicating possible structure of spleen microenvironment. BC = Billroth cords; S = sinus; A = adventitial cells; L = lining cells; I = erythroid islets with central nurse macrophage; B = basement membrane. Arrows indicate main blood flow. (Modified from Pictet et al. 1969a.)

ciation exists between the two types of cell with erythroblasts embedded in and almost completely surrounded by, macrophage cytoplasm. An affinity or recognition mechanism must operate since nurse macrophages do not ingest the developing erythroblasts. However, erythrophagocytosis is frequently observed in identical macrophages which must therefore recognise effete, damaged or abnormal erythroid cells.

It is probable that nurse cell macrophages have an important but as yet unknown role in supporting or sustaining haemopoietic differentiation over and above any simple function as iron storage or transfer cells. They are observed in all tissues engaged in erythropoiesis, in marrow (Sorenson 1962; Bessis and Breton-Gorius 1962; Tanaka et al. 1966; Berman 1967), spleen (Pictet et al. 1969b; Orlic et al. 1965), foetal liver (Zamboni 1965) and yolk sac (Sorenson 1961). In the polycythaemic mouse spleen, proerythroblast islands are seen around a central macrophage within 12–24 hours after erythropoietin treatment (Orlic et al. 1965). Since there was no evidence of ferritin transfer and proerythroblast islets developed so rapidly, erythropoietin-sensitive cells are presumably also organised in clusters around a central macrophage. Such evidence for intimate association of macrophages and a progenitor cell population emphasises the importance of such organisation. Islets of mixtures of several cell types and even pure islets of granulocytes and plasma cells have been reported (Pictet et al. 1969b) indicating such organisation is not necessarily restricted to erythropoiesis.

The purpose of this macrophage-haemopoietic cell association is unresolved but a number of possibilities can be considered:

(1) Macrophages may induce the differentiation of uncommitted stem cells and lead to production of progenitor cell aggregates or islets. This proposal is rendered less likely by the typical macrophage morphology of the central 'nurse cell'. The evidence for the origin of macrophages from circulating haemopoietic precursors sharing a common ancestor in the haemopoietic stem cell, was reviewed in Chapter 5. Thus the complexity of the haemopoietic inducing microenvironment, if expressed through the nurse macrophage, would still require an underlying diversification mechanism peculiar to each organ and probably determined by the fixed mosaic structure of the primary organ stroma. From the point of view of simplicity of organisation, such a two-tiered system is inherently unsatisfactory. Furthermore, though macrophages are generally a slowly proliferating, relatively radioresistant, population it is unlikely that they would be intact following 4000–6000 R irradiation, yet in rats such doses did not inhibit normal haemopoietic regeneration although a delayed wave of secondary aplasia was observed 2 months

after irradiation (Knopse et al. 1968). Since donor macrophages from grafted marrow would have replaced the host population in this system, secondary aplasia was presumably due to damage to a population of stromal cells with a very slow turnover and not replaced by circulating cells. This view is supported by the correlation of aplasia with loss of sinusoidal structure, and the observation that it could only be prevented by direct injection of normal marrow into the aplastic bone-marrow cavity. Evidently the haemopoietic environment can be regenerated from a cell population which does not circulate and is distinct from the haemopoietic stem-cell population.

Evidence is reviewed in Chapter 10 that the defect in haemopoiesis in Sl/Sl anaemic mice resides in the haemopoietic microenvironment. Since Sl/Sl haemopoietic cells can engage in normal haemopoiesis over long periods in irradiated non-Sl recipients, where presumably donor macrophages had replaced those of the host, the defect does not reside in macrophages which participate in the organisation of the erythroblastic islets of recipient marrow and spleen.

(2) Macrophage 'nurse' cells may simply function to detain differentiating haemopoietic cells, preventing their release into the circulation prior to full differentiation. Certainly in early embryogenesis and post-irradiation re-covery, all stages of haemopoietic differentiation appear in the circulation suggesting in both instances that the restraining or detaining capacity of the haemopoietic environment has not developed normal function.

(3) Macrophages may function to facilitate cell interaction. It is beyond the scope of this monograph to review in detail the role of macrophages in the immune response (see Nelson 1969 for a review), but there is considerable evidence to indicate that macrophages may be particularly important in facilitating interaction between different populations of immunocytes and with antigen. In particular, macrophages are required for an immune response *in vitro* to sheep red cells, a response requiring interaction of thymus-derived antigen-sensitive cells and bone-marrow-derived antibody-forming precursor cells (Shortman et al. 1970). Recent data has suggested that the macrophage requirement in such a system can be replaced by media condi-tioned by macrophages (Dutton 1969). This latter observation suggests that this macrophage factor may function as an aggregation factor. Certainly in dispersed cell cultures, free cells rapidly aggregate in a matter of hours, into islets or 'micro-organs' and this seems a critical requirement for retention of functional immune capacity *in vitro* (Auerbach, R., personal communication). In this context the role of macrophages in general haemopoietic homeostasis may be considered to operate either by facilitating close interaction between

stem cells and/or progenitor cells with the inducing cell component of the haemopoietic microenvironment. Alternatively they may facilitate close interaction or aggregation occurring between cells at the same stage of differentiation, permitting either the positive stimulus of autostimulation, or self-conditioning, or a negative feedback operating to control specifically population size.

(4) Mechanisms must operate to control the rate of entry and release of circulating stem cells. In this limited sense the macrophage population may serve as a trap or sieve for circulating cells. At the gross level the availability of space on the macrophage membrane may control the rate of flux in a particular haemopoietic line. Certainly the picture is frequently seen of tiers of cells surrounding a central macrophage with the most differentiated cells to the outside. If macrophage contact is a pre-requisite for further differentiation such a picture may represent growth control operating in a crude lebensraum manner.

(5) Surveillance function of macrophages: close interaction between macrophages and erythroid cells may lead either to maturation or phago-cytosis depending on some form of membrane recognition process. It is possible that, phylogenetically, this form of recognition by macrophages may have had a broad defensive role, but at least with respect to the haemo-poietic system macrophages may have the capacity to recognise membrane incompatibility due to damage, ageing or somatic mutation of haemopoietic cells and convert from nurse cells to phagocytes.

It may be of course that the 'macrophage' cells in haemopoietic micro-environments are quite unrelated to genuine macrophages, sharing with them only a certain similarity in morphology and the capacity for phago-cytosis. Subsequent studies may show these cells to be just as specific as thymic epithelial cells in terms of their function in regulating haemopoiesis.

Stromal cells intrinsic to haemopoietic organs and originating from em-bryonic mesenchyme of the early organ anlage are capable of differentiating into the complex vascular and reticular framework characterising spleen and marrow. To what extent the adventitial and lining reticulo-endothelial elements are derived from this mesenchyme is not known. Certainly the Kupffer cells of liver are of haematogenous origin and it may in the future be more rational to distinguish between the stromal elements of the R-E system differentiating from the fixed mesenchyme, and the labile components of haematogenous origin such as the macrophages and Kupffer cells. The adventitial reticular-cell network of the intersinusoidal regions of marrow and spleen red pulp may determine the nature of haemopoiesis occurring in these sites. These cells fulfil the criteria of 'fixed' cells showing minimum proliferation and considerable radioresistance. Caffrey et al. (1966) labelled marrow reticular cells by repeated tritiated thymidine treatment until all cells were labelled. The incidence of labelled reticular cells was not significantly reduced 1 year after labelling, and no reduction in intensity or incidence of labelling was observed in the period of haemopoietic regeneration following sublethal irradiation. These results showed that reticular cells were not participating in the production of haemopoietic stem cells nor were they stimulated to proliferate in this situation. Such stable populations are probably the components engaged in intimate interaction with haemopoietic stem cells regulating differentiation and proliferation as discussed in Chapter 3, in relation to haemopoietic spleen colony morphology, and in Chapter 10 in relation to genetic defects in haemopoiesis. Granulocytic- and erythroid-determining environments may be related to gross anatomical relationships of stem cells and stromal reticular elements; e.g., proximity to adventitial cells or lining cells, distance from sinuses or position within the spaces of Billroth. Alternatively, the reticulum cell framework though morphologically uniform, may exhibit functional differences and thereby form a cellular mosaic of different microenvironments, quantitatively differing in spleen and marrow. Complex haemopoietic differentiation is observed in foetal liver and to a lesser extent in yolk sac. In the case of liver, intimate contact between liver parenchymal cells and developing haemopoietic cells is seen. At first sight it would seem improbable that a similar capacity to generate a haemo-poietic microenvironmental mosaic should be shared by liver parenchymal cells of entodermal origin, and the mesenchymal mesoderm of the reticular framework of marrow and spleen though this possibility cannot be excluded *a priori*. Alternatively the mesenchymal cells of the septum transversum that interact with the entodermal diverticulum in the genesis of the liver and form the hepatic stroma may, during the embryonic phase, function in a similar capacity to the stromal cells of adult haemopoietic tissue.

It is clear from this brief review of the architectural arrangement of the cells determining splenic microenvironments that simple morphological approaches have not yet been able to characterise what are the essential cellular components of a spleen microenvironment. Further advances in this area will need the use of simpler model systems *in vitro*, possibly using dissociated cells subjected to cell-separation procedures and identifiable by functional markers.

One interesting general question which can be posed regarding the spleen is whether the different microenvironmental areas within the organ can sense and have their behaviour influenced by the level of functional activity of similar areas elsewhere in the spleen. Does the total amount of regenerating colony tissue affect the growth rate of individual colonies or their content of stem cells? Analysis of spleen colony size at day 14 revealed no consistent size difference between colonies in spleens containing few colonies vs. spleens containing up to 80 colonies (Moore, M. A. S. and Metcalf, D., unpublished data). Similarly no obvious difference was observed in stem-cell content between these colonies. Similar data have been obtained by Lahiri and Van Putten (1969) and Schofield and Lajtha (1969), although the latter workers reported some difference in the initial rate of accumulation of CFU's.

The behaviour of spleen grafts in mice has given some evidence for the existence of overall regulation of proliferative activity. Thus single sub-cutaneous spleen grafts from neonatal donors grew to the larger size and exhibited more active erythropoiesis in splenectomised than in sham-operated recipients (Metcalf 1963b). Analysis of multiple spleen grafts has also provided evidence of overall regulation of haemopoietic activity in the spleen. Unlike the situation with thymus grafts which are quite autonomous, the growth of individual spleen grafts is influenced by the presence of other spleen grafts in the same recipient. The more numerous the spleen grafts, the smaller the size attainable by each graft and the total spleen-graft mass attainable in splenectomised recipients plateaus out at 100–200 mg, which approximates the mass of a normal spleen (Metcalf 1964c).

Splenectomy of an animal already carrying a spleen graft causes an unusual sequence of events in the graft. The red pulp becomes dilated by spaces which are initially cell free but which subsequently contain active erythropoietic and granulopoietic cells (Metcalf 1965). Although the lymphoid elements parallel the behaviour of erythroid elements following splenectomy of the host, the effects are not the same on other cells in the spleen. The mast-cell content of spleen-graft red pulp is dramatically *reduced* by splenectomy of the host (Metcalf 1965) and the megakaryocytic content is similarly reduced. The changes are too complex for detailed interpretation but they suggest that modification of the functional activity of splenic tissue (or removal of this tissue) can influence cell populations in other splenic tissue in the body and that in part this is likely to be due to changes in non-haemopoietic elements determining the various microenvironments which occur *before* changes in haemopoiesis take place.

At this point a digression is appropriate. The striking behaviour of the stromal elements of spleen grafts in appearing to anticipate the future need for more haemopoiesis following splenectomy of the host raises a question of broader scope regarding haemopoietic microenvironments in the developing haemopoietic system. Does an organ anlage develop in anticipation of the arrival of haemopoietic cells or is it passively expanded by the proliferation of cells which have seeded out and commenced proliferation? Most workers have probably tacitly assumed that the latter process occurs, but the morphology of neonatal haemopoietic organs does not suggest that the organs at any stage are tightly packed with haemopoietic cells, and it seems likely that the stromal cells of the developing organ can actually modify their activity prior to the arrival of stem cells. The biological processes involved in such anticipatory behaviour have not been investigated; but whatever the mechanisms are which ensure that a lymph node or spleen anlage develops initially and subsequently modifies itself in preparation for the arrival of stem cells, it can be assumed that these mechanisms continue to operate in adult life and modify the behaviour of the cells determining organ microenvironments.

In an organ as complex as the spleen, it is pertinent to raise the question of whether the different haemopoietic populations themselves influence the proliferation of each other. In situations where there is a limited supply of metabolites, an extreme proliferative stimulus for one cell class might cause a restriction in the degree of cell proliferation of other cell classes. A more likely situation arises from the common ancestry of the erythroid, granulocytic and megakaryocytic cells. Here so many cells may become committed to one pathway that there is a depletion of new cells available to enter alternative pathways. Such interactions might be due to changes in the microenvironment if the proliferative stimulus led to an increase in the number or size of microenvironmental foci for one particular cell class. A possible example of this is the reduction in erythropoiesis seen in mice injected with Freund's complete adjuvant which induces a pronounced increase in granulocyte and macrophage formation (McNeill 1970a).

Scattered observations have led some to propose that some lymphocytes may have non-immunological functions, specifically that they may possess growth regulatory functions (Burch and Burwell 1965) or trephocytic functions (Loutit 1962). In the latter speculation it is envisaged that lymphocytes may provide building blocks, e.g. complex nuclear material, which promotes or facilitates the proliferation of other cell classes. In the context of the spleen, do splenic lymphocytes influence in any way the proliferation of other haemopoietic cells?

In a study of the growth of mixed organ grafts it was observed that combination of thymus tissue with spleen increased the size attained by the spleen

fragments (Metcalf 1964a). This size increase appeared to affect all components of the splenic tissue – lymphoid, erythroid, granulocytic and megakaryocytic. Combination of a variety of other tissues with spleen produced
no similar growth increment and conversely, thymus fragments did not
potentiate the growth of kidney, lung or brain tissue. The mechanism responsible for this growth potentiation was not established, but it did not
appear to be associated with obvious migration of thymic lymphocytes into
the splenic tissue.

Auerbach (1960) has made somewhat similar observations *in vitro*.
Addition of thymic cells to spleen explants from neonatal mice was observed
to cause an increase in granulopoiesis in the cultured spleens.

The injection of parental thymic cells to irradiated F_1 hybrid mice receiving parental bone-marrow cells has been shown to increase the number
and growth rate of all types of haemopoietic colonies in the spleen. On the
other hand, thymectomy did not affect spleen colony-growth rates (Goodman and Shinpock 1968; Goodman J. W., personal communication).

An even clearer example of growth potentiation by lymphoid cells was
observed in agar cultures of bone-marrow cells. Addition of thymic or lymph-
node lymphocytes potentiated the growth rate of both granulocytic and
macrophage colonies. In this effect, allogeneic cells were equally as effective
as syngeneic cells and studies using lymphoid cells labelled with tritiated
thymidine showed that the proliferating colony cells extensively reutilised
labelled nuclear material from the added lymphoid cells (Metcalf 1968).
It is not suggested that the trephocytic effects of lymphoid cells observed in
these experiments are necessarily unique for lymphoid cells and other
disintegrating cells might release material with similar properties. However,
in an organ like the spleen, large numbers of lymphoid cells are present, and
these cells might be able under some circumstances to significantly modify
the proliferative behaviour of other haemopoietic cells.

6.5.1   Summary

The non-lymphoid parts of the spleen contain specialised areas of small size
which constitute microenvironments regulating the proliferation of erythroid,
granulocytic and megakaryocytic cells. The properties of these microenvironments are:

(1) to commit incoming multipotent stem cells to a single pathway of
differentiation;

(2) to support and possibly regulate the generation of clones of differen-

tiating cells from these committed stem cells, probably in collaboration with humoral regulators;

(3) to allow extensive but not unlimited self-generation of multipotent stem cells, and to conserve stem cells from total extinction even in the face of extreme haemopoietic demand;

(4) to restrict exit of cells from the microenvironment until full maturity is reached;

(5) to anticipate or respond to changing demands for haemopoiesis by becoming active or dormant.

6.6 Bone-marrow microenvironment

The bone marrow is a major site in the body for the formation of red cells, neutrophils, eosinophils, monocytes, megakaryocytes and appears in most species to generate considerable numbers of lymphocyte-like cells. It is also the major repository in post-embryonic life of haemopoietic stem cells, together with their immediate descendents, the specific progenitor cells.

Many of the characteristics of the bone-marrow microenvironment which must exist to make this cellular proliferation and differentiation possible have already been discussed. The difference between the spleen and bone marrow is essentially one of emphasis. In the bone marrow there is a far greater degree of self-perpetuation of stem cells than in the spleen and in the mouse at least, there would also appear to be relatively more microenvironmental foci supporting granulocytic proliferation than in the spleen.

There is a great need for a detailed morphological analysis in mammals of intact bone-marrow tissue to determine the exact distribution of these various proliferating populations as it can be anticipated there must be specialisation at the microscopic level in the regions generating different cell classes.

In the chicken, a remarkable segregation of haemopoietic cells has been shown to occur (Bizzozero 1890; Sabin 1928; Bayon 1930). In electron-micrographs, apparently pure populations of granulopoietic cells have been observed to lie in aggregates outside the vascular sinusoids, whilst erythropoiesis is exclusively confined to regions within the sinusoids (Mladenov et al. 1967). If this regional segregation occurs in other species it would strongly suggest the existence of discrete microenvironmental regions with properties similar to those discussed in relation to the spleen.

Unfortunately, we still know so little of the morphology of stem and progenitor cells that conventional morphological approaches probably will not help answer many of the most intriguing questions regarding the regulation of differentiation at the stem cell level. From the evidence in Chapter 3 it is clear that within the bone-marrow microenvironment, differentiation of multipotent stem cells occurs to give rise to progenitor cells of erythroid, granulocytic, megakaryocytic, monocytic and lymphoid cells. Some of this differentiation, e.g. of lymphoid progenitor cells, must be exquisitely subtle and yet the barrier to morphological identification of these cells at present prevents attempts at analysis of the many cell-cell interactions which must be occurring.

The events occurring between the formation of multipotent stem cells and the generation of identifiable cells of the various classes can be presumed to be essentially similar in the bone marrow to those discussed in the spleen. Again multipotent stem cells must migrate within the bone-marrow cavity, lodge in microenvironments supporting specific types of cell proliferation, and there become committed to that pathway and to commence proliferation.

One point which is never experimentally relevant in studying spleen colonies is the question of the life span of these individual microenvironments. If it is assumed that the bone marrow is a reasonably stable structure, the arrangement of cells creating a particular microenvironment might be expected to be relatively permanent. Having served as 'host' for one stem cell which enters haemopoiesis, does it subsequently become seeded by a sporadic sequence of new stem cells generated elsewhere in the marrow? If so, the haemopoietic cells within any one microenvironmental focus at any one point in time would not necessarily represent the progeny of the original stem cell which seeded. Alternatively, microenvironmental foci may be entirely labile, impermanent structures, which wax and wane as new ones arise in previously vacant areas of the bone marrow. Some fluctuation occurs in the total cellularity of bone marrow and in the distribution of haemopoietic cells within the shaft, in response to age changes and relatively physiological stimuli, but the cellular basis for this in terms of microenvironments is at present unknown. Here it should be reiterated that the capacity of the bone marrow to modify its cellularity is rather limited, and where demands for additional haemopoiesis become severe, the spleen tends to respond more vigorously and to play a relatively more important role in haemopoiesis. The microenvironments of the bone marrow appears to be so constructed as to allow the entry and exit of stem cells to the circulation. In the normal animal this process may be essentially one-way (bone marrow to blood) but in the repopulation of irradiated animals by injected bone-marrow cells, it is readily demonstrable that the flow can be temporarily reversed although the bone marrow is less efficient than the spleen in trapping stem cells (see Chapter 3). This process is presumably not a passive overflow process due to tissue crowding as the rate of release can be modified by such factors as antigenic stimulation (Barnes and Loutit 1967). Until more is known of the morphology and properties of stem cells, i.e. whether they are actively motile cells, little more can be said regarding the process of release of stem cells.

This general problem of the mechanism of the release of cells from the bone-marrow microenvironment applies to all populations in the bone marrow. Electron-microscopic studies have shown that the walls of the capillaries and sinusoids in the bone marrow are not intact but have lacunae which could allow relatively free cell entry and exit (Hudson and Yoffey 1966). The problem is in fact not how cells can leave but why they do not. In the normal animal there is a remarkable degree of precision in the regulation of cell release from the bone marrow. The only cells entering the blood are mature cell elements, whether these be reticulocytes or neutrophils. In the case of cells which are actively motile when fully differentiated, e.g. polymorphs, it is easy enough to visualise a process whereby a mature cell could acquire sufficiently active motility to break loose from the bone-marrow microenvironment. However, in the case of the reticulocyte this problem must have another solution, as no evidence exists that a reticulocyte possesses active motility and, on general grounds, it should be relatively inert compared with even a nucleated red cell. Why then does a reticulocyte have the capacity to leave the bone marrow whilst a normoblast does not? Here questions of cell-surface structure and stickiness could be relevant but these await further investigation.

The vascular sinusoids of the marrow consist of a trilaminar wall of lining or littoral cells, basement membrane and a layer of adventitial cells enclosing a central lumen. The adventitial layer is incomplete and cytoplasmic processes or even whole cells may extend from this layer to produce a degree of compartmentalising of the perisinusoidal spaces (Weiss 1965). The sinus wall is a responsive structure and increasing numbers of apertures develop in the course of massive reticulocyte release in anaemia or granulocyte release following endotoxin treatment (Weiss 1965, 1970). The process of cell release into the circulation may be due to maturing haemopoietic cells displacing the adventitial layer in a region where the basement membrane is absent and producing first a thinning and then a breakdown of the lining layer of littoral cells. Adventitial cells may serve more actively to effect the exit of cells to the blood since they may undergo swelling and encroach into the perisinusoidal haemopoietic spaces displacing the haemopoietic cell population (Weiss 1970).

As was discussed in the section on lymphoid microenvironments, present evidence indicates that antibody-forming cell progenitors (AFC-P) originate in the bone marrow. Furthermore the capacity of antigen-coated glass bead columns to deplete bone-marrow populations of these cells (Singhal and Wigzell 1970) indicates that these cells have acquired specific reactivity to individual antigens within the bone-marrow microenvironment. We speculated in Chapter 5 that these cells may be members of the small lymphocyte-like population in the bone marrow, but this remains to be established. Nothing is known of the localisation of lymphoid cells or AFC-P's in the bone marrow and thus nothing can be said regarding the possible existence of specific lymphoid microenvironments in the bone marrow. It may be that it is sufficient for stem and progenitor cells to exhibit a relatively high degree of mitotic activity to generate by random-chance cells with reactivity to diverse antigens, but the process may be subject to much more precise regulation. Antigenic stimulation appears to be unnecessary for the generation of AFC-P's. Reports that antigens stimulate the proliferation of AFC's in the bone marrow have been made but the technique used merely measured ^{14}C thymidine uptake in unfractionated bone-marrow populations (Singhal and Richter 1968) and may well have been measuring antigen-induced proliferation of progenitors of granulocytes and macrophages (McNeill 1970a; Metcalf 1971). This latter process probably results indirectly from the production of elevated serum levels of CSF in antigen-injected animals and since the phenomenon can be reproduced entirely *in vitro* in suspensions of bone-marrow cells (McNeill 1970b; Metcalf 1971) it does not appear to require the intervention of a special microenvironment.

6.7 General discussion

This account of the function of the haemopoietic microenvironments has emphasised the uncertainties which still exist regarding the regulation of haemopoiesis. Certain generalisations can be attempted however:

(a) Microenvironments can exist as small and specialised regions within haemopoietic tissues.

(b) Microenvironments can be shut down or reactivated to meet changing demands for blood-cell production.

(c) Microenvironments appear to selectively localise or retain appropriate precursor cells.

(d) Microenvironments are specific for one cell class and usually operate by inducing differentiation in uncommitted multipotent stem cells, the exception being in the peripheral lymphoid organs where cells entering the microenvironment appear to be progenitor cells with predetermined reactivity patterns.

(e) The action of humoral regulating factors may be influenced by the microenvironment in which the responsive progenitor cells reside.

(f) The microenvironment selectively retains haemopoietic cells until full maturation is achieved and can regulate the survival of differentiating cells (e.g. in the thymus) and control their exit.

(g) The overall production of blood cells in scattered microenvironments appears to be regulated by a series of control systems involving specific feedback control in conjunction with stem-cell migration or recirculation in the case of lymphoid progenitor cells.

Factors determining the differentiation of the microenvironmental cells remain to be characterised. Haemopoietic cells contain all the information required for their further differentiation and specialisation; yet these processes require exogenous epigenetic stimuli. Both humoral factors and micro-environmental influences provide this exogenous stimulus for differentiation. The diversity of the products of such stimuli suggest that we are dealing with a chain of differentiative interactions leading to the production of micro-environmental induction mosaics. To develop such microenvironmental complexity multiple interactive stages must be present during the course of development.

In primary lymphoid tissue such as the thymus and bursa at least three inductive interactions are apparent during the course of development; an initial interaction between endoderm and ectoderm, followed by an epithelial-mesenchymal induction, and subsequently an interaction between immigrant stem cells and epithelium. This sequence of heterotypic interactions may be followed by homotypic interactive processes occurring between like cells which may be of particular importance in the development of the complex mesenchymal environments of spleen, lymph nodes and bone marrow. Homotypic interactions between undifferentiated mesenchymal cells leading to regional specialisation of inducing cells of the microenvironment may in turn be related to such parameters as cell-population density and aggregation, with further differentiation occurring once critical cell concentrations are achieved.

References

Ada, G. L., 1967, Specialised cell functions in the lymphoid and reticuloendothelial cell series. In: Immunity, cancer and chemotherapy, edited by E. Mihich. New York, Academic Press, p. 17.

Ada, G. L. and G. J. V. Nossal, 1971, Antigens, lymphoid cells and the immune response. New York, Academic Press.

Ada, G. L., C. R. Parish, G. J. V. Nossal, and A. Abbot, 1967, Cold Spring Harbor Symposia on Quantitative Biology *32*, 381.

Archer, O. K., D. E. R. Sutherland, and R. A. Good, 1964, Lab. Invest. *13*, 259.

Arnesen, K., 1958, Acta pathol. microbiol. Scand. *43*, 339.

Aschoff, L., 1924, Ergebn. Inn. Med. *26*, 1.

Auerbach, R., 1966, Embryogenesis of immune systems. In: CIBA Symposium on the thymus: experimental and clinical studies, edited by G. E. W. Wolstenholme and R. Porter. London, Churchill, p. 39.

Azazaki, K., 1962, Tohoku J. Exp. Med. *76*, 107.

Balfour, B. M. and J. H. Humphrey, 1967, Localization of γ-globulin and labeled antigen in germinal centres in relation to the immune response. In: Germinal centers in immune responses, edited by H. Cottier, N. Odartchenko, R. Schindler, and C. C. Congdon. New York, Springer-Verlag, p. 80.

Barnes, D. W. H. and J. F. Loutit, 1967, Lancet *2*, 1138.

Bayon, H. P., 1930, J. Comp. Path. Therap. *43*, 188.

Berman, I., 1967, J. Ultrastruct. Res. *17*, 291.

Bessis, M. C. and J. Breton-Gorius, 1962, Blood *19*, 635.

Bizzozero, G., 1890, Arch. Mikroskop. Anat. Entwicklungsmech. *35*, 424.

Borum, K., 1969, Acta pathol. microbiol. scand. *76* 515.

Brumby, M. and D. Metcalf, 1967, Proc. Soc. Exp. Biol. Med. *124*, 99.

Burch, P. R. and R. G. Burwell, 1965, Quart. Rev. Biol. *40*, 252.

Burnet, M., 1962, Brit. Med. J. *2*, 807.

Caffrey, R. W., N. B. Everett, and W. O. Rieke, 1966, Anat. Rec. *155*, 41.

Cain, W. A., M. D. Cooper, P. J. van Alten, and R. A. Good, 1969, J. Immunol. *102*, 671.

Carlens, O., 1928, Anat. Entwicklungsgesch. *86*, 393.

Cerottini, J. C. and K. J. Brunner, 1967, Immunology *13*, 395.

Chiller, J. M., G. S. Habicht, and W. O. Weigle, 1970, Proc. Nat. Acad. Sci. (Wash.) *65*, 551.

Clark, S. L., 1966, Cytological evidence of secretion in the thymus. In: CIBA Symposium on the thymus: experimental and clinical studies, edited by G. E. W. Wolstenholme and R. Porter. London, J. and A. Churchill, p. 3.

Cooper, G. N. and K. Turner, 1967, Aust. J. Exp. Biol. Med. Sci. *45*, 363.

Cooper, M. D., D. Y. Perey, M. F. McKneally, A. E. Gabrielsen, D. E. R. Sutherland, and R. A. Good, 1966, Lancet *1*, 1388.

Cooper, M. D., D. Y. Perey, A. E. Gabrielsen, D. E. R. Sutherland, M. F. McKneally and R. A. Good, 1968, Int. Arch. Allergy, *33*, 65.

Cornes, J. S., 1965, Gut *6*, 225.

Craddock, C. G., G. S. Nakai, H. Fukuta, and L. M. Vanslager, 1964, J. Exp. Med. *120*, 389.

Cronkite, E. P., C. R. Jansen, H. Cottier, K. Rai, and I. R. Sife, 1964, Ann. N.Y. Acad. Sci. *113*, 566.

De Petris, S., G. Karlsbad, B. Pernis, and J. L. Turk, 1966, Int. Arch. Allergy, *29*, 112.

De Sousa, M. B., 1968, Exp. Hemat. *17*, 4.

De Sousa, M. A. B. and D. M. V. Parrott, 1967, The definition of a germinal center area as distinct from the thymus-dependent area in the lymphoid tissue of the mouse. In: Germinal centers in immune responses, edited by H. Cottier, N. Odartchenko, R. Schindler, and C. C. Congdon. New York, Springer-Verlag, p. 361.

Dougherty, T. F., M. L. Berliner, G. L. Schneebeli, and D. L. Berliner, 1964, Annals N.Y. Acad. Sci. *113*, 825.

Dukor, P., J. F. A. P. Miller, W. House and V. Allman, 1965, Transplantation *3*, 639.

Dutton, R. W., 1969, Discussion section. In: Mediators of cellular immunity, edited by H. S. Lawrence and M. Landy. New York, Academic Press, p. 84.

Dwyer, J. M. and I. R. Mackay, 1970, Lancet *1*, 1199.

Ellis, S. T., J. L. Gowans, and J. C. Howard, 1967, Cellular events during the formation of antibody. In: Cold Spring Harbor symposium on quantitative biology *32*, 395.

Evans, E. P., D. A. Ogden, C. E. Ford, and H. S. Micklem, 1967, Nature *216*, 36.

Fichtelius, K. E., 1968, Exp. Cell. Res. *49*, 87.

Fichtelius, K. E., O. Groth, and S. Liden, 1970, Int. Arch. Allergy *37*, 607.

Fitch, F. W., R. Stejskal, and D. A. Rowley, 1968, Exp. Hemat. *17*, 20.

Fitch, F. W., R. Stejskal, and D. A. Rowley, 1969, In: Lymphatic tissues and germinal centers in immune response. Adv. Exp. Med. Biol., edited by H. Cottier and C. C. Congdon. New York, Plenum Publishing Corp. (in press).

Ford, C. E., 1966, Traffic of lymphoid cells in the body. In: CIBA Symposium on the thymus: experimental and clinical studies, edited by G. E. W. Wolstenholme and R. Porter. London, J. and A. Churchill, p. 131.

Fresen, O. 1960, Tohoku J. Exp. Med. *73*, 1.

Gajl, K. J., A. J. Fish, H. J. Meuwissen, D. Frommel, and R. A. Good, 1969, J. Exp. Med. *130*, 1367.

Gesner, B. M. and V. Ginsburg, 1964, Proc. Nat. Acad. Sci. *52*, 750.

Gilmour, D. G., G. A. Theis, and G. J. Thorbecke, 1970, J. Exp. Med. *132*, 134.

Goldschneider, I. and D. D. McGregor, 1968, J. Exp. Med. *127*, 155.

Goodman, J. W. and S. G. Shinpock, 1968, Proc. Soc. Exp. Biol. Med. *129*, 417.

Gowans, J. L. and E. J. Knight, 1964, Proc. Roy. Soc. B *159*, 257.

Griscelli, C., P. Vassalli, and R. T. McClusky, 1969, J. Exp. Med. *130*, 1427.

Hall, J. G. and B. Morris, 1965, Brit. J. Exp. Path. *46*, 450.

Hanna, M. G. Jr. 1965, Intern. Arch. Allergy appl. Immunol. *26*, 230.

Hanna, M. G. Jr., D. C. Swartzendruber, and C. C. Congdon, 1966, Exp. Mol. Pathol., Suppl. *3*, 75.

Haskill, J. S., T. A. McNeill, and M. A. S. Moore, 1970, J. Cell. Physiol. *75*, 181.

Hudson, G. and J. M. Yoffey, 1966, Interchange of lymphocytes between marrow and blood. In: The lymphocyte in immunology and haemopoiesis, edited by J. M. Yoffey. London, Ed. Arnold, p. 131.

Iorio, R. J., A. D. Chanana, E. P. Cronkite, and D. D. Joel, 1970, Cell. Tissue Kinet. *3*, 161.

Ishidate, M. and D. Metcalf, 1963, Aust. J. Exp. Biol. Med. Sci. *41*, 637.

Ito, T. and T. Hoshino, 1961, Anat. Anz. *109*, 436.

Jacobson, E. B. and G. J. Thorbecke, 1969, J. Exp. Med. *130*, 287.

Kennedy, J. C., P. E. Treadwell, and E. S. Lennox, 1970, J. Exp. Med. *132*, 353.

Kinsley, M. H., 1936, Anat. Rec. *65*, 23.

Knospe, W. H., J. Blom, and W. H. Crosby, 1968, Blood *31*, 400.

Koburg, E., 1967, Cell production and cell migration in the tonsil. In: Germinal centers in immune responses, edited by H. Cottier, N. Odartchenko, R. Schindler, and C. C. Congdon. New York Springer-Verlag, p. 176.

Lahiri, S. K. and L. M. van Putten, 1969, Cell Tissue Kinet. *2*, 21.

Lang, G. and G. L. Ada, 1967, Immunology *13*, 523.

Loutit, J. F., 1962, Lancet, 1106.

Mandel, T., 1969, Aust. J. Exp. Biol. Med. Sci. *47*, 153.

Marshall, A. H. E., An outline of the cytology and pathology of the reticular tissue. London, Oliver and Boyd.

Matsuyama, M., M. Wiadrowski, and D. Metcalf, 1966, J. Exp. Med. *123*, 559.

McGregor, D. D. and J. L. Gowans, 1963, J. Exp. Med. *117*, 303.

McNeill, T. A., 1970a, Immunol. *18*, 61.

McNeill, T. A., 1970b, Immunology *18*, 39.

Metcalf, D., 1962, Leukaemogenesis in AKR mice. In: CIBA Symposium on tumour viruses of murine origin, edited by G. E. W. Wolstenholme and M. O'Connor. London, J. and A. Churchill, p. 233.

Metcalf, D. 1963a, Aust. J. Exp. Biol. Med. Sci. *41*, 437.

Metcalf, D., 1963b, Aust. J. Exp. Biol. Med. Sci. *41*, 51.

Metcalf, D. 1964a, Interactions between the thymus and other organs. In: The thymus, edited by V. Defendi and D. Metcalf. Philadelphia, Wistar Institute Press, p. 53.

Metcalf, D., 1964b, The thymus and lymphopoiesis. In: The thymus in immunobiology, edited by R. A. Good and A. E. Gabrielsen. New York, Harper and Row, p. 150.

Metcalf, D., 1964c, Transplantation *2*, 387.

Metcalf, D., 1965, Aust. J. Exp. Biol. Med. Sci. *43*, 533.

Metcalf, D., 1966, The nature and regulation of lymphopoiesis in the normal and neoplastic thymus. In: CIBA Symposium on the thymus: experimental and clinical studies, edited by G. E. W. Wolstenholme and R. Porter. London, J. and A. Churchill, p. 242.

Metcalf, D., 1968, J. Cell. Physiol. *72*, 9.

Metcalf, D., 1971, Immunology (in press).

Metcalf, D. and M. Wiadrowski, 1966, Cancer Res. *26*, 483.

Metcalf, D., N. Sparrow, K. Nakamura, and M. Ishidate, 1961, Aust. J. Exp. Biol. Med. Sci. *39*, 441.

Meuwissen, H. J., G. T. Kaplan, D. Y. Perey, and R. A. Good, 1969, Proc. Soc. Exp. Biol. Med. *130*, 300.

Micklem, H. S., 1967, Exp. Hemat. *14*, 25.

Miller, J. F. A. P. and G. F. Mitchell, 1969, Interaction between two distinct cell lineages in an immune response. In: Lymphatic tissues and germinal centers in immune response, edited by L. Fiore-Donati and M. G. Hanna, Jr. New York, Plenum Press, p. 455.

Miller, J. F. A. P. and G. F. Mitchell, 1970, J. Exp. Med. *131*, 675.

Mitchell, G. F. and J. F. A. P. Miller, 1968, Proc. Natl. Acad. Sci. *59*, 296.

Miyakawa, M., 1959, Ann. N.Y. Acad. Sci. *78*, 221.

Mladenov, Z., U. Heine, D. Beard, and J. W. Beard, 1967, J. Natl. Cancer Inst. *38*, 251.

Movat, H. Z. and N. V. P. Fernando, 1965, Exp. Mol. Pathol. *4*, 155.

Murray, R. G. and P. A. Woods, 1964, Anat. Rec. *150*, 113.

Nakamura, K. and D. Metcalf, 1961, Brit. J. Cancer *15*, 306.

Nelson, D. S., 1969, Macrophages and Immunity. Amsterdam, North-Holland Publ. Co.

Nossal, G. J. V., 1964, Annals N.Y. Acad. Sci. *120*, 171.

Oettgen, H. F., R. Silber, P. A. Miescher, and K. Hirschorn, 1966, Clin. exp. Immunol. *1*, 77.

Orlic, D., A. S. Gordon, and J. A. Rhodin, 1965, J. Ultrastruct. Res. *13*, 516.

Parrott, D. M. V., 1967, The integrity of the germinal center: an investigation of the differential localization of labeled cells in lymphoid organs. In: Germinal centers in immune responses, edited by H. Cottier, N. Odartchenko, R. Schindler, and C. C. Congdon. New York, Springer-Verlag, p. 168.

Parrott, D. M. V., M. A. B. de Sousa, and J. East, 1966, J. Exp. Med. *123*, 191.

Perey, D. Y. and R. A. Good, Lab. Invest. *18*, 15.

Perey, D. Y. E., J. Finstad, B. Pollard, and R. A. Good, 1968, Lab. Invest. *19*, 591.

Pernis, B., G. Chiappino, A. S. Kelus, and P. G. B. Gell, 1965, J. Exp. Med. *122*, 853.

Peterson, R. D. A., M. D. Cooper, and R. A. Good, 1965, Amer. J. Med. *38*, 579.

Pictet, R., L. Orci, W. G. Forssman, and L. Girardier, 1969a, Zeitschrift für Zellforsch. Mikro-Anatomie *96*, . . .

Pictet, R., L. Orci, W. G. Forssman, and L. Girardier, 1969b, Zeitschrift für Zellforsch. Mikro-Anatomie *96*, 400.

Playfair, J. H. L., 1969, Nature *222*, 883.

Pollara, B., J. Finstad, and R. A. Good, 1968, Exp. Hematol. *17*, 1.

Pollard, M., 1970, Fed. Proc. *29*, 811 (Abs.).

Ravens, J. R., 1968, J. Reticuloendo. Soc. *5*, 559.

Sabin, F. R., 1928, Physiol. Rev. *8*, 191.

Schlesinger, M., 1970, Prog. Exp. Tumor Res. *13* (in press).

Schlesinger, M. and D. Hurvitz, 1968a, J. Exp. Med. *127*, 1127.

Schlesinger, M. and D. Hurvitz, 1968b, Israel J. Med. Sci. *4*, 1210.

Schofield, R. and L. G. Lajtha, 1969, Cell Tissue Kinet. *2*, 147.

Schwarz, M. R., 1967, Proc. Soc. Exp. Biol. Med. *125*, 701.

Shearer, G. M. and Cudkowicz, G., 1969, J. Exp. Med. *130*, 1243.

Shortman, K., E. Diener, P. Russell, and W. D. Armstrong, 1970, J. Exp. Med. *131*, 461.

Silverstein, A. M., B. I. Osburn, and R. A. Prendergast, 1970, Fed. Proc. *29*, 699 (Abs.).

Simon, G. and R. Pictet, 1964, Acta Anat. *57*, 163.

Singhal, S. K. and M. Richter, 1968, J. Exp. Med. *128*, 1099.

Singhal, S. H. and Wigzell, H., 1970, J. Exp. Med. *131*, 149.

Smith, C. and Kieffer, D. A., 1957, Proc. Soc. Exp. Biol. Med. *94*, 601.

Sordat, B., M. Sordat, M. W. Hess, R. D. Stoner, and H. Cottier, 1970, J. Exp. Med. *131*, 77.

Sorensen, G. D., 1961, Lab. Invest. *10*, 178.

Sorensen, G. D., 1962, Amer. J. Path. *40*, 297.

Stoner, R. D. and N. M. Hale, 1955, J. Immunol. *75*, 203.

Sutherland, D. E. R., O. K. Archer, and R. A. Good, 1964, Proc. Soc. Exp. Biol. Med. *115*, 673.

Swartzendruber, D. C., 1966, Am. J. Pathol. *48*, 613.

Tanaka, Y., G. Brecher, and B. Bull, 1966, Blood *28*, 758.

Taylor, R. B., 1969, Transp. Revs. *1*, 114.

Theis, G. A., E. B. Jacobson, and G. J. Thorbecke, 1968, Exp. Hemat. *17*, 9.

Thomas, C. E., 1967, Amer. J. Anat. *120*, 527.

Thorbecke, G. J., 1967, In: Discussion to Session 13. In: Germinal centres in immune responses, edited by H. Cottier, N. Odartchenko, R. Schindler, and C. C. Congdon. New York, Springer-Verlag, p. 347.

Trowell, O. A., 1961, Int. J. Rad. Biol. *4*, 163.

Turk, J. L. and J. Oort, 1968, Exp. Hemat. *17*, 26.

Wakefield, J. D. and G. J. Thorbecke, 1968, J. Exp. Med. *128*, 153.

Warner, N. L., 1967, Folia Biol. *13*, 1.

Weber, W. T., 1967, Exp. Cell. Res. *46*, 464.

Weiss, L., 1963, Amer. J. Anat. *113*, 51.

Weiss, L., 1965, J. Morph. *117*, 467.

Weiss, L., 1970, Blood *36*, 189.

Weissman, I., 1967, J. Exp. Med. *126*, 291.

W. H. O. technical report series No. 448, 1970, Factors Regulating the Immune Response. Report of a WHO Scientific Group. Geneva, World Health Organization, p. 20.

Wolf, N. S. and J. J. Trentin, 1968, J. Exp. Med. *127*, 205.

Woodruff, J. and B. M. Gesner, 1968, Science *161*, 176.

Young, I., J. Allen, and H. Friedman, 1968, Exp. Hematol. *17*, 20.

Zamboni, L., 1965, J. Ultrastruct. Res. *12*, 509.

CHAPTER 7

Humoral regulation of haemopoiesis

7.1 General introduction

The essential problem in the regulation of haemopoiesis is that, starting with aggregates of stem and progenitor cells scattered throughout the body, a regular and controlled supply of short-lived end cells must be delivered to the peripheral blood where the individual cells are in motion. This situation is inherently more complex than exists with a single solid organ like the liver which has a relatively uniform population of cells. Regardless of whether haemopoiesis is based on a rather crude system of demand and supply or is modulated by more subtle systems involving specific feedback inhibitors, the only logical system for regulating cell production would seem to require the operation of humoral regulatory factors. Humoral regulators would be capable of supplying a proliferative stimulus which was uniformly distributed to the scattered aggregates of haemopoietic cells, of supplying a system for monitoring the total number of end-product cells and, if need be, capable of mediating feedback inhibition of cell production. Even our present limited knowledge makes it clear that many regulators must exist and that the haemopoietic cells must be bathed continually in a mixture of these different humoral regulators.

Certain questions can be posed regarding the specific problem of differentiation in haemopoietic cells: what regulates the division of stem and progenitor cells and determines whether the cells shall be in a G_0 phase or in active cell cycle? What determines whether a dividing cell forms more differentiated progeny or daughters similar to the parent cell (self-generation)? What mechanism results in a permanent loss of the capacity of a differentiating cell to divide any further?

Different stages of commitment to the pathways of differentiation exist, and as discussed in the preceding chapter, short-range local microenvironmental influences induce the initial commitment of the multipotential stem cells. This commitment may be independent of humoral regulators but may lead to the appearance of membrane receptors specific for a particular humoral regulator. The subsequent fate of what is now a specific target cell could well be determined by (a) the concentration of the appropriate humoral regulator, (b) the potential life span of the cell, (c) the availability of receptor sites on the target cell membrane, (d) the position of the cell in cell cycle, (e) the time elapsed since differentiation from the stem cell (points (d) and (e) may influence (c)), (f) the influence of the microenvironment on accessibility of receptor sites and interaction with a humoral regulator, (g) stochastic factors, (f) feedback influences from more differentiated cells.

Differentiation in dividing cell populations raises one central question – can a cell divide asymmetrically to form two daughter cells whose subsequent behaviour will differ? Oddly enough, this simple question has never been decisively answered for any haemopoietic cell, and our current inability to answer this fundamental question leaves the answers to more specific questions in a state of considerable uncertainty.

At first sight the question seems capable of only one answer, namely that some cells at least must divide asymmetrically. After all, the fertilised ovum gives rise to an animal containing a multitude of different cells and surely this must be due to repeated asymmetrical division. Furthermore, in an irradiated adult animal, a single stem cell can be shown to produce populations of erythroid, granulocytic, lymphocytic and megakaryocytic cells. Does not this also mean that some of the cells must divide asymmetrically? Unfortunately, neither of these dramatic examples actually proves asymmetrical division *at the single cell level*. It is equally possible that a cell divides symmetrically to form two identical progeny but that subsequent events lead one of these daughter cells to divide symmetrically to form progeny of one type and the other daughter to divide symmetrically to form progeny of another type.

In a situation in which a haemopoietic cell gives rise ultimately to progeny of two types, how might this process be controlled by a humoral regulator? Conceptually it is easier to envisage the action of a regulator if cells divide asymmetrically. Suppose e.g. that during division not all gene products (repressors, messenger RNA's, membrane receptors, etc.) are distributed equally to both daughter cells, then differential sensitivity of the two daughters to the action of the same humoral regulator may be anticipated. Such an inexact process of cell division may play a normal role in haemopoietic differentiation and on general principles the concept cannot be rejected outright since current immunological theory holds that error processes (somatic mutational events) are intimately involved in lymphoid differentiation and the generation of immunological diversity.

The other general solution to the mechanism of action of humoral regulators is to postulate that daughter cells are identical and that regulator action determines the subsequent behaviour of these cells and their descendants. Regulator action on these uniform target cells would then be envisaged as occurring on a random basis, an individual target-cell responding following chance contact with the regulator molecule when in a susceptible state. The magnitude of production of progeny of a certain type would then be determined by the relative concentration of the appropriate regulator in the medium around the target-cell population and the frequency of target cells in a susceptible state.

It is tacitly assumed that commitment to particular pathways of differentiation in haemopoiesis is irreversible with progenitor cells or their more differentiated progeny being incapable of dedifferentiation. While it seems unlikely that dedifferentiation is a common event in normal haemopoiesis, it cannot be excluded *a priori* and may occur in certain abnormal situations.

It is the intention of this chapter only to discuss *specific* humoral regulators of haemopoietic cells but it must be pointed out that there are many nutritional factors and hormones which have profound effects on haemopoietic cells. Outstanding in this group are the adrenal corticosteroids which have an intense cytolytic action on lymphoid cells and profoundly inhibit proliferative activity of lymphopoietic cells. A well-documented case has been presented for the conclusion that these hormones represent the physiological inhibitors of lymphopoiesis which balance the positive proliferative stimuli of the thymic microenvironment and of antigens in the peripheral lymphoid organs (Dougherty et al. 1964). The sex steroids and growth hormone also have important effects on haemopoietic cells as do the B-vitamins. A proper discussion of this large and complex field is outside the scope of the present book, but some aspects of this subject have been ably reviewed elsewhere (Dougherty 1952; Kaplan et al. 1954: New York Academy of Science Symposium 'Leukopoiesis in Health and Disease', 1964).

7.2 *Erythropoietin*

The existence of a humoral factor regulating erythropoiesis was first proposed by Carnot and Deflandre (1906). These workers observed that plasma from rabbits, made anaemic by bleeding, increased peripheral red-cell counts when injected into normal rabbits. An important piece of evidence that a humoral factor not only existed but was biologically effective in physiological situations was the demonstration by Reissman (1950) that the induction of anoxia in one member of a pair of parabiotic rats was followed by stimulation of erythropoiesis in both members of the parabiotic pair. Stohlman et al. (1954) provided further evidence for the existence of a humoral factor by studies on a patient with polycythaemia secondary to hypoxia associated with a patent ductus arteriosus, and Hodgson and Toha (1954) showed that the plasma and urine of bled rabbits exhibited erythropoietic stimulating activity in experimental animals.

These initial experiments led to the proposal that a humoral factor existed in the plasma which regulated the level of erythropoiesis, at least in abnormal situations such as blood loss or anoxia, and presumably also operated in the normal animal to regulate the normal level of erythropoiesis. The active factor was termed 'erythropoietin'. Subsequent work has adequately confirmed the existence and importance of the regulator, erythropoietin.

The erythropoietic system exhibits a number of features which greatly facilitate *in vivo* studies on possible humoral regulators: (a) the level of erythropoiesis in a normal animal is extremely stable in comparison with either lymphopoiesis or granulopoiesis, (b) erythropoiesis is the simplest of all blood-cell systems involving the production in the bone marrow and spleen of cells which have a one-way passage to the circulation, and (c) there are a number of convenient procedures for assessing the level of erythropoiesis. Procedures for determining the level of erythropoiesis are based (1) on the enumeration of end products in the blood, either reticulocytes or mature red cells, (2) determining the total numbers of erythropoietic cells by conventional differential counts, or (3) the use of isotopic Fe as a specific marker for estimating the number and activity of haemoglobin-synthesising cells.

These relatively simple measurements provide the basis for several *in vivo* assay systems for measuring increased erythropoiesis after stimulation by erythropoietin. It is possible to demonstrate erythropoietin effects in normal animals, but such animals must be given relatively large amounts of erythropoietin to obtain a significant response (see review by Jacobson et al. 1960). A major advance in this work was the realisation that the sensitivity of the assay system was improved if erythropoiesis was first depressed in the assay animal. Most assay systems in current use employ a preliminary suppression of normal erythropoiesis by hypertransfusion-induced polycythaemia (Fried et al. 1957; Jacobson et al. 1960), starvation (Fried et al. 1957; Hodgson et al. 1958), or hypoxia (Cotes and Bangham 1961).

These techniques have been standardised sufficiently well to allow uniform assay procedures in different laboratories (Cotes 1968; Camiscoli et al. 1968). However, the various *in vivo* assay systems still suffer a common defect in requiring large amounts of erythropoietin to demonstrate a biological effect. Because of this shortcoming, progress on the chemical characterisation of erythropoietin has been slow. Although several *in vitro* systems have recently been studied which allow some effects of erythropoietin to be analysed (Dukes 1968; Krantz 1968), these systems have not yet been adapted as useful routine assay systems for erythropoietin.

Animals in which erythropoiesis has been suppressed by hypertransfusion develop a sequential series of changes following the injection of erythropoietin which commence 24 hours after injection and finish 7 days after injection. There is an initial rise in the number of early erythroid cells in the bone marrow, reaching maximum levels at 2–3 days after injection and coinciding with a rise in Fe incorporation in the bone marrow. These responses are followed by a rise in reticulocyte levels in the peripheral blood, reaching maximum levels at 4 days after injection (Stohlman et al. 1968).

Injection of erythropoietin in split doses, with intervals of up to 1–4 days between injections, increases the magnitude of the biological response to erythropoietin (Reichlin and Harrington 1960; Fogh 1968).

7.2.1 *Mechanism of action of erythropoietin*

Studies by Alpen and Cranmore (1959), Jacobson et al. (1959a, 1960) and Alpen et al. (1962) have clearly localised a major site of action of erythropoietin to the erythropoietic progenitor cells. Under the inductive action of erythropoietin, these cells initiate haemoglobin synthesis, and it is possible that erythropoietin acts as a derepressor of the genes determining haemoglobin synthesis. In these initial studies, careful analysis of labelling patterns, grain count data and mitotic indices of erythroid populations in erythropoietin-stimulated animals indicated that erythropoietin did not shorten the cell-generation times between the proerythroblast and the normoblast (Alpen and Cranmore 1959) and did not shorten the time of the maturation sequence from normoblast to mature red cell. The increased numbers of reticulocytes and red cells resulting from erythropoietin stimulation appeared to be due essentially to the induction by erythropoietin of a larger number of progenitor cells to initiate haemoglobin synthesis, each progenitor cell generating only the same number of red cells in the same time interval as in an unstimulated animal.

These observations are of great historical significance in the study of hae-mopoietic regulators because they documented two novel concepts regarding haemopoiesis. First they showed that the production of increased numbers of mature blood cells could be achieved without increasing proliferation rates, simply by recruiting additional progenitor cells and allowing subsequent events to proceed at a normal rate. Previous to these experiments, it was assumed that any agent stimulating an increased production of blood cells would have to increase the rate of division of cells in the proliferative compartment of that cell class. This expected situation was already causing some doubts because of the data being obtained from the analysis of cell cycle times of dividing haemopoietic cells using tritiated thymidine. These data indicated that cell cycle times were already very short in normal haemopoietic cell populations and it seemed doubtful whether these could be shortened appreciably by any type of stimulus. The recruitment system for achieving greater numbers of end cells obviated any need to shorten already short cell cycle times.

The second novel concept documented by this work was the existence of a step of commitment in the maturation of erythropoietic progenitor cells (ESC's). The availability of ^{59}Fe as a marker for haemoglobin-synthesising cells allowed a precise identification of the earliest cell type synthesising haemoglobin. In erythropoietin-stimulated (bled) animals use of this isotope documented the fact that when erythropoiesis was increased, a large number of erythropoietic cells appeared which had previously been unlabelled by ^{59}Fe (Alpen and Cranmore 1959) indicating that these cells were a second population of erythropoietic cells which had appeared subsequent to ery-thropoietin stimulation. This constituted evidence that these cells were derived from progenitor cells not previously characterisable as being in the erythropoietic sequence. At the very least, this commitment must represent a derepression of genes controlling haemoglobin synthesis and possibly other types of derepression are involved also. Just how erythropoietin achieves this within the target cell is not fully understood, but recent *in vitro* studies have begun to clarify the process and have indicated, in addition, that erythropoie-tin also influences the functional activity of more differentiated erythropoietic cells.

Biochemical studies on the influence of erythropoietin in *in vitro* cultures of haemopoietic cells have produced evidence that erythropoietin exerts its action at the chromosomal level by permitting the transcription of certain repressed gene sequences. Marrow cultures showed reduced haem synthesis in the first few hours *in vitro*, even in the presence of erythropoietin but by 10 hours and thereafter, erythropoietin-stimulated cultures showed a marked increase in haem synthesis over controls (Krantz et al. 1963; Gross and Goldwasser 1969; Gallien-Lartigue and Goldwasser 1965).

Erythropoietin also stimulated an increased incorporation of glucosamine (Dukes et al. 1963) and of extracellular iron (Hrinda and Goldwasser 1969) into marrow cultures. The results indicated that increased incorporation occurred prior to stimulation of haem synthesis and that these three effects required DNA-dependent RNA synthesis and protein synthesis. Erythropoietin also enhanced the production of the enzyme δ-amino-levulinic acid (ALA) synthetase in rabbit bone marrow, with a 6-hour induction period of DNA-dependent RNA synthesis and protein synthesis (Bottomley and Smithee 1969). Since ALA-synthetase is the rate-limiting enzyme in haem biosynthesis, physiological derepression of the enzyme may be an important site of action for erythropoietin. A similar site of action has been shown for steroid metabolites which stimulate haemoglobin production in cultures of chick blastoderm (Levere and Granick 1967).

Recent studies have shown that erythropoietin stimulates the production of RNA of different sizes from 4-150S but that only the 150S RNA appears to be unique to the action of erythropoietin (Gross and Goldwasser 1969). It is probable that some part of this RNA is functioning as messenger RNA mediating some aspects of the action of erythropoietin. In this context a 9S RNA from mouse reticulocytes has been isolated and appeared to have many of the characteristics of a true m-RNA for haemoglobin (Evans and Lingrel 1969). Erythropoietin may also augment the production of r-RNA and t-RNA, in addition to m-RNA, which may account for its influence both on the induction of differentiation of the ESC's and its influence on later stages of erythroid differentiation (Pavlov 1969).

The early stimulation of haem production and glucosamine incorporation resulting from erythropoietin action on adult marrow cells *in vitro* requires DNA-dependent RNA synthesis but is not dependent on prior DNA synthesis (Ortega and Dukes 1970). In contrast, 13-day mouse foetal liver cultures responded to erythropoietin by initially producing small quantities of RNA followed after a short period by elevated DNA synthesis, which preceded the main increase in RNA and protein synthesis (Paul and Hunter 1969). Probably in foetal cultures, erythropoietin actively maintains the immature erythroblasts, stimulates their RNA synthesis and permits their continued DNA synthesis (Chui et al. 1969).

Under some conditions, e.g. with large doses of erythropoietin or in severe anaemia, erythropoietin appears able to induce the formation of mature red cells with cell volumes larger than normal (macrocytosis) (Stohlman et al. 1968). Conversely, in iron deficiency anaemia, erythropoietin can induce a microcytosis. These observations also raised the possibility that erythropoietin may have an additional site of action in erythropoiesis – namely on the differentiated erythropoietic cells. This phenomenon, in which erythropoietin causes the production of macrocytes under conditions of severe red-cell depletion, has been interpreted by some as constituting an alternative way for rapidly increasing red-cell production, e.g. by missing normal division steps. These workers have likened this process to pressing a 'panic button', forcing the erythropoietic cells to generate additional erythrocytes with a minimum time lag.

If erythropoietin functions as a normal regulator of erythropoiesis, it must be presumed that erythropoietin action does not normally lead to the production either of macrocytes or microcytes and that the experiments demonstrate a potential function of erythropoietin which is never expressed – at least under normal conditions. However, Stohlman et al. (1968) proposed an interesting alternative which combines the accepted mode of action of erythropoietin on erythropoietic cells with these other observations. They proposed that essentially erythropoietin is an inducer and regulator of haemoglobin synthesis. In the initial step in red-cell formation, erythropoietin therefore acts as an inducer committing the erythropoietic progenitor cell to commence haemoglobin synthesis and to become the first definable cell in the erythropoietic series. As divisions proceed, erythropoietin continues to regulate haemoglobin synthesis, and Stohlman et al. proposed that it is the haemoglobin content of the cytoplasm which is the actual regulator of cell division. They suggested that a cytoplasmic haemoglobin concentration of approximately 20% may shut down DNA synthesis in dividing erythropoietic cells. Under normal conditions this stage is reached at the normoblast level and results in an inhibition of further reduction divisions and ultimately in the loss of the cell nucleus with the formation of the mature red cell. When haemoglobin synthesis is excessive, the critical haemoglobin concentration may be reached earlier, halting mitosis earlier in the reduction division sequence and resulting in macrocyte formation from these larger cells. In iron deficiency anaemia, where the availability of iron is a rate limiting factor, haemoglobin synthesis may be so slow that the cells are able to undergo one further division beyond the normoblast stage, resulting in a further size reduction in the cells and the development finally of microcytes from these cells.

This intriguing concept appears compatible with what is known of erythro-poietin at the present time, but one final aspect of the derivation of the first haemoglobin-synthesising blast cell from the multipotential stem cell requires further comment. Erythropoiesis only occurs in two locations in the body – the bone marrow and spleen, despite the presence of stem cells in the blood, and therefore, potentially at least, in almost any tissue in the body. From the discussion in Chapter 3 it is clear that erythropoietin cannot induce the transformation of stem cells to erythropoietin-sensitive cells and that this process is dependent primarily on the microenvironment in the bone marrow or spleen. The possibility cannot be excluded that erythropoietin may collaborate in this inductive action of the microenvironment, although ESC's appear to be generated in polycythaemic mice having very low plasma erythropoietin levels (see Chapter 3).

7.2.2   The site of origin of erythropoietin

The site of origin of humoral regulators has been the subject of great practical and theoretical interest to workers in experimental haematology. In the past the thinking on this problem has been dominated by what is known of the older and better established humoral regulators – the hormones. Hormones, characteristically are produced by cells of one specific type, whose distribution in the body is usually but not always restricted to a single organ, e.g. the acidophil cells of the pituitary producing prolactin or the beta cells of the pancreas producing insulin. It is true that certain evidence suggests that some cells producing specific hormones can occur in more than one organ, but the overwhelming principle from hormone studies is that such regulators should be traceable to specific cells in one or a few organs. This historical development of our views on hormones may turn out to be restrictive for an understanding of other, equally specific, humoral regulators, since there is no fundamental reason why cells producing hormones or regulators need of necessity be located in a single organ. Similarly there is no compelling reason why many different types of cells cannot, amongst their other specialised functions, also produce a specific factor serving as a regulator. Although most cells of the body exhibit greater or lesser degrees of specialisation, it has never been seriously suggested that a cell, however specialised, can only perform a single function.

The second general concept which has arisen regarding regulators of cell proliferation is that they should occur in balanced pairs or groups – one regulator or group of regulators stimulating cell division, whilst another

balances this stimulus by a roughly equal inhibitory influence. A development of this concept has been the suggestion that the mature cells produced
by cellular proliferation might themselves be the source of the inhibitory
regulator. This is the essence of the chalone concept elaborated and investigated by Bullough and his colleagues (Bullough 1967). While this second
general concept is again internally logical and may turn out to be valid, there
is already sufficient evidence from experimental haematology to indicate
that the chalone concept cannot represent the only type of stimulatory-
inhibitory system regulating haemopoiesis. E.g., the adrenal corticosteroids
are powerful inhibitors of lymphopoiesis while there is no firm evidence yet
that small lymphocytes contain or release inhibitors of lymphopoiesis.

These background concepts of the origin of specific regulators have clearly
dominated experimental work on the origin of erythropoietin, and much of
the current controversy regarding its origin stems from an attempt to find a
single organ source for this specific regulator.

In the initial studies, erythropoietin was demonstrated in the serum and
plasma. This prompted an analysis of the effects of organ resection on
assayable levels of erythropoietin in the plasma. It was shown that nephrectomy led to a dramatic fall in plasma erythropoietin levels (Jacobson et al.
1957; Mirand and Prentice 1957; Jacobson et al. 1959b). This evidence that
the kidney might be the major production site of erythropoietin received
support from several sources: (a) Erythropoietin was demonstrable in the
urine; (b) Studies on the perfusion of kidneys from anoxic animals *in vitro*
indicated that erythropoietin was released in the perfusate (Kuratowska et al.
1961; Fisher and Birdwell 1961); (c) Extracts of kidney from hypoxic animals
exhibited erythropoietic activity (Contrera et al. 1965; Lagrue et al. 1960);
and (d) erythropoietin levels were high in patients with several types of renal
disease including renal cancer (Mirand 1968).

Histological studies on kidney tissues from experimental animals exhibiting high circulating erythropoietin levels suggested that there was a consistent
association between high erythropoietin levels and increased granularity of
the juxtaglomerular apparatus (Osnes 1958; Hirashima and Takaku 1962;
Oliver and Brody 1965; Demopoulos et al. 1965; Mitus and Toyama 1965).
On the other hand, specific anti-sheep erythropoietin developed in rabbits
was shown to react only with the glomerular cells in the kidney of sheep and
not with the juxtaglomerular apparatus (Frenkel et al. 1968).

The above evidence strongly suggested that the kidney was the sole or
major site of erythropoietin production in the body. However, certain other
observations are in conflict with this conclusion. Some erythropoietin can

still be produced in the absence of the kidney (Mirand and Prentice 1957; Mirand et al. 1959; Erslev 1960; Jacobson 1962; Lange and Gallagher 1962), and Nathan et al. (1964) have shown that erythropoiesis continues in anephric man. Other sites of erythropoietin production have not been clearly characterised but some evidence has implicated the pituitary (Van Dyke 1959), liver (Burke and Morse 1962) spleen (De Franciscis et al. 1965) and hypothalamus (Mirand 1968) if not in the production of erythropoietin, then in regulating erythropoietin production by other tissues. In the newborn, the sites of erythropoietin production may differ from those in the adult. Carmena et al. (1968) observed that hypoxia in newborn rats did not increase plasma erythropoietin levels as much as in adult animals. However, nephrectomised newborn rats exposed to anoxia developed erythropoietin levels which were 50% of those in intact anoxic controls, whereas nephrectomy in adult rats completely prevented any response to anoxia. This suggests that extrarenal sources or erythropoietin may be relatively more important in the foetal and neonatal animal than in adult life.

More recently the suggestion has been raised that the kidney may not actually produce erythropoietin but an enzyme-like factor (renal erythropoietic factor) (REF) which converts an erythropoietin-precursor in the plasma to erythropoietin. Thus Kuratowska et al. (1964) reported the presence of a factor in saline perfusates of anoxic kidneys which produced erythropoietic activity when incubated with normal plasma. Similarly, mitochondrial fractions from kidney cells were found to have no erythropoietic activity but resulted in the production of erythropoietically-active material when incubated *in vitro* with normal serum (Contrera and Gordon 1966, 1968; Contrera et al. 1966; Kuratowska 1968). REF was also produced by organ cultures of rat kidney (Sherwood et al. 1970).

These findings highlight the difficulties involved with *in vivo* assay systems since the apparent demonstration of erythropoietin in plasma by injecting the plasma into an intact animal would not discriminate between the genuine presence of erythropoietin in the plasma and the presence only of an erythropoietin precursor which was activated by the kidney of the assay animal.

If the findings of Gordon and his co-workers are confirmed the question of the tissue origin of the erythropoietin-precursor is thrown wide open. One preliminary suggestion is that the liver may produce the erythropoietin-precursor (Katz et al. 1968), but much more work needs to be done on this question.

It has been suggested recently that the action of certain agents on erythropoiesis may be via the renal erythropoietic factor. Testosterone appears to play an important role in the regulation of erythropoiesis. Testosterone was observed to stimulate erythropoiesis in patients (McCullagh and Jones 1941, 1942), and this basic observation has been confirmed repeatedly (see review by Jacobson et al. 1968). Testosterone is known to be an anabolic agent with growth stimulating activity for a number of tissues, but its effects on erythropoiesis appear to be greater than that on many other tissues. This has raised the question of whether testosterone may also act in collaboration with erythropoietin or stimulate erythropoietin production. Mirand et al. (1965a) and Fried and Gurney (1965) showed that testosterone increased plasma erythropoietin levels in mice, rats, rabbits and tamarins, but the precise mechanism of action of testosterone remains unclear (see discussion by Gordon et al. 1968). Gordon et al. (1968) obtained evidence that testosterone exerted its action on erythropoiesis primarily by stimulating the production of REF. Androgens were unable to stimulate erythropoiesis in nephrectomised mice (Fried and Gurney 1968) and rises in erythropoietin stimulated by testosterone were paralleled by increases in REF (Gordon et al. 1968). By contrast, oestrogens depressed erythropoiesis and depressed erythropoietin levels but this action did not require the presence of the kidney (Mirand and Gordon 1966).

The renal erythropoietic factor, or erythrogenin, is not related immunologically or chemically to erythropoietin and may function as an enzyme which cleaves off an active moiety from the serum substrate to produce erythropoietin (Gordon 1970). In this context the system is similar in organisation to the renin-angiotensin systems; however, the renal and plasma factors involved are different. A positive feedback system has been proposed whereby the release of REF from the kidney during early periods of hypoxia may increase substrate production in addition to activating it to functional erythropoietin; a negative feedback may also exist with erythropoietin inhibiting further production of itself by an inhibitory effect at the serum-substrate level (Zanjani and Gordon 1970).

The above concept of a renal erythropoietic factor has not received total acceptance as yet, and Erslev and Kazal (1969) were unable to demonstrate an erythropoietin-generating effect of renal extracts using hypertransfused, rather than the hypoxia-induced, polycythaemic mice used by Gordon. There is also some evidence that failure to detect erythropoietin in renal extracts was due to the presence of a renal erythropoietin inhibitor which was quite potent (1 g of kidney homogenate could inactivate 5–10 units of erythropoietin) and appeared not to be an enzyme (Erslev et al. 1970).

7.2.3 Production, metabolism and fate of erythropoietin

The current uncertainties regarding the origin of erythropoietin, the unavailability of erythropoietin in pure form and the necessity to use *in vivo* assay systems for erythropoietin all combine to make it difficult to follow the production and fate of erythropoietin in the body.

The trigger mechanism eliciting erythropoietin production has been assumed to be the oxygen tension in the tissues. Thus in anoxia, tissue O_2 tension might be expected to be low, triggering erythropoietin production, and conversely in polycythaemia O_2 tension might be so high as to provide no stimulus for erythropoietin production. The validity of this concept was challenged by Erslev and Thorling (1968), who pointed out that, based on considerations of blood viscosity, blood flow and cardiac output, optimal oxygen flow should occur at the normal haematocrit level of 45%. Thus, polycythaemia should result in tissue anoxia and the increased production of erythropoietin. The role of the viscosity of the blood as a regulator of erythropoietin production has been investigated experimentally by Kilbridge et al. (1969), who showed that dehydration caused both an increased blood viscosity and depressed plasma levels of erythropoietin. Furthermore these workers showed that the hypertransfusion of methaemoglobinised human red cells to mice led to a fall in plasma-erythropoietin levels despite the fact that such cells were incapable of oxygen transport.

Studies on the effect on erythropoietin levels of hypoxia with varying red-cell mass also suggested that red-cell mass could influence erythropoietin production by a mechanism not dependent on blood oxygen-carrying capacity (Necas and Neuwirt 1970). The site of renal erythropoietin (or REF) production could conceivably be influenced both by blood oxygen levels and by red-cell mass (independent of oxygen levels) if both factors operated by an influence on hydrostatic pressure in a specific region of the kidney. The effect is not produced by generalised elevation of blood pressure which suggests that the hydrostatic effect may be localised in some specialised area of the kidney where possibly plasma skimming by renal vessels may act to amplify the influence of changes of haematocrit on hydrostatic pressure or local oxygen availability. Increased hydrostatic pressure mediated by increased haematocrit might inhibit erythropoietin production, whereas decreased oxygen levels (either in oxygen-carrying capacity of blood or in partial pressure of oxygen) might lower hydrostatic pressure as a result of local production of vasodilatory anaerobic metabolites and hydrogen ions by a region of the kidney.

An alternative hypothesis is the suggestion that polycythaemic animals may have an inhibitor of erythropoietin possibly of red-cell origin which would exert a chalone-like inhibitory action modulating erythropoietin levels.

Several reports have indicated that plasma from polycythaemic animals or man contains a factor which inhibits the activity of erythropoietin in assay animals (Krzymowski and Krzymowska 1962; Reynafarje et al. 1964; Whitcomb and Moore 1968). However, other authors (Erslev and Thorling 1968) have failed to confirm the existence of such an inhibitor in the serum or serum extracts of polycythaemic rabbits, rats and mice, and studies on the influence of red-cell haemolysates on erythropoiesis have demonstrated a stimulating, rather than an inhibiting influence (Lambardini et al. 1968). The existence of a specific erythropoietin inhibitor is in some doubt at present, and its role in regulating erythropoietin production can only be highly speculative.

The disappearance time of erythropoietin in the plasma of mice was studied by Stohlman (1959) in rats previously exposed to reduced barometric pressure and a half life of approximately 10 hours was observed. The rate of disappearance appeared to be greater in animals with excessive amounts of erythropoietic tissue. Similarly Dukes and Goldwasser (1962) reported that incubation of cells from hypoxic marrow *in vitro* with sheep erythropoietin depleted the medium of recoverable erythropoietin, whereas incubation with normal bone-marrow cells did not. It was postulated that utilisation by bone-marrow cells was an important fate for erythropoietin and that the rate of decay of erythropoietin in the plasma was proportional to the erythropoietic mass. Lo Bue et al. (1968) showed that when sheep erythropoietin was perfused through isolated rat legs *in vitro* the number of erythroblasts was increased and there was a significant decrease in the erythropoietin content of the fluid leaving the perfused limb. This may represent utilisation of erythropoietin by bone-marrow cells but it might equally well be due to degradation or inactivation of the perfused erythropoietin.

The plasma half life of endogenous erythropoietin in cobalt-stimulated nephrectomised dogs was measured by Naets and Wittek (1965). A half life of approximately 8 hours was observed, but no difference was observed in the erythropoietin half life between dogs with normal or hyperplastic bone marrow. Bozzini (1966) followed the decay of injected dog erythropoietin in normal dogs and dogs with both stimulated and depressed erythropoiesis. The results confirmed those of Naets and Wittek indicating half lives of 7.3 hours for normal dogs, 8.1 hours for erythropoietically-depressed dogs, and 8.8 hours for stimulated dogs. The similarity in erythropoietin decay times in these studies suggested that bone-marrow utilisation does not play a major role in determining plasma erythropoietin half life.

The importance of the role of erythropoietin breakdown or utilisation by erythropoietic cells or other tissues e.g., liver and kidney (Kuratowska 1968) appears an unresolved question, but the above studies indicate that the half life of erythropoietin in the plasma is relatively short, and of the order of 8–10 hours.

One of the major fates of erythropoietin appears to be excretion into the urine. Erythropoietin is demonstrable in normal human urine, and there appears to be a surprisingly wide (up to ten-fold) variation in erythropoietin output in individual subjects over 24-hour periods (Adamson et al. 1966). Evidence has also been presented for the occurrence of diurnal variations in erythropoietin excretion and for day-to-day variations in individual subjects.

Although the question needs further examination, there appear to be good correlations between plasma and urine erythropoietin levels both in normal subjects (Adamson 1968) and in patients with various types of anaemia. Thus both plasma and urine levels of erythropoietin were observed to show a direct relationship with the severity of anaemia in congenital hypoplastic anaemia, thalassaemia major, sickle cell anaemia and iron-deficiency anaemia (Hammond et al. 1960). Adamson and Finch (1968) showed that bleeding of normal subjects led to a rise in erythropoietin excretion in the urine and concluded that urine erythropoietin levels passively reflected plasma-erythropoietin levels. These observations suggested that urine erythropoietin is not selectively cleared from the plasma by the kidney and that no renal threshhold exists for erythropoietin; but future work may show that this situation may not hold true in all disease states affecting plasma-erythropoietin levels.

7.2.4 Biochemical nature of erythropoietin

Investigation of the biochemical nature of erythropoietin has been hampered by the necessity to use large amounts of material for *in vivo* assays. The most successful purification studies reported have been from anaemic sheep plasma (Goldwasser and White 1959; White et al. 1960; Campbell et al. 1961; Goldwasser et al. 1962a, b; and Goldwasser and Kung 1968). Purification with respect to protein of 930,000-fold was achieved but the recovery (2.2%) was too low to permit tests for homogeneity of the material or adequate physical and chemical determinations. Other studies have utilised anaemic human urine as the source material (Lowy and Keighley 1968) but the best purification achieved was only 20-fold. Isoelectric focusing appears to be a useful procedure for obtaining partial purification with good recovery of erythropoietin from sheep plasma, erythropoietin focusing in the vicinity of pH 3.0 (Lukowsky and Painter 1970).

Investigations on partially purified erythropoietin have revealed the following properties: relative heat stability (Borsook et al. 1954) inactivation by trypsin, chymotrypsin (Slaunwhite et al. 1957; Lowy et al. 1958), pepsin, papain, aminopeptidase, hyaluronidase (Winkert and Gordon 1960), neuraminidase (Lowy et al. 1960; Winkert and Gordon 1960), but not by RNA-ase, lysozyme, α-amylase, β-amylase and β-glucuronidase (Lowy and Borsook 1962; Winkert and Gordon 1960). Removal of sialic acid by neuraminidase appears to destroy the biological activity of erythropoietin *in vivo* but not when assayed *in vitro*.

The molecular weight of erythropoietin has been determined as about 68,000 by γ-ray inactivation (Hodgson, G., personal communication), and a sedimentation coefficient of approximately 5S was obtained from ultracentrifugation studies (Goldwasser and Kung 1968). These data agree with estimates from gel-filtration studies which indicate that erythropoietin has a molecular weight of 60,000 (Lukowsky and Painter 1968). Electrophoretically, erythropoietin in rabbit and mouse plasma banded in the α-globulin-albumin region (Lowy et al. 1959; Allen and Moore 1968). From the present evidence therefore, erythropoietin appears to be a sialic acid-containing glycoprotein of molecular weight 60–70,000.

Immunological studies have shown that human erythropoietin is antigenic in the rabbit, and antibodies can be prepared to human erythropoietin (Schooley and Garcia 1962; Lange et al. 1964). Such antibodies neutralised the erythropoietic-stimulating effects of human erythropoietin in mice and cross-neutralised erythropoietin from mice, rats, sheep and rabbits. However, some evidence was obtained that although human and rabbit erythropoietin were similar, they may not necessarily be identical (Schooley et al. 1968) and anti-human erythropoietin did not block the action of endogenous erythropoietin in Japanese quail (Rosse and Waldmann 1966). The neutralising activity of anti-erythropoietin antisera was localised in the 19S gamma-globulin region (Schooley and Garcia 1965).

The injection of erythropoietin antibodies into normal mice reduced haematocrit and reticulocyte levels and the uptake of ^{59}Fe but had no apparent effect on the level of *in vivo* stem cells in the bone marrow (Schooley et al. 1968). On the other hand, erythropoietin antibodies did reduce the number of colony-forming cells in the spleens of hypoxic mice. In an *in vitro* system using suspensions of rabbit bone-marrow cells, erythropoietin was found to stimulate an increased iron incorporation. This response was prevented by the addition of anti-erythropoietin antibodies (Lange et al. 1968).

7.2.5   Evidence that erythropoietin acts as a normal regulator

It has been suggested from time to time that erythropoietin may play an important regulatory function only in certain disease states, e.g. anaemia or following bleeding. However, several lines of evidence support the concept that erythropoietin is of importance in regulating erythropoiesis in the normal animal: (1) erythropoietin is demonstrable in significant amounts in the plasma and urine of normal subjects and animals (Mirand et al. 1965b; Alexanian 1966; Van Dyke et al. 1966). (2) The injection of anti-erythropoietin antibodies into normal mice results in the development of severe anaemia (Schooley and Garcia 1962). (3) Relatively minor procedures such as moderate bleeding or hypertransfusion in normal subjects or animals produce prompt changes in plasma erythropoietin levels and corresponding changes in the level of erythropoiesis (Adamson 1968).

It can be assumed that erythropoiesis in the normal animal is probably affected by other regulatory controls, since most cells in the body are regulated by multi-control systems. However, erythropoietin appears to be outstanding as the primary regulatory mechanism for erythropoiesis.

7.2.6   Erythropoietin levels in disease states

In disease states in which anaemia is present, erythropoietin levels have been found to be elevated both in the plasma and urine (Piliero et al. 1956; Prentice and Mirand 1957; Gurney et al. 1957; Van Dyke et al. 1957; Gordon 1959). In general, the level of erythropoietin paralleled and varied inversely with the haematocrit. Thus in congenital hypoplastic anaemia, thalassaemia major, sickle-cell anaemia and iron-deficiency anaemia, both serum and urine levels have been shown to parallel the degree of anaemia (Hammond et al. 1968) and in severe anaemia due to hookwork infestation, urinary excretion of erythropoietin is particularly high (Gutnisky et al. 1968).

Cyclic fluctuations in serum erythropoietin levels have been observed in patients with haemolytic anaemia when passing through acute aplastic crises. Serum and urine levels of erythropoietin were high before haemopoietic recovery, fell with the reinitiation of haemopoiesis, but exhibited a temporary rebound for a short period after the initiation of erythropoiesis (Hammond et al. 1968).

Injections of normal human plasma have been shown to increase erythropoiesis in patients with congenital erythroid hypoplasia despite high levels of endogenous erythropoietin. This suggested that endogenous erythropoietin may be functionally inactive in some types of patients with anaemia, even though capable of stimulating erythropoiesis in assay animals (Hammond et al. 1968). Here it is possible that only erythropoietin-precursor is present in high levels and is not being activated by the renal erythropoietic factor in the patient or possibly a plasma protein required for transport or activation of erythropoietin is lacking in such patients. This again highlights the problem of erythropoietin assay, where the material to be assayed needs to be injected into the intact animals in which interactions may occur leading to activation or inhibition of erythropoietin.

The disease polycythaemia vera presents a number of interesting facets regarding regulation of erythropoiesis by erythropoietin. In this disease, erythropoiesis is excessive with the production of excessive numbers of mature red cells and a consequent polycythaemia. In a normal animal such polycythaemia would be expected to depress erythropoietin production, thereby shutting down erythropoiesis and restoring normal red cell levels. Plasma-erythropoietin levels have indeed been shown to be low in patients with polycythaemia vera, and urinary excretion of erythropoietin is abnormally low (Noyes et al. 1962; Adamson and Finch 1968). When patients with this disease are bled, there is an increased excretion of erythropoietin in the urine (Adamson and Finch 1968) indicating that the production of erythropoietin in such patients is not defective. It might have been postulated that the precursor cells in such patients were abnormally sensitive to low levels of erythropoietin and that excessive erythropoiesis might occur even with very low plasma levels of erythropoietin. However, *in vitro* studies have shown the converse to be true. Polycythaemic bone-marrow cells responded very poorly to erythropoietin *in vitro* compared with normal cells as assessed by ^{59}Fe haem synthesis (Krantz 1968). Plasma erythropoietin from polycythaemic patients stimulated normal bone-marrow cells in an apparently normal fashion suggesting that abnormal erythropoietic stimulating factors were not present in the plasma in this disease state. Polycythaemia vera may therefore represent a semi-neoplastic state of erythropoietic progenitor cells, in which derepression into the erythropoietic pathway is not erythropoietin-dependent but proceeds autonomously due to genetic abnormalities in the cells themselves. Further studies may reveal other diseases in which there are abnormalities in responsiveness of erythropoietic precursor cells to erythropoietin.

Certain diseases have been observed to be sometimes associated with excessive red-cell production and polycythaemia. This association has been described with hydronephrosis, carcinoma and cysts of the kidney, cerebellar haemangioblastoma, Wilms' tumour, and carcinoma of the liver. Analysis of the plasma and urine of such patients has shown high levels of erythropoietin to be present (Gurney 1962; Donati et al. 1963a, b; Rosse et al. 1963; Lehman et al. 1963; Thurman et al. 1966; Gallagher and Donati 1968; Mirand 1968). In the case of renal diseases this association may be due to abnormalities in production in the kidney of REF. Evidence exists that some non-renal tumours may actually elaborate erythropoietin or erythropoietin-like substances. Thus plasma erythropoietin levels were observed to fall following resection of Wilms' tumours (Mirand 1968). Erythropoietin has been detected in cystic fluid of cerebellar haemangioblastoma, sometimes in the absence of elevated erythropoietin levels in the plasma (Gallagher and Donati 1968) and in cyst fluid or tumour tissue in hypernephroma, cerebellar haemangioblastoma and phaeochromocytoma (Waldmann et al. 1968). The active factor in such tumour extracts was inactivated by anti-erythropoietin antibodies (Waldmann et al. 1968). Production of erythropoietin or erythropoietin-like substances by tumour cells may be autonomous and not subject to feedback regulation by haematocrit levels. Thus rats bearing an adrenal cortical tumour developed polycythaemia, and in these animals erythropoiesis was not inhibited by hypertransfusion (Waldmann et al. 1968).

Jepson and Lowenstein (1966) reported that an inhibitor was present in the plasma of two patients with erythroblastopenia (red-cell aplasia). This inhibited the biological effectiveness of erythropoietin in polycythaemic assay mice. The nature and origin of this inhibitor is unknown. Many of such patients have thymic tumours, and erythropoiesis has been observed to improve following removal of the tumour. Possibly some tumours elaborate erythropoietin inhibitors but this question and the possible significance of such a phenomenon in the production of anaemia in patients with other types of carcinoma is in need of further investigation.

7.3 Thrombopoietin

The history of the detection of a humoral factor controlling platelet formation has been similar to that of erythropoietin. Toi (1956) and Yamamoto

(1957) observed slight increases in platelet levels in rabbits following the injection of serum from patients with acute blood loss and the serum of bled dogs was found to increase platelet levels when injected into normal dogs (De Nicola et al. 1958). Thrombopoietic activity has also been detected in normal plasma, serum and urine (Odell et al. 1961; Linman and Pierre 1962).

The assay of the active humoral factor, thrombopoietin, at present depends on the injection of the test material into animals and the subsequent measurement either of platelet levels (Krizsa et al. 1968) or the uptake of iso-topically-labelled methionine (^{75}Se-Selenomethionine). Methionine is incorporated into the cytoplasm of immature but not mature megakaryocytes (Cohen et al. 1965; Evatt and Levin 1969) and has proved a reasonably specific index of thrombopoiesis.

A single injection of thrombopoietin was found to induce an 8-fold increase in blood platelet levels, the peak response occurring at 3–4 days, and platelet levels remained high for up to 10 days (Kelemen et al. 1958; De Nicola 1968). The delay of 3–4 days before a peak response is consistent with the known maturation time from primitive megakaryocytes to platelets in the rat (Ebbe and Stohlman 1965) and suggests that thrombopoietin may act on megakaryocyte progenitors or primitive megakaryocytic cells (see Chapter 3). Multiple injections of active material did not appear to increase the peak response, which may indicate that the responsiveness to thrombopoietin may be limited by the number of available target cells.

On present reports, there appears to be a wide species variation in responsiveness to thrombopoietin. In the rat, relatively large volumes of thrombocytopenic serum must be injected to produce a measurable response (Odell et al. 1961; De Gabriele and Penington 1967a). One important complication of *in vivo* assays for thrombopoietin appears to be the fact that foreign proteins elicit rises in blood platelet levels (Odell et al. 1964). This makes it difficult to assess reports on the detection of thrombopoietin in normal human serum or plasma when assayed in experimental animals. However, despite variation of assay results, the evidence supports the existence of a humoral thrombopoietic factor (Abildgaard and Simone 1967).

The site of action of thrombopoietin has not been clearly characterised, but the observations reported in Chapter 3 suggest that thrombopoietin may recruit progenitor cells into the definable megakaryocytic cell series and increase the rate of maturation of megakaryocytes.

Transfusion of platelets has been observed to depress the production of platelets (Cronkite et al. 1961; De Gabriele and Penington 1967b), suggest-ing the operation of a feedback mechanism similar to that involved in the depression of erythropoiesis by hypertransfusion.

The site of production of thrombopoietin is not known. Nephrectomy did not influence platelet production (De Gabriele and Penington 1967b), but some experiments (De Nicola 1968) have indicated that the pituitary and adrenals may be involved at least in regulating thrombopoietin production. A thrombocytosis-inducing factor has also been extracted from human and animal liver but is present in liver only during its phase as an extramedullary site of haemopoiesis. It has been suggested from time to time that the spleen exerts a humoral influence on platelet formation (Damashek and Estren 1948), but such a role has not been firmly documented. In thrombocytopenic purpura a non-dialysable extract of spleen produced a significant rise in platelet counts within 4–6 days (Cooney et al. 1965) and spleen extracts were also claimed to increase megakaryocyte regeneration in sublethally irradiated guinea pigs (Johnson and Strike 1962). Since platelet elevation accompanies administration of many non-specific substances the role of the spleen in the production of a specific thrombopoietin must still be in question.

Evidence on the chemical nature of thrombopoietin shows that this sub-stance has some similarities to both erythropoietin and colony stimulating factor. Thrombopoietin appears to be heat labile and non-dialysable and to be inactivated by extremes of pH. It migrates electrophoretically in the betaglobulin region (Yamamoto 1957; Kelemen et al. 1958; Rak et al. 1959) and appears to be a glycoprotein (Linman and Pierre 1962; Schulman et al. 1965). It was also found to be inactivated by trypsin (Rak et al. 1959), but to survive lyophilisation and freezing (Penington 1968). Other platelet-stimulating factors with different properties have been described by Komiya et al. (1962) and Linman and Pierre (1963), but these have been less well documented.

Plasma levels of thrombopoietin have been observed to be elevated following acute bleeding in man (Toi 1956; Yamamoto 1957) dogs (De Nicola et al. 1958) and rats (Odell and McDonald 1961). Thrombopoietin levels were also elevated in experimental animals following treatment with myeleran or antiplatelet serum (Spector 1961) and X-irradiation, UV irradiation or splenectomy (Rak et al. 1961a, b). Patients with acute idiopath-ic thrombocytopenic purpura (ITP) had elevated levels of thrombopoietin but not patients with chronic idiopathic thrombocytopenic purpura (Schul-man et al. 1959; Kelemen et al. 1960). Serum from acute ITP patients increased platelet levels in patients with chronic ITP (Schulman et al. 1959,

1960) suggesting that possibly thrombocytopenia in the latter patients may have been due to the deficiency in thrombopoietin.

Erythropoietin levels in chronic ITP were normal (Schulman et al. 1960) clearly showing that the erythroid and megakaryocytic series are regulated by two distinct humoral factors and not by a single factor, as postulated by Linman and Pierre (1963).

Even though plasma thrombopoietin activity seemed normal or elevated in acute ITP, fresh plasma improved the condition and appeared to induce some remissions (Schulman et al. 1965).

Although work on regulation of platelet formation is technically more difficult than the analysis of regulation of erythropoiesis, the results so far tend to suggest that platelet formation may be regulated by a humoral factor which is a close analogue of erythropoietin.

7.4 Colony-Stimulating Factor (CSF)

The existence of the colony-stimulating factor (CSF) was first demonstrated by studies on the growth of mouse bone marrow and spleen cells in agar culture (Bradley and Metcalf 1966; Pluznik and Sachs 1965, 1966). In these studies it was shown that certain cells in the mouse bone marrow and spleen could proliferate *in vitro*, and form colonies, provided a feeder layer of cells was placed in another layer of agar under the haemopoietic cells. Subsequent work showed that the feeder-layer cells need not be capable of proliferation (Pluznik and Sachs 1966) and indeed could be substituted by medium harvested from liquid cultures of feeder-layer cells (Pluznik and Sachs 1966; Bradley and Sumner 1968). Other studies showed that small volumes of mouse serum (Bradley et al. 1967a; Robinson et al. 1967; Metcalf and Foster 1967a), human serum (Foster et al. 1968b) or human urine (Robinson et al. 1969b; Metcalf and Stanley 1969) could be incorporated in the agar medium and serve as a suitable stimulus for colony formation *in vitro* by the haemo-poietic cells. The active principle which stimulated colony formation was given the simple descriptive name of the 'colony-stimulating factor' (CSF) (Robinson et al. 1967). Other workers (Ichikawa et al. 1967) have described this factor as an 'inducer' of colony formation and have applied the name 'mashran'. For simplicity, and because it is still unknown whether this factor is a genuine inducer, we shall refer to the active principle throughout this discussion as the 'colony-stimulating factor' (CSF). Biochemical studies on CSF in mouse serum (Stanley et al. 1968) and human urine (Stanley and

Metcalf 1969) have indicated that CSF is macromolecular in nature, and is probably a glycoprotein having some similarities to erythropoietin and it seems possible that CSF is the analogue of erythropoietin for the granulocyte-monocyte cell series.

The history of the detection and characterisation of CSF has been almost the converse of that erythropoietin. The existence of erythropoietin was first detected by *in vivo* studies and most of what is known of erythropoietin action has been deduced from *in vivo* experiments. On the other hand, satisfactory and sensitive *in vitro* assay systems for erythropoietin have not yet been developed, and as a consequence large-scale survey work on erythropoietin levels in normal and abnormal states has been slow, and progress with the chemical purification and characterisation of erythropoietin has been difficult.

Because of the availability of a simple and highly sensitive *in vitro* assay system for CSF, much is known of its distribution in body fluids and organs in normal and abnormal states, and good progress has been made in chemically purifying CSF on a large-scale basis. The present difficulty with CSF is to firmly establish its true role *in vivo* in the normal and abnormal animal, because of the multiplicity of factors which appear capable of modifying granulocyte and macrophage production *in vivo*.

7.4.1   In vitro action of CSF

When an adequate concentration of CSF is incorporated in agar cultures of bone-marrow cells, certain of the cells commence proliferation and by 7–10 days form large cell aggregates (colonies), which may consist of pure populations of granulocytic cells, pure populations of macrophages or mixed populations of both cell types (Bradley and Metcalf 1966; Ichikawa et al. 1966; Metcalf et al. 1967a). Observations indicate that colonies arise by the proliferation of single cells (Pluznik and Sachs 1966; Bradley and Metcalf 1966) and not by the aggregation of the bone-marrow cells originally plated (Robinson et al. 1967). In the absence of CSF no such colony formation occurs *in vitro*. The colony-stimulating factor can therefore be characterised in a general fashion as a factor capable of stimulating the proliferation of granulocyte and macrophage cells *in vitro*.

As was discussed in Chapter 3, the target cells for CSF action *in vitro* (*in vitro* CFC's) appear to be the progenitors of granulocytes and some macrophages. It is uncertain whether the macrophage progenitors stimulated to proliferate *in vitro* by the action of CSF are representative of all macrophage progenitors or only one special type of progenitor. The other fact regarding the nature of the initial target cell of CSF which needs repetition is that the *in vitro* CFC shares a common ancestor with the erythropoietin-sensitive cells (ESC's). Hypertransfusion-induced polycythaemia, in reducing the number of erythropoietic cells in the bone marrow, sharply increases the number of *in vitro* CFC's and conversely anaemia induced by bleeding increases erythropoiesis and depresses the number of *in vitro* CFC's (Bradley et al. 1967b; Metcalf 1969a).

As was discussed in earlier chapters, *in vitro* CFC's are the progeny of CFU's but the conversion of CFU's to *in vitro* CFC's cannot be achieved by CSF alone and probably requires the intervention of the specialised bone-marrow or spleen microenvironment. If CSF is involved at all in the transformation, it must act only in collaboration with this mandatory micro-environmental influence.

In the routine assay of biological material for CSF content, a standard number of mouse bone-marrow cells (e.g. 50,000 or 75,000 per ml) is cultured in the presence of the unknown material to be assayed. Colony counts are performed after 7 days of incubation and the CSF activity expressed as the number of colonies stimulated to develop. Studies have shown that the number of colonies forming is determined by the concentration of CSF rather than the total amount of CSF in the culture (Metcalf 1970). The relation between CSF concentration and colony numbers is linear throughout an intermediate range of CSF concentrations and forms a reliable basis for the assay of CSF concentrations. The full relationship is a sigmoid one (Figure 7.1) with colony numbers falling precipitously at low CSF concentrations and reaching plateau levels with progressively higher concentrations of CSF

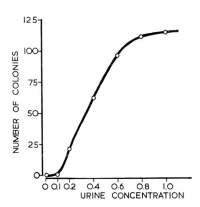

Fig. 7.1. Sigmoid dose-response relationship between concentration of urine CSF and number of colonies forming in cultures of 75,000 C57BL bone-marrow cells.

as all available *in vitro* CFC's become stimulated to form colonies. Since the number of *in vitro* colony-forming cells is limited in the target population, it is obvious that to assay CSF levels in highly active material, serial dilutions of the CSF source must be employed until the linear portion of the dose-response curve is reached.

The fact that both the number and size of colonies developing in agar are determined by the concentration of CSF documents an important facet of regulator-haemopoietic target-cell interaction, which can be presumed to apply for other regulators. The data clearly indicate that some colony-forming cells are extremely sensitive to stimulation by CSF, whereas others require much higher concentrations of CSF before being stimulated. In other words, there is a distinct heterogeneity in responsiveness to stimulation amongst the target cells. On the other hand, the progeny of a particular colony-forming cell must be relatively uniform with respect to their threshhold for stimulation by CSF, and indeed must have a similar sensitivity to that of the parent cell, otherwise all colonies initiated by moderate concentrations of CSF would be of *uniformly* small size due to their population being a random mixture of cells with high and low threshhold sensitivities to CSF. This is never observed, and it is a characteristic feature of bone-marrow colonies in any one culture that they exhibit a wide range of sizes (see Figure 3.20) (Metcalf and Foster 1967a).

Discussion was entered into earlier on the heterogeneity of haemopoietic stem cells and progenitor cells based on parameters of cell size, adherence to glass-bead columns and buoyant density. Data obtained in our laboratory suggest that within any one fractionated population of bone-marrow cells, where fractionation is based either on adherence or buoyant density, there is the full spectrum of sensitivity of *in vitro* colony-forming cells to stimulation by CSF. Thus the heterogeneity in sensitivity to stimulation by CSF appears not to be correlated with other types of heterogeneity so far documented in the *in vitro* CFC population.

Figure 3.20 exemplifies one of the problems in interpretation of data obtained from the agar culture of bone-marrow cells. In this figure are plotted the size and frequency of all cell aggregates in a 7-day culture of 25,000 C57BL mouse bone-marrow cells stimulated by an excess concentration of CSF. It will be noted that the culture contained a whole spectrum of cell aggregates ranging in size from 3 to 700 cells. In other cultures the upper size limit can be from 3–5,000 cells. Only the larger of such aggregates are scored routinely as 'colonies'. Under some culture conditions, e.g. when low numbers of cells are plated and high concentrations of CSF are used, the dividing line is fairly obvious between aggregates that are colonies and aggregates that are too small to be classified as colonies. The nature of the cells forming small aggregates in culture ('cluster-forming cells') was discussed in Chapter 3. Difficulties arise in discriminating between colonies and smaller cell aggregates with some sources of CSF, e.g. urine, which stimulate a high background of small aggregates and when low concentrations of CSF are used.

The general difficulty with the quantitation of *in vitro* colony-formation is that there is no characteristic, or minimal, size for an *in vitro* colony. The major factor determining the size attained by a colony after 7 days of incubation is the concentration of CSF present in the medium (Robinson et al. 1967; Metcalf and Foster 1967a; Metcalf and Stanley 1969; Metcalf 1970) (Figure 7.2). However, a number of other factors also modify colony size.

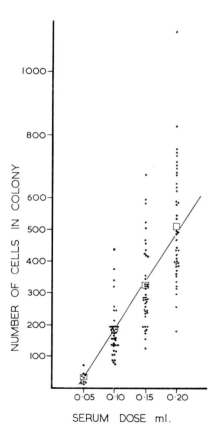

Fig. 7.2. Increase in mean size of 7-day bone-marrow colonies developing in cultures stimulated by increasing amounts of mouse serum CSF. Each point represents a single colony. (From Robinson et al. 1967, reproduced by permission of J. Cell. Physiology.)

These are (a) the number of colonies present in the culture dish and the number of cells originally plated (Metcalf 1968), (b) the time during the incubation period when the colony-forming cells commence proliferation (see later), (c) the presence of inhibitory cells or cell-breakdown products, as seen with foetal liver cultures or yolk-sac cultures (Moore and Metcalf 1970), and (d) the general adequacy of the culture medium, the foetal calf serum and the incubating conditions. Usually, if colonies are small, the background clusters of cells are also correspondingly small and the eye has no difficulty in perceiving the difference between colonies and background clusters. Nevertheless it should be emphasised that culture conditions can be so arranged that genuine colonies can contain as few as 10–20 cells after 7 days of incubation.

Since CSF concentration has a major influence on colony growth rates, colony size can also be used as an assay system for CSF (Robinson et al. 1967; Metcalf and Stanley 1969), but such measurements are more tedious than the simple enumeration of colony numbers. As there is no apparent cell death in growing colonies, at least in the first 3–4 days of culture, colony size represents an index of cellular proliferation. If colonies grow more rapidly with high concentrations of CSF than with low it might be assumed that this constitutes evidence that CSF acts as a proliferative stimulus, e.g. by shortening cell cycle times. The difficulty with this simple interpretation is that colonies contain a heterogeneous population of dividing and non-dividing cells, e.g. metamyelocytes and polymorphs. This allows two alternative explanations for an increased colony growth rate: (a) shortening of mean cell cycle times, or (b) modification of differentiation in the progeny of dividing cells so that a higher proportion remains parental in type and capable of further division. The available data on CSF action do not yet allow any final decision between these two alternatives but the evidence favours (b) or a combination of (a) and (b), since colony growth rates tend to correlate with the percentages of primitive cells in the colony – the more rapid the growth rate, the higher the percentage of primitive cells (Metcalf, D., unpublished data).

It has been shown that bone-marrow cells themselves can produce detectable amounts of CSF (Metcalf 1970) and this may, in part be the basis for the more rapid growth rate of colonies when large numbers of bone-marrow cells are plated (Metcalf 1968). Similarly, it is conceivable that the colony cells themselves may also elaborate CSF, and this may be the basis for the observation that colony crowding potentiates colony growth (Metcalf 1968). However, other factors may be released by colony cells which may be growth stimulating. Studies using tritiated thymidine have shown that dividing colony cells reutilise nuclear material from other cells breaking down in the culture (Metcalf 1968). If such reutilised material promotes cell proliferation, then colony crowding or high concentrations of plated bone-marrow cells might also potentiate colony growth by this mechanism.

Intriguing information has been obtained regarding the mechanism of action of CSF *in vitro* from a time-sequence analysis of the events occurring in cultures of bone-marrow cells (Metcalf 1969b, 1970). In these studies, small numbers (10,000 or 25,000) of cells were plated, to allow *all* cells in the culture plates to be analysed. Urine was used as the source of CSF since urine-stimulated colony formation is characterised by the compact, discrete, nature of the cell aggregates which develop (Metcalf and Stanley 1969).

When cultures of 10,000 bone-marrow cells were examined at daily intervals after incubation, it was observed that cell aggregates appeared in the cultures and grew progressively larger but also that new aggregates continuously developed in the agar between existing aggregates. By scoring all aggregates larger than 3 cells in individual cultures it was shown that there was a characteristic linear increase in the number of discrete aggregates as incubation proceeded (Figure 7.3) (Metcalf 1969b). Cluster counts extrapolated back to zero at approximately 12 hours after incubation, but this does not indicate a lag period of this duration because two divisions must occur before an aggregate is scorable (since it contains 3 or more cells). Size analysis of all clusters in such cultures made it evident that (1) at any one point in time most clusters are small because they represent recently-initiated aggregates, (2) most clusters grow in size progressively for at least 2–3 days after initiation, and (3) clusters growing large enough to be scored as 'colonies', of necessity, tend to arise early in the incubation period. Indeed, plate mapping studies showed that more than 50% of colonies scored at day 7 of incubation were already present as aggregates of 3–30 cells by days 2–3 of incubation (Metcalf 1969b).

This situation in which cluster-forming cells or colony-forming cells progressively become activated to divide in culture after a variable lag period of 0–6 days is highly unusual when compared with other *in vivo* and *in vitro* data from cells or tissues responding to a proliferative stimulus (Swann 1958; Epifanova and Terskikh 1969). In most cases there is a lag period of around 8–48 hours before any proliferation occurs, followed by an exponential accumulation of proliferating cells reaching an early plateau, by which time, all cells in the original population which are capable of responding are now proliferating, e.g. as is seen in the response of lymphocytes *in vitro* to

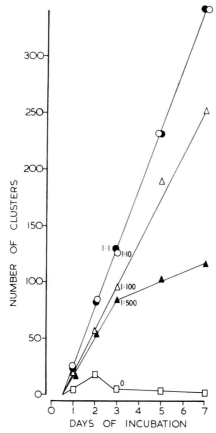

Fig. 7.3. Effect of the concentration of CSF on the rate of accumulation of clusters in cultures of 25,000 C57BL bone-marrow cells. Note abortive cluster formation in unstimulated cultures. Cultures were plated with 0.15 ml of increasing dilutions of a human urine concentrate containing CSF. (From Metcalf 1970, reproduced by permission of J. Cell. Physiology.)

phytohaemagglutinin (Mackinney et al. 1962). The exponential type of proliferative response with its characteristic initial lag period is usually interpreted as indicating that the proliferative stimulus is acting as an inducer, bringing target cells first from a G_0-like state into active cell cycle. If this interpretation is correct, it seems reasonable to conclude that CSF does not function as an inducer in the agar-culture system. This conclusion must remain tentative until further evidence has been accumulated on the cell cycle status of colony-forming cells in the intact animal.

When increasing concentrations of CSF were used in culture, the slope of the linear accumulation with time of new clusters rose more steeply, but reached a maximum slope which approximated 60°. Thus CSF appears to be able to shorten the mean lag period before cells commence proliferation *in vitro* – a function which is related to the log of CSF concentration (Metcalf 1970). The use of concentrations of CSF even 100-fold above the concentration giving a maximum response did not increase the slope further (Figure 7.3), suggesting that no concentration of CSF, however high, can initiate immediate proliferation in all potential cluster- or colony-forming cells. Conversely, in cultures in which no CSF was added, some cluster formation did occur. However, such clusters were few in number, and new cluster formation ceased after 3–4 days, at which time existing cell aggregates usually disintegrated, so that by day 7 of incubation no clusters were seen in unstimulated plates (at least when small numbers of bone-marrow cells were plated). This abortive formation of clusters in unstimulated cultures may represent a low level of intrinsic proliferative capacity in colony-forming and cluster-forming cells independent of CSF but may simply be due to the fact that bone-marrow cell suspensions can themselves produce low levels of CSF (Metcalf 1970). This latter explanation seems more likely, as unstimulated aggregate formation is more evident when large numbers of bone-marrow cells are cultured.

The cellular basis for the fact that some colony-forming and cluster-forming cells can remain dormant in culture for up to 6 days before commencing proliferation is not known, but represents a further type of heterogeneity in the cell population initiating colonies and clusters. Again, preliminary studies have indicated that this heterogeneity does not correlate with adhesiveness, buoyant density or sensitivity to stimulation by CSF. Most *in vitro* CFC's are in continuous cell cycle but a small fraction may be in a G_0 state (Iscove et al. 1970) and these may contribute to the population of *in vitro* CFC's commencing proliferation late in the incubation period.

When developing colonies at 2–3 days of incubation were transferred to recipient plates lacking CSF, colony growth ceased immediately and many such colonies disintegrated (Metcalf and Foster 1967b). Similar data were reported by Paran and Sachs (1968) using CSF in spleen cell-conditioned medium. This indicates that dividing colony cells require CSF continuously and that CSF is not simply a trigger substance firing off the first division in the original colony-forming cell. Similarly, incubation of colony-forming cells with CSF, followed by washing off of all CSF before culturing did not result in initiation of CFC proliferation (Robinson et al. 1967; Bradley et al. 1969).

Assays for residual CSF in cultures in which colony formation had occurred, revealed a moderate degree of depletion of CSF in the medium (Metcalf 1970). This is consistent with the possibility that dividing colony cells may actually use CSF as a metabolite during division. However, other alternative explanations are possible: (a) colony cells may non-specifically adsorb CSF from the culture medium, or (b) cell products or breakdown products may degrade or inactivate CSF. The question of whether colony-forming cells each require only a single trigger molecule for activation or utilise appreciable amounts of CSF during proliferation must await the development of isotopically-labelled pure preparations of CSF.

One of the disturbing findings from the analysis of CSF action *in vitro* has been the demonstration that if cluster-forming or colony-forming cells are incubated *in vitro* in the absence of CSF for 2 or 3 days they either rapidly die or lose their proliferative capacity (Metcalf 1970). This phenomenon is not necessarily related to the continuous requirement of CSF by dividing colony cells since the cell survival concerned relates to survival of cells *before* the cell has actually initiated its first division – an event which may normally be delayed *in vitro* for 5–6 days. This finding raises the bogey of all such tissue culture work that the 'growth factor' being studied is simply a survival factor, allowing cells to remain healthy and to express their intrinsic proliferative activity. Distinctions between 'survival, with expression of intrinsic proliferative potential' and 'growth stimulation' can at times approach meaningless semantics, but *in vitro* culture systems are notoriously prone to contain suboptimal amounts of nutritional substances and to give rise to misleading observations on the existence of growth promotors. Until more is known of the biochemical action of CSF, this remains an unresolved worry in the interpretation of *in vitro* studies on CSF and it places more importance on the elucidation of possible actions of CSF *in vivo* where such basic problems of adequate nutritional supplies for cells can be assumed to be irrelevant.

Before leaving the analysis of the *in vitro* action of CSF, discussion must be made of the influence of CSF on cell differentiation in colony cells. During growth, *in vitro* colonies exhibit a number of changes in their cell populations which both complicate an analysis of CSF action and yet offer a valuable tool for the analysis of problems in haemopoietic cell differentiation.

When fully developed at 7–10 days of incubation, *in vitro* colonies are composed of populations of granulocytic cells, macrophages or mixtures of both cell types (Metcalf et al. 1967a; Ichikawa et al. 1966). If serum or urine is used as the source of CSF, most colonies finally contain macrophages, whereas with feeder layers or conditioned medium as the source of CSF, mature colonies of all three types are common. However, studies using urine stimulation of colony formation have shown that most macrophage colonies originate from clusters which are purely granulocytic (Metcalf 1969b), and which subsequently transform to macrophage colonies after passing through an intermediate stage in which cells of both classes are present. Thus the probability is strong that most colonies, regardless of their final composition, originate from proliferating granulocytic cells. Although indirect evidence from cell isolation studies and colony formation with limiting dilutions of bone-marrow cells (Pluznik and Sachs 1966; Bradley and Metcalf 1966) suggest strongly that individual colonies are clones and are derived from single colony-forming cells, the possibility has not yet been excluded that as a colony increases in size it may incorporate into the colony population other viable cells in the agar around the colony. Studies on inter-colony cells have shown that the vast majority are macrophages and these cells might represent the progenitors of the macrophage cells which ultimately become the dominant colony population in some types of cultures, e.g. with serum or urine CSF. However, there is evidence to suggest that macrophages arise within developing granulocytic colonies by transformation of immature granulocytes to macrophages:

(a) As discussed in Chapter 3, single cells have been transplanted from D2 clusters containing more than 99% of granulocytic cells to recipient cultures. After 3–5 days, 35% of these transplanted cells were recovered as single cells or clusters, and of these 50–60% were typical macrophages. Thus some, but not all, colony granulocytes can transform to macrophages (Metcalf 1971a).

(b) At an intermediate stage in colony growth when both populations are present, many granulocytic cells have a morphology compatible with such a transformation. Myelocyte nuclei are commonly seen in which the ring-shaped nucleus appears to be transforming to a spherical nucleus and metamyelocytes are seen in which the nucleus appears to be rounding up and to be becoming excentric.

(c) At limiting cell dilutions, e.g. 10 or 100 bone-marrow cells per culture, only an occasional colony develops but some of these contain both cell populations, despite the fact that few if any other cells could have been present in the culture medium adjacent to the single colony.

(d) Large granulocytic colonies can develop in cultures containing high concentrations of conditioned medium CSF or serum from endotoxin-treated mice. In these cultures there is a dense inter-colony background of macrophages and yet the granulocytic colonies commonly do not contain a single macrophage. This is even more spectacularly evident when conditioned medium from myelomonocytic leukaemia WEHI-3 (see later) is used. With this conditioned medium, occasional giant granulocytic colonies develop which are very loose in structure and occupy up to 20 times the volume occupied by a normal colony. Despite the loose nature of these colonies and the large volume of agar enclosed within the limits of the colony, many such giant colonies have been observed which did not contain a single macrophage. Thus invasion of colonies by macrophages can be excluded for at least some colonies.

(e) During typical colony formation stimulated by urine CSF, the developing colonies are initially densely packed, discrete, granulocytic aggregates and yet at 3–4 days of incubation most such dense aggregates contain a few macrophages often buried deep within the tight cluster of surrounding granulocytes.

(f) Evidence has been obtained from an analysis of the myelomonocytic leukaemia WEHI-3 that the neoplastic granulocytes and monocytes in the population have a common ancestor (Warner et al. 1969). These leukaemic cells form colonies *in vitro* resembling normal *in vitro* colonies (Metcalf et al. 1969) and again such colonies contain mixtures of granulocytic and macrophage cells – both of which exhibit the characteristic karyotype of this tumour.

(g) Ichikawa (1969) has serially cloned myeloid leukaemic cells in agar and shown them to be capable of forming progeny of both granulocytic and macrophage cells in the presence of conditioned medium.

From this data sufficient indirect evidence appears to exist to conclude that probably the granulocytic and macrophage cells in many mixed colonies are derived from the same colony-forming cell. If this conclusion can be proved beyond doubt, the *in vitro* culture system will provide clear evidence that granulocytes and at least some macrophages of bone-marrow origin share a common precursor cell (the *in vitro* colony-forming cell) and will provide an excellent system for analysing the regulation of differentiation into two specialised blood cell types.

Certain factors have been found to modify the transformation of developing granulocytic colonies to macrophage colonies.

(a) With urine CSF, the percentage of granulocytic colonies which develops is dependent on the concentration of CSF used (Metcalf, D., unpublished data). With high CSF concentrations, a higher proportion of colonies at day 7 of incubation are granulocytic or mixed colonies that in cultures using lower concentrations of CSF. However, this may not represent a direct action of CSF, for parallel studies have shown that colony crowding in such cultures has an even more marked influence on colony composition. When cultures contain large numbers of colonies, the proportion of granulocytic colonies is higher than in cultures with few colonies. Taken together, the two sets of experiments suggest that colony crowding, rather than CSF concentration, is the critical factor and that interaction between colony cells may somehow be able to influence the differentiation of some colonies in such a way as to prevent transformation to macrophages.

(b) Where culture conditions are poor and colony growth is slow (e.g. with unsuitable foetal calf serum or partially toxic plastic culture dishes) premature transformation to macrophage populations occurs. Thus by day 3 most such colonies will be pure populations of macrophages.

(c) When CSF is withheld from bone-marrow cultures for 2–3 days, all developing clusters and colonies are macrophage in composition from the earliest point at which they can be identified (the three cell stage) (Metcalf 1970).

(d) Similarly, the clusters which normally initiate later in the incubation period (after 4–5 days) are usually macrophage in composition from the outset (Metcalf 1969b).

These data suggest that the *in vitro* transformation of granulocytes to macrophages seen in many colonies may occur as a reaction to generally unfavourable environmental conditions, possibly because the macrophages are more resistant cells under such circumstances. It should not be misconstrued from this that colony macrophages are necessarily unhealthy cells. These cells initially exhibit high mitotic activity and are actively phagocytic (Metcalf et al. 1967a) and electronmicrograph sections of such macrophages indicate that they are healthy as judged from the morphology of their cellular substructure (Figure 3.15). However, the possibility remains that macrophage colony formation *in vitro* could be to some degree an artefact and not necessarily a true representation either of the preferred behaviour of some granulocytic colony cells or of the normal origin of macrophages.

The development of a medium conditioned by myelomonocytic leukaemia (WEHI-3) cells which could stimulate the formation of an unusually high percentage of granulocytic colonies, including the unique giant granulocytic colonies, raised certain doubts regarding the initial assumption that all *in vitro* colony-forming cells are essentially similar in nature.

We have referred already to the heterogeneity of such cells with respect to CSF, the size of colonies they generate, their lag period prior to initiation of proliferation and their heterogeneity with respect to adhesiveness and buoyant density. Is it also possible that some *in vitro* CFC's are preprogrammed only to form granulocytic colonies and others to form mixed or macrophage colonies?

The experiment which made such a possibility likely was an analysis of colony formation resulting when urine CSF (stimulating mainly macrophage colonies) was mixed with myelomonocytic leukaemia (MML) conditioned medium (stimulating mainly granulocyte colony formation). Analysis of the colonies resulting (Table 7.1) showed that the two types of CSF appeared to operate independently in the cultures, the number of granulocytic and macrophage colonies which developed being the sum of the number and type of colonies developing with either type of CSF alone (Metcalf, D., unpublished data).

If it is assumed that there are two different types of CSF or accessory factors, one (urine type) tending to produce macrophage colonies and the other (MML type) tending to produce granulocyte colonies, then if all CFC's were identical, the composition of all colonies might be expected to reflect the competitive interaction of the two influences on the CFC's and their progeny. Thus, as in the present experiment, if the effective concentrations of the two types of CSF were approximately equal, by random chance about half the cell population in every colony might be expected to be macrophages. In fact it was observed that many colonies 'bred true' and tended to be composed of either granulocytes or macrophages. This *in vitro* situation is of some general interest as an essentially similar situation occurs *in vivo*, where common ancestral and progenitor cells of erythroid or granulocytic cells reside in a mileu containing both erythropoietin and CSF; yet the evidence suggests that, having commenced proliferation, erythropoietic cells form only erythroid cells, and *vice versa*.

TABLE 7.1

Effect of mixture of two different types of CSF-containing material on number and type of bone-marrow colonies*

Human urine concentrate 0.1 ml	Myelomonocytic leukaemia con-ditioned medium 0.1 ml	Mean total no. of col-onies*	Mean number of colonies*		
			Macrophage	Granulocytic	Giant granulocytic
+	—	32	27	5	0
—	+	77	30	42	5
+	+	102	45	52	5

* All cultures contained 75,000 C57BL bone-marrow cells. Mean data from four replicate cultures.

Studies on colony formation *in vitro* using urinary CSF have shown that most colonies at 7 days of incubation are composed of macrophages. However, plate mapping and cluster-transfer studies have indicated that more than 50% of such colonies commence as granulocytic clusters, which at day 2 of incubation were identical in size and cellular composition with the clusters in plates stimulated by MML conditioned medium (Metcalf 1969b). This allowed reciprocal cluster-transfer experiments to be carried out to determine the subsequent fate of such clusters when transferred to cultures containing the other type of CSF. Table 7.2 shows the results of such a study and indicates clearly that clusters initiated by one type of CSF continue to behave on transfer as if they had remained in the donor plate. Thus urine and serum CSF-initiated clusters become macrophage in composition on recipient

TABLE 7.2

Cytological analysis of transferred clusters after incubation for 5 days in recipient cultures

Stimulus in donor plates	Stimulus in recipient plates	Number of clusters transferred	Percent recovery of transferred clusters	Percent of transferred clusters or colonies			
				Macro-phage*	Mixed macro-phage and gran-ulocytic	Granu-locytic**	Giant granu-locytic**
Human urine concentrate	Urine	45	74	97	3	0	0
	Serum	45	76	100	0	0	0
	MML con. med.	45	94	95	5	0	0
C57BL mouse serum	Urine	45	85	95	5	0	0
	Serum	45	91	98	2	0	0
	MML con. med.	45	91	98	2	0	0
Myelomono-cytic leukaemia conditioned medium	Urine	45	27	17	50	33	0
	Serum	45	44	60	30	10	0
	MML con. med.	47	68	12	38	47	3

* Clusters or colonies containing > 90% macrophages.
** Clusters or colonies containing > 90% granulocytes.

plates with MML-conditioned medium, whilst MML-initiated clusters (although appearing identical at day 2 to the other types of clusters) tended to develop into granulocytic colonies on recipient plates with urine or serum.

These data make it probable that at least some CFC's differ from others in that they are preprogrammed to develop into granulocytic colonies (provided culture conditions permit this), whilst others initially form granulocytic clusters which later become macrophage colonies, largely independently of the nature of the medium. The full implications of these findings remain to be established, but at present they can be regarded as further evidence of the heterogeneity of *in vitro* CFC's and probably as being evidence that preprogramming of progenitor cells can restrict the subsequent pattern of proliferation and differentiation of these cells without the further intervention of any microenvironmental influences.

The availability of conditioned media and particularly of sera from endotoxin-treated mice (see later), which stimulate the development of large numbers of purely granulocytic colonies, has raised some interesting questions regarding the proliferative pattern of the cells involved. It is relatively easy to culture from mouse bone marrow colonies of granulocytes containing up to 5000 cells, and analysis of such colonies at the two-cell stage indicates that at this stage both cells have large ring-shaped nuclei. From the morphological description of granulopoietic cells in the mouse (Boggs et al. 1967a) the latter cells would be classified as promyelocytes and on the various schemes of granulopoiesis deduced from thymidine-labelling data *in vivo* such cells should be capable of generating by symmetrical divisions at most 4–8 cells (Cronkite 1969; Athens 1969). Is granulopoiesis *in vitro* abnormal or are the data from *in vivo* studies misleading and incorrectly interpreted? It is quite possible that the present morphological classification of early granulocytic cells in the mouse is incorrect and that the above cells may be promyeloblasts but, even so, this would only allow the generation of up to 64 or 128 cells. Recently Athens (1969) has discussed data which suggest that the older concepts of symmetrical divisions may be incorrect and that asymmetrical divisions may occur in this cell series. If so, then theoretically any dividing granulocytic cell could produce unlimited numbers of progeny. Why then do promyeloblasts appear only to give rise to 64 progeny cells *in vivo*? The solution to this problem may come from further *in vitro* studies amplifying the observations that colony size is determined by CSF concentration, and that colonies show extreme heterogeneity in size and responsiveness to stimulation. It may be that the data obtained *in vivo* indicate the *mean* situation. Some early granulocytes may be able to generate only a few progeny, whilst others can generate some thousands of cells. Furthermore this intrinsic proliferative capacity may be greatly modified by micro-environmental conditions and above all by the level of CSF and other humoral regulators. Thus, *in vitro* CFC's may well generate an average of 64 progeny under steady-state conditions in normal animals, but with increasing demand, be able to generate many thousands of progeny. For this reason the haemopoietic tissues may well be capable of great flexibility in total granulocyte production without showing corresponding fluctuations in the number of progenitor cells (*in vitro* CFC's). As shall be seen later, the injection of CSF to mice appears capable of inducing increased granulocyte production without substantially altering the number of *in vitro* CFC's.

The full implications of granulocyte colony growth *in vitro* must await further experimental data, but at this stage it seems wise to view existing models of granulopoiesis (and also of erythropoiesis) with some scepticism as the proposed patterns of proliferation may not be as inflexible as previously supposed.

7.4.2 Source of CSF

CSF was originally detected as a product elaborated by certain cells *in vitro*, e.g. neonatal mouse-kidney cells (Bradley and Metcalf 1966) lymphoma cells (Bradley, T. R. and Metcalf, D., unpublished data) or fibroblasts (Pluznik and Sachs 1965). It was shown shortly thereafter that CSF was detectable in the serum of most normal mice (Robinson et al. 1967; Metcalf and Foster 1967a). Initial studies suggested that CSF was not detectable in the serum of normal humans (Foster et al. 1968b), but subsequent work (Chan and Metcalf 1970; Chan et al. 1971) revealed that inhibitors are present in most normal human sera which mask the presence of CSF. Prior dialysis of normal sera against water led to the removal by precipitation of these inhibitors, and subsequent assays revealed detectable levels of CSF in all normal human sera.

The regular presence of CSF in serum is mandatory if CSF is to be considered as a normal humoral regulator (see later) but raises the question of the organ or tissue origin of the CSF found in the serum. Studies on serum CSF levels following removal of the thymus, spleen, kidneys, adrenals, gonads or a major portion of the liver (Metcalf, D., unpublished data) indicated that none of these organs constitutes a single major source of serum CSF. Parallel studies using cell suspensions from various organs as feeder layers suggested that many organs contain cells which can secrete or release CSF on culture in agar (Bradley and Metcalf 1965; Bradley et al. 1969). Of these, the most active appeared to be embryonic cells, and neonatal kidney cells. Somewhat similar data were obtained from an analysis of the capacity of cells from various organs to release or secrete CSF into tissue culture fluid on conventional culture in liquid medium. Cells from the embryo and certain organs, such as the kidney, thymus and bone marrow, appeared exceptional in their capacity to release or secrete CSF and thereby condition the medium (Bradley and Sumner, 1968). The obvious drawback to making conclusions from such work is the possibility that cells from certain organs may contain or secrete CSF but have such a poor survival in agar or liquid culture that they cannot reveal their content, or production, of CSF. This led to an alternative approach of assaying extracts of various organs for their static content of CSF. This study revealed that some organs contain large amounts of CSF, e.g. pregnant uterus, lung and spleen (Bradley, T. R. and Sumner, M. A., unpublished data). However, this approach also suffers from the serious drawback that only stored CSF is assayed and that an organ may secrete large amounts of CSF to the serum yet not store significant amounts of CSF. Recently, Robinson et al. (1969a) have estimated the colony-stimulating activity of perfusate fluid from intact pig spleens or livers maintained *in vitro*. Spleen perfusate contained high levels of CSF for 16 hours and liver perfusates for 40 hours, suggesting that both organs contained and/or secreted substantial amounts of CSF. Interestingly, a closed perfusion system was used, and in the case of both organs CSF levels eventually fell to zero, suggesting that cells in these organs, or their breakdown products, can degrade CSF or block the biological action of this factor.

In so far as the present evidence goes, the implication is strong that serum CSF is not derived from a single organ but is a secretory product of (or released by) many organs in the body. This means either that many different cells in the body have the capacity to produce CSF or alternatively that cells common to many organs in the body, e.g. reticuloendothelial cells may elaborate CSF.

One complicating factor in determining the tissue origin of CSF is the possibility that some organs like the submaxillary gland may contain large amounts of CSF but normally not release it to the serum. If this possibility occurs, then the submaxillary gland could not be regarded as playing a significant role in the regulation of haemopoiesis, since presumably only CSF entering the serum would have the capacity to stimulate progenitor cells in the various haemopoietic organs. An approach to this question seems possible because of the recent finding that CSF extractable from different organs differs biochemically, specifically with respect to charge as revealed by electrophoretic mobility and by binding to calcium phosphate gels (Stanley, E. R. and Sheridan, J., unpublished data). Thus it has been observed that CSF extractable from lung, spleen and kidney resembles serum CSF in these properties but that CSF extracted from submaxillary gland is quite distinct (Sheridan, J., unpublished data). Further analysis of serum and organ CSF's may provide a clearer insight into the question of which organs contribute significantly to the CSF detected in the serum.

One of the important questions regarding humoral regulators concerns their half life in the serum and their metabolic fate. Such questions can best be answered when pure preparations of identifiable humoral factors are available which can be injected and monitored in recipient animals. Although CSF has not yet been extracted in purified form, high-potency preparations of CSF have been prepared from human urine and injected into adult C57BL mice. The fall in serum concentrations of CSF was monitored by the use of a discriminatory antibody, prepared in rabbits to human urine CSF, which inactivated human CSF at high dilution but had no neutralising activity against mouse serum CSF (Stanley et al. 1970). The data obtained indicate a mean half life of human CSF in mouse serum of 2.9 hours (Metcalf and Stanley 1971). It might be argued that since human and mouse CSF differ antigenically, human CSF might be eliminated abnormally rapidly in the mouse. However, the observed half-life of about 3 hours agrees well enough with an approximate figure for the half life of mouse CSF in serum of less than 4 hours deduced from a study of CSF levels in mice recovering from the acute effects of LDH virus infection (Foster et al. 1968a). Nothing is yet known of the serum CSF half-life in abnormal situations such as infections, leukaemia or renal disease in which CSF levels are known to be high in the serum.

Analysis of the urine of humans and mice has shown that detectable levels of CSF are present in normal, unconcentrated urine. In view of the known ability of kidney cells to release CSF in liquid culture, attempts were made to establish whether urinary CSF represented CSF cleared from the serum by the kidney or CSF secreted into the urine by kidney cells. Mice subjected to bilateral nephrectomy or ureter ligature developed rises in serum CSF levels in the first 24 hours post-operation (Chan 1970; Foster and Mirand 1970). Further evidence that urinary CSF represents CSF cleared from the serum was obtained from an analysis of the mechanism by which the injection of cortisone in mice causes a pronounced fall within 3 hours of serum CSF levels (Metcalf 1969c). Cortisone injection was found to cause an acute diuresis in mice, and assay of the urine from such mice revealed sufficiently high levels of CSF to account for that lost in the serum. In confirmation of this conclusion, cortisone failed to reduce serum CSF levels in mice nephrectomised immediately before the injection of cortisone. Furthermore, injected human CSF has been recovered in large amounts in the urine of C57BL mice within 12 hours of injection (Chan, S. H., personal communication). This evidence suggests that excretion in the urine is a major fate of serum CSF, and an analysis of patients with acute leukaemia has indicated that the rate of loss of CSF in the urine is in part related to the level of CSF in the serum (Metcalf et al. 1971). However, there are sufficient anomalies between serum and urine CSF levels to make it evident that the situation with CSF is not as simple as appears to exist with erythropoietin, where there is a clear parallel in most cases between plasma and urine erythropoietin levels.

Another possible fate of serum CSF is inactivation, or excretion, by the liver. Some evidence for the occurrence of such a process has been referred to earlier from the work of Robinson et al. (1969a). Partial hepatectomy in mice was not followed by consistent rises in serum CSF levels, but destruction of most of the liver by carbon tetrachloride was followed in some cases by moderate rises in serum CSF levels (Chan, S. H., unpublished data). Similarly in some, but certainly not the majority, of cases of advanced cirrhosis in man, serum CSF levels were found to be elevated in the absence of any intercurrent infections (Foster et al. 1968b).

As discussed earlier, there is some evidence that CSF may be utilised by dividing haemopoietic cells (Metcalf 1970) but adsorption or non-specific breakdown of CSF by these cells cannot be excluded.

Despite the apparently specific chemical nature of CSF (see later), it may be that CSF is a membrane component present on many cells and released in small amounts during normal cellular metabolism and in larger amounts following cell breakdown. This suggestion is difficult to prove or disprove but some indirect evidence supports this view: (a) CSF release by cells *in vitro* increases as incubation proceeds and in cultures of bone-marrow or thymic cells this is associated with increasing cell death, (b) serum CSF levels are high in infections and leukaemia where increased cell breakdown can be anticipated, (c) whole-body irradiation elevates serum CSF levels, the rise in CSF being proportional to the dose of irradiation (Hall 1969), and (d) cytosine arabinoside, a cytotoxic agent, elevates serum CSF levels in mice and leads to increased urinary excretion of CSF in leukaemic mice and humans (Metcalf et al. 1971; Chan, S. H., unpublished data). All these situations are complex and the rise in CSF levels could have other explanations, but release from cell membranes is as likely as any.

Does this type of origin of CSF detract from the suggestion that CSF is a specific normal regulator of granulocyte and monocyte formation? Since the normal functions of granulocytes and macrophages presumably include removal of disintegrating and damaged cells it is logical that the production of these cells be stimulated by a factor released from disintegrating cells; and since such cell breakdown occurs regularly in the normal body, CSF would have as much right to be regarded as a 'normal' regulator, as erythropoietin. Indeed, in the special case of breakdown of granulocytes, CSF would constitute a highly specific positive feedback mechanism ensuring homeostasis in total granulocyte numbers.

Other agents have been shown to cause transitory rises in serum CSF levels in mice. The injection of a variety of bacterial antigens, endotoxin, conjugated serum proteins and antigen-antibody complexes causes 10–100-fold elevations in serum CSF levels within 3 hours of injection, levels falling to normal within the next 24 hours (Metcalf, D., unpublished data). Repeated injections of antigens such as polymerised flagellin elicited repeated serum peaks of CSF raising the additional possibility that in the normal animal CSF production and release into the serum may be triggered by a continuous low level of bacterial antigens or other bacterial products entering the blood from exposed body surfaces.

An interesting side result from experiments involving the injection of large amounts of human urine CSF intravenously to adult mice was the finding that levels of serum CSF of mouse origin actually rose 2–3 hours after such injections. This type of response is essentially similar to that just discussed as following the injection of other antigenic materials, but since human CSF can be shown to have biological activity *in vivo* (see later) the results suggest that plasma CSF levels may exert no inhibitory feedback regulation on CSF production or release.

7.4.3 Biochemistry of CSF

The initial studies on the biochemical nature of CSF were carried out on serum CSF from normal or leukaemic mice (Robinson et al. 1967; Metcalf and Foster 1967a; Stanley et al. 1968) and on conditioned medium produced by mouse cells (Pluznik and Sachs 1966; Bradley et al. 1969). These studies indicated that CSF was heat-labile (being inactivated at temperatures ranging from 75–90 °C, depending on the type of CSF), non-dialysable and ether-and UV-resistant. Further studies with mouse serum CSF indicated that it was resistant to RNA-ase and DNA-ase, migrated electrophoretically in the α globulin-post albumin region, had a buoyant density of approximately 1.34 in CsCl and a sedimentation coefficient of between 4.5 and 7.0 S (Stanley et al. 1968).

More detailed studies on CSF in normal and leukaemic human urine indicated that urinary CSF differed slightly from serum CSF. Urine CSF was again heat-labile and non-dialysable, but stable to RNA-ase, DNA-ase, ether, 8M urea and pH's from 2–12. Urine CSF was precipitated by ammonium sulphate between 40–68 % and by ethanol between 32–47 %. Earlier studies indicated an apparent discrepancy between the molecular weight of CSF as determined by gel filtration (approximately 190,000) and by zone sedimentation in sucrose gradients (approximately 45,000) (Figure 7.4) both estimates being based on the assumption that CSF had hydrodynamic properties similar to BSA (Stanley and Metcalf 1969). A similar discrepancy was noted by Austin and Till (1970) in gel filtration and sedimentation studies on the colony-stimulating factor in L cell-conditioned medium.

Subsequent studies have revealed that human urine CSF exhibits anomalous behaviour on Sephadex and DEAE-cellulose when in the presence of large amounts of contaminating protein. Estimates of molecular weight from gel filtration, starting with increasingly purified material, give results agreeing closer and closer with the estimate of 3.4 S (45,000) derived from sedimen-

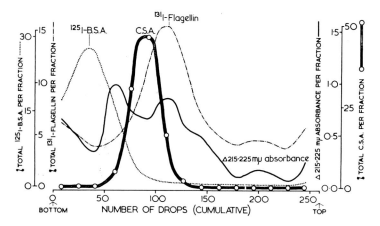

Fig. 7.4.   Zone sedimentation of concentrated human urine on a 10–25% sucrose gradient (49 hours, 115,000 g, 4° pH 6.0). Colony-stimulating activity (CSA) is shown peaking between ^{125}I-BSA marker (M.W. approx. 69,000) and ^{131}I-flagellin marker (M.W. approx. 40,000) close to the ^{131}I-flagellin peak. (From Stanley and Metcalf 1969, reproduced by permission of Aust. J. Exp. Biol. Med. Sci.)

tation studies in sucrose gradients at a variety of temperatures and pH's (Stanley and Metcalf 1971). This estimate also agrees with data from the behaviour of CSF on gradient gel electrophoresis (Stanley, E. R. and Metcalf, D., unpublished data).

Procedures have been developed for the large-scale extraction of partially purified CSF from 176 litre batches of normal human urine, using sequential batch chromatography on DEAE-cellulose, calcium phosphate and column chromatography and gel filtration on DEAE-cellulose, Sephadex G-150, and hydroxylapatite. Recovery of CSF from such procedures was approximately 20% with 4,000-fold purification with respect to protein (Stanley and Metcalf 1969; Stanley, E. R. and Metcalf, D., unpublished data). Electrophoretic separation of small amounts of these CSF preparations on polyacrylamide gels has achieved an approximate 50,000-fold purification with respect to protein.

The activity of partially purified CSF was destroyed by periodate, mercaptoethanol and high concentrations of pronase and subtilisin, but was resistant

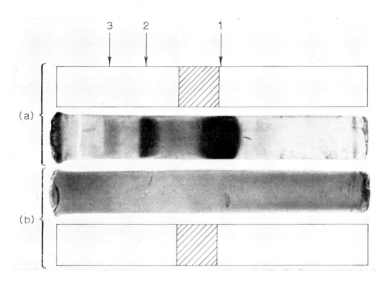

Fig. 7.5. Effect of papain treatment on partially purified (× 4000) human urine CSF. Preparations separated electrophoretically on 7.5% polyacrylamide gel at pH 9.4 and stained with Coomassie blue. CSF was located in hatched area in starting material (a). Major contaminants in this preparation were monomeric (1) and polymeric (2, 3) forms of HSA. Following papain digestion (b) there was almost complete disappearance of contaminating protein bands, while size-charge characteristics of CSF (lower hatched area) were unchanged, with 90% recovery of starting CSF.

to trypsin, papain and pepsin. Combination of papain digestion of batch-prepared CSF with subsequent electrophoretic separation on polyacrylamide gels has achieved CSF preparations approximately 100,000-fold purified with respect to protein (Figure 7.5) (Stanley, E. R. and Metcalf, D., unpublished data).

The *in vitro* colony stimulating activity of partially purified batches of CSF was not destroyed by digestion with highly purified neuraminidase, although this finding does not exclude the possibility that CSF contains small amounts of sialic acid.

It is clear from this data that CSF is present in only minute amounts in serum and urine despite the high biological activity of these fluids. Thus 170 litres of urine contain approximately 30 g of protein of which less than 300 μg is CSF, and biological activity can be detected *in vitro* with less than 100 pg of material per standard 1-ml culture. Calculations indicate that, at this concentration, colony stimulation can be achieved with only 1 molecule of CSF per 1000 μ^3 volume in the culture gel. At this level chemical estimations on active fractions for protein and carbohydrate content are wasteful of

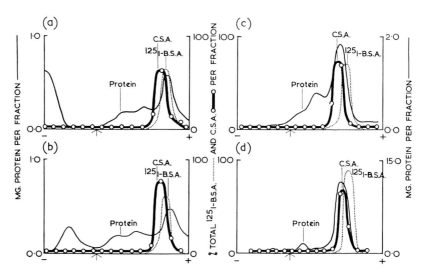

Fig. 7.6. Electrophoresis of human urine concentrates in starch-Geon supporting medium (pH 8.6). The colony-stimulating activity (CSA) of (a) a concentrate from a normal male, (b) a pool of three concentrates from normal males, (c) a concentrate from a leukaemic female, and (d) a concentrate from a leukaemic male, bands constantly to the left of the ^{125}I-BSA marker in the post-albumin region. (From Stanley and Metcalf 1969, reproduced by permission of Aust. J. Exp. Biol. Med. Sci.)

active material, which complicates further purification procedures. From the data on erythropoietin it is likely that similar problems apply in the purification of this regulator. Comparative study of normal and leukaemic human urine indicated no major physical differences between CSF in the two types of material (Stanley and Metcalf 1969) (Figure 7.6).

From the present data, CSF appears to have a molecular weight of approximately 45,000 and probably is a glycoprotein with some general similarities to erythropoietin.

As previously mentioned, human urine CSF has been shown to be antigenic in the rabbit (Stanley et al. 1970). The antibody activity was shown to reside in both the 7S and 19S gammaglobulin regions. No precipitin lines were observed on the immunoelectrophoresis against human urine concentrates but the antibody, when mixed in culture with CSF, inhibited colony formation. Based on this inhibition assay, it was demonstrated that human serum and urine CSF are antigenically similar, but distinct from CSF present in mouse serum or urine and medium conditioned by mouse embryo cells.

7.4.4 *Indirect evidence that CSF functions as a humoral regulator in the normal animal*

The indirect evidence in support of the concept that CSF acts as a regulator of the production of granulocytes and macrophages *in vivo* comes from observations on CSF levels in mouse and man.

Serum from most normal mice contains sufficiently high concentrations of CSF to be detectable in assays on unconcentrated serum (Bradley et al. 1967a; Robinson et al. 1967; Foster and Metcalf 1967a). In a number of mouse strains, e.g. C3H and BALB/c, the presence of CSF in the serum is partially masked by lipoidal material, which inhibits colony formation. This inhibitory material can be removed by centrifugation, ether extraction or dialysis against water when it forms a precipitate which can be removed by centrifugation (Stanley et al. 1968). Initial surveys (Foster et al. 1968b) appeared to show that CSF was not detectable in the serum of normal humans, using mouse bone-marrow cells as the assay system. However, subsequent work in this laboratory (Chan et al. 1971) showed that CSF is present in significant amounts in all normal human sera, but its detection is normally obscured by the same type of lipoidal inhibitors as found in some mouse sera.

It should be emphasised here that the levels of CSF detectable in the serum of normal mice and humans are highly significant in terms of physiological activity. E.g., in a typical assay on CSF levels in normal mouse serum, 0.1

ml of serum is incorporated in 1 ml of agar medium containing 75,000 target bone-marrow cells. In such a culture it is common for 75 colonies to develop after 7 days of incubation. Stimulation of proliferation of bone-marrow cells has been shown to be related to the concentration of CSF in the medium (Metcalf 1970). Thus, a 1:10 dilution of serum still contains a sufficiently high concentration of CSF to stimulate extensive proliferation of the target cells over a 7-day incubation period. Data from the decay curves of human urine CSF levels in the sera of mice injected with urine concentrates suggest that serum CSF is in free exchange with tissue CSF (Metcalf and Stanley 1971). From this it can be concluded that in the normal mouse bone marrow, target cells are normally bathed in fluid containing a $10 \times$ higher concentration of CSF than is needed *in vitro* to act as a powerful proliferative stimulus. Similar conclusions can be drawn from an analysis of serum CSF levels in normal humans. It must be concluded therefore that if CSF action *in vivo* in any way resembles CSF action *in vitro*, CSF concentrations in the plasma of normal mice and humans represent a very strong proliferative stimulus for their appropriate target cells.

Parallel surveys on urine from normal humans of all ages have revealed detectable colony-stimulating activity in all such urines. Again initial studies appeared to indicate that CSF was undetectable in some unconcentrated urine preparations, but the dose-response curve of colony formation with decreasing amounts of CSF is sigmoid, and urines containing relatively small amounts of CSF sometimes fail to stimulate colony formation. Furthermore lipoidal substances are present in some urines, which can inhibit colony formation *in vitro*. This is a particular problem with urine from normal mice. If concentration of such urines 2–8-fold is carried out using a variety of methods, particularly if the concentration technique achieves a partial removal of inhibitory factors, e.g. by adsorbing CSF on calcium phosphate gels, tests on such concentrates invariably reveal colony-stimulating activity. Less extensive tests have been made on other body fluids, but thoracic duct lymph and ascites and pleural fluids in mice have been shown to contain CSF.

As with erythropoietin, the daily excretion of CSF in man shows a rather wide variation over a 10-fold range, although most data from normal subjects fall within a 4-fold range. CSF excretion also shows some diurnal variation and unexplained day-to-day variations (Metcalf and Stanley 1969). Until further work is performed on the occurrence and levels of inhibitory factors in urine, the significance of the apparently wide variations in daily excretion rates of CSF cannot be fully assessed.

CSF levels appear to be unusually high in the serum of embryonic mice.

This period coincides with the period of very rapid increase in haemopoietic cells in the body (9–12 days of embryonic life), although these two processes may not necessarily be related (Moore and Metcalf 1970).

7.4.5 *In vivo effects of material containing CSF*

In this work the content of CSF in the injected material was expressed in units, one unit being the amount of CSF required to stimulate one colony to develop from 75,000 bone-marrow cells. In practice, assays are performed on the linear portion of the dose-response curve, i.e. in the 20–100 colony range. Thus, if 0.1 ml of the test material stimulates 50 colonies to develop, on the above definition this material contains 50 units of CSF.

The injection of 0.1 ml of human urine concentrates (containing 25,000 units) intraperitoneally to 6-day old mice produced a temporary elevation of blood polymorphs and monocytes, but no significant changes in lymphocyte and nucleated red-cell levels (Figures 7.7, 7.8). Following a single injection, levels of these cells reached a maximum at 24–48 hours after injection and returned to pre-injection levels by 72 hours. Granulocyte and monocyte levels

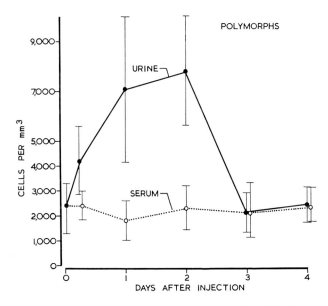

Fig. 7.7. Blood-polymorph levels in neonatal C57BL mice following a single I.P. injection of 25,000 units of human urine CSF. Control mice injected with diluted human serum. Each point mean value of 12 mice with standard deviations.

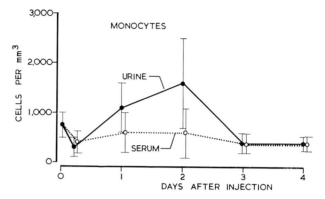

Fig. 7.8. Blood-monocyte levels in neonatal C57BL mice following a single I.P. injection of 25,000 units of human urine CSF. Control mice injected with diluted human serum. Each point mean value of 12 mice with standard deviations.

at 3 and 6 hours after injection were not elevated, nor was the bone marrow depleted of granulocytes at either of these time points. Thus, these urine concentrates of CSF appeared to lack the leucocyte releasing action described for sera and organ extracts by Gordon et al. (1964) and Bierman (1964).

A granulocyte leucocytosis in mice can be induced by the injection of a wide variety of materials and the potential non-specificity of this type of response presents diffculties in choosing suitable control materials. In experiments with urine CSF concentrates, control systems have included urinary protein concentrates from DEAE column fractions on either side of the demonstrable peak of CSF activity and diluted or concentrated to match the protein concentration of the CSF-containing fraction. These control preparations and controls using whole normal human serum diluted to a similar protein concentration, failed to induce a polymorph leucocytosis in baby mice. The general difficulty in this type of work is that since pure preparations of CSF do not yet exist, even if the induction of a granulo- cytosis is a specific effect of CSF-containing fractions, it may still be due to the action of another protein with similar physical properties in the same semi-purified concentrates.

Earlier studies in adult mice given repeated intraperitoneal injections every 6 hours of medium conditioned by syngeneic embryo cells also indicated that this material induced the development of a polymorph leucocytosis (Bradley et al. 1969). Autoradiographic studies on the appearance of labelled polymorphs in the blood indicated that labelled cells did not appear earlier in the peripheral blood of such mice, but that after 24 hours the rate of increase in labelled cells in mice injected with conditioned medium was greater than that in control mice. These studies suggested that CSF had not released preformed cells but had produced a leucocytosis by increasing the rate or magnitude of granulopoiesis in the animal. Assays for the incidence of *in vitro* colony-forming cells in such animals 6 days after commencement of the injections showed that mice injected with conditioned medium exhibited a significant rise in the spleen and blood content of colony-forming cells but no significant rise in the bone-marrow content.

In further *in vivo* studies, single injections of partially purified human urine CSF (1000-fold purified with respect to protein) containing 13–20,000 units of CSF were made intravenously to adult C57BL mice (Metcalf, D., unpublished data). Such mice developed a monocytosis which was maximal between 24–48 hours after the injection and had passed by 72 hours. No significant changes were observed in polymorph or lymphocyte levels. Studies in animals labelled with tritiated thymidine have indicated that, in mice injected with CSF, labelled polymorphs did not appear earlier in the blood than in control mice. However, the rate of accumulation of labelled cells was considerably increased in CSF-injected mice, and since labelled polymorphs accumulate exponentially in the blood this difference suggests a considerably increased level of granulopoiesis in CSF-injected mice. The monocytes in CSF-injected mice were often unusually large and basophilic and had a smoothly rounded nucleus, suggesting that these cells were slightly less mature cells than those seen normally in the peripheral blood. No obvious histological changes were observed in the haemopoietic organs 48 and 72 hours after the injection of 4–6 doses of 25,000 units of CSF.

Assays for colony-forming cells in the bone marrow of adult mice injected with CSF 24 hours previously showed a slight rise in colony-forming cells (+50%) compared with control mice injected with normal human serum. Of particular interest was the observation that cultures of bone-marrow cells from mice injected 24 hours previously with CSF showed a different pattern of progressive cluster formation *in vitro* from that shown by control bone-marrow cells. With bone-marrow cells from normal or serum-injected control mice, the accumulation of clusters invariably extrapolated back to zero at 12 hours of incubation. Corresponding data from bone-marrow cells from CSF-injected mice showed an extrapolation to zero at −12 hours, suggesting that CSF *in vivo* had altered many cluster-forming cells so that they were able to commence proliferation almost immediately after plating out *in vitro* (Figure 7.9). Since CSF *in vitro* appears to shorten the lag period before new cluster-forming cells commence proliferation, this suggests that CSF injected

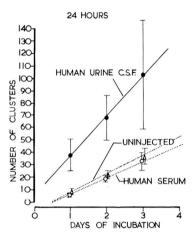

Fig. 7.9. Accumulation of clusters in cultures of 10,000 bone-marrow cells from adult C57BL mice injected intravenously 24 hours earlier with 15,000 units of human urine CSF. Control mice injected with diluted human serum. Note larger number of clusters in cultures from CSF-injected mice and apparent extrapolation to zero approximately 24 hours earlier than in control cultures. Each point mean data from cultures from six individual mice with standard deviations.

in vivo may have a somewhat similar effect to that observed *in vitro*.

These effects of a single injection of CSF disappeared between 48–72 hours after injection. In view of the short half life of injected human CSF in mice (approximately 3 hours), in other studies mice were injected at 6–12 hourly intervals for up to 72 hours, but this procedure neither accentuated the responses observed nor prolonged them beyond the duration normally observed following a single injection. This unexpected finding cannot be fully interpreted at present but it suggests that the recruitment or proliferation of *in vitro* colony-forming cells in the intact animal may be limited by the flow of precursor or resting cells into the susceptible CFC pool and that no matter how much CSF is given the response may be limited by the slow entry of new cells into the susceptible (stimulatable) pool. We discussed earlier the *in vitro* evidence indicating that CSF was unable to effect the transformation of *in vivo* colony-forming cells (CFU's) to *in vitro* colony-forming cells. Reasons were given earlier for suspecting that granulopoiesis can be increased without necessarily increasing the number of *in vitro* CFC.s and the present results may provide supporting evidence for this conclusion. If *in vitro* CFC's can divide asymmetrically in generating granulocytes and if cluster-forming cells are intermediate progeny in such a sequence then the present observation of a greater rise in cluster-forming cells than *in vitro* CFC's would be in line with this suggestion.

The *in vivo* data so far obtained are consistent with the interpretation that CSF does have a significant biological effect *in vivo*, leading to the generation of increased numbers of granulocytes and monocytes. The mechanism by which this is achieved remains uncertain but could include stimulation of the division of cells from the *in vitro* colony-forming cell to the myelocyte class and possibly the recruitment of additional *in vitro* colony-forming cells from precursor cells.

7.4.6 *CSF levels in abnormal states*

Elevation of serum and urine CSF levels have been observed in the acute stages of viral and bacterial infections in man (Foster et al. 1968b; Metcalf and Wahren 1968; Wahren et al. 1970; McNeill, T. A., unpublished data) and following LDH-virus infection and possibly other acute infections in mice (Foster et al. 1968a). In general, elevated levels fell promptly during the convalescent period, levels in the urine falling before those in the serum. Complementing these observations is the finding that serum CSF levels are unusually low in germfree mice, although such mice were capable of developing high CSF levels in response to leukaemia (Metcalf et al. 1967b) or unilateral ureteral ligature (Foster and Mirand 1970).

In a study of patients with infectious mononucleosis (Metcalf and Wahren 1968) it was observed that serum levels of CSF in the acute stages of the disease correlated well with the subsequent progress of the patients. The majority of patients developed high serum CSF levels and had a brief clinical illness, whilst the small proportion failing to develop elevated CSF levels tended to have a prolonged, difficult, clinical course.

It is well recognised that blood granulocyte levels are usually elevated in acute bacterial infections. Many workers have shown that the injection of products from bacteria ranging from lipopolysaccharide endotoxin to more specific products, e.g. of pertussis, produce polymorph leucocytoses in experimental animals, often of prodigious proportions. The significance of an elevated blood level of granulocytes must be assessed with care, as analysis has shown in acute infections that blood granulocyte levels do not necessarily reflect the level of granulopoiesis at that time (Athens 1969). Despite these reservations there is little doubt that bacterial products can strongly stimulate granulopoiesis. In part, this may represent a direct stimulation of primitive granulocytes by these products, but *in vitro* and *in vivo* studies have shown that such materials may also stimulate granulo-poiesis through CSF.

Bradley et al. (1969) showed that the injection of pertussis vaccine increased the incidence of *in vitro* CFC's in the bone marrow, spleen and blood. McNeill (1970c) showed that the *in vivo* injection of mice with substances such as *Salmonella adelaide* flagellin, endotoxin and Freund's complete adjuvant increased both serum levels of CSF and the number of *in vitro* CFC's in the bone marrow and spleen. More detailed studies on the acute response of serum CSF levels in mice to the injection of flagellin, endotoxin and a variety of bacterial vaccines showed that characteristically there was an acute rise in serum CSF levels reaching values up to 100 times normal levels (Metcalf, D., unpublished data). The response was maximal at 3–6 hours and was maintained for varying periods but had largely passed off by 24 hours. Repeated injections of flagellin at daily intervals resulted in repeated peaks of serum CSF 3–6 hours later.

In parallel *in vitro* studies using mouse bone-marrow cells in agar culture, McNeill (1970a) and Metcalf (1971b) showed that none of these bacterial antigens was capable of direct stimulation of colony formation *in vitro*. However, bacterial antigens added to minimal concentrations of CSF enhanced the number and size of colonies which developed. This action of antigen was dose-dependent and the potentiating effect required the presence of a serum factor which physical studies showed was an alphamacroglobulin (McNeill 1970b). This alphamacroglobulin was not specific for different antigens, e.g. it could be absorbed out by sheep red cells and the sera lost its activity when tested in a flagellin plus CSF system. The alphamacroglobulin was present in detectable amounts even in foetal mouse serum and may be related to the alphaglobulin shown by *in vivo* studies to potentiate the growth of spleen colonies in irradiated recipients and to promote radiation survival (Hanna et al. 1967).

In subsequent work it was shown that bone-marrow cells are able to produce CSF in liquid medium and that the addition of polymerised flagellin and serum to these cultures increased the production of CSF (Metcalf 1971b). These studies may indicate the reason why antigens potentiate the development and growth of bone-marrow colonies in agar cultures and suggest further that antigens and bacterial products may elevate serum CSF levels by stimulating the production of CSF by various tissues. These studies do not necessarily exclude the possibility of a direct growth stimulating action of bacterial products on granulopoietic cells, but in any case the CSF may well play an important intermediatory role in such processes.

Recent observations suggest that the abnormally high colony-stimulating activity seen in the serum following the injection of endotoxin or antigens may not be due to the CSF described so far or, alternatively, that the serum contains a factor modifying the action of CSF. Normal mouse serum stimulates the development of macrophage and occasional mixed colonies.

Similarly, partially purified CSF from human urine stimulates predominantly macrophage colonies and only with high concentrations of CSF does a small percentage of granulocytic colonies develop.

It is characteristic of colonies stimulated by serum from endotoxin- or antigen-injected mice that most are either granulocytic or mixed. Furthermore, unlike the effects of lowering the concentration of urine CSF, no fall in the percentage of granulocytic colonies occurs when such sera are progressively diluted. Preliminary electrophoretic separation of such sera has shown colony-stimulating activity to be located in the same region as CSF in normal mouse serum and that the granulocyte colony-stimulating activity is located in this region. Furthermore, addition of the inactive fractions from such separated sera to urine CSF did not result in the development of granulocytic colonies, suggesting that a 'granulocyte modifying factor' was not present in the inactive fractions. Analysis of tissue CSF from such animals using the selective elution pattern from $CaPO_4$ gels to characterise the active material, has provided evidence, particularly in the submaxillary gland, of a new type of elution pattern, consistent either with the presence of a modified type of CSF or of a different type of molecule with colony-stimulating activity.

Further work is required to clarify the situation but the most reasonable provisional conclusion appears to be that this 'reactive type' CSF may be a variant of 'normal' CSF, possibly having minor structural differences from normal CSF.

There is an extensive body of evidence indicating that serum and urine levels of CSF are elevated in mice and humans with various types of leukaemia. This will be discussed in Chapter 9, along with evidence of another possible variant of CSF produced by myelomonocytic leukaemic cells.

As might be anticipated from the fact that the kidney clears CSF from the urine, high serum levels of CSF have been observed in patients with advanced renal disease or in anephric patients on dialysis (Chan, S. H., unpublished data).

7.4.7 Role of CSF in vivo

The above evidence from *in vitro* and *in vivo* studies and the data on CSF levels in disease states suggest that CSF acts *in vivo* as a regulator of granulocyte and monocyte proliferation. There is a good general correlation between situations in which elevated serum CSF levels have been observed and situations, e.g. infections, tumour-bearing states or leukaemia, in which granulocyte and monocyte production are increased. However, a number of observations appear to suggest that CSF is not the only regulator for such cells: (a) There is no precise correlation in individual normal mice between serum CSF levels and blood-polymorph levels or bone-marrow levels of colony-forming cells (Metcalf, D., unpublished data). (b) Similarly in leukaemic AKR mice no correlation in individual mice exists between serum CSF levels and blood-polymorph levels or bone-marrow levels of *in vitro* colony-forming cells (Hibberd and Metcalf 1971). (c) In germfree mice, serum CSF levels are low, whereas blood-polymorph levels are normal as are the total bone-marrow content of granulocytic cells and the bone-marrow content of *in vitro* colony-forming cells (Boggs et al. 1967a; Metcalf et al. 1967b; Metcalf and Foster 1969). (d) During the regeneration of haemopoietic cells following whole-body irradiation, even though *in vitro* colony-forming cell levels rise progressively, as do blood-polymorph levels, the serum levels of CSF are not elevated (Hall 1969). (e) Blood-polymorph levels in cortisone-treated mice remain normal even though serum levels of CSF are grossly depressed (Metcalf 1969c).

These situations are all potentially highly complex as granulopoiesis and monocyte formation can be expected to be dependent not only on CSF levels but on the number of available *in vitro* CFC's and their ability to respond to stimulation in these various situations. Furthermore the magnitude of granulopoiesis is difficult to assess from blood-polymorph levels or even bone-marrow cell counts, and a careful analysis will be required in each of these situations to determine the true level of granulopoiesis.

For the present it seems reasonable to conclude that CSF does function *in vivo* as a regulator of granulopoiesis and monocyte formation, at the same time recognising that other regulators may also exist and may be of importance in certain situations.

7.4.8 *Other factors regulating granulopoiesis*

A number of workers have described experiments indicating the existence of a humoral factor which can cause an acute rise in blood-leucocyte levels (mainly granulocytes) by release of preformed cells to the blood. In investigations on the mechanisms involved in inflammation, Menkin (1956) reported that pleural and peritoneal exudates, certain tissue extracts and plasma from dogs with inflammatory effusions produced an acute, but brief, rise in granulocyte levels when injected intravenously into dogs. The active factor was termed the 'leucocytosis promoting factor' (LPF).

In a series of studies Gordon and his co-workers (see review by Gordon

1955; Gordon et al. 1964) produced evidence for the occurrence of an essentially similar factor which they termed 'leucocytosis inducing factor' (LIF). This also induced an acute, short-lasting, leucocytosis, which was shown to be the result of liberation into the blood of preformed granulocytes from the bone marrow and sites of sequestration in the peripheral circulation. The basic assay system used was to produce a leucocytosis in rats by the injection of large volumes of plasma from treated donor rats. Treatments which were found to induce LIF activity in the plasma were repeated leuca-phoresis (leucocyte removal by peritoneal lavage) and the injection of typhoid-paratyphoid vaccine. Biochemical studies showed that the active factor was non-dialysable and heat labile, precipitable by 35–75% ammonium sulphate and migrated in the alphaglobulin region.

Bierman (1964) reported studies on a similar factor termed 'leukopoietin G', which, because of the timing and duration of the granulocytosis probably also operated by leucocyte release. The assay system used was again the injection of test material into rats, and observations were limited to peripher-al blood counts. Leukopoietin G was reported to be present in the plasma of normal humans, rats, cattle and pigs, and to be present in increased amounts in the plasma and urine of patients with granulocytic leukaemia. Extracts of kidney, spleen, lung and thymus were also found to induce a leucocytosis. Boggs et al. (1966) reported that plasma from dogs injected with cytotoxic drugs, vinblastine or endotoxin induced an acute granulocytosis when in-jected intravenously into dogs. This factor was heat labile at 60 °C and showed species specificity in its action.

There is sufficient unanimity between these reports to make it probable that a factor exists in the plasma which can cause an acute elevation of granulocyte levels by mobilising preformed granulocytes. Such a factor must be an important control mechanism for maintaining normal blood-granulocyte levels, but is not really relevant to the question of the regulation of granu-lopoiesis, since no evidence has been presented suggesting a stimulating effect of this factor on granulocyte production.

Of a less certain nature are the results reported by a number of investigators in which more slowly developing responses occurred in granulocyte levels following the injection of biological material. Wearn et al. (1939) reported that the injection of urine extracts from patients with granulocytic leukaemia induced an accumulation of immature granulocytes in the spleen and bone marrow of guinea pigs. Subsequent studies (Turner and Miller 1943; Erf et al. 1946; Foster and Miller 1950) suggested that this factor was also demonstrable in the serum and organs of patients with granulocytic leukaemia and in normal liver extracts. Hirschman et al. (1945) produced similar changes with injections of urine fractions over an 8-day period. The active factor in these studies was found to be non-dialysable, sensitive to trypsin, relatively heat and pH stable and it was suggested that the active material could be a protein or glycoprotein.

Steinberg (1958) and Steinberg et al. (1958, 1959, 1965) reported that multiple injections of normal bovine and human serum into rabbits produced a maturation arrest of granulopoiesis in the bone marrow, lymphoid hyperplasia and increased extramedullary haemopoiesis in the spleen. Blood-leucocyte levels were either normal or occasionally subnormal. Heated sera by contrast was observed to produce a marked leucocytosis with granulocyte hyperplasia in the bone marrow.

These experiments are difficult to interpret because of the lack of haematological investigations which might have thrown light on the underlying mechanisms. It is possible that the responses observed are the consequence of unusual features of the guinea pig and rabbit, but accepting the data on face value they would indicate that some factor or factors are present in the serum and urine of leukaemic patients, which can affect granulocyte behaviour.

Studies have also been made on the mechanisms underlying the development of a leucocytosis in mice carrying transplanted mammary tumours. Saline extracts of granulocytosis-producing tumours resulted in the development of a leucocytosis which persisted 7–13 days (Delmonte and Liebelt 1965; Delmonte et al. 1966). The active material was non-dialysable, heat stable, precipitable by ethanol and ammonium sulphate, and was not retarded on passage through Sephadex G75 columns.

Another *in vivo* approach used to investigate the presence of humoral factors affecting granulopoiesis has been the use of the spleen-colony technique of Till and McCulloch (1961). Delmonte and Liebelt (1966) demonstrated an increased incidence of spleen colony formation following the injection of extracts of mouse tumours and mammalian kidney. Extensive studies have been made by Boggs et al. (1967b) using the endogenous system of spleen colony formation. The injection of normal dog, human and rat plasma into mice before sublethal irradiation increased the number of spleen colonies which subsequently developed, but no effect was seen with serum from syngeneic or related mouse strains. Endotoxin was excluded as being the basis for the observed results. These observations have intriguing similarities to those made in this laboratory where the injection of mice with flagellin, endotoxin, various bacterial vaccines and conjugated serum proteins caused marked elevations in serum levels of CSF (Metcalf, D., unpublished data) and the results of Boggs et al. (1967b) may have been due to the production or release of humoral factors following the injection of their foreign material.

7.4.9 Résumé

The discussion in this section has made it clear that at least two humoral factors exist which can affect granulocytic cells. One of these, the leucocyte-releasing factor, does not seem to be strictly relevant to questions of haemopoiesis. The other, CSF clearly affects the proliferation and differentiation of granulocytes and macrophages, as based on *in vitro* studies, but more work is required to establish its exact role in regulating granulopoiesis *in vivo*.

On general grounds, it is probable that other humoral regulators of granulopoiesis may exist and possibly some of the miscellaneous observations on humoral factors *in vivo* briefly discussed above might prove to be evidence for such factors. The general difficulty in all the above miscellaneous investigations was the need to use intact animals to assay biological activity. As a consequence, little progress was made either in chemically characterising the factors or in establishing the origin and occurrence of these factors in normal and abnormal situations. It is possible that a number of these factors may have been CSF.

7.5 Chalones and other inhibitors

It is well established in endocrinology that the production of individual hormones is regulated by feedback inhibitory systems which are often triggered by the hormones themselves (Furth 1969). Thus, thyroid hormone appears to act as an inhibitor of the hypothalamic-pituitary axis reducing the production of thyroid-stimulating hormone and thereby depressing the production of thyroid hormone. Such systems are intellectually satisfying since they provide an obvious system for regulating hormone-target-cell interaction. In the context of haemopoiesis, if specific regulators exist and stimulate by one mechanism or another, the production of various blood-cell classes, then by analogy with known endocrine systems, it is logical to expect that similar feedback inhibitory systems might operate to modulate the production and stimulating effects of these humoral regulators. Certainly this would provide an adequate system for explaining how blood cells are normally maintained at very precise levels in the normal animal.

Such feedback inhibitors would be conceived of as being humoral factors produced elsewhere in the body and having a depressing effect either on the production of stimulating factor, such as erythropoietin or CSF, or by inhibiting the capacity of their target cells to respond to stimulation. An alternative system proposes that the mature end cells of a proliferative sequence contain and release specific factors with the power to inhibit mitosis. Furthermore, the mitotic inhibition is specific for each particular differentiating cell series (Bullough and Laurence 1960). The factors have been called 'chalones' (Bullough 1962) and are defined as 'an internal secretion produced by a tissue for the purpose of controlling by inhibition the mitotic activity of cells of the same tissue' (Bullough 1967). The best characterised chalone is produced by epidermal cells and appears to inhibit epidermal mitoses *in vivo* and *in vitro* with inhibition augmented in the presence of adrenalin and a glucocorticoid (Bullough 1965, 1967). The epidermal chalone was tissue specific, but not species or class specific and was a water-soluble, heat-labile factor, probably a glycoprotein, of molecular weight 35–40,000 (Bullough et al. 1967; Hondius, Boldingh and Laurence 1968).

Chalone control has also been implicated in haemopoiesis, since extracts of granulocyte-rich (but not granulocyte-pure) preparations from the peritoneal cavity were found to depress tritiated thymidine uptake in liquid cultures of bone marrow (Rytomaa 1969). A similar inhibitory factor was present in serum of rats bearing transplantable granulocytic neoplasms (the Shay chloroleukaemia) and could be extracted from leukaemic cells (Rytomaa and Kiviniemi 1967). The active material was found to be dialysable, relatively heat-stable and on gel filtration had an apparent molecular weight of 4,000 (Rytomaa and Kiviniemi 1968a). The mitotic inhibitory capacity of this postulated granulocyte chalone appeared to be specific for granulopoiesis (though specificity control was incomplete) was not influenced by adrenalin though was potentiated by low concentrations of hydrocortisone and the inhibition appeared to be reversible (Rytomaa and Kiviniemi 1969).

It has been claimed that chalones can inhibit the growth of some malignant tumours *in vivo*. Epithelial chalone inhibited squamous-cell carcinoma in rabbits (Bullough and Laurence 1968a), melanocyte chalone inhibited malignant melanoma in mice and hamsters (Bullough and Laurence 1968b), and granulocyte chalone inhibited myelocytic chloroleukaemia in rats (Rytomaa and Kiviniemi 1968b). In all cases the work is of only a preliminary nature and control material has been inadequate so far. Since granulocytic chalone can be extracted from chloroleukaemic cells, is present in high concentration in the serum of tumour-bearing animals and yet the tumour cells are still responsive to mitotic inhibition, it was proposed that the lesion in neoplasia is a reduction in intracellular chalone concentration due at least in part to an unusually high rate of chalone loss to the blood (Rytomaa and Kiviniemi 1968b).

A possible erythrocytic chalone was reported in fresh normal serum but gel filtration on Sephadex G-75 could not separate this factor from granulocyte chalone and both substances eluted in the same zone corresponding to a molecular weight of about 4,000 (Rytomaa and Kiviniemi 1968a).

An antagonistic factor has also been reported to stimulate granulocytic proliferation and has been termed granulocyte 'antichalone'. The source of this factor is unclear but in situations of acute demand it was detected in rat serum (Rytomaa 1969). Gel filtration of leucaphoresed serum suggested a molecular weight of 30–35,000 for the antichalone, and dialysis of tissue extracts to remove chalone indicated that the antichalone may be produced by the same tissue as the chalone (Rytomaa 1969).

The whole question of establishing the biological role of inhibitory factors is fraught with difficulty, not the least being that of specificity. Chalones are still in the early stages of characterisation, and though a strong case can be presented for epidermal chalone, the situation of the postulated haemopoietic chalones is less clear and awaits further study. *In vivo* studies on granulocyte chalone action on granulocytic spleen colony formation, erythropoietin responsiveness and numbers of CFU's and *in vitro* CFC's indicated that chalone had no effect on these systems apart from a questionable stimulation of *in vitro* CFC numbers (known to be sensitive to elevation by antigenic stimuli), no effect on CFU regeneration following sublethal irradiation, and no effect on growth rate of *in vitro* CFC's (Lajtha, L. G., personal communication).

In the *in vitro* culture system for growing granulocytes and macrophage colonies, a number of inhibitory factors have been described. Ichikawa et al. (1967) described a dialysable factor in medium conditioned by spleen, peritoneal or colony macrophages which inhibited the growth of both macrophage and granulocytic colonies *in vitro* but not the growth of a granulocytic leukaemia. In subsequent studies Paran et al. (1969) described a non-dialysable inhibitor produced or released by semi-purified granulocytes which also inhibited the growth of macrophage and granulocytic colonies *in vitro*. Red cells did not appear to contain this inhibitor, but no other control studies were described.

In this laboratory dialysable inhibitors of both macrophage and granulocytic colony formation have been demonstrated in medium conditioned by bone-marrow, spleen, thymus and lymph-node cells, as well as in medium conditioned by a variety of neoplastic haemopoietic cells. Inhibition of colony growth was apparent within 12 hours of initiation of cultures and was associated with extensive death of the bone-marrow cells cultured. There is so far little evidence of specificity in terms of cellular origin of this inhibitory material, other than that lymphoid cell suspensions produce relatively small amounts in comparison with bone-marrow cells. It is quite possible that these low-molecular-weight inhibitors are relatively non-specific enzymes or toxic cell-breakdown products.

Analysis of normal mouse and human sera fractionated by electrophoresis has shown the existence of at least two non-dialysable inhibitors which inhibit the proliferation of colony cells, and it is likely that these inhibitors are lipoproteins (Stanley et al. 1968; Chan and Metcalf 1970; Chan et al. 1971). The inhibitors in normal human serum also show a certain species specificity being inhibitory for human CSF but not for mouse CSF when tested on mouse bone-marrow cells. These particular inhibitors would therefore appear to act in some way other than via a toxic effect on bone-marrow cells.

The difficulties in interpreting the biological significance of the above *in vitro* data are that there is as yet no evidence for tissue specificity in such experiments and that there is no guarantee that material which inhibits colony formation *in vitro* necessarily has any comparable activity *in vivo*. E.g., lipoprotein inhibitors are present in large amounts in the sera of C3H and BALB/c mice compared with levels in C57BL mice (Stanley et al. 1968), but levels of granulopoiesis in the three strains are essentially similar. The literature abounds with examples of *in vitro* artefacts of this nature and much more work is required before any special biological significance can be attached to these inhibitors.

The chalone concept is not without a satisfying logic but at the present time there are no concrete data which establish the existence or importance of such inhibitors in haemopoiesis.

7.6 Thymic humoral factor

The thymus can be shown to influence the total cellularity and proliferative activity of the peripheral lymphoid organs. There is an extensive literature on the effects of thymectomy at various ages in different species which has been reviewed in full elsewhere (see Metcalf 1966; Miller and Osoba

1967), and here only the major effects of thymectomy will be summarised.

Thymectomy in the adult mouse leads to a slowly developing weight loss of the lymph nodes and atrophy of spleen lymphoid follicles (Metcalf 1960). Analysis of this process has shown that there is a selective depletion of small lymphocytes in these organs, and histological studies have localised the lymphocyte depletion to the areas involved in lymphocyte recirculation (the loose cortex of the lymph nodes and the periarteriolar areas of the spleen lymphoid follicles) (Metcalf 1960; Metcalf and Brumby 1966). Thymectomy in neonatal animals produces an even more striking depletion of lymphocyte levels in the blood, thoracic duct fluid and lymphoid organs, suggesting that the thymic influence on lymphopoiesis is quantitatively more important in the neonatal animal than in adult life (Miller 1962; Waksman et al. 1962; Good et al. 1962; Parrott et al. 1966; Miller and Mitchell 1969).

Since most peripheral lymphocytes seem likely to be involved in one immune response or another, it is not surprising that thymectomy has a marked influence on some types of immune response, particularly those of cell-mediated type, e.g. homograft rejection and humoral responses to certain antigens, e.g. sheep red cells and BSA (Miller 1962; Good et al. 1962; Jankovic et al. 1962; see review by Miller and Osoba 1967). In the adult animal similar depressed immune responses follow thymectomy, although they are much slower in onset and quantitatively less severe (Good et al. 1962; Miller 1965; Metcalf 1965; Taylor 1965). The degree of immunological impairment in thymectomised adult animals can be accentuated by combining thymectomy with whole-body irradiation (Miller et al. 1964; Globerson and Feldman 1964) or with treatment by anti-lymphocyte serum (Monaco et al. 1965).

The high susceptibility of neonatally thymectomised mice to infections and early death explains in part the apparently greater effects of thymectomy on lymphoid organs in the neonatal animal than in the adult animal. The secondary infections can be expected to stress the animal leading to further lymphoid atrophy mediated by the adrenal corticosteroids and malnutrition. This probably results in a snowballing effect on lymphocyte depletion leading terminally to profound lymphoid organ atrophy.

Thymus grafts, provided grafting is carried out before the final irreversible vicious circle of infection and stress is entered, will restore the cellularity of the peripheral lymphoid organs, correct or prevent the development of depressed immune responses, and prevent death in the case of neonatal thymectomy.

These remarkable effects of the thymus on peripheral lymphoid organs and immune responses clearly indicate that the thymus has a profound regulatory influence on lymphopoiesis elsewhere in the body. The controversial aspect of this regulatory influence concerns the question of whether the influence is due solely to the production by the thymus of lymphoid cells, or is due to the production by the thymus of a humoral factor affecting lymphopoiesis elsewhere in the body. The third and more likely alternative is that the thymus has a dual, cellular and humoral, function.

The attempt to demonstrate the existence of a thymic humoral factor has been complicated by the fact that the thymus undoubtedly generates vast numbers of lymphoid cells and the well-documented evidence that some of these lymphoid cells certainly seed in the peripheral lymphoid organs when they proliferate in response to antigens and potentiate the proliferation in these organs of bone-marrow-derived lymphoid progenitor cells. Many feel that this cell-seeding function of the thymus can, by itself, adequately explain the observed effects of thymectomy in causing lymphocyte depletion, depressed lymphopoiesis and depressed immune responses.

However, as we discussed earlier, the epithelial cells of the thymus have the morphology of secretory cells (Arnesen 1958; Clark 1966) and do appear to regulate lymphopoiesis at least in the thymus. Is it possible that the thymus, in addition to its function as a producer of lymphocytes, also influences lymphopoiesis elsewhere in the body via a humoral factor? The evidence for the existence of a humoral factor will be discussed in semi-chronological order, dealing first with observations on the effects of thymus extracts both *in vivo* and *in vitro*, and then with indirect evidence supporting these observations.

7.6.1 *Effects of thymus extracts on lymphopoiesis*

Direct attempts to demonstrate a thymic humoral factor by the injection of thymus extracts encounter the same problems of dosage schedules, half life of injected material, variation in responsiveness of animals and possible feedback inhibitors, as were discussed earlier for *in vivo* testing of erythropoietin and CSF. Two additional problems make the task even more difficult: (a) Lymphocyte levels are highly labile in small laboratory animals and vary widely with environmental conditions such as diet, minor trauma, crowding, and temperature. Furthermore, lymphocyte levels do not necessarily reflect levels of lymphopoiesis. (b) Lymphoid cells are stimulated to proliferate by antigens. Thus, thymus extracts from foreign species will almost certainly be antigenic for the test animal and possibly syngeneic thymus extracts might also prove antigenic if they contain antigens not normally released to the body. The reported effects of injections of thymus extracts on lymphoid tissues must therefore be interpreted with caution before being accepted as valid evidence for a thymic humoral factor which regulates lymphopoiesis.

Based on the experience with erythropoietin, the most useful *in vivo* assay system for a lymphopoietic factor should be a lymphocyte-depleted animal. Thus, a neonatal animal, neonatally-thymectomised animal or an adult animal subjected to thymectomy with or without irradiation, might be expected to provide the most sensitive type of assay system.

Observations on the effect of thymus extracts in intact adult animals have been conflicting. In extensive investigations no effects were observed of syngeneic thymus extracts in adult mice on blood lymphocyte levels or lymphoid organ cellularity (Metcalf 1964, 1966), but Bomskov and Sladovic (1940) reported that oily extracts of thymus produced a lymphocytosis in rats, guinea pigs, pigeons and man; Comsa (1956) produced a lymphocytosis in guinea pigs with thymus extracts; and Nakamoto (1957) reported the production of a lymphocytosis in rabbits following the injection of foreign thymus extracts. Similarly Gregoire and Duchateau (1956) reported that thymus extracts increased lymph-node weights and cellularity in the guinea pig.

Metcalf (1956a, b) observed that sera from patients with chronic lymphoid leukaemia and lymphosarcoma, but not with other types of leukaemia, produced a lymphocytosis in neonatal mice. In extending these observations, it was observed that extracts of human or mouse thymus (homogenised in saline using silica) produced a temporary lymphocytosis when injected intracerebrally into neonatal mice. The magnitude of the response was small (a 2-fold elevation) and the lymphocytosis reached maximum levels 7 days after injection. Similar extracts from other lymphoid tissues, such as the lymph node and spleen as well as extracts from liver, lung, brain, kidney and gonads, failed to produce a lymphocytosis (Metcalf 1956c). The active factor in the thymus extract was termed the 'lymphocytosis stimulating factor' (LSF). Lymphocytosis stimulating activity appeared to be associated with the medullary tissue of the thymus and not the cortical tissue, and the active factor appeared to be heat-labile (Metcalf 1956c). Sera from mice with lymphoid leukaemia also produced a lymphocytosis in neonatal mice as did preleukaemic sera from the high leukaemia strain AKR. Sera from thymectomised AKR mice showed no lymphocytosis stimulating activity (Metcalf 1959a). Mouse thymus extracts also produced a temporary lymphocytosis in thymectomised adult C57BL mice (Metcalf and Buffett 1957) and irradiation appeared to elevate serum levels of lymphocytosis stimulating activity (Metcalf 1959b).

Camblin and Bridges (1964) also observed the development of a lymphocytosis following the injection of rat-thymus extracts but not of rat-spleen extracts into neonatal rats made lymphopenic by small doses of whole-body irradiation combined with large doses of irradiation to the thymic region. De Somer et al. (1963) reported that medium from cultures of minced thymus tissue produced a peripheral leucocytosis in adult mice and prevented the development of immunological defects in neonatally thymectomised mice.

Bezssnoff and Comsa (1958) reported the chromatographic separation of thymus extracts, and in a subsequent report (Comsa 1965) obtained evidence that an active fraction prevented post-thymectomy deaths in guinea pigs and the fall in lymphocytes in the lymph nodes, spleen and bone marrow following thymectomy. No control tissue extracts were used. Hand et al. (1967) reported an extraction procedure for calf-thymus extracts, monitoring fractions for lymphocytosis-stimulating activity by injecting them into neonatal mice. Again no control tissues were used in this study. Fractions were obtained by gel electrophoresis which elevated lymphocyte/polymorph ratios in mice at a dose of 0.1 γ protein/mouse. This material was non dialysable, heat labile and appeared to have a molecular weight of 10,000–30,000.

Klein et al. (1965) reported that calf-thymus extracts, when injected into adult mice, increased the rate of incorporation of isotopically labelled thymidine into the DNA of lymph-node lymphocytes, although studies in our laboratory showed such an effect to be non-specific and to be produced also by spleen- and lymph-node extracts (Metcalf, D. and Ada, G. L., unpublished data). In extending this work, Goldstein et al. (1966) and Klein et al. (1966) reported the partial purification of a factor from calf-thymus extracts (thymosin), which increased lymph-node weights in mice and increased tritiated thymidine incorporation *in vitro* by suspensions of rat and rabbit mesenteric lymph-node cells. The active material appeared to be a relatively heat-stable, carbohydrate-containing protein with a molecular weight less than 10,000.

Subsequent work using thymosin preparations (Law et al. 1968) suggested that these preparations could restore the capacity of spleen cells from neonatally thymectomised C57BL mice to induce graft-vs.-host disease in neonatal BALB/c mice. Similarly prepared extracts of spleen failed to produce this effect. Treatment of thymectomised mice with thymosin was also reported to lead to the development of higher lymphocyte levels than in control thymectomised mice. Antisera were prepared in rabbits to calf thymosin which formed precipitin lines with thymosin preparations *in vitro*, and these antisera were cytotoxic for thymus cells and agglutinated calf-thymic lymphocytes (Hardy et al. 1969). Calf-thymosin preparations were reported to accelerate rejection of first- and second-set allogeneic skin grafts in adult mice, whereas antisera to thymosin significantly prolonged the survival of such grafts (Hardy et al. 1968).

In a parallel series of studies, Trainin and co-workers have provided further evidence for the existence and biological activity of a factor in thymus tissue which affects lymphocyte function. Trainin et al. (1966) reported that thymus extracts from sheep, calves and rabbits induced a lymphocytosis when repeatedly injected into normal or thymectomised newborn and adult mice. Increases were also noted in the cellularity and mitotic activity of spleen-lymphoid follicles. Subsequent work (Small and Trainin 1967) showed that calf-thymus extracts increased the plaque-forming response to sheep red cells in C3H mice thymectomised on the 3rd day of life, but kidney extracts had no effect in such animals. Trainin and Linker-Israeli (1967) showed that injections of calf-thymus extracts improved the rejection by neonatally thymectomised C3H mice of skin and tumour allografts and the capacity of spleen cells from neonatally thymectomised C57BL mice to initiate graft-vs.-host reactions in F_1 hybrid mice. Again, calf-kidney extracts were without comparable activity. Goldstein et al. (1970) reported that thymus extracts could induce some degree of skin-graft rejection when injected into neonatally thymectomised mice, but the factor did not lead to any reconstitution of the anti-sheep red-cell response.

More recently, Trainin et al. (1969) have made use of the technique of organ culture of spleen fragments developed by Globerson and Auerbach (1967) to investigate the effects of thymus extracts. The addition of syngeneic mouse-thymus extract to cultures of spleen cells from neonatally thymectomised C57BL mice allowed these cells to initiate *in vitro* graft-vs.-host responses in spleen-fragment explants. Syngeneic spleen and lymph-node extracts prepared in the same manner had no such effect. Of some interest was the demonstration that incubation of thymus extracts with spleen cells for as short a period as 1 hour, allowed immunological reactivity to develop in these cells.

7.6.2 *Indirect evidence for thymic humoral factor*

Numerous studies have provided indirect evidence for the existence of a thymic humoral factor.

(a) *Diffusion chamber experiments.* The fact that thymus grafts restore lymphocyte levels and immunological competence in neonatally thymectomised mice suggested the use of thymus grafts in cell-impermeable diffusion chambers as a method for investigating the existence of a thymic humoral factor. Experiments in neonatally thymectomised mice (Osoba and Miller 1963, 1964; Osoba 1965a; Levey et al. 1963; Law et al. 1964a) showed that syngeneic thymus tissue in such chambers led to partial restoration of immunological reactivity in neonatally thymectomised mice to allogeneic skin grafts and sheep red cells, and restored the susceptibility of such animals to infections by the lymphocytic choriomeningitis virus (Levey et al. 1963b). Lymphocyte levels were not restored to normal in the experiments of Osoba and Miller (1963, 1964), but Levey et al. (1963a) reported some restoration of blood-lymphocyte levels. Similar diffusion-chamber experiments have been performed in thymectomised adult mice, rats, hamsters and rabbits (see review by Osoba and Miller 1967). Osoba (1968) has reported more recently that thymus grafts in millipore diffusion chambers increased the number of antibody-forming cell progenitors (AFC-P) in thymectomised irradiated mice injected with bone-marrow cells. The validity of the assumption that such chambers are always intact and impermeable to lymphoid cells has been questioned (Reese and Israel 1969).

Observations on the thymus tissue in such diffusion chambers have indicated that lymphoid cell survival was extremely poor and that the only cells persisting in a viable state for any length of time appeared to be thymic epithelial and reticulum cells (Osoba and Miller 1964).

(b) *Restorative effects of pregnancy.* Osoba (1965b) reported that pregnancy in neonatally thymectomised mice was followed by the development of a normal capacity to respond to allogeneic skin grafts and sheep red cells. Pseudopregnancy did not restore immune responsiveness. These observations do not exclude other mechanisms associated with pregnancy, but chromosome analysis of the lymphoid cells in the mother appeared to exclude possible migration of lymphoid cells from the foetus to the mother as the basis for the improved immune responses. It is possible that the mechanism involved in immunological recovery was passage of thymic humoral factor from the foetal thymus to the mother with the placenta serving as a natural diffusion chamber membrane.

(c) *In vitro diffusion chamber experiments.* Globerson and Auerbach (1967) developed an *in vitro* organ culture system using spleen fragments from irradiated mice. Immunological competence of such fragments was assayed by the capacity of the dissociated spleen cells to induce graft-vs.-host reaction *in vitro* in other spleen fragments. Cells from cultured irradiated spleen fragments were unable to induce graft-vs.-host reactions but restoration of immunological competence was observed if the spleen fragments were cultured in the presence of thymus tissue but not in the presence of bone-marrow, liver or kidney tissue. This inductive effect of thymus tissue could be demonstrated to occur when the thymus was separated from the spleen tissue by a millipore membrane, suggesting strongly that the effect was mediated by a diffusible factor.

(d) *Thymectomy and thymic tumour grafts.* Law et al. (1964b) reported that grafts of slowly-growing thymic epithelial tumours from C57BL mice (induced by the polyoma virus) could partially restore lymphocyte levels and immunological reactivity in neonatally thymectomised C57BL mice. This work has recently been extended by Stutman et al. (1968, 1969) using carcinogen-induced thymic tumours. These workers showed that grafts of these epithelial tumours prevented post-thymectomy wasting, allowed improved growth of lymphoid organs and restored immunological reactivity (assessed by allograft immunity and graft-vs.-host reactivity) in neonatally thymectomised allogeneic hosts. Such thymomas were also effective when enclosed in millipore diffusion chambers (Stutman et al. 1969). These experiments also suggested that the cells in the spleen of the neonatally thymectomised recipient which could be activated immunologically by the thymoma tended to die or become inactivated if thymoma grafting was delayed up to 45 days following neonatal thymectomy. In these experiments, the thymoma allografts were also observed to induce the development of partial tolerance to skin grafts from the mouse strain of origin of the thymoma (Stutman et al. 1968).

7.6.3 Discussion

Taken together, the various experiments discussed above constitute sufficiently strong evidence to accept provisionally the existence of a humoral factor released by thymic tissue which can modify lymphocyte function. Because of the absence of good *in vivo* and *in vitro* assay systems, progress in this field has been slow and many pertinent questions remain unanswered. One important problem which has not been sufficiently investigated is the uniqueness or otherwise of this thymic factor. Many of the experiments described above had the serious deficiency in design of not employing adequate control tissues. This comment applies particularly to the failure to use extracts of other lymphoid organs, e.g., the lymph nodes, spleen, Peyer's patches, or appendix. We referred in Chapter 3 to the existence in chickens of the bursa of Fabricius which exerts a thymus-like role in the chicken, and there is some evidence that the bursa also may elaborate a humoral factor. Humoral immune responses were partially reconstituted in bursectomised birds by bursal extracts or bursal grafts enclosed in diffusion chambers (St. Pierre and Ackerman 1965; Jankovic and Leskowitz 1965; Jankovic et al. 1967), but the reconstitution may have been due to an adjuvant-mediated stimulation of pre-existing immune potential.

The exact mode of action of thymic humoral factor can only be speculated upon at the present time because of current uncertainty regarding the nature of the collaboration between thymus-derived (T) and bone marrow-derived (B) cells during immune responses. One possible action of a thymic humoral factor might be to potentiate the proliferation of cells during the T-B interaction. Since thymectomy in adult life has no measurable effect on lymphopoiesis or the generation of antibody-forming cells for many months, the target cells of thymic hormone may only need a limited (perhaps once only) exposure to thymic hormone – unlike the situation with CSF. Indeed, if the experiments of Trainin et al. are confirmed, this exposure time may be very short indeed.

7.7 Humoral factors in immune responses

The most obvious humoral factor implicated in immune responses is of course antibody, but a detailed consideration of the role of antibody is outside the scope of this book. What is evident in the immune response is that homeostatic mechanisms exist which regulate the magnitude and direction of an immunological reaction. Humoral regulatory factors are implicated in this homeostasis, and one of the main mechanisms is undoubtedly the ability of antibodies to suppress their own synthesis (for review see Uhr and Moller 1968). Antibody-induced suppression of the generation of both 19S and 7S antibody-producing cells can be brought about by actively-synthesised or passively-administered antibody with 19S-producing cells being more sensitive to suppression than 7S-producing cells (Wigzell 1967). The kinetics of inhibition suggest that the effect is mediated at the antigen level, with antibody removing the antigenic stimulus and this might be of particular importance *in vivo* if the antigen is not readily metabolised.

A further control mechanism is the increase in the rate of catabolism of immunoglobulin when serum levels are abnormally high. The catabolic effect is selective since it can distinguish between IgG and IgM class elevation, but it does not distinguish one antibody from another (Uhr and Moller 1968).

In certain forms of immune responses involving predominantly cell-mediated reactions *in vitro*, a considerable number of humoral factors have been described and are presumed to originate from the antigen-stimulated lymphocytes. The exact status of most of these factors is still unclear and many of the effects ascribed to different factors may be the property of a single factor. Furthermore, most of the effects have so far only been demonstrated *in vitro* and consequently extrapolation to an *in vivo* role is difficult.

7.7.1 Macrophage inhibition factor (MIF)

Following the contact of sensitized lymphocytes with specific antigen a factor is released from the stimulated cells which is capable of inhibiting macrophage migration (Bloom and Bennett 1966; David 1966, 1968; Falk et al. 1969). This macrophage-inhibition factor is released within 6 hours of antigenic stimulation, long before lymphocyte transformation, and its inhibitory activity is antigen-independent (Bloom 1969). MIF is a relatively heat stable, non-dialysable factor sensitive to neuraminidase and chymotrypsin, and appears to be a protein with a molecular weight on gel filtration of 70,000 which migrates electrophoretically in the albumin region (Bloom 1969).

Two other factors, macrophage activating factor and macrophage aggregation factor, may be the same as MIF (David 1971).

7.7.2 Chemotactic factor

A factor chemotactic for macrophages is also released by sensitised lymphocytes under the same conditions as MIF and has a similar molecular weight upon gel filtration (60,000) (Bloom 1969; Ward et al. 1969). Chemotactic factor is heat-stable and is eluted from G 100 Sephadex with the albumin marker. Although precise results in different laboratories are not yet in agreement, MIF and chemotactic factor appear to be different and have been separated by polyacrylamide gel electrophoresis (Bloom 1969; David 1969).

7.7.3 Transfer factor, blastogenic factor, and mitogenic factor

Transfer factor is designated as a specific factor or factors in leukocytes responsible for transfer of delayed hypersensitivity (see Lawrence 1969 for a review). Transfer factor has the capacity to confer sensitivity on previously non-sensitised individuals and this property can be serially transferred. The dilutional aspect suggested that the factor was not a potent form of antigen or an unique form of immunoglobulin. Biochemical studies revealed that transfer factor was a dialysable moiety of low molecular weight (10,000) and was resistant to DNA-ase, RNA-ase and trypsin (Lawrence 1969). The dialysable transfer factor could be a small polypeptide or polynucleotide, and though rather small to act as an information-transferring molecule, may act as an activator of select lymphocyte populations.

In vivo transfer of tuberculin sensitivity has been obtained in guinea pigs by means of plasma obtained from sensitised donors after whole-body irradiation (Dupuy et al. 1969). This guinea pig transfer factor was, however, non-dialysable.

In vitro transfer of tuberculin sensitivity to human lymphocytes has also been reported in a study where sensitised human lymphocytes cultured for 36 hours with tuberculin elaborated a soluble non-dialysable material which caused non-sensitive lymphocytes to respond to tuberculin *in vitro* by transformation and proliferation (Valentine and Lawrence 1969). Transfer of haemocyanin sensitivity has also been demonstrated *in vitro* with a non-dialysable factor (Baram and Condoulis 1969).

Earlier studies revealed the existence of blastogenic or mitogenic factors released by antigen-stimulated lymphocytes and capable of inducing mitosis in other, non-antigen stimulated populations of lymphocytes (Kasakura and Lowenstein 1965; 1967; Gordon and MacLean 1965; Bloom and Bennett 1968). Kasakura and Lowenstein (1967) suggested the blastogenic material was soluble transplantation antigen, which has been shown to stimulate allogeneic lymphocyte cultures (Vira et al. 1968). Valentine and Lawrence (1969) considered for a number of reasons that their factor was not transplantation antigen. Bach (1969a) found that the blastogenic factor produced by the lymphocytes of one individual alone would stimulate to some extent isogeneic as well as allogeneic cells and blastogenic factor was produced by mixed leucocyte cultures from monozygotic twins in the absence of antigenic differences and obvious blast transformation (Kasakura 1970). The relationship of the non-dialysable blastogenic factors to dialysable transfer factor is not yet clear and the latter is liberated by lymphocytes within 1 hour of incubation with antigen, whereas the former is produced after 18–24 hours. The possibility that transfer factor is rendered non-dialysable because it becomes complexed with antigen during the course of incubation requires further investigation (Lawrence 1969).

There is also a report of an additional potentiating factor which is present in the supernatant fluid of leucocyte cultures, both stimulated and unstimulated, which in some cases potentiates antigen-induced lymphocyte transformation so that the response obtained is greater than the sum of stimulation by antigen alone or blastogenic factor alone (Martin and Bach 1970).

7.7.4   Lymphotoxin (LT)

Cytotoxicity can be exerted by non-immunised lymphocytes stimulated by non-specific agents such as PHA or by immune lymphocytes specifically stimulated by antigen (Granger et al. 1969; Ruddle and Waksman 1968; Kolb and Granger 1968; see review by Perlmann and Holm 1969). The cytotoxic effect can be mediated by a soluble factor, lymphotoxin, which is released by stimulated lymphocytes within 36 hours. The target cells exposed to lymphotoxin undergo a concentration-dependent cytolysis, though cells exposed to sublethal doses of the factor develop resistance to cytolysis (Granger 1969). Granger suggested that very few, perhaps only one molecule of lymphotoxin per cell may be sufficient for damage or destruction. Biochemical characterisation has shown that lymphotoxin has a molecular weight of 80–85,000 and that the factors from human and murine cells differ in physical properties. Purification of human lymphotoxin by ammonium-sulphate precipitation and DEAE cellulose-column chromatography has shown that LT and MIF are closely related, and may possibly be the same factor (Granger 1969).

LT may be the same as the cloning inhibitory factor which, without killing the seeded cells, e.g. HeLa cells, inhibited their capacity to divide and thereby blocked colony formation (Bloom 1969; Lebowitz and Lawrence 1969). LT is probably the factor involved in inhibiting division of allogeneic or syngeneic rat fibroblasts in the system reported by Perlmann and Holm (1968).

The specificity of cytotoxic damage by immunised lymphocytes was confined to the initial antigen recognition stage which activates the lymphocyte to kill target cells on a non-specific basis (Lundgren 1970). PHA-induced cytotoxicity was detected considerably earlier than cytotoxicity produced by immunised lymphocytes (Lundgren and Moller 1969). It is possible that this difference in timing is due to quantitative rather than qualitative differences in the reaction. The delay with antigen-stimulated cytotoxicity may represent the time taken for amplification of the reactive cell population by proliferation, production of antigen-antibody complexes which are known to transform lymphocytes to a cytotoxic state, and by production of non-antibody amplification factors such as blastogenic and transfer factors (Lundgren et al. 1968a).

There is some disagreement as to the mechanism of cytotoxicity and Lundgren and Moller (1969) do not support the concept of release of lymphotoxic factor believing that close contact is required between target cell and effector cell. The soluble lymphotoxin produced in culture could be an enzyme(s) released by contaminating granulocytes (Lundgren et al. 1968b). However, Bach (1969b) has shown that extensively purified (98–99%) lymphocytes in a mixed leucocyte culture produced just as much cytotoxic factor as did cultures of unpurified cells.

7.7.5   Skin reactive factor

Exposure of lymphocytes from immunised guinea pigs to antigen *in vitro* results in release of a soluble substance able to induce inflammatory reactions when injected into the skin of normal guinea pigs (Bennett and Bloom 1968; Krejci et al. 1969). The skin reaction is characterised by an indurated and erythematous lesion appearing within 3 hours and maximal at 6–10 hours with an early and pronounced mononuclear cell infiltration and later polymorph infiltration (Bloom 1969). The lesion is very similar to that seen in an active, delayed-type, cutaneous lesion but has an accelerated time course. A further factor was reported by Ramseier (1969) as being released following the interaction *in vitro* between competent mouse lymphoid cells and a target-cell population. The factor was assayed by its capacity to provoke polymorph accumulations in the skin of hamsters. Non-specific factors such as PHA may cause the release of skin reactive factor (Pick et al. 1969, 1970). Biochemical studies have shown that skin reactive factor was present even in purified preparations of MIF, and has a similar molecular weight (Turk 1969). This observation, and the fact that skin reactive factor was produced under the same conditions as lymphotoxin, suggests that skin reactive factor may be lymphotoxin or more probably a mixture of MIF and lymphotoxin.

7.7.6   Other factors

In addition to the above factors, specifically or non-specifically stimulated lymphocytes release interferon (Green et al. 1969) an agent known to cause human tissue culture cells to become resistant to viral infection, and antibodies (Heise et al. 1968).

There is some evidence to suggest that humoral factors may be produced by macrophages and may play some role in immune responses. A conditioned medium-reconstituting factor produced by adherent cells, possibly macrophages, was shown to be required for proliferation in mixed leucocyte cultures of highly purified lymphocytes (Bach et al. 1971). An *in vitro* immune response was obtained by mixed populations of adherent and non-adherent spleen cells but not by either population on its own (Dutton 1969). The adherent cell effect was still present following 1000 R irradiation and could be replaced by supernatant from cultures of adherent cells. The supernatant from immunised adherent cells was several times more active than the supernatant from non-immunised cells in reconstituting the immune response *in vitro* (Dutton 1969).

In general, specific inhibitors of lymphocyte proliferation produced by lymphocytes (lymphocyte chalones) have not been reported, though in a recent study an inhibitory factor was obtained in aqueous extracts of normal human lymphocytes (Garcia-Giralt et al. 1970). This factor inhibited DNA synthesis in normal lymphoid cell strains and in strains of lymphoblastic leukaemia. Upon purification the factor appeared to be a protein of molecular weight about 40,000 and apparently was not cytotoxic.

7.7.7 Conclusion

The importance of the various factors under review in the manifestation and control of the *in vivo* immune response remains to be determined. Potentially such factors are of considerable importance, though at the present time the proliferation of reports of different 'factors' only serves to confuse the issue. It is to be hoped that future studies will concentrate on establishing a common identity for factors manifesting a divergence of reactions otherwise the Emperor's New Clothes Factor (ENCF) (David 1969) may well achieve reality.

Many of the factors reported may be implicated in the amplification and propagation of the immune response, particularly in cell-mediated immunity. Such factors may, however, have important implications for cell collaboration in humoral immunity since it could be postulated that factors released by antigen-stimulated T cells may activate and/or recruit a responsive B cell population. However, the evidence of immunological specificity in B and T cell collaboration indicates that most factors under discussion, apart from transfer factor, could only partially account for collaboration since they do not appear to have specificity in an immunological sense. The possibility of a specific humoral factor in B and T cell collaboration is still an open question, and close parallels may be found in the controversy over the mediation of cellular immunity by cell contact only or by diffusible lymphotoxin. The T cell may, e.g., release informational molecules which program B cells for specific antibody formation. More probably any factor released by T cells is immunoglobulin in nature, either an intact immunoglobulin (IgX) or a part of an immunoglobulin molecule. Such a factor may be cytophilic and attach to dendritic reticular cells where it may function to present, or focus, antigen to the appropriate reactive B cell. An antigen-specific factor released by peritoneal exudate cells has been implicated in cell collaboration and it appeared to replace the T cell requirement for an *in vivo* immune response to heterologous erythrocytes (Kennedy et al. 1970).

7.8 *General conclusion*

Regulation of haemopoiesis is based on a hierachy of chemical messages. At the intracellular level are repressor molecules produced by regulator genes; at the extracellular level are the microenvironmental inducing agents that operate sequentially in development and differentiation to limit the genetic potentialities of cells; and finally chalones and humoral regulators which regulate mitotic activity and allow the system to adapt to environmental change. This chapter has considered the latter two categories of regulators, though it is possible that local inducing agents may act at a distance on haemopoietic differentiation in certain abnormal experimental situations, and the status of thymus hormone is important in this context.

All the regulating factors under discussion directly or indirectly modify gene action and induce differentiation and/or control the development of the differentiated state. Differentiation has been defined as '...the sum of processes by which acquisition of specific metabolic competences (or loss thereof) distinguishes daughter cells from each other or from the parental cell' (Gross 1968). Operationally, assessment of the differentiated state requires the identification of specific macromolecules, morphological features or metabolic activities which uniquely characterise the cell and are demonstrably absent in other cells. In the case of haemopoiesis, cells undergo a step of 'determination' which limits them to particular pathways of differentiation. These are the progenitor cells, but the cells at this stage may not manifest any features, such as haemoglobin synthesis, that uniquely characterise a particular differentiation pathway. This determination step undoubtedly restricts the genetic potential of the cell but only in an indirect sense of achieving responsiveness to a specific humoral regulator can differentiation be demonstrated.

The determination step, affected by the inductive influence of the haemopoietic microenvironment may be presumed to induce the production of membrane receptor sites specific for only one humoral regulator. The recognition of the stimulus of the regulatory molecule by the target cell is therefore specific and results in transformation of the signal into an effect on intracellular processes which directly or indirectly influences gene action. The humoral regulator may either activate repressed genes or gene sequences in the target progenitor cell required for the synthesis of specific macromolecules which characterise the differentiated cell, or may facilitate the expression of such gene sequences already derepressed by the preceding determinative influence of the haemopoietic microenvironment.

The stimulus to modify gene action may be conveyed to the nucleus directly by the humoral regulator or indirectly by some factor produced as a consequence of interaction between the membrane receptor and regulator molecules. In this latter context the action of a great many hormones appear to be mediated within the target cell by the action of cyclic 3, 5-AMP (see Robison et al. 1968 for a review). Cyclic AMP may be produced by the activity of a membrane adenyl cyclase enzyme linked to a receptor site specific for a particular humoral regulator and could then function to regulate the transcription of genetic information by an effect on enzymes controlling phosphorylation of histones (Langan 1969). So far no information is available to support a role for cyclic AMP in the mediation of humoral regulator action in haemopoiesis, though W. Braun (personal communication) has evidence that cyclic AMP enhances antibody formation *in vivo* and *in vitro* and may therefore mediate some of the effects of humoral factors implicated in immune responses.

Most of the humoral factors discussed in this chapter share a general chemical similarity in so far as they are proteins, possibly glycoproteins, have a short biological half life, are subject to homeostatic regulation, and have a common capacity both to activate progenitor cells into a differentiation sequence and to influence the rate of differentiation at later stages of the cell-maturation pathway.

There is evidence *in vitro* for an influence of variations in the concentration of a humoral regulator (e.g. CSF) on the number of differentiated cells produced by a single target cell. *In vivo* it is probably more usual for increased haemopoietic demand to be met by an increase in the number of target cells (a function of the microenvironment) rather than an increase in the size of the differentiated cell clone produced by each target cell (a possible function of humoral regulators), but the latter mechanism undoubtedly exists and may in some cases be an important process. Such clonal expansion may be brought about by initial regulator-dependent derepression of particular gene sequences which then come under repressor control by the gene product. A balance between accumulation of gene products and the repression or induction of other genes in an organised, systematic manner probably determines the orderly chronological sequence of division and differentiation steps. The continual activity of humoral regulators throughout subsequent differentiation may override local regulatory factors intrinsic to the cell. In this manner the concentration of a humoral regulator may influence the rate of differentiation and may determine whether in the early stages of differentiation, cells divide to form parental-type progeny or undergo a further maturation step with consequent reduction in division capacity.

References

Abildgaard, C. F. and J. V. Simone, 1967, Seminars in Hematol. *4*, 424.

Adamson, J. W., 1968, Blood *32*, 597.

Adamson, J. W. and C. A. Finch, 1968, Annals N.Y. Acad. Sci. *149*, 560.

Adamson, J. W., R. Alexanian, C. Martinez, and C. A. Finch, 1966, Blood *28*, 354.

Alexanian, R., 1966, Blood *28*, 344.

Allen, R. C. and D. J. Moore, 1968, Annals N.Y. Acad. Sci. *149*, 63.

Alpen, E. L. and D. Cranmore, 1959, Observations on the regulation of erythropoiesis and on cellular dynamics by Fe59 autoradiography. In: Kinetics of cellular proliferation, edited by F. Stohlman. New York, Grune and Stratton, p. 290.

Alpen, E. L., D. Cranmore, and M. E. Johnston, 1962, Early observations on the effects of blood loss. In: Erythropoiesis, edited by L. O. Jacobson and M. Doyle. New York, Grune and Stratton, p. 184.

Arnesen, K., 1958, Acta pathol. microbiol. Scand. *43*, 339.

Athens, J. W., 1969, Granulocyte kinetics in health and disease. In: Human tumor cell kinetics. Natl. Cancer Instit. Monograph 30, p. 135.

Austin, P. E. and J. E. Till, 1970, Proc. Canad. Fed. Biol. Sciences *13*, 100.

Bach, F. H., 1969a, In discussion. In: Mediators of cellular immunity, edited by H. S. Lawrence and M. Landy. New York, Academic Press, p. 292.

Bach, F. H., 1969b, In discussion. In: Mediators of cellular immunity, edited by H. S. Lawrence, and M. Landy. New York, Academic Press, p. 362.

Bach, M. L., B. Alter, D. Zoschke, S. Solliday, and F. H. Bach, 1971, A soluble adherent cell fraction permitting purified lymphocyte response. Trans. Proc. (in press).

Baram, P. and W. V. Condoulis, 1969, Fed. Proc. *28*, 629 (Abs.).

Bennett, B. and B. R. Bloom, 1968, Proc. Nat. Acad. Sci. (Washington) *59*, 756.

Bezssonoff, N. A. and J. Comsa, 1958, Ann. d'Endocrinol. *19*, 222.

Bierman, H. R., 1964, Annals N.Y. Acad. Sci. *113*, 753.

Bloom, B. R., 1969, Biological activities of lymphocyte products. In: Mediators of cellular immunity, edited by H. S. Lawrence and M. Landy. New York, Academic Press, p. 249.

Bloom, B. R. and B. Bennett, 1966, Science *153*, 80.

Bloom, B. R. and B. Bennett, 1968, Fed. Proc. *27*, 13.

Boggs, D. R., G. E. Cartwright, and M. M. Wintrobe, 1966, Amer. J. Physiol. *211, 51.*

Boggs, D. R., P. A. Chervenick, J. C. Marsh, H. I. Pilgrim, G. E. Cartwright, and M. M. Wintrobe, 1967a, Proc. Soc. Exp. Biol. Med. *125*, 325.

Boggs, D. R., J. C. Marsh, P. A. Chervenick, C. R. Bishop, G. E. Cartwright, and M. M. Wintrobe, 1967b, J. Exp. Med. *126*, 851.

Bomskov, C. and L. Sladovic, 1940, Deut. med. Wochschr. *66*, 589.

Borsook, H., A. Graybiel, and G. Keighley, 1954, Blood *9*, 735.

Bottomley, S. S. and H. A. Smithee, 1969, J. Lab. Clin. Med. *74*, 445.

Bozzini, C. E., 1966, Nature *209*, 1140.

Bradley, T. R. and D. Metcalf, 1966, Aust. J. Exp. Biol. Med. Sci. *44*, 287.

Bradley, T. R. and M. A. Sumner, 1968, Aust. J. Exp. Biol. Med. Sci. *46*, 607.

Bradley, T. R., D. Metcalf, and W. Robinson, 1967a, Nature *213*, 926.

Bradley, T. R., W. Robinson, and D. Metcalf, 1967b, Nature *213*, 511.

Bradley, T. R., D. Metcalf, M. Sumner, and R. Stanley, 1969, Characteristics of *in vitro* colony formation by cells from haemopoietic tissues. In: Hemic cells in vitro, edited by P. Farnes. In Vitro *4*, p. 22.

Bullough, W. S., 1962, Biol. Rev. *37*, 307.

Bullough, W. S., 1965, Cancer Res. *25*, 1683.

Bullough, W. S., 1967, The evolution of differentiation. London, Academic Press.

Bullough, W. S. and E. B. Laurence, 1960, Proc. roy. Soc. B, *151*, 517.

Bullough, W. S. and E. B. Laurence, 1968a, Europ. J. Cancer *4*, 587.

Bullough, W. S. and E. B. Laurence, 1968b, Europ. J. Cancer *4*, 607.

Bullough, W. S., E. B. Laurence, O. H. Iversen, and K. Elgjo, 1967, Nature *214*, 578.

Burke, W. T. and B. S. Morse, 1962, Studies on the production and metabolism of erythropoietin in the rat liver and kidney. In: Erythropoiesis, edited by L. O. Jacobson and M. Doyle. New York, Grune and Stratton, p. 111.

Camblin, J. G. and J. B. Bridges, 1964, Transplantation *2*, 785.

Camiscoli, J. F., A. H. Weintraub, and A. S. Gordon, 1968, Annals N.Y. Acad. Sci. *149*, 40.

Campbell, B. J., R. J. Schlueter, G. F. Weber, and W. F. White, 1961, Biochim. Biophys. Acta *46*, 279.

Carmena, A. O., D. Howard, and F. Stohlman, 1968, Blood *32*, 376.

Carnot, P. and G. Deflandre, 1906, Compt. Rend. Acad. Science *143*, 384.

Chan, S. H., 1970, Proc. Soc. Exp. Biol. Med. *134*, 733.

Chan, S. H. and D. Metcalf, 1970, Nature *227*, 845.

Chan, S. H., D. Metcalf, and E. R. Stanley, 1971, Brit. J. Haematol. *20*, 329.

Chui, D., M. Djaldetti, P. A. Marks, and R. A. Rifkind, 1969, Blood *34*, 837.

Clark, S. L., 1966, Cytological evidence of secretion in the thymus. In: The thymus: experimental and clinical studies, edited by G. E. W. Wolstenholme and R. Porter. London, J. and A. Churchill, p. 3.

Cohen, P., M. H. Codley, and F. H. Gardner, 1965, J. Clin. Invest. *44*, 1036.

Comsa, J., 1956, C. R. Soc. Biol. *150*, 516.

Comsa, J., 1965, Amer. J. Med. Sci. *250*, 79.

Contrera, J. F. and A. S. Gordon, 1966, Science *152*, 653.

Contrera, J. F. and A. S. Gordon, 1968, Annals N.Y. Acad. Sci. *149*, 114.

Contrera, J. F., J. F. Camiscoli, A. H. Weintraub, and A. S. Gordon, 1965, Blood *25*, 809.

Contrera, J. F., A. S. Gordon, and A. H. Weintraub, 1966, Blood *28*, 330.

Cooney, D. P., W. F. Blatt, R. Louis-Ferdinand, and B. A. Smith, 1965, Scand. J. Haemat. *2*, 195.

Cotes, P. M., 1968, Annals N.Y. Acad. Sci. *149*, 12.

Cotes, P. M. and D. R. Bangham, 1961, Nature *191*, 1065.

Cronkite, E. P., 1969, Kinetics of granulopoiesis. In: Human tumor cell kinetics, edited by S. Perry. National Cancer Institute Monograph *30*, p. 51.

Cronkite, E. P., V. P. Bond, T. M. Fliedner, D. A. Paglia, and E. R. Adamik, 1961, In: Blood platelets: Henry Ford Hospital Symposium, edited by S. Johnston et al. Boston, Little-Brown, p. 595.

Damashek, W. and S. Estren, 1948, The spleen and hypersplenism. New York, Grune and Stratton.

David, J. R., 1966, Proc. Nat. Acad. Sci. (Washington) *56*, 72.

David, J. R., 1968, Fed. Proc. *27*, 6.

David, J. R., 1969, In: Mediators of cellular immunity, edited by H. S. Lawrence and M. Landy. New York, Academic Press, p. 262.

David, J. R., 1971, Mediators of cellular immunity. Transp. Proc. (in press).

De Franciscis, P., G. de Bella, and S. Cifaldi, 1965, Science *150*, 1831.

De Gabriele, G. and D. G. Penington, 1967a, Brit. J. Haemat. *13*, 210.

De Gabriele, G. and D. G. Penington, 1967b, Brit. J. Haemat. *13*, 202.

Delmonte, L. and R. A. Liebelt, 1965, Science *148*, 521.

Delmonte, L. and A. Liebelt, 1966, Fed. Proc. *25*, 232.

Delmonte, L., A. G. Liebelt, and R. A. Liebelt, 1966, Cancer Res. *26*, 149.

Demopoulos, H. B., B. Highman, D. Altland, M. A. Geroing, and G. Kaley, 1965, Amer. J. Path. *46*, 497.

De Nicola, P., 1968, Exp. Biol. Med. *3*, 200.

De Nicola, P., G. A. Cappelletti, and F. Soardi, 1958, Haematologica *43*, 779.

De Somer, P., P. J. Denys, and R. Leyten, 1963, Life Sci. *2*, 810.

Donati, R. M., R. D. Lange, and N. I. Gallagher, 1963a, Arch. Int. Med. *112*, 960.

Donati, R. M., J. M. McCarthy, R. D. Lange, and N. I. Gallagher, 1963b, Ann. Int. Med. *58*, 47.

Dougherty, T. F., 1952, Physiol. Rev. *32*, 379.

Dougherty, T. F., M. L. Berliner, G. L. Schneebeli, and D. L. Berliner, 1964, Annals N.Y. Acad. Sci. *113*, 825.

Dukes, P. P., 1968, Annals. N.Y. Acad. Sci. *149*, 437.

Dukes, P. P. and E. Goldwasser, 1962, On the utilisation of erythropoietin. In: Erythropoiesis, edited by L. O. Jacobson and M. Doyle. New York, Grune and Stratton, p. 125.

Dukes, P. P., F. Takaku, and E. Goldwasser, 1963, Endocrinology *74*, 960.

Dupuy, J. M., D. Y. E. Perey, and R. A. Good, 1969, Lancet *1*, 551.

Dutton, R. W., 1969, Discussion. In: Mediators of cellular immunity, edited by H. S. Lawrence and M. Landy. New York, Academic Press, p. 84.

Ebbe, S. and F. Stohlman, Jr., 1965, Blood *26*, 20.

Epifanova, O. I. and V. V. Terskikh, 1969, Cell Tissue Kinet. *2*, 75.

Erf, L. A., D. L. Turner, and F. R. Miller, 1946, Blood *1*, 379.

Erslev, A., 1960, Acta Haemat. *23*, 226.

Erslev, A. J. and L. A. Kazal, 1969, Blood *34*, 222.

Erslev, A. J. and E. B. Thorling, 1968, Annals N.Y. Acad. Sci. *149*, 173.

Erslev, A. J., L. A. Kazal, and O. P. Miller, 1970, In: XIII International Congress of Hematology, Abstract Volume. Munich, Lehmanns Verlag, p. 11 (Abs.).

Evans, M. J. and J. B. Lingrel, 1969, Biochemistry *8*, 3000.

Evatt, B. L. and J. Levin, 1969, J. Clin. Invest. *48*, 1615.

Falk, R. E., L. Collste, and G. Moller, 1969, Nature *224*, 1206.

Fisher, J. W. and B. J. Birdwell, 1961, Fed. Proc. *20*, 81.

Fogh, J., 1968, Annals N.Y. Acad. Sci. *149*, 217.

Foster, C. G. and F. R. Miller, 1950, Proc. Soc. Exp. Biol. Med. *75*, 633.

Foster, R. S. and E. A. Mirand, 1970, Proc. Soc. Exp. Biol. Med. *133*, 1223.

Foster, R., D. Metcalf, and R. Kirchmyer, 1968a, J. Exp. Med. *127*, 853.

Foster, R., D. Metcalf, W. A. Robinson, and T. R. Bradley, 1968b, Brit. J. Haematol. *15*, 147.

Frenkel, E. P., W. Suki, and J. Baum, 1968, Annals N.Y. Acad. Sci. *149*, 292.

Fried, W. and C. W. Gurney, 1965, Nature *206*, 1160.

Fried, W. and C. W. Gurney, 1968, Annals N.Y. Acad. Sci. *149*, 356.

Fried, W., L. F. Plzak, L. O. Jacobson, and E. Goldwasser, 1957, Proc. Soc. Exp. Biol. Med. *94*, 237.

Furth, J. 1969, Harvey Lectures *63*, 47.

Gallagher, N. I. and R. M. Donati, 1968, Annals N.Y. Acad. Sci. *149*, 528.

Gallien-Lartigue, O. and E. Goldwasser, 1965, Biochim. Biophys. Acta, *103*, 319.

Garcia-Giralt, E., E. Lasalvia, and G. Mathe, 1970, In: XIII International Congress of Hematology, Abstract Volume. Munich, Lehmanns Verlag, p. 55 (Abs.).

Globerson, A. and R. Auerbach, 1967, J. Exp. Med. *126*, 223.

Globerson, A. and M. Feldman, 1964, Transplantation *2*, 212.

Goldstein, A. L., F. D. Slater, and A. White, 1966, Proc. Natl. Acad. Sci. *56*, 1010.

Goldstein, A. L., Y. Asanuma, J. R. Battisto, M. A. Hardy, J. Quint, and A. White, 1970, J. Immunol. *104*, 359.

Goldwasser, E. and C. K. H. Kung, 1968, Annals N.Y. Acad. Sci. *149*, 49.

Goldwasser, E. and W. F. White, 1959, Fed. Proc. *18*, 236.

Goldwasser, E., W. F. White, and K. B. Taylor, 1962a, On the purification of sheep plasma erythropoietin. In: Erythropoiesis, edited by L. O. Jacobson and M. Doyle. New York, Grune and Stratton, p. 43.

Goldwasser, E., W. F. White, and K. B. Taylor, 1962b, Biochim. Biophys. Acta *64*, 487.

Good, R. A., A. P. Dalmasso, C. Martinez, O. K. Archer, J. C. Pierce, and B. W. Papermaster, 1962, J. Exp. Med. *116*, 773.

Gordon, A. S., 1955, Annals N.Y. Acad. Sci. *59*, 907.

Gordon, A. S., 1959, Physiol. Rev. *39*, 1.

Gordon, A. S., 1970, Biochemical mechanisms underlying hematopoietic cell differentiation. In: Plenary Session, Scientific Contributions XIII International Congress of Hematology. Munich, Lehmanns Verlag, p. 7.

Gordon, A. S., E. S. Handler, C. D. Siegel, B. S. Dornfest, and J. Lobue, 1964, Annals N.Y. Acad. Sci. *113*, 766.

Gordon, A. S., E. A. Mirand, J. Wenig, R. Katz, and E. D. Zanjani, 1968, Annals N.Y. Acad. Sci. *149*, 318.

Gordon, J. and L. D. Maclean, 1965, Nature *208*, 795.

Granger, G. A., 1969, Cytotoxicity or stimulation by effector molecules. In: Mediators of cellular immunity, edited by H. S. Lawrence, and M. Landy. New York, Academic Press, p. 324.

Granger, G. A., S. J. Shacks, T. W. Williams, and W. P. Kolb, 1969, Nature *221*, 1155.

Green, J. A., S. R. Cooperband, and S. Kibrick, 1969, Science *164*, 1415.

Gregoire, C. and G. Duchateau, 1965, Arch. de Biol. *67*, 269.

Gross, M. and E. Goldwasser, 1969, Biochemistry *8*, 1795.

Gross, P. R., 1968, Ann. Rev. Biochem. *37*, 631.

Gurney, C. W., 1962, Relationship of erythropoietin production to renal abnormalities. In: Erythropoiesis, edited by L. O. Jacobson and M. Doyle. New York, Grune and Stratton, p. 359.

Gurney, C. W., E. Goldwasser, and C. Pan, 1957, J. Lab. Clin. Med. *50*, 534.

Gutnisky, A., L. Malgor, M. L. Nohr, and D. van Dyke, 1968, Annals N.Y. Acad. Sci. *149*, 564.

Hall, B. M., 1969, Brit. J. Haematol. *17*, 553.

Hammond, D., N. Shore, and N. Movassaghi, 1968, Annals N.Y. Acad. Sci. *149*, 516.

Hand, T., P. Caster, and T. D. Luckey, 1967, Biochem. and Biophys. Res. Commun. *26*, 18.

Hanna, M. G., P. Nettesheim, W. D. Fisher, L. C. Peters, and M. W. Francis 1967, Science *157*, 1458.

Hardy, M. A., J. Quint, A. L. Goldstein, D. State, and A. White, 1968, Proc. Natl. Acad. Sci. *61*, 875.

Hardy, M. A., J. Quint, A. L. Goldstein, A. White, D. State, and J. R. Battisto, 1969, Proc. Soc. Exp. Biol. Med. *130*, 214.

Heise, E. R., S. Hans, and R. S. Weiser, 1968, J. Immunol. *101*, 1004.

Hibberd, A. D. and D. Metcalf, 1971, Israel J. Med. Sci. 7, 202.

Hirashima, K. and F. Takaku, 1962, Blood *20*, 1.

Hirschmann, H., R. W. Heinle, and J. T. Wearn, 1945, Proc. Soc. Exp. Biol. Med. *58*, 5.

Hodgson, G. and J. Toha, 1954, Blood *9*, 299.

Hodgson, G., M. Perreta, D. Yudilevich, and I. Eskuche, 1958, Proc. Soc. Exp. Biol. Med. *99*, 137.

Hondius Boldingh, W. and E. B. Laurence, 1968, Europ. J. Biochem. *5*, 191.

Hrinda, M. E. and E. Goldwasser, 1969, Biochim. Biophys. Acta. *195*, 165.

Ichikawa, Y., 1969, J. Cell. Physiol. *74*, 223.

Ichikawa, Y., D. H. Pluznik, and L. Sachs, 1966, Proc. Natl. Acad. Sci. *56*, 488.

Ichikawa, Y., D. H. Pluznik, and L. Sachs, 1967, Proc. Natl. Acad. Sci. *58*, 1480.

Iscove, N. N., J. E. Till, and E. A. McCulloch, 1970, Proc. Soc. Exp. Biol. Med. *134*, 33.

Jacobson, L. O., 1962, Sites of formation of erythropoietin. In: Erythropoiesis, edited by L. O. Jacobson and M. Doyle. New York, Grune and Stratton, p. 69.

Jacobson, L., E. Goldwasser, W. Fried, and L. Plzak, 1957, Nature *179*, 633.

Jacobson, L. O., E. Goldwasser, C. W. Gurney, W. Fried, and L. Plzak, 1959a, Annals N.Y. Acad. Sci. *77*, 551.

Jacobson, L. O., E. Goldwasser, and C. W. Gurney, 1959b, Control of red cell formation. In: The kinetics of cellular proliferation, edited by F. Stohlman. New York, Grune and Stratton, p. 344.

Jacobson, L. O., E. Goldwasser, and L. W. Gurney, 1960, Transfusion-induced poly-cythaemia as a model for studying factors influencing erythropoiesis. In: CIBA Symposium on haemopoiesis: cell production and its regulation, edited by G. E. W. Wolstenholme and M. O'Connor. London, Churchill, p. 423.

Jacobson, W., R. L. Sidman, and L. K. Diamond, 1968, Annals N.Y. Acad. Sci. *149*, 389.

Jankovic, B. D. and S. Leskowitz, 1965, Proc. Soc. Exp. Biol. Med. *118*, 1164.

Jankovic, B. D., B. H. Waksman, and B. G. Arnason, 1962, J. Exp. Med. *116*, 159.

Jankovic, B. D., K. Isakovic, and J. Howat, 1967, Experientia *23*, 1062.

Jepson, J. H. and L. Lowenstein, 1966, Blood *27*, 425.

Johnson, J. B. and T. A. Strike, 1962, Acta Haemat. *28*, 194.

Kaplan, H. S., C. S. Nagareda, and M. B. Brown, 1954, Recent Progress in Hormone Research *10*, 293.

Kasakura, S., 1970, Nature *227*, 507.

Kasakura, S. and L. Lowenstein, 1965, Nature *208*, 794.

Kasakura, S. and L. Lowenstein, 1967, Nature *215*, 80.

Katz, R., G. W. Cooper, A. S. Gordon, and E. D. Zanjani, 1968, Annals N.Y. Acad. Sci. *149*, 120.

Kelemen, E., I. Cserhati, and B. Tanos, 1958, Acta haematol. *20*, 350.

Kelemen, E., D. Lehoczky, I. Cserhati, F. Krisza, and K. Rak, 1960, Lancet *1*, 1134.

Kennedy, J. C., P. E. Treadwell, and E. S. Lennox, 1970, J. Exp. Med. *132*, 353.

Kilbridge, T. M., W. Fried, and P. Heller, 1969, Blood *33*, 104.

Klein, J. J., A. L. Goldstein, and A. White, 1965, Proc. Natl. Acad. Sci. *53*, 812.

Klein, J. J., A. L. Goldstein, and A. White, 1966, Ann. N.Y. Acad. Sci. *135*, 485.

Kolb, W. P. and G. A. Granger, 1968, Proc. Nat. Acad. Sci. (Washington) *61*, 1250.

Komiya, E., G. Shibamoto, H. Katsunuma, R. Kawakubo, H. Ito, M. Woda, T. Sugimoto, K. Hoshi, S. Sato, K. Kawashimo, and I. Yoneyama, 1962, Proc. 8th Intern. Congr. Hematol. *3*, 1915.

Krantz, S. B., 1968, Annals N.Y. Acad. Sci. *149*, 430.

Krantz, S. B., O. Gallien-Lartigue, and E. Goldwasser, 1963, J. Biol. Chem. *238*, 4085.

Krejci, J., J. Pekarek, J. Johanovsky, and J. Svejcar, 1969, Immunol. *16*, 677.

Krisza, G., G. Gergely, and K. Rak, 1968, Acta haemat. *39*, 112.

Krzymowski, T. and H. Krzymowska, 1962, Blood *19*, 38.

Kuratowska, Z., 1968, Annals N.Y. Acad. Sci. *149*, 128.

Kuratowska, Z., B. Lewartowski, and E. Michalak, 1961, Blood *18*, 527.

Kuratowska, Z., B. Lewartowski, and B. Lipinski, 1964, J. Lab. Clin. Med. *64*, 226.

Lagrue, G., P. Boivin, and A. Branellec, 1960, Etudes Clin. Biol. *5*, 816.

Lambardini, J., L. Sanchez-Medal, L. Arriaga, D. Lopez, and J. F. Smyth, 1968, J. Lab. Clin. Med. *72*, 419.

Langan, T. A., 1969, J. Biol. Chem. *244*, 5763.

Lange, R. D. and N. I. Gallagher, 1962, Clinical and experimental observations on the relationship of the kidney to erythropoietin production. In: Erythropoiesis, edited by L. O. Jacobson and M. Doyle. New York, Grune and Stratton, p. 361.

Lange, R. D., E. Gardner, C. S. Wright, and N. I. Gallagher, 1964, Brit. J. Haematol. *10*, 69.

Lange, R. D., L. F. O'Grady, J. P. Lewis, F. E. Trobaugh, 1968, Annals N.Y. Acad. Sci. *149*, 281.

Law, L. W., N. Trainin, R. H. Levey, and W. F. Barth, 1964a, Science *143*, 1049.

Law, L. W., T. B. Dunn, N. Trainin, and R. H. Levey, 1964b, Studies of thymic function. In: The thymus, edited by V. Defendi and D. Metcalf. Philadelphia, Wistar Institute Press, p. 105.

Law, L. W., A. L. Goldstein, and A. White, 1968, Nature *219*, 1391.

Lawrence, H. S., 1969, Advances in Immunol. *11*, 196.

Lebowitz, A. and H. S. Lawrence, 1969, Fed. Proc. *28*, 630 (Abs.).

Lehman, C. J., A. J. Erslev, and R. M. Myerson, 1963, Amer. J. Med. *35*, 439.

Levere, R. D. and S. Granick, 1967, J. Biol. Chem. *242*, 1903.

Levey, R. H., N. Trainin, and L. W. Law. 1963a, J. Nat. Cancer Inst. *31*, 199.

Levey, R. H., N. Trainin, L. W. Law, P. H. Black, and W. P. Rowe, 1963b, Science *143*, 1049.

Linman, J. W. and R. V. Pierre, 1962, Proc. Soc. Exp. Biol. Med. *110*, 463.

Linman, J. W. and R. V. Pierre, 1963, J. Lab. Clin. Med. *62*, 374.

Lobue, J., F. C. Monette, J. F. Camiscoli, A. S. Gordon, and P. C. Chan, 1968, Annals N.Y. Acad. Sci. *149*, 257.

Lowy, P. H. and H. Borsook, 1962, Preparation and properties of erythropoietin concentrates from rabbit plasma and human urine. In: Erythropoiesis, edited by L. O. Jacobson and M. Doyle. New York, Grune and Stratton, p. 33.

Lowy, P. H. and G. Keighley, 1968, Annals N.Y. Acad. Sci. *149*, 54.

Lowy, P. H., G. Keighley, H. Borsook, and A. Graybiel, 1958, Nature *181*, 1802.

Lowy, P. H., G. Keighley, H. Borsook, and A. Graybiel, 1959, Blood *14*, 262.

Lowy, P. H., G. Keighley, and H. Borsook, 1960, Nature *185*, 102.

Lukowsky, W. and R. H. Painter, 1968, Canad. J. Biochem. *46*, 731.

Lukowsky, W. and R. H. Painter, 1970, Proc. Canad. Fed. Biol. Sciences *13*, 97.

Lundgren, G., 1970, Clin. Exp. Immunol. *6*, 661.

Lundgren, G. and G. Moller, 1969, Clin. Exp. Immunol. *4*, 435.

Lundgren, G. and L. Collste, and G. Moller, 1968a, Nature *220*, 289.

Lundgren, G., C. Zukoski, and G. Moller, 1968b, Clin. Exp. Immunol. *3*, 817.

MacKinney, A. A., F. Stohlman, and G. Brecher, 1962, Blood *19*, 349.
Martin, J. and F. H. Bach, 1970, Nature *225*, 238.
McCullagh, E. P. and T. R. Jones, 1941, Cleveland Clinic Quart. *8*, 79.
McCullagh, E. P. and T. R. Jones, 1942, J. Clin. Endocrinol. *2*, 243.
McNeill, T. A., 1970a, Immunology *18*, 39.
McNeill, T. A., 1970b, Immunology *18*, 49.
McNeill, T. A., 1970c, Immunology *18*, 61.
Menkin, V., 1956, Biochemical mechanisms in inflammation. Springfield, Ill., C. C. Thomas.
Metcalf, D., 1956a, Brit. J. Cancer *10*, 169.
Metcalf, D., 1956b, Brit. J. Cancer *10*, 431.
Metcalf, D., 1956c, Brit. J. Cancer *10*, 442.
Metcalf, D., 1959a, Canadian Cancer Conference *3*, 351.
Metcalf, D., 1959b, Rad. Res. *10*, 313.
Metcalf, D., 1960, Brit. J. Haematol. *6*, 324.
Metcalf, D., 1964, The thymus and lymphopoiesis. In: The thymus in immunobiology, edited by R. A. Good and A. E. Gabrielsen. New York, Harper and Row, p. 150.
Metcalf, D., 1965, Nature *208*, 1336.
Metcalf, D., 1966. The thymus. Recent Results in Cancer Research 5. Heidelberg, Springer-Verlag.
Metcalf, D., 1968, J. Cell. Physiol. *72*, 9.
Metcalf, D., 1969a, Brit. J. Haematol. *16*, 397.
Metcalf, D., 1969b, J. Cell. Physiol. *74*, 323.
Metcalf, D., 1969c, Proc. Soc. Exp. Biol. Med. *132*, 391.
Metcalf, D., 1970, J. Cell. Physiol. *76*, 89.
Metcalf, D., 1971a, J. Cell. Physiol. *77*, 277.
Metcalf, D., 1971b, Immunology (in press).
Metcalf, D. and M. Brumby, 1966, J. Cell. Physiol. *67*, Suppl. 1, 149.
Metcalf, D. and R. F. Buffett, 1957, Proc. Soc. Exp. Biol. Med. *95*, 576.
Metcalf, D. and R. Foster, 1967a, J. Natl. Cancer Instit. *39*, 1235.
Metcalf, D. and R. Foster, 1967b, Proc. Soc. Exp. Biol. Med. *126*, 758.
Metcalf, D. and R. S. Foster, 1969, In vitro colony-forming cells in the bone marrow of germfree mice. In: Germfree biology: experimental and clinical aspects. New York, Plenum Press, p. 383.
Metcalf, D. and E. R. Stanley, 1969, Aust. J. Exp. Biol. Med. Sci. *47*, 453.
Metcalf, D. and E. R. Stanley, 1971, Brit. J. Haematol. *20*, 547.
Metcalf, D. and B. Wahren, 1968, Brit. Med. J. *3*, 99.
Metcalf, D., T. R. Bradley, and W. Robinson, 1967a, J. Cell. Physiol. *69*, 83.
Metcalf, D., R. Foster, and M. Pollard, 1967b, J. Cell. Physiol. *70*, 131.
Metcalf, D., M. A. S. Moore, and N. L. Warner, 1969, J. Natl. Cancer Instit. *43*, 983.
Metcalf, D., S. H. Chan, F. W. Gunz,, P. Vincent and F. B. M. Ravich, 1971, Blood (in press).
Miller, J. F. A. P., 1962, Proc. Roy. Soc. B, *156*, 415.
Miller, J. F. A. P., 1965, Nature *208*, 1337.
Miller, J. F. A. P. and G. F. Mitchell, 1969, Transplant. Rev. *1*, 3.
Miller, J. F. A. P. and D. Osoba, 1967, Physiol. Rev. *47*, 437.
Miller, J. F. A. P., E. Leuchars, A. M. Cross, and P. Dukor, 1964, Annals N.Y. Acad. Sci. *120*, 205.
Mirand, E. A., 1968, Annals N.Y. Acad. Sci. *149*, 94.
Mirand, E. A. and A. S. Gordon, 1966, Endocrinology *78*, 325.
Mirand, E. A. and T. C. Prentice, 1957, Proc. Soc. Exp. Biol. Med. *96*, 49.
Mirand, E. A., T. C. Prentice, and W. R. Slaunwhite, 1959, Annals N.Y. Acad. Sci *77*, 677.

Mirand, E. A., A. S. Gordon, and J. Wenig, 1965a, Nature *206*, 270.

Mirand, E. A., A. H. Weintraub, A. S. Gordon, T. C. Prentice, and J. T. Grace Jr. 1965b, Proc. Soc. Exp. Biol. Med. *118*, 823.

Mitus, W. J. and K. Toyama, 1965, Arch. Pathol. *78*, 658.

Monaco, A. P., M. L. Wood, and P. S. Russell, 1965, Science *149*, 432.

Moore, M. A. S. and D. Metcalf, 1970, Brit. J. Haematol. *18*, 271.

Naets, J. P. and M. Wittek, Nature *206*, 726.

Nakamoto, A., 1957, Acta haematol. Jap. *20*, 187.

Nathan, D. G., E. Scheipak, F. Stohlman, and F. Merrill, 1964, J. Clin. Invest. *43*, 2158.

Necas, E. and J. Neuwirt, 1970, In: XIII International Congress of Hematology, Abstract Volume. Munich, Lehmanns Verlag, p. 9 (Abs.).

New York Academy of Sciences, 1964, Annals N.Y. Acad. Sci. *113*, 513.

Noyes, W. D., B. M. Domm, and L. C. Willis, 1962, Blood *20*, 9.

Odell, T. T. and T. P. McDonald, 1961, Fed. Proc. *20*, 51.

Odell, T. T., T. P. McDonald, T. C. Detwiler, and F. L. Howsden, 1961, Blood *18*, 796 (Abs.).

Odell, T. T., T. P. McDonald, and F. L. Howsden, 1964, J. Lab. Clin. Med. *64*, 418.

Oliver, W. J. and G. L. Brody, Circulation Res. *16*, 83.

Ortega, J. A. and P. P. Dukes, 1970, Bioch. Biophys. Acta *204*, 334.

Osnes, S., 1958, Brit. Med. J. *2*, 1387.

Osoba, D., 1965a, J. Exp. Med. *122*, 633.

Osoba, D., 1965b, Science *147*, 298.

Osoba, D., 1968, Proc. Soc. Exp. Biol. Med. *127*, 418.

Osoba, D. and J. F. A. P. Miller, 1963, Nature *199*, 653.

Osoba, D. and J. F. A. P. Miller, 1964, J. Exp. Med. *119*, 177.

Palos, L. A., 1968, Lancet *2*, 918.

Paran, M., Y. Ichikawa, and L. Sachs, 1969, Proc. Natl. Acad. Sci. *62*, 81.

Parrott, D. M. V., M. A. B. de Sousa, and J. East, 1966, J. Exp. Med. *123*, 191.

Paul, J. and J. A. Hunter, 1969, J. Mol. Biol. *42*, 31.

Pavlov, A. D., 1969, Biochim. Biophys. Acta. *195*, 156.

Penington, D. G., 1968, Proc. Roy. Soc. Med. *61*, 601.

Perlmann, P. and G. Holm, 1968, In: Immunopathology. Vth International Symposium: mechanisms of inflammation induced by immune reactions, edited by P. A. Miescher and P. Grabar. New York, Grune and Stratton, p. 325.

Perlmann, P. and G. Holm, 1969, Advances in Immunol. *11*, 117.

Pick, E., J. Krejci, K. Cech, and J. L. Turk, 1969, Immunol. *17*, 741.

Pick, E., J. Krejci, and J. L. Turk, 1970, Nature *225*, 236.

Piliero, S. J., P. T. Medici, B. Pansky, A. L. Luhby, and A. S. Gordon, 1956, Proc. Soc. Exp. Biol. Med. *93*, 302.

Pluznik, D. H. and L. Sachs, 1965, J. Cell. Comp. Physiol. *66*, 319.

Pluznik, D. H. and L. Sachs, 1966, Exp. Cell Res. *43*, 553.

Prentice, T. C. and E. A. Mirand, 1957, Blood *12*, 993.

Rak, K., I. Cserhati, and E. Kelemen, 1959, Med. Exptl. *1*, 125.

Rak, K., F. Krizsa, and I. Cserhati, 1961a, Med. Exptl. *5*, 91.

Rak, K., F. Krizsa, E. Sovenyi, and I. Cserhati, 1961b, Experientia *17*, 518.

Ramseier, H., 1969, J. Exp. Med. *130*, 1279.

Reese, A. J. M. and M. S. Israel, 1969, Brit. J. Exp. Path. *50*, 461.

Reichlin, M. and W. J. Harrington, 1960, Blood *16*, 1298.

Reissman, K. R., 1950, Blood *5*, 372.

Reynafarje, C., J. Ramos, J. Faura, and D. Villavicencio, 1964, Proc. Soc. Exp. Biol. Med. *116*, 649.

Robinson, W., D. Metcalf, and T. R. Bradley, 1967, J. Cell. Physiol. *69*, 83.

Robinson, W. A., R. C. Atkins, and B. Pike, 1969a, Proc. Soc. Exp. Biol. Med. *132*, 431.

Robinson, W. A., E. R. Stanley, and D. Metcalf, 1969b, Blood *33*, 396.

Robison, G. A., R. W. Butcher, and E. W. Sutherland, 1968, Ann. Rev. Biochem. *37*, 149.

Rosse, W. F. and T. A. Waldmann, 1966, Blood *27*, 654.

Rosse, W. F., T. A. Waldmann, and P. Cohen, 1963, Amer. J. Med. *34*, 76.

Ruddle, N. H. and B. H. Waksman, 1968, J. Exp. Med. *128*, 1267.

Rytomaa, T., 1969, Granulocytic chalone and antichalone. In: Hemic cells in vitro, edited by P. Farnes. Baltimore, Williams and Wilkins, p. 47.

Rytomaa, T. and K. Kiviniemi, 1967, Regulation system of blood cell production. In: Control of cellular growth in adult organisms, edited by H. Teir and T. Rytomaa. London, Academic Press, p. 106.

Rytomaa, T. and K. Kiviniemi, 1968a, Cell Tissue Kinet. *1*, 329.

Rytomaa, T. and K. Kiviniemi, 1968b, Europ. J. Cancer *4*, 595.

Rytomaa, T. and K. Kiviniemi, 1969, Cell Tissue Kinet. *2*, 263.

Schooley, J. C. and J. F. Garcia, 1962, Proc. Soc. Exp. Biol. Med. *109*, 325.

Schooley, J. C. and J. F. Garcia, 1965, Blood *25*, 204.

Schooley, J. C., J. F. Garcia, L. N. Cantor, and V. W. Havens, 1968, Annals N.Y. Acad. Sci. *149*, 266.

Schulman, I., M. Pierce, A. Lukens, and Z. Currimbhoy, 1959, Am. J. Dis. Child. *98*, 633.

Schulman, I., M. Pierce, A. Lukens, and Z. Currimbhoy, 1960, Blood *16*, 943.

Schulman, I., C. F. Abildgaard, J. Cornet, J. V. Simone, and Z. Currimbhoy, 1965, J. Pediat. *66*, 604.

Sherwood, J. B., S. H. Robinson, L. Bassan, S. Rosen, and A. S. Gordon, 1970, XIII International Congress of Hematology, Abstract Volume. Munich, Lehmanns Verlag, p. 168 (Abs.).

Slaunwhite, W. R., E. A. Mirand, and T. C. Prentice, 1957, Proc. Soc. Exp. Biol. Med. *96*, 616.

Small, M. and N. Trainin, 1967, Nature *216*, 377.

Spector, B., 1961, Proc. Soc. Exp. Biol. and Med. *108*, 146.

Stanley, E. R. and D. Metcalf, 1969, Aust. J. Exp. Biol. Med. Sci. *47*, 467.

Stanley, E. R. and D. Metcalf, 1971, Proc. Soc. Exp. Biol. Med. *137*, 1029.

Stanley, E. R., W. A. Robinson, and G. L. Ada, 1968, Aust. J. Exp. Biol. Med. Sci. *46*, 715.

Stanley, E. R., T. A. McNeill, and S. H. Chan, 1970, Brit. J. Haematol. *18*, 585.

Steinberg, B., 1958, Arch. Pathol. *65*, 237.

Steinberg, B., A. A. Dietz, and R. A. Martin, 1958, Lab. Investig. *7*, 35.

Steinberg, B., A. A. Dietz, and R. A. Martin, 1959, Acta haematol. *21*, 78.

Steinberg, B., F. H. F. Cheng, and R. A. Martin, 1965, Acta haematol. *33*, 279.

Stohlman, F., 1959, Annals N.Y. Acad. Sci. *77*, 710.

Stohlman, F., C. E. Roth, and J. C. Rose, 1954, Blood *9*, 721.

Stohlman, F., S. Ebbe, B. Morse, D. Howard, and J. Donovan, 1968, Annals N.Y. Acad. Sci. *149*, 156.

St. Pierre, R. L. and G. A. Ackerman, 1965, Science *147*, 1307.

Stutman, O., E. J. Yunis, and R. A. Good, 1968, J. Natl. Cancer Instit. *41*, 1431.

Stutman, O., E. J. Yunis, and R. A. Good, 1969, J. Exp. Med. *130*, 809.

Swann, M. M., 1958, Cancer Res. *18*, 1118.

Taylor, R. B., 1965, Nature *208*, 1334.

Thurman, W. G., H. Grabstold, and P. H. Lieberman, 1966, Arch. Int. Med. *117*, 280.

Till, J. E. and E. A. McCulloch, 1961, Rad. Res. *14*, 213.

Toi, S. L., 1956, In: Die zentralnervöse Regulation des Blutbildes, edited by E. Komiya. Stuttgart, Thieme.

Trainin, N. and M. Linker-Israeli, 1967, Cancer Res. *27*, 309.

Trainin, N., A. Bejerano, M. Strahilevitch, D. Goldring, and M. Small, 1966, Israel J. Med. Sci. *2*, 549.

Trainin, N., M. Small, and A. Globerson, 1969, J. Exp. Med. *130*, 765.

Turk, J. L., 1969, Discussion. In: Mediators of cellular immunity, edited by H. S. Lawrence and M. Landy. New York, Academic Press, p. 301.

Turner, D. L. and F. R. Miller, 1943, Proc. Soc. Exp. Biol. Med. *54*, 177.

Uhr, J. W. and G. Moller, 1968, Adv. In Immunol. *8*, 81.

Valentine, F. T. and H. S. Lawrence, 1969, Science *165*, 1014.

Van Dyke, D., 1959, Annals N.Y. Acad. Sci. *77*, 543.

Van Dyke, D. C., J. F. Garcia, and J. H. Lawrence, 1957, Proc. Soc. Exp. Biol. Med. *96*, 541.

Van Dyke, D. C., M. L. Nohr, and J. H. Lawrence, 1966, Blood *28*, 535.

Vira, D. C., O. Degani, J. Dausset, and D. A. L. Davies, 1968, Nature *219*, 704.

Wahren, B., K. Lantorp, G. Sterner, and A. Espmark, 1970, Proc. Soc. Exp. Biol. Med. *133*, 934.

Waksman, B. H., B. G. Arnason, and B. D. Jankovic, 1962, J. Exp. Med. *116*, 187.

Waldmann, T. A., W. F. Rosse, and R. L. Swarm, 1968, Annals N.Y. Acad. Sci. *149*, 509.

Ward, P. A., H. G. Remold, and J. R. David, 1969, Science *163*, 1079.

Warner, N. L., M. A. S. Moore, and D. Metcalf, 1969, J. Natl. Cancer Instit. *43*, 963.

Wearn, J. T., F. R. Miller, and R. W. Heinle, 1939, Trans. Assn. Amer. Phys. *54*, 278.

Whitcomb, W. H. and M. Moore, 1968, Annals N.Y. Acad. Sci. *149*, 462.

White, W. F., C. W. Gurney, E. Goldwasser, and L. O. Jacobson, 1960, Recent Prog. Hormone Res. *16*, 219.

Wigzell, T. 1967, Cold Spring Harbor Symp. Quant. Biol. *32*, 507.

Winkert, J. W. and A. S. Gordon, 1960, Biochim. Biophys. Acta *42*, 170.

Yamamoto, S., 1957, Acta Haematol. Japan *20*, 163.

Zanjani, E. D. and A. S. Gordon, 1970, In: XIII International Congress of Hematology, Abstract Volume. Munich, Lehmanns Verlag, p. 167 (Abs.).

CHAPTER 8

Senescence of haemopoietic tissues

In cell systems as complex as the haemopoietic tissues it might be anticipated that age-related failures in one or more of the many components might occur and have measurable effects on the functional capacity of these tissues. However, it is not particularly easy to demonstrate such deficiencies in cell production or function, a fact which attests to the great functional reserve of the haemopoietic tissues and the effectiveness of multiple, overlapping, control systems.

8.1 Ageing and the immune system

It is a common clinical observation that, despite the use of antibiotics, death in old age is often caused by, or significantly associated with, infections. This would suggest that in old age immune responses are not as effective as in the young. However, when the response to a specific antigen is tested it is somewhat surprising that the depression observed in the immunological response is less than might be expected. In a study of antibody formation to S. adelaide flagellin, Rowley and Mackay (1969) observed lower levels of natural antibody in old subjects but no difference between peak titres of antibody following immunisation in old and young subjects. Similarly the levels of 'natural' agglutinins to sheep red cells (Paul and Bunnell 1932) rabbit cells (Friedberger et al. 1929) and blood-group antigens (Thomsen and Kettel 1929) were lower in old age, but normal responses were reported to typhoid vaccine (Brenner et al. 1951) and lower responses to tetanus toxin (Virag and Kochar 1966). If autoantibodies can be accepted in part as indicating abnormal responsiveness of immune tissues, then these disturbances do become more common in old age; and a study by Wittingham et al. (1969) indicated that 50% of subjects over the age of 60 years exhibited autoantibodies to one or other normal tissue antigens.

Experience with animals is limited, as few investigators seem prepared to keep large populations of experimental animals for studies in old age. Again as in humans, ageing mice seem less able to mount effective immune responses and commonly die with chronic ulcers and abscesses which suggests that defects in the immune system develop with advancing age. In some mouse strains, a decreased ability to generate antibodies or antibody-forming cells has been noted in old age (Makinodan and Peterson 1964; Albright and Makinodan 1966; Metcalf et al. 1967; Celada 1968), and Teller et al. (1964) reported that aged mice exhibited a diminished capacity to reject transplants of foreign tumour cells. On the other hand, some strains of mice exhibit no such age-related deficiencies (Metcalf et al. 1967).

Thus the situation in both the mouse and man may be that in old age, genetically-related defects in immunological responses often do develop but that these result from a combination of minor deficiencies in more than one of the multiple components of the immune system rather than a single major defect.

The size and cellularity of the lymphoid organs become reduced with advancing age. This is seen dramatically in the thymus and bursa where weight decrease commences in early adult life and continues at a slower rate throughout life. Similar but less marked changes develop later in life in the lymph nodes and spleen lymphoid follicles (Metcalf et al. 1967). As the areas chiefly affected are the thymus-dependent areas it is possible that this reduced cellularity is secondary to the slow decline in the number of cells produced in, and released from, the thymus. The age-related decline in cellularity of the thymus is not due to age-changes in the body as aged animals adequately support the growth of neonatal thymus grafts, nor is there an appreciable reduction in the supply of thymus-repopulating stem cells in old age as the aged animal can adequately repopulate multiple neonatal thymus grafts (Metcalf 1965). We discussed in Chapter 6 the evidence indicating that thymus cellularity was determined by the epithelial micro-environment within the organ, and it is this micro-environment which appears to develop the age-related changes leading to decreased lymphopoiesis.

The basis for the decreased cellularity in lymph nodes and spleen lymphoid tissue is likely to be more complex as in part this is secondary to a reduction in the entry of new thymus-derived cells. However, multiple thymus grafting in aged mice did not significantly increase the lymphocyte content of the lymph nodes or spleen suggesting that again the microenvironmental cells of these organs may have developed age-related changes preventing them from accepting, or fostering the proliferation of, thymus-derived cells (Metcalf et al. 1967). Similar conclusions were reached by Celada (1968) from an analysis of the capacity of spleen cells from immunised mice to produce antibody on transfer to recipients of varying ages. Cells injected into aged recipients produced less antibody following challenge than cells injected into young recipients. It was postulated that there was a reduction in 'biological space' available for the seeding and proliferation of injected cells in the aged animal. This biological space could be increased by pre-irradiation of the recipient (Albright and Makinodan 1966; Celada 1968).

However, defective immune responses in aged mice seem unlikely to be due simply to a reduction in suitable microenvironmental foci for supporting the generation of antibody-forming cells, since multiple spleen grafts from neonatal donors, either alone or in combination with multiple neonatal thymus grafts, failed to restore antibody or antibody-forming cell responses to sheep red cells to the level seen in young mice (Metcalf et al. 1967).

Albright and Makinodan (1966) analysed the ability of unprimed spleen cells to respond to sheep or rat red cells after transfer to irradiated recipients of uniform age. Subsequent work by others suggests that the technique used would represent an assay of focus-forming units – that is the presence of both T and B cells. The responsiveness of a fixed number of spleen cells rose progressively to 40 weeks of age, but after this time fell progressively with increasing age in mice aged 40–130 weeks. A similar decline was noted in the responsiveness of spleen cells from primed animals, but this decline occurred with a decay half life of 26 weeks, which was more rapid than that observed in primary responsiveness. An analysis of this situation suggested that individual FFU's in aged mice were able to generate normal numbers of antibody-forming progeny and normal total amounts of antibody, but only 19S antibody was generated with no subsequent 7S antibody production. In the (C57BL $\times$ C3H)F_1 mice analysed, some decline in the total spleen content of CFU's was noted with increasing age although the capacity of these cells for self-generation was not studied.

The observations of Albright and Makinodan are compatible with the interpretation that in ageing there is a decline in the number or effectiveness of microenvironmental foci in the spleen capable of sustaining focus-forming units and their subsequent proliferative activity following antigenic stimulation. Such a deficiency would be revealed in assays for FFU's, but would not necessarily depend on a deficiency in the number of CFU's in the animal, even though for the same general reasons the total spleen content of CFU's may decline in old age. Reciprocal transfer experiments in irradiated old and young recipients, suggested that the aged spleen microenvironment might be less able to support the proliferation of old donor cells than the spleen in young recipients, indicating, in addition, some intrinsic changes in the cells themselves.

Obviously the situation is complex in aged mice of those strains in which immunological defects can be demonstrated, and the situation is in need of re-examination using systems which can clearly discriminate between T and B components.

8.2 Senescence of haemopoietic stem cells

A general decrease in haematological values is associated with ageing in mice and includes depression of erythrocyte counts, haemoglobin levels, hae-matocrit, mean corpuscular volume and mean corpuscular haemoglobin concentration (Ewing and Tauber 1964). These changes are not, however, of sufficient magnitude to warrant a diagnosis of anaemia. Spleen size and spleen iron incorporation, increased with age but haematocrit and blood-iron up-take decreased (Yukas and Storer 1967). These latter investigators also studied the influence of age on radiation sensitivity of mice and observed that marrow and intestinal radiosensitivity showed dissimilar ageing patterns with marrow resistance increasing to a maximum at 17–19 months and intestinal resistance decreasing from 3 months. They concluded that '…maximum fitness in the mouse, in terms of resistance to radiation, is not attained in early adult life but is associated with middle age (a consoling point for ageing radiation biologists)'.

Studies on the influence of age on the stem-cell and progenitor-cell compartments are unfortunately fragmentary, and considerable species and strain differences undoubtedly exist. Yukas and Storer (1967) reported that the femoral CFU content doubled by 18 months but returned to normal values by 24 months in C57BL/6J mice. No difference in the incidence of marrow CFU's was found in mice between 12–43 weeks (Kretchmar and Conover 1967) and no change in CFU numbers was seen in RFM/Un mice up to 52 weeks of age (Davis et al. 1968). Moore, M. A. S. (unpublished observations) found a striking increase in both frequency and absolute numbers of CFU's in the marrow of old (2.5 years) male CBA mice when compared to young mice of the same strain (see Table 8.1). No difference in the frequency of CFU's was seen in the spleen but absolute numbers showed a slight reduction in aged mice. A similar fall with age in spleen CFU

TABLE 8.1

Influence of ageing on the stem cell (CFU) population

Age (weeks)	Marrow		Spleen	
	CFU/10⁵	CFU total per femur	CFU/10⁵	CFU total
130	212	23,200	1.3	2,600
130	135	28,400	1.9	2,760
130	133	29,300	1.0	1,800
130	167	19,000	0.8	1,000
130	114	18,000	1.1	1,870
8	26 ± 2*	$2,900\pm120$	1.6 ± 0.3	$3,100\pm370$

CFU content of femoral marrow and spleen of young and old male CBA mice.
* Data for young mice are means $\pm$ S.E. of CFU values of 40 animals.

content was noted by Albright and Makinodan (1966). Endogenous spleen colony-forming capacity also increased progressively with age. Following 625 R total body irradiation, 19 months old mice had 4–5 times more endogenous colonies than did 3 months old mice; spleen weight, and spleen and blood iron incorporation were all considerably elevated in the old mice (Yukas and Storer 1967). A considerable increase in endogenous colony background was also found in old vs. young RFM mice subjected to 750 R (Davis et al. 1968). This increase was associated predominantly with increased numbers of megakaryocytic spleen colonies, and it is probably relevant that an increase in numbers of megakaryocytes has been reported in spleens of old mice (McFadden 1967).

Ageing influences may potentially involve humoral regulators, the haemopoietic microenvironment or the haemopoietic stem cell. There is unfortunately little information on the nature of the defects in haemopoiesis in ageing but the microenvironment has been shown to be defective since young bone marrow formed only half the number of spleen colonies in 36–43 weeks old irradiated mice that formed in 12–16 weeks old recipients (Kretchmar and Conover 1967).

Hayflick (1965, 1966) has described the limited replicative life span of human diploid fibroblast cultures. Restriction in fibroblast growth potential was revealed in serial subculturing experiments where cultures entered a terminal phase with progressively increasing population doubling times and eventual failure to replicate further. The number of passages obtained was inversely related to the age of the donor, which suggested that restriction in growth potential was a manifestation of senescence at the cellular level (Hayflick 1965, 1966; Goldstein et al. 1969). The so-called 'immortal' cell lines do not show this senescence effect, but such lines invariably show gross karyotypic changes and are almost certainly virus-transformed or neoplastic. Estimates by different workers of the cell doubling capacity of fibroblast cultures vary according to culture conditions and depend on assumptions made with respect to plating efficiency and proliferation during the establishment of the culture. The doubling capacity of human fibroblasts was 50 ± 10 doublings in the report of Hayflick (1965), and approximately 44 in the data of Martin et al. (1970). In the latter study the age-related decline in doubling capacity was investigated with fibroblast cultures established from foetal material and from donors of all age groups, and a highly significant reduction in doubling capacity was observed with 0.2 ± 0.05 cell doublings lost each year between the 1st and 9th decades of life. Further correlation between ageing and cell-doubling capacity was revealed in studies on patients with certain autosomal recessive inherited diseases such as Werner's syndrome, Progeria and Rothmund's syndrome, which are characterised by a variety of degenerative features that caricature normal ageing processes. Patients with these conditions all showed a marked deficiency in *in vitro* growth potential of fibroblast cultures (Martin et al. 1970).

Primary cultures established from different tissues achieved different numbers of doublings, since skin fibroblast cultures achieved more doublings than cultures established from bone marrow and cultures from skeletal muscle achieved intermediate values (Martin et al. 1970). Species differences also influence passaging capacity since embryonic fibroblast cultures from short-lived species such as mice, rats, hamsters and chickens achieved only 15 doublings compared with 50 doublings by human fibroblasts, and fibroblasts from adults of these species underwent considerably fewer than 15 divisions (Hayflick 1968).

In vivo studies have also demonstrated intrinsic ageing mechanisms in somatic tissue. Mouse skin grafts e.g. were maintained in serial passage for $4\frac{1}{2}$–5 years, a period considerably in excess of the normal lifespan of the original donor, but the grafts ultimately became shrunken and hairless (Krohn 1962). Mouse bone marrow serially passaged in irradiated recipients also lost its ability to promote survival and haemopoietic recovery (Barnes et al. 1962; Van Bekkum and Weyzen 1961). Using 1-year passage intervals, several marrow lines were maintained for up to 40 months and one line was carried for seven passages over a period of 5 years (Micklem and Loutit 1966).

Impairment of proliferative capacity of passaged marrow appeared to depend upon the number of marrow cells transplanted and the differentiation demand in the recipient. Recipients rendered polycythaemic or infused with lymphoid cells showed enhanced marrow proliferative competence (Bennett et al. 1964). A correlation between marrow small lymphocyte numbers and marrow proliferative capacity in serial transplantation has also been claimed (Cudkowicz et al. 1964). The effect of repetitive irradiation upon the proliferative capacity of CFU's was studied by Boggs et al. (1967). In this experiment, spleen endogenous colony numbers, weight and iron uptake showed a progressive decline during the course of six sequential exposures to 600 R at 6-weekly intervals. Further increase in the intervals between irradiation did not increase the number of irradiation exposures the animal could withstand. A similar observation was made in serial marrow passaging experiments, where increase in the interval between passages did not influence the number of passages obtained (Cudkowicz et al. 1964).

Decline in marrow or spleen passaging capacity is associated with a reduction in CFU content. Siminovitch et al. (1964) grafted 10^7 marrow cells into primary irradiated recipients and maintained serial passage at 14-day intervals for 4–5 generations until termination, when recipient spleens contained few or no CFU's. In Table 8.2 the results of a similar passage experiment are shown. This serial transfer was initiated by a marrow graft of 30 CFU's from old (2.5 years) mice and was maintained for four passages before extinction. Such results demonstrate the tremendous proliferative

TABLE 8.2

Proliferative capacity of aged stem cells

Passage number	Transplant cell source	Duration of passage (days)	Total cells per spleen	Spleen CFU per 10^5	Spleen CFU total
1°	Old Marrow*	14	2.2×10^8	3.64	8,000
2°	Spleen	14	2.1×10^8	0.98	2,060
3°	Spleen	14	1.3×10^8	0.17	220
4°	Spleen	11	3.5×10^7	0.01	4

Decline in colony-forming ability seen on serial passage of old CBA marrow in lethally irradiated CBA recipients.
* Passage initiated with 15,000 marrow cells (containing 30 CFU) from a 130-week old CBA male donor.

reserve capacity of the haemopoietic stem-cell population even in very old animals. Table 8.3 documents a further facet of marrow serial passaging experiments. The decline in CFU numbers and termination of passaging capacity occurred in the course of four passages with 14-day passage intervals. Increasing the duration of the first passage to 8 weeks did not extend passaging capacity, nor did extension of first passage to 8 weeks and second passage to 27 weeks. Even when the penultimate passage was extended to 18–23 weeks the transferred spleen cells were incapable of reconstituting a CFU population in an irradiated recipient. Three points emerge from this study: (a) duration of passage intervals does not significantly affect the number of passage generations, (b) the decline in stem-cell passaging capacity does not show recovery over a prolonged period, (c) stem-cell proliferative demand to support haemopoiesis for up to 30 weeks during interpassage periods did not accelerate the rate of CFU decline.

Is this decline in CFU passaging capacity an *in vivo* correlate of the fibroblast culture experiments and thus an example of ageing at the somatic cell level, or is it an artefact due to trauma in passage, abnormal differentiation pressure or inhibitory influence of the spleen environment? Trauma of passage is excluded by the endogenous regeneration experiments of Boggs et al. (1967), where decline was still evident even though the cells were not subjected to handling. The extent of decline was less dramatic in the endogenous regeneration experiments than in the serial grafting studies. This difference is probably due to the stem-cell survival fraction, which may be at least $3-6 \times 10^3$ CFU's following 600 R and contrasts with the much lower numbers of CFU's used to initiate the marrow grafting experiments (e.g. only 30 CFU's initiated the passage shown in Table 8.2). The influence of abnormal differentiation pressure diverting stem cells into differentiated cell compartments and delaying CFU recovery should be overcome by prolonging the passage interval since this would allow eventual recovery of the stem-cell compartment once normal haemopoietic recovery was accomplished. The lack of effect of such a procedure argues against the role of abnormal differentiation pressures in producing restriction in passaging capacity. An inhibitory influence of the spleen environment must be considered, since haemopoietic regeneration occurs predominantly within the spleen rather than the more normal site for haemopoiesis and stem-cell proliferation in the marrow. This possibility is to some extent excluded since passaging carried out exclusively with cells taken from bone marrow rather than spleen terminates after a similar number of passage generations.

Analysis of stem-cell proliferation is complicated by many factors such as

TABLE 8.3

The effect of variation in passage intervals on CFU passaging capacity

Passage number	Duration of passage (days)	CFU per spleen	Duration of passage (days)	CFU per spleen	Duration of passage (days)	CFU per spleen	Duration of passage (days)	CFU per spleen	Duration of passage (days)	CFU per spleen	Duration of passage (days)	CFU per spleen
1°	14	7,200	56	10,060*	56	10,060	56	10,060	56	10,060	56	10,060
2°	14	9,300	14	12,600	187	2,360	13	7,500	13	7,500	13	7,500
3°	14	230	14	465	12	260	161	1,000	130	1,210	142	14
4°	14	6	14	40	11	0	12	0	11	0	11	0
Total passage time (days)	56		98		266		242		210		222	

The first passage initiated by a graft of young marrow containing 300 CFU's and the passage was maintained by transfer of 1/15th of the total spleen.

* All passages from primary hosts after 56 days taken from the same pool.

transition of proliferating stem cells into resting compartments, operation of population size control mechanisms inhibiting stem-cell proliferation, heterogeneity in individual stem cell self-replication capacity, and redistribution of stem cells between different haemopoietic tissues (see Chapter 3).

The haemopoietic system is particularly suitable for studies on the restriction of somatic cell proliferative capacity since at least two self-replicative cell types can be ennumerated with considerable efficiency and can be serially passaged. One, the CFU stem-cell population has been most extensively studied but the other, the antigen-reactive cell, has not. Serial transfer of the precursors of antibody-forming cells (both 7S and 19S plaque-forming cells) has been accomplished using 7-day intervals and transferring immunised cells with antigen (Moller 1968). Such transfers were invariably successful for 2–4 passages with no decline in numbers of antibody-forming cells (PFC) developing in the spleen. During the 5–6th transfer the number of PFC's developing declined rapidly and usually were no longer produced within one or two further transfers despite repeated antigenic stimulation. Moller estimated that the PFC progenitor cell divided 38 times during the first four passages and had the capacity to generate 10^{12} antibody-producing cells. The interpretation of this experiment is complicated since the antigenic stimulus used was the sheep erythrocyte and therefore two progenitor cells are implicated in the genesis of the haemolysin-forming cell, the thymus-derived antigen reactive cell (ARC) and the antibody-forming cell precursor (AFC-P). Consequently the demonstrated restriction in proliferative capacity applies only to whichever of the two cell types is rate limiting for the production of antibody-forming cells in the passage system.

The most direct experimental approach for estimating cell-doubling capacity has involved serial passaging of spleen colonies. In this system individual stem cells (CFU's) are cloned, and CFU's, *in vitro* CFC's and total differentiated cells can be estimated during the exponential phase of colony growth where exit of cells is minimal (see Figure 8.1 for experimental design). Adult marrow CFU's produced spleen colonies which upon second passage contained very few or no detectable CFU's. This 'decline' following the recloning of spleen colonies did not appear to depend upon the CFU content of the primary colony (Siminovitch et al. 1964).

We have observed a similar decline in spleen colony passaging experiments (see Figure 8.2) with 2nd passage colonies containing only 1–10 % of the CFU's found in primary colonies and third passage colonies containing generally no detectable CFU's (Moore, M. A. S. and Metcalf, D., unpublished observation). It may seem surprising that spleen colonies containing

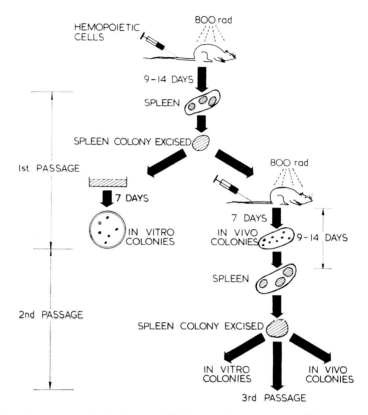

Fig. 8.1.   Experimental design for serial CFU passaging experiments. Primary irradiated recipients are injected with low numbers of adult or embryonic haemopoietic cells. At various intervals thereafter individual spleen colonies are removed from the spleen, made into single-cell suspensions, and after counting are cultured for *in vitro* CFC assay, or injected into two groups of secondary irradiated recipients. One group is sacrificed at 7 days for CFU assay, the second group constitutes the second passage generation and individual spleen colonies are removed at various intervals for further passage with simultaneous *in vitro* CFC and CFU assay.

10^6–10^7 differentiated cells should develop with no detectable CFU's, but since CFU analysis was only performed at late stages of colony development (10–14 days) it may be presumed that CFU's were present and proliferated at earlier stages of colony development, but subsequently underwent irreversible differentiation. The population of *in vitro* CFC's within individual spleen colonies also declined upon serial colony passage but decline was less severe than with CFU's, with the result that the *in vitro* CFC/CFU ratio was considerably increased in the penultimate passage of spleen colonies.

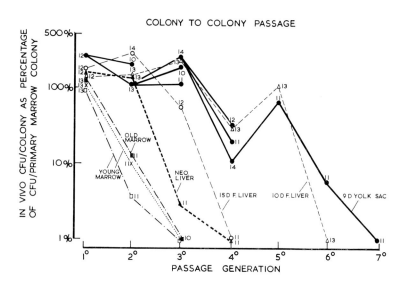

Fig. 8.2. CFU content of spleen colonies serially passaged in (C57BL × CBA)F₁ mice with 11–14-day passage intervals. CFU values are expressed as the percentage of the CFU content of primary colonies of equivalent age of adult marrow origin. Each point is mean of CFU assays on a minimum of 20 individual spleen colonies, the age of the colonies (in days) at time of sampling is shown at each passage. Young marrow was from 8-weeks donor CBA and (C57BL × CBA)F₁ mice, old marrow from 130-weeks old CBA mice. Neonatal and foetal liver and yolk-sac CFU's were from (C57BL × CBA)F₁ mice.

In terminal passage colonies neither *in vitro* CFC's nor CFU's could be detected by the 10th day of colony growth and since neither stem cells nor progenitor cells were present, the production of differentiated cells was curtailed and the average cellularity of terminal passage colonies was one-third to one-half of normal.

Using the colony-to-colony passage design we have observed no difference in passaging capacity of CFU's from the marrow of young mice (8 weeks of age) or from old mice (1.5–2.5 years), but differences were found when neonatal or embryonic CFU's were used (see Figure 8.2). In contrast to the three passages obtained with marrow, CFU's from neonatal liver underwent four passages before extinction, and the earliest embryonic stem cells tested, from 9-day yolk sac, were passaged for 6–7 generations. Light-density CFU's (embryonic type, see Chapter 4) separated by density-gradient centrifugation from 10-day foetal liver also showed extensive passaging capacity, while CFU's from 15-day foetal liver showed a passaging capacity intermediate between early embryonic and neonatal liver CFU's.

Stem-cell generation times were similar in primary colonies of both adult and embryonic origin and were maintained in the second passage of neonatal liver CFU's and in the 2nd and 3rd passages of yolk-sac CFU's. Stem-cell generation times of 6–7 hours have been estimated during the exponential phase of spleen colony growth (see Chapter 3) and if allowance is made for an initial lag period before proliferation of CFU's commences and for a terminal reduction in proliferation at later stages of colony growth, an estimate of a 12-hour mean stem-cell generation time is not unreasonable during the course of passage. Adult stem cells can thus divide approximately 28 times before any defect in proliferation (decline) is evident, whereas neonatal stem cells can divide 56 times and early embryonic stem cells can divide 84 times. Estimates of generation times in spleen colonies exhibiting decline in CFU population size have not been made, and therefore the absolute number of stem-cell doublings cannot be estimated. However, clear differences between embryonic, neonatal and adult stem cells are revealed both in terms of the number of passages before decline is evident, and the number of passages undergone in the course of decline prior to final extinction.

This difference in passaging capacity cannot be explained by defective differentiation of embryonic stem cells in an adult environment with consequent 'sparing' of stem cells, since embryonic CFU's produced spleen colonies with the same total cellularity and proportion of differentiated cells as did adult CFU's. Differences in spleen seeding efficiency of CFU's likewise could not account for the magnitude of the difference, and in any case such an effect would tend to minimise any difference in passaging capacity since embryonic CFU's appear to have a lower seeding efficiency in the adult spleen and may consequently be underestimated. Embryonic stem cells may be less susceptible to inhibitory factors in the adult environment than adult stem cells. This possibility is harder to eliminate, but data presented in Chapter 4 showed that embryonic stem cells (characterised by large size and light density) actually generated adult-type stem cells within a period of 7 days in the adult irradiated animal. Furthermore, adult irradiated animals reconstituted with embryonic stem cells after many months still contained CFU's with increased passaging capacity compared with animals reconstituted with adult stem cells (Moore, M. A. S., unpublished observations). It would seem unlikely that embryonic stem cells had persisted unchanged and resisted differentiation to adult stem cells after such long periods in the adult environment. The most probable explanation is that embryonic stem cells have the capacity to divide a greater number of times, or sustain a higher rate of proliferation, than stem cells from an adult animal. In a competitive situation where mixed inocula of adult marrow and foetal liver cells were used to reconstitute irradiated recipients, foetal liver-derived cells eventually overgrew and replaced the adult marrow-derived cells (Micklem and Loutit 1966). Since the proliferative demand in this experiment was unlikely to lead to exhaustion of stem-cell division capacity the experiment indicates that embryonic stem cells can sustain a higher rate of proliferation for longer periods than can adult stem cells. Differences in CFU doubling times have been reported in the exponential growth phase of spleen colonies derived from CFU's from different sources (Schofield 1970). The shortest doubling time was seen in colonies derived from foetal liver CFU's (16 hours) which contrasted with 19-hour doubling seen in colonies from spleen CFU's and 25-hour doubling with marrow-derived CFU's. Differences were seen even in second passage colonies where doubling times were longer than in primary colonies, since second-passage spleen-derived CFU's had doubling times of 26 hours, which were considerably shorter than the 32-hour doubling times seen with second-passage marrow-derived CFU's. Schofield has suggested that two populations of CFU's exist, one with a doubling time in excess of 30 hours and the other less than 15 hours, and that the proportion of the two types differs in different haemopoietic organs, and varies upon serial passage. An alternative explanation is that CFU doubling time is determined by the previous proliferative history of the cell and the number of divisions it has undergone. This would explain why foetal-liver-derived CFU's, having undergone less proliferation than adult CFU's, can sustain a higher rate of proliferation, and would also explain the lengthening of doubling time upon serial passage. The difference between marrow- and spleen-derived CFU's is intriguing and may indicate a lack of homogeneity in the proliferative history of the CFU population in the adult animal.

Restriction in doubling capacity of haemopoietic stem cells (and of lymphoid progenitor cells) may be the consequence of somatic mutational mechanisms with an increasing incidence of errors until a point is reached when cells with such a level of errors, that they can no longer proliferate, outnumber cells with intact reproductive potential. In this sense decline in stem-cell passaging capacity can be considered as an example of senescence at the single-cell level. Increasing levels of error accumulation may result in extension of cell cycle times due to reduced efficiency of the cell-replication process, and this in turn could lead to increased susceptibility to differentiation. Since different tissues have different doubling potentials, and the doubling capacity of a particular cell population is influenced by species differences, a fixed rate of accumulation of somatic errors cannot provide the sole answer for restriction in proliferative capacity. Additional factors that must be considered are: DNA repair mechanisms, selective forces which can selectively eliminate aberrant cells, and programmed restriction of mitotic potential. The latter concept implies that each class of differentiated cell is programmed in some as yet unknown way to undergo a fixed number of divisions. Such an intrinsic control mechanism would have the advantage of restricting cell proliferation prior to a point when accumulated error would become a major cause of cell death and would counteract the increasing probability of neoplastic transformation due to somatic mutation.

In view of the preceding considerations it may at first appear puzzling that no difference in passaging capacity was observed when CFU's from young or very old mice were compared, and yet marked differences were found in the embryonic and neonatal periods. The answer to this apparent paradox is to be found in the yolk-sac migration concept of haemopoietic development (see Chapter 4). Since stem cells in adult haemopoietic organs were initially derived from the first stem cells to have developed in yolk-sac blood islands they must have undergone proliferation throughout the entire course of embryonic as well as postnatal and adult haemopoietic development. The stem-cell generation time during embryonic haemopoiesis is probably as short as 6–7 hours and consequently stem cells could potentially have undergone some 50 divisions during this embryonic period. This accumulated proliferative experience would adequately account for the more limited passaging capacity of neonatal CFU's when compared with early embryonic CFU's.

If continuous logarithmic expansion of the stem-cell population was to continue once the adult stem-cell population size was achieved (1.4×10^6 stem cells in an 8-week old mouse) the stem-cell population could be effectively replaced every 6 hours for the whole life span of the animal (1,000 days) by the expenditure of only 10–11 population doublings. The sensitivity of detection of stem-cell doubling capacity in serial colony passaging experiments is too low to reveal such differences and consequently it has not yet proved possible to demonstrate an age-related decline in the adult animal nor indeed any effect resulting from increasing the interval between passages.

Calculations of the number of generations required to produce the whole output of human erythrocytes and leukocytes in 60 years of life from a single cell has been estimated at only 54 generations by logarithmic expansion, whereas in a tangential system of stem-cell production (see Figure 8.3) an equivalent result requires 1.2×10^4 generations (Kay 1965). It is unlikely

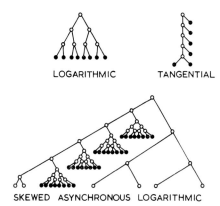

LOGARITHMIC TANGENTIAL

SKEWED ASYNCHRONOUS LOGARITHMIC

Fig. 8.3. A diagram illustrating three models of stem-cell generation. In the tangential model each stem cell (○) divides to produce one differentiated cell (●) and one stem cell. In the logarithmic model synchronous clonal expansion of the stem-cell population occurs prior to terminal differentiation. In the skewed asynchronous logarithmic scheme asymmetry is introduced by variation in stem-cell generation times. Some stem cells are in long cycle or G_0, while others undergo rapid logarithmic expansion to support continuing demand for differentiated cells.

that either extreme situation is normally operating but that some form of compromise operates, either an intermediate logarithmic-tangential or skewed asynchronous form of stem-cell generation (Figure 8.3). Synchronous logarithmic expansion is probable in the embryonic phase of haemopoiesis, but asynchrony may develop when the rate of haemopoietic expansion ceases to be exponential and may become more pronounced as the growth phase terminates in the young adult animal. If at this stage many stem cells enter a non-proliferating G_0 stage as a result of decreased proliferative pressure or feedback inhibition then any demand for stem-cell differentiation could be met by activation of a small number of resting stem cells which could then undergo clonal proliferation and differentiation. This mechanism of clonal succession (Kay 1965) in its most extreme form could supply normal demands for differentiating haemopoietic cells by activating as few as 25 stem cells per day if each stem cell was capable of undergoing the same degree of proliferation and differentiation, as is seen during the course of spleen colony formation. Such an extreme asynchronous situation is unlikely for a number of reasons: (a) it implies that the vast majority of stem cells once entering a G_0 state remain inactive for the life span of the animal; (b) the stem-cell reserve would be suficient for 130 years of normal haemopoietic demand, which would appear to be an overgenerous reserve for an animal with a life-span of 2–3 years; (c) a highly sophisticated stem-cell activation mechanism would be required to selectively activate 0.002 % of the total stem-cell population per day without influencing the remainder; (d) such extreme clonal succession would result in heterogeneity in passaging capacity of CFU's equivalent to at least one passage generation and this has not been observed. G_0 stem cells selected on the basis of vinblastine resistance did not show better passaging capacity than CFU's in normal marrow in active cell cycle (see Section 3.2). We would therefore propose an intermediate situation in the adult haemopoietic system with some degree of clonal succession where some stem-cell clones proliferate extensively to satisfy the requirement for differentiated cells and the remainder of the population undergoing a far slower turnover in response to depletion of stem cells by differentiation. Such a modified asynchronous logarithmic model with clonal succession explains experimental observations in normal animals and the failure to detect major age differences in the adult animal. The major differences seen in the embryonic and neonatal period are the consequence of synchronous logarithmic expansion during the growth phase. In serial passaging experiments, decline in stem-cell passaging capacity is consequently most rapidly revealed in situations where logarithmic expansion of the stem-cell population is initiated (e.g. spleen colony passaging) and where stem-cell division capacity is rapidly exhausted. The absence of an effect on passaging capacity when passage intervals are considerably extended is therefore due to cessation of logarithmic proliferation once the haemopoietic system is reconstituted, with restoration of a resting population of stem cells and establishment of asynchrony and clonal succession with consequent conservation of stem-cell doubling capacity.

References

Albright, J. F. and T. Makinodan, 1966, J. Cell. Comp. Physiol. *67*, Suppl. 1, 185.

Barnes, D. W. H., J. R. Loutit, and H. S. Micklem, 1962, Ann. N.Y. Acad. Sci. *99*, 347.

Bennett, M., G. M. Shearer, A. C. Upton, and G. Cudkowicz, 1964, Nature *204*, 351.

Boggs, D. R., J. C. Marsh, P. A. Chervenick, G. E. Cartwright, and M. M. Wintrobe, 1967, J. Exp. Med. *126*, 871.

Brenner, L. O., S. O. Waife, and M. G. Wohl, 1951, J. Gerontol. *6*, 229.

Celada, F., 1968, The immunologic defence in relation to the Aged. In: Cancer and aging, edited by A. Engel and T. Larsson. Stockholm, Nordiska Bokhandelns Forlaig, p. 97.

Cudkowicz, G., A. C. Upton, G. M. Shearer, and W. L. Hughes, 1964, Nature *201*, 165.

Davis, M. L., A. C. Upton, G. E. Cosgrove, and L. C. Satterfield, 1968, Proc. Soc. Exp. Biol. Med. *128*, 1149.

Ewing, K. L. and O. E. Tauber, 1964, J. Gerontol. *19*, 165.

Friedberger, E., G. Bock, and A. Furstenheim, 1929, Z. Immun-Forsch *64*, 294.

Goldstein, S., J. W. Littlefield, and J. S. Soeldner, 1969, Proc. Nat. Acad. Sci. (Washington) *64*, 155.

Hayflick, L., 1965, Exp. Cell. Res. *37*, 614.

Hayflick, L., 1966, Cell culture and the aging phenomenon. In: Topics in the biology of aging. New York, Interscience Publishers Inc., p. 83.

Hayflick, L., 1968, Sci. Amer. *218*, No. 3, p. 32.

Kay, H. E. M., 1965, Lancet *2*, 418.

Kretchmar, A. L. and W. R. Conover, 1967, Exp. Hemat. *14*, 48.

Krohn, P. L., 1962, Proc. Roy. Soc. B, *157*, 128.

Makinodan, T. and W. J. Peterson, 1964, J. Immunol. *93*, 886.

Martin, G. M., C. A. Sprague, and C. J. Epstein, 1970, Lab. Invest. *23*, 86.

McFadden, K. D., 1967, Canad. J. Zool. *45*, 1035.

Metcalf, D., 1965, Nature *208*, 87.

Metcalf, D., R. Moulds, and B. Pike, 1967, Clin. Expt. Immunology *2*, 109.

Micklem, H. S. and J. F. Loutit, 1966, Tissue grafting and radiation. New York/London, Academic Press.

Moller, G., 1968, J. Exp. Med. *127*, 291.

Paul, J. R., and W. W. Bunnell, 1932, Amer. J. Med. Sci. *183*, 90.

Rowley, M. J. and I. R. Mackay, 1969, Clin. Exp. Immunology *5*, 407.

Schofield, R., 1970, Cell Tissue Kinet. *3*, 119.

Siminovitch, L., J. E. Till, and E. A. McCulloch, 1964, J. Cell. Comp. Physiol. *64*, 23.

Teller, M. N., G. Stohr, W. Curlett, M. L. Kubisek, and D. Curtis, 1964, J. Natl. Cancer Instit. *33*, 649.

Thomsen, O. and K. Kettel, 1929, Proc. Soc. Exp. Biol. Med. *127*, 664.

Van Bekkum, D. W. and W. W. H. Weyzen, 1961, Pathol. Biol. *9*, 888.

Virag, S. and L. Kochar, 1966, Zh. Mikrobiol. *43*, 99.

Wittingham, S., J. Irwin, I. R. Mackay, S. Marsh, and D. C. Cowling, 1969, Aust. Annals Med. *18*, 130.

Yukas, J. M. and J. B. Storer, 1967, Rad. Res. *32*, 596.

CHAPTER 9

Neoplasia of haemopoietic cells

This book is not the place in which to discuss the complexities of the aetiology of leukaemia or of allied diseases. However, there are certain aspects of these diseases which it is pertinent to consider in the light of the preceding discussion of the origin and regulation of normal haemopoietic cells.

The best general definition of a cancer cell is that it is a cell 'capable of progressive proliferation, without restraint by the body' (Furth 1959). In this definition the keyword is 'restraint', for under suitable conditions many normal cells are capable of sustained proliferation. Two distinct components are involved in the capacity of the body to 'restrain' cell proliferation and abnormalities in either, or both, may lead to the development of a population of neoplastic cells: (a) the body must possess an appropriate set of cellular or humoral regulators capable of regulating the growth and differentiation of the cells in question, and (b) the cells themselves must be responsive to these regulators, responsiveness needing to be a heritable trait also possessed by the progeny of these cells.

Normally, restraint of cellular proliferative activity is accompanied by differentiation in these cells, but we have already seen from the discussion of multipotent (undifferentiated) haemopoietic stem cells in mice that normal cells can retain and regularly exhibit the capacity to divide for periods beyond the life span of the animal. The periods during which this proliferative capacity is restrained (G_0 periods) do not appear to be accompanied by any parallel differentiation. What may distinguish a haemopoietic stem cell as 'normal' is the fact that the cell does not pass through continuous cell cycles but rather spends shorter or longer periods in a non-cycling state. This would clearly suggest that such cells were subject to regulatory control mechanisms. Recent evidence, however, suggests that *intermittent* proliferative activity may also be a feature of at least some leukaemic cells (Mauer et al. 1969; Clarkson 1969), so this criterion may not be an absolute one for normal cells.

It is still not entirely certain that all forms of leukaemia are genuine neoplasms, but since leukaemia does involve unusual proliferative activity of haemopoietic cells, and the diseases are progressive in nature leading finally to death, a *prima facie* case exists for classifying all leukaemias into the above very loose definition of cancer, although it must be emphasised that for a disease like chronic lymphoid leukaemia in humans, this assumption could well be wrong.

In inbred animals, it is possible to apply a rather restrictive criterion in testing an abnormal cell population for neoplasia. If the cells in question proliferate progressively after transplantation to a histocompatible recipient and cause death of the animal, most would accept this as indisputable evidence that the cell population contained cancer cells. The same test can be applied to leukaemic cell populations in inbred mice, and if the leukaemic cells grow progressively on transplantation to a normal syngeneic recipient, leading to death of the animal, such leukaemic cells can be said unequivocably to be neoplastic. The cells involved in the common forms of leukaemia in the mouse (lymphoid and granulocytic) usually fulfil this transplantation criterion. With other types of leukaemia and certain allied diseases, e.g. the Hodgkin's-like reticulum cell tumours of SJL mice, transplantability is not invariable and it is likely that many of these neoplasms of haemopoietic cells may fail to fulfil the transplantation criterion either because of the dependence of the abnormal cells on disturbances in host regulators for their progressive growth or because the highly antigenic nature of the cells leads to their immunological suppression by a normal recipient. Thus, transplantability in normal animals is positive evidence for a neoplastic state, but non-transplantability does not exclude a neoplastic state.

Transplantation of haemopoietic cells highlights the essential difference between leukaemic and normal haemopoietic cells. The clearest example of this is a comparison of the behaviour of normal and leukaemic cells in forming spleen colonies. As was shown by Bruce and Meeker (1964), lymphoid leukaemic cells can form colonies of leukaemic cells in the spleen when injected into syngeneic, unirradiated, AKR recipients. As we have discussed earlier, normal haemopoietic stem cells also produce spleen colonies in irradiated syngeneic recipients (Till and McCulloch 1961) and w/w stem cells can produce colonies in the spleen of unirradiated W/W^v recipients (McCulloch et al. 1964). In the initial stages of growth, all three types of colony have a superficial resemblance to one another. The difference between normal and leukaemic cells relates to the events occurring subsequent to colony formation. In the case of normal haemopoietic stem cells, cellular proliferation continues with merging together of individual colonies, but the exponential increase in the size of the cell population ceases once the normal total body complement of haemopoietic tissue has been attained. In other words, faced with demands by tissues depleted of haemopoietic cells, normal cells can proliferate exponentially in a manner essentially similar to neoplastic cells but this proliferation is responsive to inhibition by feedback regulators, presumably monitoring the total population size of haemopoietic cells. In contrast, the leukaemic cells in AKR spleen colonies also proliferate progressively causing merging together of individual colonies, but no shutdown of this proliferative activity appears possible and the animal dies shortly thereafter with progressively enlarging deposits of leukaemic cells throughout the body.

The general questions of interest regarding leukaemic cells are: (a) to what degree can neoplastic cells differentiate?; (b) how responsive are they to regulation by normal mechanisms, either microenvironmental or humoral?; (c) what disturbances in haemopoietic regulation occur in leukaemia and do these disturbances significantly modify the progress of the disease?; and (d) do disturbances in humoral regulators ever lead to the development of leukaemia?

9.1 Capacity of leukaemic cells for differentiation

Most leukaemic cell populations exhibit obvious evidence of mitotic activity, and many of the cells in the leukaemic population appear to be primitive members of the particular cell class. What is equally true, however, is that almost every leukaemic population contains cells which exhibit varying degrees of differentiation. E.g., in lymphoid leukaemia in the mouse, small lymphocyte-like cells can be shown to be part of the tumour population (Metcalf et al. 1965; Metcalf and Wiadrowski 1966; Metcalf and Brumby 1967); in chronic granulocytic leukaemia in humans, polymorphs can be shown to be members of the leukaemic cell population, and in myelomonocytic leukaemia in the mouse, both polymorphs and monocytes can be shown to belong to the tumour population (Warner et al. 1969). Often these differentiated cells exhibit abnormalities which allow them to be distinguished from their normal counterparts. E.g., the high alkaline-phosphatase content of leukaemic small lymphocytes distinguishes them from normal lymphoid cells (Metcalf et al. 1962); the low alkaline-phosphatase content of polymorphs in chronic granulocytic leukaemia distinguishes them from normal polymorphs (Wachstein 1946), and the tetraploid DNA content of poly-morphs and monocytes in one subline of a myelomonocytic leukaemia (War-ner et al. 1969) distinguishes them from normal cells of these types. However, in one critical aspect such differentiated cells exhibit normal behaviour – they have lost the capacity for further division. In fact, the leukaemias offer the clearest examples in oncology of the proposition that cancer cells *can* respond to normal differentiating influences even to the degree of becoming non-dividing end cells with a finite life span.

Since most leukaemic populations characteristically contain blast cells and some less differentiated ancestral cells, it is reasonable to speculate whether the neoplastic event usually occurs at the haemopoietic stem-cell level. Here we are on less certain ground. There are leukaemias, which, because of the uniformly undifferentiated appearance of the leukaemic cells, have been termed 'stem cell leukaemias', but the morphology of such cells does not allow a distinction to be made between neoplasms of multipotent stem cells, partially committed stem cells, progenitor cells, or even possibly merely of blasts cells. Little attempt appears to have been made in stem-cell leukaemias in mice to investigate the possibility that these might be genuine neoplasms of multipotent stem cells and that the cells might, under appropriate conditions, be able to form recognisable progeny of more than one haemopoietic cell class. As mentioned above, leukaemic cells can be shown to form spleen colonies in unirradiated syngeneic recipients, and these colonies have many resemblances to normal haemopoietic colonies in irradiated animals, indicating that an investigation of the above problem might be feasible and rewarding.

Two recent studies have demonstrated that leukaemic cells can be multi-potential in terms of the morphology of their progeny cells. In a study of a myelomonocytic leukaemia in BALB/c mice, it was shown that the leukaemic population included both granulocytes and monocytes (Warner et al. 1969). Certain cells in the population were shown to form mixed colonies of neo-plastic, granulocytic and monocytic cells *in vitro* and these colonies contained colony-forming cells, that is, the cells initiating colonies were a type of leukaemic stem cell capable of some self-replication (Metcalf et al. 1969; Metcalf and Moore 1970). In a somewhat similar study, Ichikawa (1969) showed that an undifferentiated myeloid leukaemic population was capable of being cloned repeatedly in agar culture and of forming colonies in agar which contained both differentiated granulocytes and macrophages.

An intriguing natural situation occurs in man in which stem cells may be involved in the neoplastic processes and be capable of producing neoplastic cells of one class and apparently normal cells of another class. In almost all cases of chronic granulocytic leukaemia, it has been demonstrated that the leukaemic cells exhibit the abnormal Philadelphia chromosome and that this abnormality is not present in non-haemopoietic cells in these patients. The Philadelphia chromosome is also present in the erythroid and mega-karyocytic cells which appear to be normal in these patients but is absent from the lymphoid cells (Nowell and Hungerford 1960, 1961; Whang et al. 1963). One of the possible explanations of these observations is that the Philadelphia chromosome abnormality develops in the common stem cells of the erythroid and granulocytic series after they have separated from the lymphoid stem cells. What is unclear, however, is whether the Philadelphia abnormality, per se, represents the neoplastic change or whether it merely renders the cells abnormally prone to subsequent neoplasia. If the latter is the case it could then be postulated that the susceptibility to neoplastic change depends on the cells also passing into the granulocytic pathway of differentiation.

9.2 *Responsiveness of leukaemic cells to regulation*

In the initial stages of all leukaemias, the proliferating members of the leukae-mic population are restricted in location to those organs which support the proliferation of normal haemopoietic cells. This fact, coupled with the obvious cellular differentiation seen in leukaemic populations, clearly indicates that to a large degree the initial leukaemic populations are regulat-able by, and dependent on, the same microenvironmental and humoral factors that regulate normal haemopoiesis. There could of course be subtle differences in how completely the leukaemic cells are responsive to regulation, which may take time to reveal themselves in the form of progressively expanding leukaemic populations, but an argument could be made for the case that many of the overt signs of leukaemia which develop later depend on secondary changes developing in the initial leukaemic population, e.g. aneuploidy, loss of antigens, etc. In advanced leukaemia, leukaemic cells occur and proliferate in tissues not capable of supporting normal haemopoi-esis. The most likely basis for this behaviour of leukaemic cells is the second-ary loss of dependence of leukaemic cells on normal microenvironmental factors for sustaining cell proliferation.

A misapprehension which is still common regarding leukaemic cells is that they divide more rapidly (that is, have shorter cell cycle times) that corresponding normal cells. However, detailed kinetic studies have shown that the opposite is the case. Studies on mouse lymphoid leukaemia (Metcalf and Wiadrowski 1966) and on acute leukaemia in humans (Astaldi and Mauri 1953; Mauer and Fisher 1962; Gavosto et al. 1964) have consistently shown that leukaemic blast cells proliferate with longer cell cycle times than do their normal counterparts. This evidence implies that the capacity of a leukaemic cell population to expand exponentially does not depend on short cell cycle times but on the tendency for daughter cells to remain parental in type and therefore capable of further division. Even small changes in the proportion of daughter type (non-dividing) and parental type (dividing) offspring in a dividing cell population will quickly allow an exponential expansion of the population, a situation which could allow a large fraction of cells in the leukaemic population to be differentiated at any one point in time and yet allow the population to expand exponentially.

The exact form of the abnormality in this pattern of daughter-cell differentiation reveals itself in the overall pattern of differentiation in the leukaemic population. Studies on such differentiation patterns in lymphoid leukaemia in the mouse, using both cytological and Coulter counter cell size analyses, have shown that identical patterns are present throughout the different leukaemic deposits in individual animals, and that these patterns are reproduced with some precision on transplantation of small numbers of the leukaemic cells to normal recipients (Metcalf et al. 1965; Metcalf and Brumby 1967). This suggests that the cause of the abnormal pattern is a heritable intrinsic abnormality in the stem cells of the leukaemic population which is not modified by variations in the regulatory environment in different individual animals. Analysis of many different lymphoid leukaemias in individual mice with spontaneous lymphoid leukaemia has shown that no two leukaemic cell populations have exactly the same abnormal patterns of differentiation. If, as we have suggested, an underlying genetic abnormality which leads to irregularities in differentiation is the essence of the neoplastic change, then one must conclude that there may be a very large number of ways in which the genetic mechanisms regulating the pattern of differentiation can be altered and still allow the progeny of such a cell to behave as a neoplastic population.

Recently the growth of two leukaemias has been analysed in the agar-culture system with respect to the responsiveness of the leukaemic cells to stimulation by a normal regulator. We discussed earlier the fact that colony formation *in vitro* by normal granulocyte and macrophage progenitors is totally dependent on the presence of the colony-stimulating factor (CSF), supplied either in the form of serum, urine or conditioned medium. The number and growth rate of normal colonies are dependent on the concentration of CSF.

An analysis of a transplantable subline of the myelomonocytic leukaemia WEHI-3 in BALB/c mice (Metcalf et al. 1969) showed that some of the leukaemic cells could form colonies *in vitro* which closely resembled normal haemopoietic colonies in gross morphology. Cytological analysis showed that such colonies contained mixed populations of granulocytic and monocytic cells, and these cells were shown to be tumour cells (a) by identification in all dividing colony cells of the characteristic 39 chromosome karyotype of this subline, and (b) by obtaining myelomonocytic leukaemia after transplantation of individual colonies to normal BALB/c mice. Some leukaemic cells appeared to be capable of forming colonies *in vitro* in the absence of added CSF, particularly when large cell numbers were plated in each culture. However, the addition of CSF in the form of urine, serum or conditioned medium increased the number of colonies developing and the growth rate of individual colonies. This suggested that whilst the growth of some leukaemic cells appeared to be autonomous with respect to CSF, many of the cells were in a 'responsive' state, intermediate between the total dependency of normal

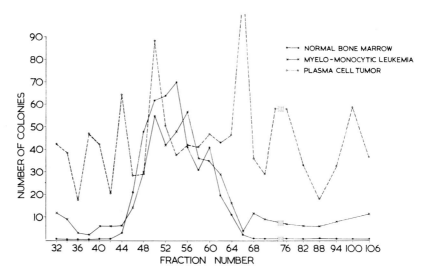

Fig. 9.1. Sephadex column fractionation of conditioned medium showing that the fractions active in stimulating normal bone-marrow colony growth *in vitro* also stimulate the growth of *in vitro* colonies of myelomonocytic leukaemic cells. Growth of colonies of plasma-cell tumour cells was not affected by these fractions.

cells on CSF and a state of complete autonomy with respect to this growth regulator. The CSF used in these experiments was not highly purified, and it was possible that the leukaemic cells might have been responding to some other growth factor but fractionation of urine and conditioned medium on Sephadex columns showed that the fractions containing colony stimulating activity for normal bone-marrow cells coincided exactly with those stimulating myelomonocytic cells, and the probability is strong that the same CSF was involved in both cases (Figure 9.1).

Further studies on the apparent autonomy of some of the myelomonocytic cells to CSF showed that this particular leukaemia can produce detectable amounts of CSF both in agar and liquid culture. Thus myelomonocytic leukaemic cells had the highly unusual capacity of being able to stimulate colony formation by normal haemopoietic cells when mixed in small numbers with the normal cells in agar cultures (Metcalf et al. 1969). These normal colonies contained an unusually high proportion of granulocytes, and some had an unique dispersed morphology and were composed entirely of mature granulocytes. Because the cells of this leukaemia themselves produce significant amounts of CSF, there is now some doubt about the original conclusion that some of the leukaemic cells were autonomous with respect to CSF, and all of the leukaemic cells may have been responsive in varying degrees to stimulation by this regulator.

Further experiments with this myelomonocytic leukaemia demonstrated that the *in vitro* colonies produced by these cells themselves contained *in vitro* colony-forming cells as well as more differentiated progeny. Thus the cells forming the original colonies can be regarded as leukaemic stem cells (Metcalf and Moore 1970). An analysis of the leukaemic populations produced by implanting *in vitro* colonies in the spleen, kidney or thymus in normal BALB/c mice revealed that these populations did not have a uniform content of stem cells. Leukaemic populations in the spleen contained a much higher percentage of stem cells than did apparently similar populations in the subcutaneous tissues, the kidney or the thymus (Table 9.1). This raises the interesting concept that the capacity of leukaemic stem cells to self-generate is not a fixed genetically-determined property of a particular leukaemic population but is greatly influenced by the microenvironment in which the leukaemic cells reside – further evidence of the responsiveness of neoplastic haemopoietic cells to normal regulatory influences.

A similar series of observations has been made by Ichikawa (1969) on a granulocytic leukaemia, arising in SL mice, which was adapted to growth in liquid cultures. The leukaemic cells appeared to be a uniformly undifferen-

TABLE 9.1

Incidence of colony-forming cells in spleen and kidney tumours produced by implantation of *in vitro* colonies of myelomonocytic leukaemia WEHI-3* (From Metcalf and Moore, 1970)

Original tumour no.	Mean no. *in vitro* colonies/10^5 original tumour cells		Number of days after colony implantation	Mean no. of *in vitro* colonies/10^5 tumour cells**			
				Spleen		Kidney	
	Unstimulated	Stimulated†		Unstimulated	Stimulated†	Unstimulated	Stimulated†
3B-11 generation 14	58	176	21	>10,000	>10,000	0	9
				1,310	13,820	12	82
				—	—	45	92
3B-10 generation 16	7	116	35	678	794	4	8
3B-7 generation 17	50	120	24	280	706	60	384
				2,400	2,240	10	79
				2,400	2,460	65	110
			25	1 740	1,740	220	310
				—	—	30	95
				—	—	142	424
				—	—	8	44
				—	—	80	120
				—	—	90	232

* Data from spleen and kidney tumours on same line derived from tumours in the same host animal.

** Mean colony counts from 6 replicate cultures of 50,000 tumour cells.

† Colonies stimulated by addition of 0.15 ml of human urine concentrate to each 1 ml culture.

tiated population of blast cells, but when these cells formed colonies in agar after stimulation by conditioned medium, it was noted that the colonies contained differentiating populations of granulocytic cells and also clearly characterised populations of macrophages. Colony-forming cells were sequentially cloned and still were capable of generating populations of both granulocytes and macrophages, a compelling piece of evidence for the concept that granulocytes and macrophages can have common ancestral cells. As in the myelomonocytic leukaemic studies, colony growth by these myeloid leukaemic cells was stimulated by conditioned medium, more colonies being produced than in the absence of added conditioned medium. Of more interest was the fact that conditioned medium increased the capacity of the leukaemic blast cells to differentiate to progeny of mature granulocytes and macrophages. The active component in this conditioned medium may not have been CSF, as further studies by Ichikawa (1970) have shown the active factor to be dialysable and not to stimulate normal colony-forming cells. A similar observation on the responsiveness of leukaemic cells to differentiating influences has been made using human granulocytic leukaemic cells in agar culture by Pike and Robinson (1970). It was shown that the leukaemic blast cells formed colonies containing differentiated granulocytes when grown on feeder layers of normal peripheral leucocytes and feeder layer activity correlated with the content of normal granulocytes (Robinson et al. 1970). This capacity of conditioned medium or cell-feeder layers to elicit maturation in undifferentiated leukaemic cells is one of the most intriguing findings to emerge from the use of the agar-culture technique.

In neoplasms of erythropoietic cells, some experiments have been made to determine the role of erythropoietin in the development and growth of the erythroleukaemias induced by the Friend virus (Friend 1967). The situation is complex since two variants of the Friend virus exist, one causing leukaemia associated with polycythaemia and the other associated with severe anaemia (Mirand 1968). The Friend virus appears to stimulate the proliferation of the same cells as are target cells for erythropoietin action. Thus the early morphology of a spleen a few days after virus infection is essentially similar to that of a hypertransfused mouse injected with erythropoietin (Metcalf et al. 1959). In both cases, foci of proliferating primitive erythroid cells can be found along the trabeculae of the spleen and under the spleen capsule. These foci resemble miniature versions of spleen colonies, and focus counts have been developed as a reliable system of assay for the Friend virus (Axelrad and Steeves 1964).

The Friend virus inducing the polycythaemic variety of erythroleukaemia

(FVP) was capable of initiating erythropoiesis in mice in which erythropoiesis had been suppressed by hypertransfusion. Assay of plasma and urine in FVP-infected mice revealed no elevation of erythropoietin levels. The situation may resemble that discussed earlier for polycythaemia vera in man in that the erythropoiesis measured by ^{59}Fe uptake in FVP-infected mice represents the differentiation into erythropoiesis, and proliferation, of abnormal erythroid cells in a process which is autonomous with respect to erythropoietin. Erythropoietin was observed to slightly increase the rate of growth of the total population of viral-transformed erythroid cells in FVP-infected mice as measured by spleen weight and haematocrit levels (Mirand 1968). The FVP virus selectively attacks erythroid precursors in the spleen rather than the bone marrow and splenectomy prevents or delays the development of polycythaemia even in mice injected with erythropoietin.

This Friend-virus system is worthy of further analysis since it appears to offer a possible experimental system for determining the responsiveness of neoplastic erythroid cells to erythropoietin and for determining whether the virus can induce the commitment of erythroid precursor cells independently of erythropoietin.

Experiments with the Rauscher virus, which also induces erythroleukaemia in mice, have given different results from those with the Friend virus. In mice made polycythaemic by hypertransfusion, the Rauscher virus was found to be unable to induce splenomegaly or increased ^{59}Fe uptake (Mirand 1966, 1968) and was only capable of producing a few foci of abnormal erythroid cells in the spleen (Pluznik et al. 1966). Conversely, the Rauscher virus induced more spleen foci in hypoxic than in normal mice, presumably because of the greater number of susceptible target cells.

These data suggest that the target cells for the Rauscher virus are more differentiated than those for the Friend virus and that the availability of potential target cells for the Rauscher virus is profoundly modified by the normal growth regulator, erythropoietin.

The further exploration of the Friend- and Rauscher-virus systems should be assisted by the use of the agar-culture system to study the growth characteristics of the various types of erythroleukaemic cells since Patuleia and Friend (1967) have demonstrated that erythroleukaemic cells induced by the Friend virus are able to proliferate in agar and form discrete clones of tumour cells.

In lymphoid leukaemia in the mouse, evidence has existed for many years of the possible role of haemopoietic regulators in leukaemia development. It was shown by McEndy et al. (1944) that the thymus was essential for the development of lymphoid leukaemia in high leukaemia strain mice, and this work has been extended and confirmed for other systems of lymphoid leukae-mia development in mice (see review by Metcalf 1966). The nature of the interrelationship between the thymus and lymphoid leukaemia development remains obscure. In mice such as the AKR, the first leukaemic cells appear in the thymus and all subsequently developing populations in other organs are the progeny of this initial population. This suggests either that the thymic lymphoid cells are exceptionally susceptible to leukaemic transformation or that the thymic microenvironment is conducive to leukaemic transformation. Here the problem becomes extremely complex. There is evidence from thymus-graft studies between high and low leukaemic strains of mice that the thymic epithelial cells play a critical role in lymphoid leukaemia development, but other evidence implicates the high viral content in the thymus as the critical factor. No positive evidence exists for the involvement of the thymic humoral factor in lymphoid leukaemia development and thymus tissue in diffusion chambers did not restore susceptibility to lymphoid leukaemia development in thymectomised mice (Metcalf et al. 1966).

Leukaemic cells in the thymus do not exhibit higher mitotic indices than in leukaemic deposits in other organs (Metcalf et al. 1965), suggesting that they may not be responsive to the thymic microenvironment favouring, or stimulating, high lymphocyte mitotic activity. It may be, however, that infiltration of the organ by leukaemic cells has so disrupted the architecture of the organ and disturbed the viability and function of the epithelial cells that no effective thymic microenvironment exists in a thymic lymphoma.

This raises another question, namely, whether leukaemic cells may modify the nature of the cells determining haemopoietic organ microenvironments. This is an important problem as local disruption of microenvironments by leukaemic cells may be part of the mechanism leading to abnormalities in red-cell and platelet production and abnormal immune responses which are major features of leukaemia. In a study of phagocytic reticuloendothelial cells in lymphoid leukaemic tissue in the mouse, it was observed that the ratio of normal reticuloendothelial cells to leukaemic cells remained constant during exponential growth of the leukaemic population. This was not achieved by proliferation of the reticuloendothelial cells but by recruitment of modified local normal cells in the lymphoid organs (Metcalf et al. 1967b) The role played by the reticuloendothelial cells in the biology of the leukaemic population is unknown, but some type of regulator interaction is possible and the observations raise the possibility that tissue regulation may become progressively disturbed during the growth of leukaemic cells, with consequent effects on both the leukaemic population and normal haemopoietic cells.

No studies appear to have been made on the responsiveness of lymphoid leukaemic populations to antigenic stimulation, but *in vitro* experiments have indicated that neither phytohaemagglutinin nor antigens provokes a normal level of blast transformation in the neoplastic small lymphocytes from the peripheral blood of patients with chronic lymphatic leukaemia, possibly indicating that these cells have lost their normal responsiveness to antigenic stimulation (Nowell 1960; Quaglino and Cowling 1964; Astaldi and Airo 1967). Alternatively of course, these populations of cells may be monoclonal and be responsive only to stimulation by an antigen which has not yet been used in such *in vitro* studies.

9.3 Production of haemopoietic regulators by leukaemic cells

Various workers have proposed that leukaemic populations may be character-ised (a) by excessive production of haemopoietic growth stimulating factors, (b) by failure to produce specific inhibitory substances, and (c) by failure to respond to inhibition by such substances.

Paran et al. (1968) showed that continuous cell lines of myeloid, erythroid and lymphoid leukaemic cells released a factor to the culture medium which could stimulate granulocyte and macrophage colony formation *in vitro*. Similar material appeared to be produced by cultured L1210 leukaemic cells (Metcalf, D. and Foster, R., unpublished data), and we have referred above to the production of an active factor by cultured myelomonocytic leukaemic cells (Metcalf et al. 1969). It thus appears that many leukaemic populations do produce factors which can stimulate the growth of haemopoietic cells. It should be reiterated here that such activity is not unique for leukaemic cells. Many normal cells also produce colony stimulating factor as do non-haemo-poietic neoplastic cells, e.g. sarcoma cells (Ichikawa et al. 1966). Of particular relevance to the present discussion is the fact that these growth stimulating factors also stimulate the growth of some leukaemic cells *in vitro*. The work of Metcalf et al. (1969) and Ichikawa (1969) on this question has already been discussed.

Cells of the myelomonocytic leukaemia (WEHI-3) have the highly unusual property of being able to stimulate colony formation *in vitro* when mixed with suspensions of normal bone-marrow cells. Cells of many lymphoid and erythroid leukaemias, plasma-cell tumours and reticulum-cell sarcomata were unable to stimulate colony formation in such a system even though cell survival was excellent in many cases and though many of these neoplastic populations could condition liquid medium (Metcalf et al. 1969). These observations suggest that cells of the WEHI-3 leukaemia may produce unusually large amounts of colony stimulating material. More intriguing has been the observation that a characteristic loose type of colony is formed by normal bone-marrow cells after stimulation by WEHI-3 cells or medium conditioned by these cells. These colonies contain up to 2000 cells, which at 7-days of incubation are uniformly highly differentiated polymorphs. Only one cell in 5–10,000 normal bone-marrow cells appears capable of forming such a colony, suggesting that these cells may differ from other *in vitro* CFC's. The active factor in medium conditioned by WEHI-3 cells has not been fully characterised, but it has some similarities to CSF, being non-dialysable, ether resistant and relatively heat-stable. It is possible that this active factor is a variant of normal CSF.

Pluznik (1969) and Ichikawa et al. (1969) have described a second factor produced by normal and leukaemic cells, which also stimulated leukaemic cell growth *in vitro*. Unlike CSF which is non-dialysable this second factor was dialysable and presumably was therefore of lower molecular weight. This factor was observed to be produced *in vitro* by normal embryo fibroblasts and by myeloid, erythroid and lymphoid leukaemic cells and was found to increase the cloning efficiency, and to increase colony growth rate, of myeloid, erythroid and lymphoid leukaemic cells *in vitro*. This dialysable factor did not stimulate the growth of normal haemopoietic colonies, but had the interesting property of inducing macrophage differentiation in colonies of myeloid leukaemic cells growing in agar (Ichikawa 1970).

From the evidence so far obtained, the production of factors stimulating haemopoiesis *in vitro* does not appear to be a unique property of leukaemic cells, and no quantitative experiments have been performed to indicate whether, cell-for-cell, leukaemic cells produce more of these factors than do normal cells.

A number of studies have indicated that some normal haemopoietic cells produce a factor inhibiting colony formation by haemopoietic cells in agar. Thus feeder layers of macrophages or medium conditioned by macrophages from the peritoneal cavity, spleen or macrophage colonies, were found to inhibit granulocyte and macrophage colony formation *in vitro* (Ichikawa et al. 1967). This inhibitory factor was found to be dialysable and to be more effective in inhibiting macrophage than granulocyte colony formation. Other studies showed that mature granulocytes also produced a factor inhibiting colony formation *in vitro*, and in this case the inhibitor was non-dialysable and inhibited both granulocyte and macrophage colony formation

(Paran et al. 1969). In contrast to these studies on inhibitors using normal colony-forming cells, parallel studies showed that neither of the inhibitors obtained from macrophages or granulocytes inhibited colony formation *in vitro* by leukaemic myeloid, erythroid or lymphoid cells, and indeed, both factors appeared to stimulate leukaemic colony growth rates.

On the basis of these observations Sachs (1968) postulated that in leukaemogenesis, the leukaemia-inducing agents might alter cells, so that they no longer produced feedback inhibitors and/or no longer responded to feedback inhibition. If at the same time these cells continued to produce growth stimulating factors, uncontrolled proliferation of the population of altered cells would be expected.

This concept attempts to apply the principles developed from the analysis of endocrine carcinogenesis to leukaemia development. As applied to haemopoietic cells this concept of the mechanisms leading to leukaemia development may well be partially correct, but a number of reservations must be made. In the above experiments it was not rigidly established that pure cell populations were used to produce the 'specific' macrophage and granulocyte inhibitors. In this laboratory, similar studies have shown that a dialysable inhibitor of colony formation is also elaborated by normal bone-marrow, spleen, lymph-node and thymic cells. Furthermore, a number of leukaemias (myelomonocytic leukaemia, reticulum-cell sarcoma) have been found to be excellent producers of what appears to be the same dialysable inhibitor. There has been no suggestion from our work that, cell-for-cell, leukaemic cells were less able to produce inhibitors than normal cells, and the situation may well vary from one leukaemic population to another. In addition, colony formation by myelomonocytic leukaemic cells *in vitro* was inhibited by dialysable inhibitors produced by normal haemopoietic cells to the same degree as was normal colony formation, so again lack of responsiveness to inhibitors seems not to be a universal attribute of leukaemic cells.

Somewhat similar comments can be made regarding the studies by Rytomaa and his colleagues on a granulocyte inhibitor (chalone) and a granulocyte stimulating factor (anti-chalone) (Rytomaa 1968). Extracts of granulocyte-rich cell suspensions from the peritoneal cavity were found to contain a low-molecular-weight factor inhibiting the uptake of tritiated thymidine by granulocytic cells in liquid culture *in vitro*, and evidence was obtained for a high-molecular-weight-material in the same extracts which could stimulate proliferation of granulocytic cells. Using similar preparations of 'granulocyte chalone' Rytomaa and Kiviniemi (1968) were able to inhibit the growth of a transplantable chloroleukaemia in rats, and these workers also obtained evidence that chloroleukaemic cells might contain unusually low amounts of granulocyte chalone. Again the same reservations can be made regarding the general significance of this work. Proof of the specific nature of the inhibitors is inadequate, and more than one example of a leukaemic population needs to be examined before generalisations can be entertained regarding differing patterns between normal and leukaemic cells.

Serum levels of colony stimulating factor (CSF) were observed to be elevated in humans with various types of leukaemia and lymphomata (Foster et al. 1968). A survey of CSF levels in single-serum samples from such patients showed that from 14–60% of sera had elevated CSF levels. There was a general correlation between serum CSF levels and the clinical activity of the disease in at least three diseases – Hodgkin's disease, reticulum-cell sarcoma and chronic lymphoid leukaemia. A study on serum CSF levels in children with acute leukaemia showed that at some stage in the disease *all* such patients had elevated serum CSF levels (Foster et al. 1971). Periods of elevated CSF levels occurred irregularly and often persisted for several months. No correlations were observed between serum CSF levels and the stage of the disease (i.e. whether the patient was in remission or relapse) or chemotherapy.

In a subsequent, more detailed study on urine and serum CSF levels in adult patients with acute granulocytic leukaemia, the situation has been found to be extremely complex (Metcalf et al. 1971). Studies on normal human serum have shown that an inhibitor is present which masks CSF and inhibits colony formation by mouse bone-marrow cells. This inhibitory material shows some species specificity of action, blocking colony stimulation by human CSF but not by mouse CSF, and is therefore presumably non-toxic for colony-forming cells. Pre-exposure of mouse bone-marrow cells to inhibitory material from human serum, followed by washing of the cells, did not reduce the number of colony-forming cells, but some change was induced, for colonies grown using endotoxin serum as the source of CSF were mainly macrophage-type rather than the usual granulocytic-type (Chan, S. H., unpublished data). The vast majority of normal human sera showed uniformly high inhibitor levels (Figure 9.2), but studies on sera from adult patients with acute granulocytic leukaemia showed that more than half the sera either lacked detectable inhibitors or contained sub-normal amounts of inhibitory material (Chan and Metcalf 1970; Chan et al. 1971). There were some suggestions that low serum-inhibitor levels were associated with periods of relapse in these patients with acute leukaemia. Studies on electrophoretically separated normal human serum showed that at least two

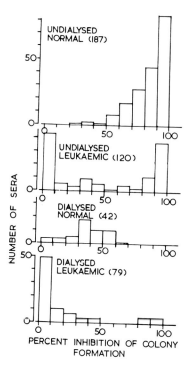

Fig. 9.2. Distribution in 187 sera from normal persons and 120 sera from patients with acute leukaemia of material inhibiting serum-stimulated bone-marrow colony formation *in vitro*. Note absence of inhibitors in many leukaemic sera. Inhibitors form precipitates following dialysis which can be removed by centrifugation, decreasing the inhibitory activity of the serum. (From Chan and Metcalf 1970; reproduced by permission of Nature.)

different non-dialysable inhibitors were present. It is possible that these inhibitors may represent specific antagonists of the stimulating factor, CSF, but no positive evidence in support of this possibility has been obtained, and the *in vivo* significance of these apparent inhibitors is purely a matter for speculation at the present time.

Comparative studies on serum and urine levels of CSF in these patients with acute granulocytic leukaemia (Metcalf et al. 1971) showed that 30% (76/251) of leukaemic sera exhibited higher CSF levels than normal, and 53% (751/1422) of corresponding 24-hour urine specimens contained higher amounts of CSF than normal. Indeed the commonest combination was that of a normal or low serum CSF with a higher than normal CSF level in the urine – suggesting that acute leukaemia might be characterisable as a disease associated with excessive loss of CSF. Sequential analyses of sera and urines from individual patients established that there were characteristic fluctuations in the urine output of CSF. When such patients suffered secondary infections, serum CSF levels and urine output of CSF rose (Figure 9.3). This is also a response shown by non-leukaemic persons with infections, but in leukaemic

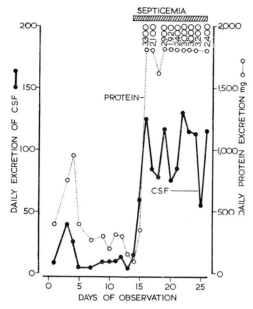

Fig. 9.3. Rise in total daily urine content of CSF in a patient with acute granulocytic leukaemia associated with the development of septicaemia.

patients in relapse, CSF levels did not rise as frequently as in patients in remission or in control patients. Other rises in urine output of CSF in the leukaemic patients followed the use of certain chemotherapeutic agents, particularly cytosine arabinoside (Figure 9.4). These observations are still in their early phase, and no firm conclusions can be reached regarding the significance of the observations.

These findings in humans with leukaemia have been paralleled by similar observations in mice with spontaneous, induced or transplanted leukaemia. Thus, serum CSF levels were shown to be elevated in most mice with lymphoid leukaemia (Robinson et al. 1967), erythroleukaemia induced by the Friend virus and lymphoid leukaemia induced by the Moloney virus (Metcalf, D. and Foster, R., unpublished data), lymphoid leukaemia induced by the Buffett virus (Metcalf and Foster 1967) and in mice with transplanted lymphoid leukaemia, plasma cell tumours and myelomonocytic leukaemia (Metcalf et al. 1969; Hibberd and Metcalf 1971).

Regardless of the cytological type of leukaemia, the colonies stimulated to develop by serum or urine from leukaemic mice or humans appear to be the same morphological type as those stimulated by CSF from normal serum or

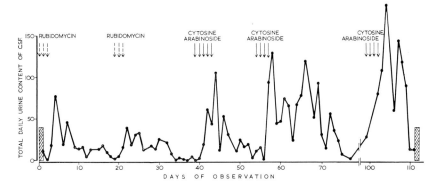

Fig. 9.4.   Rises in total daily urine content of CSF in a patient with acute granulocytic leukaemia following treatment with cytosine arabinoside. Hatched vertical bars indicate range of daily CSF output in normal subjects.

urine. These colonies were initially granulocytic and later became composed of macrophages (Metcalf et al. 1967a; Metcalf and Foster 1967; Foster et al. 1968).

Physical studies on CSF in normal and leukaemic human urine failed to reveal differences in general physical properties, electrophoretic mobility and behaviour on column chromatography (Stanley and Metcalf 1969). Furthermore, antisera developed in rabbits to leukaemic human urine concentrates inhibited equally colony formation *in vitro* stimulated by normal or leukaemic urine CSF (Stanley et al. 1970). It seems probable therefore that the elevated levels of colony-stimulating activity observed in leukaemic patients are due to elevated concentrations of CSF of normal type.

There are a number of possible explanations for the high CSF levels in leukaemia: (a) patients with leukaemia are unusually susceptible to infections, and these infections may trigger the production of CSF; (b) leukaemic cells themselves are able to secrete or release CSF in liquid culture, as discussed above, and possibly leukaemic cells produce or release similar factors *in vivo*; (c) since antigens elevate serum levels of CSF and many leukaemic cells are antigenic for the host animal, the elevated serum levels in leukaemia may reflect chronic antigenic stimulation by leukaemic cells; (d) the high CSF levels may represent a compensatory response on the part of the body to a situation involving deficient production of normal white cells and to be an attempt to stimulate additional white-cell production; and (e) the high CSF levels may have pre-existed in the preleukaemic state due to unknown causes and have contributed to the development of leukaemia.

Of the various possibilities above only (e) would suggest that elevated CSF levels in leukaemia were anything more than a secondary response to abnormal situations created by the leukaemic state.

Studies on preleukaemic humans are difficult to undertake because of the rarity of the disease. Certain diseases are associated with a predisposition to subsequent leukaemia development, e.g. aplastic anaemia or polycythaemia vera, and preliminary observations have indicated that serum and urine CSF levels can be high in such patients. The significance of such observations is at present unknown, and it is at least an open question whether the data obtained will be really applicable to the average case of leukaemia where the disease is not preceded by one of the above conditions.

Contradictory evidence was obtained in mice regarding CSF levels in the preleukaemic period. In preleukaemic AKR mice, serum CSF levels were observed to be higher than normal (Robinson et al. 1967). However, in preleukaemic Swiss mice with viral-induced disease, CSF levels did not become elevated until leukaemia was clinically well advanced (Metcalf and Foster 1967). On the other hand, in mice infected with the Friend virus, serum CSF levels were elevated within 24 hours of virus infection and remained elevated throughout the preleukaemic and leukaemic periods (Metcalf, D. and Foster, R., unpublished data).

Clearly this question of serum stimulators and inhibitors of haemopoietic cells in leukaemia is of intense interest. However, it is clear that future work in this field must pay particular attention to the following: (a) the specificity of the various stimulatory and inhibitory factors, (b) the quantitation of factor production by normal or leukaemic cells, (c) the responsiveness of leukaemic cells to stimulation or inhibition, (d) the variability of the situation from one leukaemia to another, and (e) progressive changes in leukaemic populations with respect to responsiveness to various regulators.

9.4 Conclusions

Leukaemic cells appear to be abnormal because of defective patterns of differentiation following cell division, but leukaemic cells in some respects are still partially responsive to the factors regulating normal haemopoiesis. There is increasing evidence that levels of humoral regulators are abnormal in leukaemia. It is not yet clear whether these disturbances in regulators and responsiveness to regulators are secondary changes developing after the onset of leukaemia or represent some of the factors leading to the initiation of these diseases.

References

Astaldi, G. and C. Mauri, 1953, Rev. Belg. Path. *23*, 69.
Astaldi, G. and R. Airo, 1967, In: The lymphocyte in immunology and haemopoiesis, edited by J. M. Yoffey. London, E. Arnold, p. 73.
Axelrad, A. A. and R. A. Steeves, 1964, Virology *24*, 513.
Bradley, T. R. and M. A. Sumner, 1968, Aust. J. Exp. Biol. Med. Sci. *46*, 607.
Bruce, W. R. and B. E. Meeker, 1964, J. Natl. Cancer Instit. *32*, 1145.
Chan, S. H. and D. Metcalf, 1970, Nature *227*, 845.
Chan, S. H., D. Metcalf, and E. R. Stanley, 1971, Brit. J. Haematol. *20*, 329.
Clarkson, B. D., 1969, J. Natl. Cancer Instit. Monograph No. *30*, 81.
Foster, R., D. Metcalf, W. A. Robinson, and T. R. Bradley, 1968, Brit. J. Haematol. *15*, 147.
Foster, R. S., D. Metcalf, and J. Cortner, 1971, Cancer *27*, 881.
Friend, C., 1957, J. Exp. Med. *105*, 307.
Furth, J., 1959, Cancer Res. *19*, 241.
Gavosto, F., A. Pilieri, C. Bachi, and L. Pegoraro, 1964, Nature *193*, 92.
Hibberd, A. D. and D. Metcalf, 1971, Israel J. Med. Sci. *7*, 202.
Ichikawa, Y., 1969, J. Cell. Physiol. *74*, 223.
Ichikawa, Y., 1970, J. Cell. Physiol. *76*, 175.
Ichikawa, Y., D. H. Pluznik, and L. Sachs, 1966, Proc. Natl. Acad. Sci. *56*, 488.
Ichikawa, Y., D. H. Pluznik, and L. Sachs, 1967, Proc. Natl. Acad. Sci. *58*, 1480.
Ichikawa, Y., M. Paran, and L. Sachs, 1969, J. Cell. Physiol. *73*, 43.
Mauer, A. M. and V. Fisher, 1962, Nature *193*, 1085.
Mauer, A. M., E. F. Saunders, and B. C. Lampkin, 1969, J. Natl. Cancer Instit. Monograph *30*, 63.
McCulloch, E. A., L. Siminovitch, and J. E. Till, 1964, Science *144*, 844.
McEndy, D. P., M. C. Boon, and J. Furth, 1944, Cancer Res. *4*, 377.
Metcalf, D., 1966, The thymus. recent results in cancer research 5. Heidelberg-New York, Springer-Verlag.
Metcalf, D. and M. Brumby, 1967, Int. J. Cancer *2*, 37.
Metcalf, D. and R. Foster, 1967, J. Natl. Cancer Instit. *39*, 1235.
Metcalf, D. and M. A. S. Moore, 1970, J. Natl. Cancer Instit. *44*, 801.
Metcalf, D. and M. Wiadrowski, 1966, Cancer Res. *26*, 483.
Metcalf, D., J. Furth, and R. F. Buffett, 1959, Cancer Res. *19*, 52.
Metcalf, D., N. Sparrow, and R. Wyllie, 1962, Aust. J. Exp. Biol. Med. Sci. *40*, 215.
Metcalf, D., K. Nakamura, and M. Wiadrowski, 1965, Aust. J. Exp. Biol. and Med. Sci. *43*, 413.
Metcalf, D., M. Wiadrowski, and T. R. Bradley, 1966, National Cancer Institute Monograph *22*, 571.
Metcalf, D., T. R. Bradley, and W. Robinson, 1967a, J. Cell. Physiol. *69*, 93.
Metcalf, D., M. Ishidate, and M. Brumby, 1967b, J. Natl. Cancer Instit. *38*, 527.
Metcalf, D., M. A. S. Moore, and N. L. Warner, 1969, J. Natl. Cancer Instit. *43*, 983.
Metcalf, D., S. H. Chan, F. W. Gunz, P. Vincent, and R. B. M. Ravich, 1971, Blood (in press).
Mirand, E. A., 1966, Natl. Cancer Institute Monograph *22*, 483.
Mirand, E. A., 1968, Annals N.Y. Acad. Sci. *149*, 486.
Nowell, P. C., 1960, Cancer Res. *20*, 462.
Nowell, P. C. and D. A. Hungerford, 1960, J. Natl. Cancer Instit. *25*, 85.
Nowell, P. C. and D. A. Hungerford, 1961, J. Natl. Cancer Instit. *27*, 1013.
Paran, M., Y. Ichikawa, and L. Sachs, 1968, J. Cell. Physiol. *72*, 251.

Paran, M., Y. Ichikawa, and L. Sachs, 1969, Proc. Natl. Acad. Sci. *62*, 81.

Patuleia, M. C. and C. Friend, 1967, Cancer Res. *27*, 726.

Pike, B. L. and W. A. Robinson, 1970, J. Cell. Physiol. *76*, 77.

Pluznik, D. H., 1969, Israel J. Med. Sci. *5*, 306.

Pluznik, D. H. and L. Sachs, 1965, J. Cell. Physiol. *66*, 319.

Pluznik, D. H. and L. Sachs, 1966, Exp. Cell Research *43*, 553.

Pluznik, D. H., L. Sachs, and P. Resnitzky, 1966, J. Natl. Cancer Instit. Monograph *22*, 3.

Quaglino, D. and D. C. Cowling, 1964, Brit. J. Haematol. *10*, 358.

Robinson, W., D. Metcalf, and T. R. Bradley, 1967, J. Cell. Physiol. *69*, 83.

Robinson, W. A., J. E. Kurnick, and B. L. Pike, 1970, In: Proceedings XIII International Congress of Hematology. Munich, J. F. Lehmanns Verlag, p. 350 (Abs.).

Rytomaa, T., 1969, In: *In vitro* 4, edited by P. Farnes. Baltimore, Williams and Wilkins, p. 47.

Rytomaa, T. and K. Kiviniemi, 1968, Nature *220*, 136.

Sachs, L., 1968, In: Canadian cancer conference *8*, New York, Pergamon, Canada, p. 146.

Stanley, E. R. and D. Metcalf, 1969, Aust. J. Exp. Biol. Med. Sci. *47*, 467.

Stanley, E. R., T. A. McNeill, and S. H. Chan, 1970, Brit. J. Haematol. *18*, 585.

Till, J. E. and E. A. McCulloch, 1961, Radiat. Res. *14*, 213.

Wachstein, M., 1946, J. Lab. Clin. Med. *31*, 1.

Warner, N. L., M. A. S. Moore, and D. Metcalf, 1969, J. Natl. Cancer Instit. *43*, 963.

Whang, J., E. Frei, J. H. Tjio, P. P. Carbone, and G. Brecher, 1963, Blood *22*, 664.

CHAPTER 10

Genetic defects in haemopoiesis

10.1 Introduction

Experiments of nature are infrequent in their occurrence but invaluable to our understanding of the organisation and regulation of haemopoiesis. Recognition and analysis of mutations affecting haemopoiesis in the laboratory mouse in particular have revealed the complexity of haemopoietic control mechanisms, and credit for much of this work must go to the Jackson Laboratory. Its extensive studies studies of mouse anaemias produced by the action of mutant alleles at 11 different loci have been reviewed by Russell and Bernstein (1966). A more recent review was undertaken by Pinkerton and Bannerman (1968), and the earlier literature is reviewed by Gruneberg (1952), one of the pioneers in the field.

Defective development of the immunological apparatus has not to date been extensively analysed in the laboratory mouse though the recent recognition of a thymusless strain of mouse (Pantelouris 1968) may be a prelude to identification of a number of mutant mouse genes affecting immune responses and lymphoid development. A review of genetic defects of human haemopoiesis is also presented in this chapter, particularly the numerous forms of immunological deficiency diseases described since Bruton's (1952) original recognition of agammaglobulinaemia. R. A. Good and co-workers at Minneapolis in particular have been instrumental in classifying and analysing a bewildering variety of human immunological defects and placing these in the framework of known immunological mechanisms. Other human defects, such as the aregenerative anaemias and neutropenias, are briefly reviewed. Because in many instances, the clinical conditions are of unknown aetiology, it is our hope that by presenting these in the context of the review of recent advances in experimental haematology, some cross fertilisation of ideas between the clinical and experimental fields will accrue.

10.2 W series anaemias (gene symbol W, linkage group XVII)

The W allele was first described by Little (1915) as lethal in the homozygous mouse and producing a white spotting effect in heterozygotes. The cause of death of homozygotes was first attributed to severe anaemia by Detlefsen (1923). Germ-cell defects also characterise W series homozygotes resulting in sterility, absence of oogenesis and virtual aspermia (Fekete et al. 1941; Russell and Russell 1948). The pleiotropic effects of the W locus therefore influence haemopoiesis, germ cells and pigmentation. A number of dominant alleles at the W locus have subsequently been identified (W^v, W^j, W^s, W^b, W^x). The allele W^v discovered by Little and Cloudman (1937) causes a less severe anaemia, and viability of homozygous and heterozygous mice is considerably improved. For this reason most studies have been performed on the anaemic, but viable, W^v/W^v or W/W^v mice, particularly with two F_1 hybrid genetic backgrounds (WB/Re × C57BL/6J and WC/Re × C57BL/6J), which have proved particularly favourable for survival and vigour of the anaemic mutants (Russell and Bernstein 1966).

The anaemia of mice carrying two dominant W alleles (W/W, W/W^v, W^v/W^v) is of a severe macrocytic hypoplastic type. Total red-cell counts are 40–50 % of normal with haematocrits of 39–40 % and an increase in mean red-cell volume of 50 %. Heterozygous W/+ mice have a normal blood picture, while $W^v/+$ mice show a slight reduction in total red cells and a slight increase in the mean cell volume (Russell and Bernstein 1966; Bernstein et al. 1968). The various alleles of the W locus either in homozygous or heterozygous states can be ranked in the following order of progressively increasing severity of anaemia $+/+ = W/+ = W^j/+ < W^v/+ < W^v/W^v < W/W^v < W/W = W/W^j = W^j/W^j$ (Russell and Bernstein 1966). Normal numbers of circulating leucocytes and platelets have been reported in W/W^v mice (Lewis et al. 1967; Russell and Bernstein 1966), but a slight reduction in both elements was noted by Gruneberg (1939) and Fekete et al. (1941). De Aberle (1927) found reduced white-cell counts but normal platelet counts. Chervenick and Boggs (1969) found significantly fewer neutrophils and lymphocytes than normal in the circulation of W/W^v mice at 3 months, but not in older mice. These latter workers investigated the response of W/W^v mice to endotoxin and found a reduced blood neutrophilic response in the first few hours, but later the response was similar to that of normal mice. A slight reduction in absolute numbers of circulating reticulocytes has been reported (Bernstein et al. 1968).

Anaemia can be detected in W/W embryos at 14–16 days (De Aberle 1927;

Attfield 1951; Borghesa 1959) with 16% of normal numbers of red cells at 16 days and 14% at birth. Russell and McFarland (1965) reported significantly fewer nucleated erythrocytes at all stages in the circulation of W/W foetuses suggesting defective haemopoiesis as early as the yolk-sac phase of development. An extensive survey of haemopoiesis in W/W embryos was reported by Borghesa (1959). A generalised hypoplasia of liver haemopoietic tissue was seen as early as the 12th day of gestation, prior to the onset of anaemia. Reduced numbers of haemopoietic cells both erythroid and granulocytic, were evident and more immature stages of erythroid differentiation predominated. Onset of splenic haemopoiesis was delayed in anaemic mice and when established, fewer erythroid and granulocytic cells were present. Marrow haemopoiesis initiated on the 16th and 17th day of gestation is solely granulopoietic in the embryo and was extremely deficient in anaemic mice. Hypoplastic marrow was found at birth but near-normal cellularity has been reported in adult W/W^v and W^v/W^v marrow (Russell et al. 1953). Subsequent studies have shown reduced marrow cellularity in adult W anaemic mice (Bennett et al. 1968a; McCulloch et al. 1965a; Bernstein et al. 1968) but normal spleen cellularity (McCulloch et al. 1965a). The ratio of marrow erythroid to granulocytic cells in anaemic mice was normal but the ratio of early to late erythroid cells was abnormally high, suggesting impaired erythroid maturation, and there was also evidence of maturation arrest in the myeloid series (Russell et al. 1953). Evidence of delayed erythroid maturation was provided by Altman and Russell (1964), who showed that after isotopically-labelled haem precursors were injected, erythrocytes with labelled protoporphyrin appeared in the circulation of normal mice after 3 days but not until 10 days in W/W^v mice. Chervenick and Boggs (1969) found the absolute numbers of neutrophils to be significantly reduced, and there were approximately only half as many megakaryocytes in W/W^v marrow, but the distribution of granulocytes between the mitotic and post-mitotic compartments was normal. Marrow neutrophil response to endotoxin showed an initial depression and recovery but not the overshoot seen in normal mice. The haematological data suggest that the haemopoietic lesion in W anaemic mice is not confined solely to the erythroid series, but may involve granulocytes and megakaryocytes. The deficiencies of these latter populations may, however, be secondary to competition for a common stem cell and its direction into an ineffective line of erythroid differentiation. However, this view is unlikely, since Bennett et al. (1968a) observed that prolonged polycythaemia did not correct defective leucopoiesis.

The immune response of W/W^v mice was found to be normal by McCulloch et al. (1965b), but Shearer and Cudkowicz (1967) found that the antibody-forming cells (plaque-forming cells) to sheep erythrocytes were only one-third to one-half, of the normal number, in W^v/W^v spleens, and the frequency of haemolytic focus forming units in the spleen was only half normal. In contrast, Mekor and Phillips (1969) found that plaque-forming cells to sheep erythrocytes were not depressed in W/W^v but were in fact elevated. Bone marrow-thymus synergism in the generation of plaque-forming cells was also investigated by these workers and both W/W^v marrow and thymus cells were more active than normal in generating plaque-forming cells.

10.2.1 Response of W mice to erythropoietic stimuli
(erythropoietin, hypoxia, testosterone, and Friend virus)

Gruneberg (1939) first observed the response of W anaemic mice to hypoxia and noted a 75 % increase in erythrocytes. Subsequent studies have confirmed this hypoxic stimulation of erythropoiesis (Keighley et al. 1966; Fried et al. 1967). In contrast, the response of W/W^v polycythaemic mice to erythropoietin over a 1000-fold dose range was reduced in magnitude, and approximately 150 times more erythropoietin was required to elicit an effect in W/W^v than in normal mice (Keighley et al. 1966). Despite the defective response to exogenous erythropoietin, W/W^v erythropoiesis appears normally to be regulated by erythropoietin, since plasma erythropoietin can be detected in W/W^v mice and levels were slightly higher than normal (Keighley et al. 1966). Furthermore Schooley et al. (1968) reported that W/W^v mice injected with anti-erythropoietin serum showed a marked decrease, at 5 days, in the percentage of marrow erythroid cells, blood-iron incorporation and reticulo-cyte levels, with no change in the numbers of marrow CFU's. W/W^v poly-cythaemic mice did not respond to phenylhydrazine-induced anaemic plasma from humans, rabbits or isologous w/w mice nor to hypoxic w/w plasma. In contrast, W/W^v hypoxic plasma stimulated erythropoiesis in W/W^v mice, though the response was 2–3-fold greater in w/w mice (Mirand and Prentice 1964). Though W/W^v plasma erythropoietin levels are elevated 3-fold by hypoxia (Keighley et al. 1966) it is difficult to explain the observation of Mirand and Prentice solely on the basis of this elevation, since the differential sensitivity of normal and W mice to exogenous erythropoietin is 150-fold. It is an interesting possibility that some factor other than erythropoietin with a different site of action may come into play in the erythroid response to hypoxia, and may be particularly elevated in W/W^v hypoxic plasma. Keighley et al. (1966) considered this unlikely, since they observed that hypoxic anaemic W/W^v plasma did not elevate iron incorporation in polycythaemic W mice to anywhere near the extent seen in normal animals.

The response of W anaemic mice to hypoxia stands in marked contrast to their response to erythropoietin. Continuous hypoxia results in a parallel linear increase in haematocrit levels to a maximum after 18 days in both W/W^v and normal mice. Haematocrit levels in W/W^v mice reached 58–60% (from 38%) and were only 6.5% lower than those of the normal hypoxic mice (Keighley et al. 1966; Bernstein et al. 1968). Marrow CFU levels remained unchanged during hypoxic stimulation (Fried et al. 1967). The response of polycythaemic W/W^v mice to graded brief periods of hypoxia was lower than in $+/+$ mice but the difference between genotypes was not as great as observed with exogenous erythropoietin (Keighley et al. 1966). These latter workers proposed that this near-normal response to hypoxia was not erythropoietin-mediated, but represented a direct effect of hypoxia on blood-forming tissues which was quantitatively more important in W anaemic mice. Testosterone was also reported to augment erythropoiesis in W/W^v mice, increasing red-cell mass by 45–50% and haemoglobin concentration and haematocrit by 20–25% (Fried et al. 1967).

Friend leukaemia virus induces hypervolaemic polycythaemia and macroscopic foci of erythroid cells proliferating independently of erythropoietin in spleens of susceptible mice (see Chapter 9). The influence of the W locus on susceptibility to Friend's spleen focus-forming virus was studied by Steeves et al. (1968). It was found that W/W^v mice were absolutely resistant to the virus, suggesting that the target cell for the virus was defective. The heterozygote W^v/+ was also refractory, but W/+ mice were fully susceptible. Since both heterozygotes respond equally well to erythropoietin (suggesting equal numbers of ESC's) and yet both show defective capacity to produce spleen colonies on transplantation (suggesting equally deficient CFU's) Steeves et al. (1968) suggested that the target cell was not a stem cell but rather a cell intermediate between the stem cell and the erythropoietin-sensitive cell. A monopotent erythroid colony-forming cell was suggested as the target cell; however, the existence of such a cell type has not been demonstrated in normal mice (see Chapter 3).

Alternatively, the virus may act on a target cell at a critical stage immediately following gene activation associated with differentiation from the stem cell to the ESC but prior to the expression of erythropoietin receptor sites on the membrane of these cells. Differing alleles at the W locus may influence to different extents the duration of this transitional phase and hence lead to variations in the number of target cells independent of the numbers of erythropoietin-sensitive cells and stem cells.

10.2.2   Cell grafting in W/W^v mice

w/w haemopoietic cells can colonise non-irradiated W/W^v hosts and restore a normal blood picture. Recovery was accelerated when the recipient was irradiated with 200 R (Bernstein and Russell 1959). W/W^v mice can be 'cured' with allogeneic (H2-compatible) foetal liver cells and even in some allogeneic combinations where skin grafts were rejected, haemopoietic grafts ameliorated the anaemia (Russell and Bernstein 1967). Colonisation of tolerant W/W^v mice by allogeneic CBA haemopoietic cells was detected by donor haemoglobin production (Seller and Polini 1966; Seller 1968a) and by chromosome-marker analysis which revealed that 9–18 months after injection nearly all dividing cells in the host's marrow, spleen, thymus and lymph nodes were donor in type (Seller 1968b). W series mice were also completely cured by histocompatible Steel (Sl/Sl) anaemic marrow and such chimaeras responded to erythropoietin in a perfectly normal way (Bernstein et al. 1968).

McCulloch et al. (1964) showed that anaemic unirradiated mice of geno-type W/W^v developed spleen colonies following injection of marrow from normal donors. The number of such colonies was linearly related to the dose of cells injected, and erythroid colonies were suppressed in hypertransfused recipients. Growth of donor CFU's in unirradiated W/W^v spleens was delayed in comparison with growth in normal heavily irradiated animals but the 2-hour seeding factors (f) were similar in the unirradiated W/W^v and in the irradiated normal spleen. Donor CFU proliferation in W/W^v spleens was uninfluenced by hypertransfusion (Till et al. 1967).

10.2.3   Stem cells and progenitor cells in W anaemic mice

Homozygous anaemic mice are extremely radiosensitive with an $LD_{50/30}$ of 250–350 R compared to 700–750 R in normal littermates. An intermediate radiosensitivity was seen in the heterozygotes, W^v/w and W/w (Bernstein 1962). Following sublethal (200 R) irradiation, erythroid regeneration was delayed, whereas granulocyte repopulation was closer to normal (Russell et al. 1963). McCulloch et al. (1965a, b, c) observed a gross deficiency in *in vivo* CFU's in W/W^v anaemic marrow when assayed in either normal or W/W^v irradiated recipients. As few as 0.005 CFU's per 10^5 anaemic marrow cells were found, in contrast to coisogenic normal marrow values of 12.2 per 10^5. W/W^v-derived spleen colonies were very small and most lay deep within the spleen (Lewis et al. 1965, 1967). Histological studies showed that only 11% of these colonies were erythroid and the predominant colony type was granulocytic (75%). The impaired growth of W/W^v colonies was particularly evident with erythroid colonies where even the largest were only one-tenth of the diameter of normal at day 8 of growth. Defective growth of granulocytic colonies was also detected and at 9 days of development; these corresponded in size to normal colonies of 5–6 days' development (Lewis et al. 1965, 1967). The haemopoietic defect therefore affects early stages of growth and development of all types of colonies but particularly the most rapidly growing erythroid clones. The discrepancy between the data of McCulloch et al. (1965a, b, c), showing very severe depression of CFU's, and that of Lewis et al. (1965, 1967), who found a depression of only 20–25% of normal is due to the enumeration of spleen colonies by histological techniques by the latter workers with consequent inclusion of the large number of small, underdeveloped, colonies that are not seen macroscopically. W^v/+ heterozygous marrow contained more CFU's than in the homozygote, but erythroid colonies showed defective growth and were only a quarter to half the diameter of coisogenic normal colonies of the same age on the 9th day but reached normal or near normal size at later stages of colony development (Bennett et al. 1968a). Bennett and Cudkowicz (1966) used ^{59}Fe and IUdR incorporation to study haemopoietic regeneration following transfer of W/W^v and W^v/W^v marrow into normal or polycythaemic coisogenic irradiated mice. Both erythroid and leucopoietic regeneration were defective. Heterozygous W/+, W^b/+ or W^v/+ marrow grafts also produced subnormal repopulation but were less defective than homozygous marrow, suggesting a gene-dosage effect. Defective leucopoiesis was not secondary to anaemia since prolonged polycythaemia did not correct this (Bennett et al. 1968a). *In vitro* colony-forming cells in W^v/W^v or W^v/+ marrow were neither decreased in number nor impaired in *in vitro* proliferation and differentiation (Bennett et al. 1968a). It is possible that many of the microscopic granulocytic colonies appearing in the spleen following W/W^v marrow grafting are produced by proliferation of *in vitro* CFC's rather than CFU's.

In situations where W/W^v marrow was injected into irradiated coisogenic recipients, greatly impaired CFU recovery was seen with prolongation of the lag phase prior to exponential recovery, and a considerable increase in the CFU doubling time (Sutherland et al. 1970). The regeneration of *in vitro* CFC's and peroxidase-positive cells in this situation was impaired to a modest degree, but since *in vitro* CFC regeneration is dependent on CFU differentiation rather than *in vitro* CFC self-renewal, impaired *in vitro* CFC recovery was presumably secondary to defective CFU proliferation. It appears therefore that W alleles influence both erythropoiesis and granulo-poiesis by an action at, or near, the beginning of haemopoietic differentiation at the stem cell rather than the progenitor cell level.

10.2.4   Pigment defects in W mice

Homozygous W mice are black-eyed with white coats, and the heterozygotes show variable degrees of white spotting. Defective pigmentation is due to absence of melanocytes in hair follicles. Dendritic melanocytes of the choroid layer of the eye are also absent and share with skin melanocytes a common origin from neural crest. Black-eye pigmentation in these mice is due to melanin production by retinal-epithelial cells derived embryologically from the optic cup. Mayer and Green (1968) grew 11-day mouse embryo skin together with 9-day neural crest in a chick embryo-grafting system and obtained pigmentation of W skin when cultured with normal neural crest but not with W neural crest. The pigment defect consequently resides in a defective neural-crest production of melanoblasts (or their precursors) with consequent failure of melanocyte migration into the skin.

10.2.5   Sterility in W mice

Germ-cell defects were first reported by Fekete et al. (1941) and the early data was reviewed by Borghesa (1959), who also showed that the testes and ovaries of W/W embryos were smaller than normal and nearly devoid of germ cells. The gonadal defect was not reversed by grafting into non-anaemic recipients (Russell and Russell 1948). Using an alkaline-phosphatase staining procedure to identify primordial germ cells, Mintz and Russell (1955, 1957) showed these cells were abnormal in number and location in W homozygous embryos. The abnormality appeared to be due to defective multiplication of primordial germ cells in the course of migration to the germinal ridges from the yolk sac on the 8th–9th day of gestation.

10.3   Steel anaemias (Sl, linkage group IV)

The Steel locus was first described by Sarvella and Russell (1956) and over

30 mutations have been described at this highly mutable locus (Russell and Bernstein 1966). Sl/Sl homozygotes die at 15 days' gestation but the homozygous allelic mutant Steel-Dickie (Sl^d/Sl^d) and the heterozygote Sl/Sl^d are viable. 20–25% survive to 30 days and the mean survival is 79–113 days. Sl homozygotes display the same triad of defects seen in the W-series anaemias, namely severe macrocytic anaemia, sterility, and lack of hair pigmentation. Linkage studies have shown that the Steel locus is located in linkage group IV and is not linked with W in group XVII (Wolfe 1963; Nash 1964).

The anaemia is first detected at 14 days' gestation by paleness of affected embryos and reduction of erythrocyte number to 28% of normal (Bennett 1956). The anaemia persisted into adult life with red-cell counts 40–50% of normal, haematocrits 39% and mean red-cell volume increased to 81 u^3 indicating a severe macrocytic anaemia (Russell and Bernstein 1966; Kales et al. 1966). In embryogenesis no change in the cell volume of the yolk-sac generation of primitive erythrocytes was found, despite decrease in numbers and more rapid elimination of these cells, which suggested that the Steel defect affected the primitive as well as the intermediate and definitive generations of erythropoiesis (Bennett 1956). Foetal liver and marrow showed marked reduction in haemopoiesis and shaft counts were approximately half normal values. Leucocyte levels in Sl/Sl^d mice appear normal. Lymphoid regeneration and haemolysin responses and homograft rejection were also normal (McCulloch et al. 1965c).

10.3.1   Tissue grafting in Steel mice

Irradiated Sl/Sl^d mice given normal marrow cells showed defective initial localisation of CFU's in the spleen and little or no proliferation during a 10-day period with no increase in spleen cellularity and no formation of spleen colonies (McCulloch et al. 1965a, b, c). In a more recent study, normal coisogenic marrow was injected into heavily irradiated Sl/Sl^d mice, and impaired CFU growth was demonstrated since only a 2-fold increase in spleen CFU numbers was observed by eight days (Sutherland et al. 1970). The Sl influence was less evident in the marrow environment where a 5- to 10-fold increase in CFU's was seen in the same 8-day period. The Sl/Sl^d recipients also showed a modest impairment in the recovery of the *in vitro* CFC's and peroxidase-positive cell populations. In contrast, Sl/Sl^d marrow in irradiated normal mice produced spleen colonies with a similar frequency and of similar morphology to those seen following normal marrow grafting and Sl/Sl^d CFU's showed normal growth in +/+ spleens (McCulloch et al.

1965a, b, c). *In vitro* irradiation of Sl/Sl^d marrow followed by grafting to +/+ irradiated recipients demonstrated the normal radiosensitivity of Steel CFU's (McCulloch et al. 1965a). Consequently the extreme radiosensitivity of Sl mice (LD$_{50/30}$ = 100–200 R) is probably not due to any defect either quantitative or qualitative intrinsic to the stem cells (McCulloch et al. 1965a, b, c; Russell and Bernstein 1966). The different basis for the macrocytic anaemias of Sl and W mice was demonstrated in experiments, where Sl^d/Sl marrow cells transplanted to W series anaemic recipients, cured the anaemia of the latter (Russell and Bernstein 1966; McCulloch et al. 1965a). Furthermore, intact grafts of W spleen or bone marrow (but not cell suspensions) cured Steel anaemic mice and haemopoiesis in the grafts was of host type (Holmes, M. and S. Bernstein, 1970, personal communication). The Steel defect apparently involves an environmental factor that interferes with proliferation of haemopoietic stem cells in the spleen and, to a lesser degree, marrow. This factor is not humoral since Steel mice parabiosed with normal mice did not show any improvement in growth of injected CFU's following irradiation, despite normal proliferation in the +/+ parabiotic partner (McCulloch et al. 1965a). Despite the environmental defect, irradiated Steel mice gave a normal haemolysin plaque-forming cell response to sheep erythrocytes following injection of normal (+/+) thymus cells plus bone-marrow cells and antigen (Mekor and Phillips 1969), indicating that the environment is satisfactory for an immune response.

10.3.2 Influence of erythropoietin and other factors on haemopoiesis in Steel mice

Sl/Sl^d serum contains significant quantities of erythropoietin yet these mice are unresponsive to massive doses of exogenous erythropoietin (up to a 1000-fold the minimum effective dose in normal mice) (Kales et al. 1966; Bernstein et al. 1968). However, normal irradiated mice restored with Steel marrow showed normal erythropoietin responses. Unlike W/W^v mice, the response to hypoxia was grossly deficient, with many mice dying, and the survivors showing only a slight increase in haematocrit (Kales et al. 1966; Bernstein et al. 1968). The latter investigators showed, however, that Steel mice greatly increased their haematocrit in response to intermittent hypoxia, and it would thus appear that these mice can eventually respond to hypoxia but have difficulty in adapting to a sudden and constant hypoxic stimulus. Bennett et al. (1968b) observed that Sl/Sl^d mice were completely resistant to Friend spleen focus-forming virus and the heterozygous Sl/+ and Sl^d/+

were relatively resistant. Normal marrow was also insensitive to the virus when present in the Steel environment. The Steel locus appears to affect the environment of target cells so that they are no longer available for infection or no longer able to form viral-induced foci. A defective response to endotoxin was reported by Till et al. (1968) since Sl/Sl^d mice showed no increase in spleen CFU content after endotoxin in contrast to a 10-fold increase produced in normal animals. *In vitro* CFC's did, however, respond to endotoxin stimulation in both normal (McNeill 1970) and Sl/Sl^d mice and *in vitro* CFC numbers increased from $2-6/10^6$ up to $20-100/10^6$ in the spleen of Sl/Sl^d mice following endotoxin treatment (McCulloch et al. 1970).

10.3.3   Sterility in Steel mice

The gonads of homozygous Sl mice were found to be completely devoid of germ cells and heterozygotes showed impaired oogenesis and spermatogenesis (Bennett 1956). A marked decrease in primordial germ cells was seen in 9-day embryos with no germ cells in the gonadal ridges and a variable reduction in the numbers in gut and allantoic regions. In addition to defective numbers, distribution was abnormal with clumps of primordial germ cells in the allantoic region and gut in contrast to the random scattering of cells seen in normal embryos (Bennett 1956). It was suggested by Bennett, that defective migration and/or proliferation of primordial germ cells led to their clumping and that this was the basis of the sterility seen in the Steel mice.

10.3.4   Pigmentation in Steel mice

Sl homozygous mice are black-eyed white and heterozygotes displayed dilution of coat colour. The absence of melanocytes in the skin of homozygous mice was not cured by grafting to pigmented recipients (Bennett 1956). Mayer and Green (1968) grafted combinations of Sl/Sl^d and $+/+$ normal embryonic skin and neural tube to chick embryos. No defect in Sl neural crest cells was noted since they produced pigmentation of normal skin. However, a defect resided in Sl skin since many skin grafts remained unpigmented even in the presence of normal neural crest tissue.

10.4 Speculation on the nature of the defect in Sl and W mice

Any consideration of the basis of W and Sl gene action must include the effects on germ cells and pigmentation as well as haemopoiesis. If the premise of a unitary gene action is valid, there must be one lesion which leads to defects in all these systems. Our attention must therefore be directed to revealing common factors in the regulation of the three cell types under discussion; haemopoietic stem cells, primordial germ cells, and melanoblast precursors. All three cell types possess multipotential differentiation capacities, migration ability from site of production to site of differentiation, self-replication capacity, interaction with other cell types regulating their differentiation, and an early embryological origin.

Most primordial germ cells and haemopoietic stem cells first develop in the yolk sac in the mouse embryo between 7–12 days' gestation (Moore and Metcalf 1970; Mintz and Russell 1957). The number of primordial germ cells (PGC) produced by the yolk sac is small (less than 100). These multiply to 5000 or more during the period of migration to the gonadal ridges. Germ-cell migration is claimed to be via the dorsal gut mesentry to the gonadal ridges in the mouse (Mintz and Russell 1957). Studies in the chick embryo indicate a vascular route for migration. Simon (1960) excised the germinal crescent of early chick embryos and found *in vitro* that no primordial germ cells developed in the gonads. When two blastoderms were parabiosed *in vitro* and a vascular anastomosis established, PGC's appeared in the gonads of an embryo whose germinal crescent had been excised, and transanastomotic vascular migration of germ cells was therefore strongly indicated. In the absence of gonadal rudiments, PGC's migrated from the yolk sac to the posterior region of the embryo and collected there but did not attach to the coelomic wall (Simon 1960; Wolff and Haffen 1965). Evidence for a strikingly similar developmental process in the case of haemopoietic stem cells was reviewed in Chapter 4, and briefly the results indicated that comparatively few haemopoietic stem cells develop in yolk-sac blood islands between 7–12 days' gestation, and these migrate via the circulation into the embryo where self-replication in the foetal liver expands the initial population. This liver population is responsible, after a sequence of migration to other organs and proliferation, for the establishment of the whole adult haemopoietic system.

The origin of melanoblasts has much in common with the origin of haemopoietic stem cells and PGC's. Primordial melanoblasts originate in the neural crest during the 8th–12th day of foetal development in the mouse, and migrate laterally to their defined location in the hair-bulb matrix of the receiving hair follicles (Wolfe and Coleman 1966). Mintz (1967) in a study of pigmentation in allophenic mice, produced by fusion of pairs of developing mouse eggs of different genotypes, observed a regular banding or striping of coat pigmentation. She interpreted this observation as evidence for a small population of some 34 primordial melanoblasts, each one responsible for clonal production of the melanocytes producing pigmentation of a particular area of skin. Russell and Mayer (1957) estimated from the size of colour spots induced by irradiating embryos that only 150–200 prospective pigment cells existed at $10\frac{1}{4}$ days' gestation. This number is in accord with a lower primordial number at the outset of neural crest migration on the 8th day of gestation. Weston and Butler (1966) studied neural crest migration using thymidine labelling and tissue grafting to chick embryos and concluded that pluripotent neural crest cells were not directed in their migration but rather that the precise localisation of migrating crest cells was governed by non-specific extrinsic factors combined with progressive changes in the adhesive properties of the cells themselves. Cells widely distributed in ectoderm, produced pigment, whereas the same cells aggregated and condensed in the midst of somatic mesenchyme established conditions appropriate for expression of neural traits such as ganglia formation, etc.

The lesion in W mice is most probably intrinsic to the W haemopoietic stem cell, PGC, and primordial melanoblasts, whereas in Sl mice the defect is in the environment into which the cells migrate, i.e. the haemopoietic microenvironment, the skin and the gonads. We suggest here as a unifying hypothesis that the three cell types under discussion bear on their cell surface receptor sites that are complementary, with specific macromolecules present on the surface of the cells forming part of the stroma of the organ of localisation. Since the defect in W mice involves intrinsic lesions in the three cell types concerned, this would suggest defects in receptor sites on the surfaces of these cells which we shall refer to as the W-defect. Conversely the impairment in Sl mice is related to a defect in the receptors on the microenvironmental cells which we shall term the Sl-defect. The effects of the genetic defects at the W and Sl loci are not additive, which suggests that the two genes control factors which, though not absolutely required, facilitate stem-cell proliferation (Sutherland et al. 1970). Furthermore, the defects are more apparent in the spleen than in the marrow, suggesting interorgan variation in the importance of the interaction between the stem cell and the microenvironment. Tissue formation in embryogenesis requires inductive interactions between cells, and Moscona (1963) has proposed that the specificity of tissue formation is due to interactions between complementary macromolecules on the cell surfaces. Recently Crandall and Brock (1968) have reported an interesting microbial model of cell interaction in their study of two mating types, strains 5 and 21 of a sexually agglutinated yeast

Agglutination of the two strains was due to cell surface glycoproteins, which interacted in the manner of antibody and antigen. Isolated strain 21 factor was specifically and completely absorbed only by strain 5, and *vice versa*. It is tempting to equate the W and Sl factors with specifically-aggregating cell surface glycoproteins. However, isolation of such complementary substances may prove difficult in mammalian tissue systems, both because of low concentrations and possible complexing of complementary receptors which may prevent their detection.

Can the above proposal satisfactorily account for the defects seen? In the case of cell migration, Weiss (1967) has proposed three ways in which cells get from one point to another with specificity: (a) by guidance involving ordered movement, (b) selective fixation in which randomly moving cells are trapped in selective sites, and (c) selective disposal in which both cell movement and trapping are random but cells are selectively destroyed (or cannot survive) in certain sites. In the systems under review the latter two mechanisms are probably operative but would require a recognition process involving the migrating cell and its environment. This recognition process could result in a simple trapping or aggregation, or may involve a specific stimulus to the immigrant cell to proliferate and/or differentiate. In the case of haemopoiesis, the importance of the spleen and marrow environment, not only for trapping circulating stem cells but also for directing self-replication and differentiation, has been discussed in earlier chapters.

Variation in severity of anaemia and sterility associated with the various alleles of the W and Sl loci can be explained as variations in the degree to which the possible amino acid stubstitutions in the W or Sl substances influences their complementarity and hence their efficiency or affinity in interaction. The observation that the haemopoietic lesions are predominantly erythroid, may simply reflect the greater cellular flux and greater stem-cell demand for the erythroid line (Bennett et al. 1968a). The apparently normal population of immunologically competent cells in W and Sl mice may like-wise indicate the low numbers of uncommitted stem cells required to maintain a normal lymphocyte population size. Alternatively, the stem cells in the lymphoid system may be able to differentiate normally in the thymic and bursal-equivalent epithelial environment though not in a mesenchymal one. The capacity of the mutant spleen to support normal immune reactions may also be explained by the non-involvement of stem cells but, rather, precommitted lymphoid progenitor cells that have secondarily migrated to the spleen environment.

10.5 Anaemia of flexed tail mice (f, linkage group XIV)

This transitory siderocytic anaemia arose as a spontaneous mutant and be-
haves as an autosomal recessive characteristic (Hunt and Permar 1928;
Gruneberg 1942a). The effects of this recessive gene, flexed (f), are first
detectable by the 13–15th day of gestation as a reduction in the numbers of
red cells of the intermediate foetal liver generation. Furthermore, even at this
stage the red cells are characteristically abnormal, containing little haemoglobin and many siderocytic granules detected by Prussian blue staining
(Kamenoff 1935; Gruneberg 1942b). Yolk-sac erythropoiesis appeared little
affected since cells of the primitive generation of erythrocytes were present in
normal numbers and showed abundant haemoglobinisation (Gruneberg
1942a, b). However, Russell and McFarland (1965) reported that though the
primitive generation erythrocytes were present in f/f foetuses in normal
numbers on the 12th day of gestation significantly fewer than normal were
found by the 16th day. By birth, f/f mice have less than half the normal
concentration of haemoglobin and 70–92 % of the erythrocytes are siderocytic
(Gruneberg 1942a, b). The situation rapidly improves, however, and by 7
days, red-cell numbers are near-normal and haemoglobin content of blood
considerably increased while the proportion of siderocytes drops rapidly to
3 % in this time (Gruneberg 1942a) although siderocytes are present throughout the life of the animal.

   The defect in f/f haemopoiesis is not due to deficiency in numbers of stem
cells since Thompson et al. (1966a) and McCulloch et al. (1965c) found no
reduction in numbers of spleen colonies formed by either foetal liver or by
marrow cells of 8-weeks or 7-months old adults. However, histological
studies showed that erythroid cells were much rarer in f/f colonies, and colonies derived from both adult and embryonic cells had a predominantly
granulocytic appearance. f/f spleen colonies were also considerably smaller
than normal and showed depressed ^{59}Fe incorporation but were not defective in CFU content (Thompson et al. 1966a; McCulloch et al. 1965c). Since
defective erythropoiesis is seen in spleen colonies of adult origin, the apparent
cure of the anaemia with increasing age cannot be explained by a change in
gene action. Transplanted f/f and normal marrow cells were compared for
their ability to incorporate ^{59}Fe in the spleen of irradiated recipients. By
9 days maximum iron incorporation was observed with normal marrow cells,
but with f/f marrow cells this was delayed until 13 days, although thereafter
the two groups showed similar iron incorporation (Thompson et al. 1966a).
The defect was intrinsic to the f/f haemopoietic cells, as was shown by

reconstituting f/f mice with normal haemopoietic cells, and *vice versa*, but was only manifest under conditions of rapid expansion of haemopoietic tissue found in the foetal liver or during the early phases of regeneration in adult animals but not under steady-state conditions.

The iron accumulation suggests defective haem or globin synthesis and impaired activity of the enzyme delta-aminolevulinate dehydratase (ALD) has been shown by Margolis and Russell (1965). This enzyme condenses delta-aminolevulinic acid to form porphorobilinogen and both f/f and f/+ adult mice had ALD levels in liver and spleen that were one-third of normal. Haemolysis induced by phenylhydrazine had only a slight effect on ALD activity in f/f mice in contrast to the marked increase seen in normal mice, and the intermediate effect in heterozygous f/+ mice (Margolis and Russell 1965). This dehydratase effect of the f gene is dominant in contrast to all other effects of the gene, which appear to be recessive (Russell and Bernstein 1966). Alternatively, changes in enzyme levels may simply reflect the changes in rate of erythropoiesis (Tengerdy 1966) and thus the low levels of ALD activity in phenylhydrazine-treated f/f mice would be a consequence, rather than a cause, of the defect in erythropoiesis (Fowler et al. 1967).

The defect in haemopoiesis in f/f mice is specific for erythropoiesis and no defects in capacity to produce CFU's or granulocytic elements have been detected, but the data of Fowler et al. (1967) indicate that the f locus regulates a step in erythropoiesis occurring prior to the acquisition of capacity for haemoglobin synthesis. Using ^{59}Fe autoradiography to measure rates of haemoglobin synthesis in individual cells these workers showed that cells of f/f genotype incorporated ^{59}Fe at a normal rate; however, f/f grafts produced fewer iron-incorporating cells than normal. The defect probably operates at the level of erythropoietin-sensitive cell, i.e. at the progenitor rather than the stem-cell level, and may be a quantitative defect in the size of this population or a qualitative defect influencing the rate at which the erythropoietin-sensitive cells can move into the pro-erythroblast compartment.

The associated abnormalities of rigid flexus of the tail, and also in many individuals a white belly spot were considered by Gruneberg (1942a) to be secondary to the anaemia which caused a general retardation of development during the sensitive periods of differentiation of intervertebral discs and melanocytes. However, skeletal abnormalities do not appear in W anaemic mice which are anaemic at approximately the same stage of development, and consequently the secondary nature or otherwise of the non-haemopoietic defects in flexed tail mice remains an open question.

10.6 Sex-linked anaemia (sla, linkage group XX)

This mild anaemia was first noted by Falconer and Isaacson (1962) among
the male offspring of the daughter of a male mouse which had received
500 R X-rays. Linkage studies showed the sla gene lay on the X chromosome
(Grewal 1962). As originally described the anaemia was characterised by a
haemoglobin concentration 57–81% of normal, slight microcytosis, some
hypochromia and a mild reticulocytosis. Subsequent studies of this anaemia
on a different genetic background revealed a more severe anaemia with
haemoglobin levels between 4–8 gm per 100 ml but with relatively less
reduction in haematocrit and red-cell count (Bannerman and Cooper 1966;
Bannerman and Pinkerton 1967).

Erythropoiesis was normal in irradiated normal mice rendered chimaeric
with sla marrow or spleen cell grafts indicating that the defect was not
intrinsic to the haemopoietic cells but that the primary action resided outside
the erythron (Bennett et al. 1968c). This is also indicated by the absence of a
dual red-cell population in heterozygotes which would be expected on the
basis of X-chromosome inactivation. Histochemical studies revealed defective iron storage particularly in the spleen but with excessive iron deposition
in the mucosal epithelium of the intestine (Pinkerton and Bannerman 1966).
Intestinal iron absorption was significantly less in sla mice and serum iron
and total body iron were both reduced. The diagnosis of iron deficiency
anaemia due to iron malabsorption was supported by evidence that ^{59}Fe
tracer was very effectively utilised and cleared from the plasma after intravenous injection, which is a characteristic of iron deficiency, and free
protoporphyrin levels were elevated; indicating failure of delivery of iron to
the erythroid cells due to failure of mucosal iron transfer (Pinkerton and
Bannerman 1967, 1968; Pinkerton 1968). Therapy with iron dextran administered intraperitoneally produced an immediate rise in haematocrit.

The capacity of sla progenitor and stem cells to engage in erythropoiesis
and leukopoiesis was tested by transferring sla spleen and marrow cells to
irradiated normal or polycythaemic recipients and assaying proliferation by
IUdR and ^{59}Fe uptake. Sla marrow was somewhat defective in proliferative
capacity; however, sla spleen, which was enlarged 3–4-fold, showed a 20-fold
increase in erythroid progenitor cells and a less striking elevation of leukopoietic progenitor cells (Bennett et al. 1968c). This increased spleen potential
for haemopoiesis, particularly erythropoiesis, was reversed by iron dextran
therapy, which reduced spleen cellularity and erythroid progenitor cells to
normal (Bennett et al. 1968c). The anaemia improved spontaneously with

age, but even in older mice iron deficiency was still evident suggesting that improvement with age reflected a more favourable iron balance due to decreased iron requirements (Pinkerton 1968).

10.7. Hertwig's anaemia (an, linkage group VIII)

This autosomal recessive macrocytic anaemia was discovered among the offspring of a heavily irradiated male mouse (Hertwig 1942). Homozygous an/an mice rarely survive more than a few days after birth and only 4% survive for more than 1 month with erythrocyte counts of $3-5 \times 10^6$ RBC/cubic mm (Kunze 1954). Inbreeding and enforced heterozygosity for an/+ resulted in improved survival with a mean survival time of 212 days (McFarland and Russell 1966; cited by Russell and Bernstein 1966). Macrocytosis and anisocytosis characterise this anaemia, and erythrocyte counts are 30–50% of normal. Reticulocyte levels also are reduced indicating defective erythrocyte production, and white-cell counts are low (Kunze 1954). Defective haemopoiesis was seen as early as 12–13 days' gestation in foetal liver with initially an abnormally high proportion of proerythroblasts and by 14 days' gestation, a reduction in the intermediate generation of circulating erythrocytes. Complete regression of foetal liver erythropoiesis occurred 4 days after birth, 6 days earlier than normal. Adult marrow showed decreased haemopoiesis, and the presence of megaloblastic haemopoiesis indicating maturation arrest of the erythroid series (Kunze 1954; Hertwig 1956). The spleen was very small in the young anaemic mice but became larger than normal in adults (Thoms 1951).

The basis of the defect in Hertwig's anaemia is obscure, but increased rates of haemolysis of ^{51}Cr-labelled an/an erythrocytes have been observed (Thompson et al. 1966b). A further defect was noted in the number of CFU's produced by an/an marrow in normal, irradiated recipients. The number of colonies formed depended on the age of the donor and only donor marrows older than 8 weeks produced normal colonies and showed normal colony-forming efficiency. However, donors of all ages produced spleen colonies of smaller size than normal and such colonies were predominantly defective in erythropoiesis, although defective granulopoiesis and stem-cell self-renewal were also evident (Thompson et al. 1966a; Pinkerton and Bannerman 1968). The defect has some similarities to that seen in the W series of anaemias, probably involving an intrinsic defect of the haemopoietic stem cell influencing its rate of proliferation and consequently the ability to support optimal erythropoiesis and granulopoiesis. In this context, sterility and failure of gonadal development were seen in adult an/an mice (Kunze 1954) but absence of pigmentation defects, and the linkage data clearly distinguish the genetic basis of Hertwig's anaemia from that of the W series.

10.8 Inherited microcytic anaemia (mk)

This autosomal recessive anaemia arose spontaneously and anaemic mice were observed in a newborn litter in a mixed stock involving C3H, C57BL and DBA/2 ancestors (Nash et al. 1964; Russell and Bernstein 1966). Neonatal mk mice were pale at birth but erythrocyte numbers were normal. However, erythrocyte volume was only half normal. The microcytosis was compensated by an increase in red-cell number and by 8 weeks the average red-cell count of 13×10^6/cubic mm was almost 50% higher than in normal litter mates, but microcytosis and hypochromia persisted. Reticulocyte percentages were also significantly elevated in microcytic mice. The metabolic disturbance in mk mice is unknown, but is probably confined to erythrocyte maturation.

10.9 Transitory anaemia of 'tail-short' mice (Ts)

This mutation first arose in BALB/c mice and is semi-dominant and lethal in a homozygous state (Deol 1961). The effects of this gene were first recognised in adults, as skeletal abnormalities particularly affecting the tail. However, Deol (1961) noted a marked anaemia in Ts/+ embryos at 14 days' gestation with reduced numbers of pale thin blood vessels in the embryo, placenta, and yolk sac. Between 16 days and birth, the anaemia disappeared and at birth no abnormalities in the blood picture was seen. The haemopoietic defect in Ts mice is probably confined to the yolk-sac phase of haemopoiesis, and as early as 8 days' gestation the effects of the mutation were manifest as abnormalities in yolk-sac development consisting of reduction in numbers of blood islands with consequent reduction in numbers of primitive-generation erythrocytes appearing in the circulation first noted at 9 days of gestation. It is possible that the defect in numbers of blood islands reflects a deficiency in numbers of haemangioblasts or haemangioblast-precursors that migrate into the yolk sac from the primitive-streak region. A defect of this nature would reduce the number, but not the size, of blood islands.

An alternative defect involving deficient inductive interaction between yolk-sac endoderm and mesoderm, which precedes erythroid differentiation would be more likely to affect the size, rather than the number, of individual blood islands, and this was not evident in the data presented by Deol (1961). It is highly probable that the skeletal defects are secondary to this very early onset of transitory anaemia.

10.10 Anaemia of 'diminutive' mice (dm, linkage group V)

This autosomal recessive mutant gene produces growth retardation, multiple skeletal anomalies of the entire axial skeleton and a severe neonatal macrocytic anaemia (Stevens and Mackensen 1958). Newborn mice had approximately one-third of normal numbers of erythrocytes and mean erythrocyte volume was increased by 40%. This macrocytic anaemia persisted throughout life but was less extreme in surviving adults who may be fertile. The basis of this defect is unknown, but as anaemia is present at birth, both foetal liver and adult marrow erythropoiesis must be affected.

10.11 Mouse haemolytic anaemias

10.11.1 Hereditary spherocytosis (sph)

A severe haemolytic anaemia was reported by Joe et al. (1962), arising spontaneously in a C3H mouse and behaving as an autosomal recessive defect. Affected mice were detected at birth by their pale colour and rapid development of jaundice. Homozygous sph/sph mice died within 24 hours. Haemoglobin levels and haematocrits were only 25% of normal and erythrocytes were microcytic. Reticulocyte levels were very high and nucleated erythrocytes, numerous siderocytes and spherocytes were seen.

10.11.2 Haemolytic anaemia (ha)

This recessive haemolytic anaemia is controlled by a locus unrelated to sph and presents as a severe, persisting haemolytic disease with spherocytosis, circulating nucleated erythroid and myeloid cells, marrow hyperplasia and hyperbilirubinaemia (Bernstein 1963; Russell and Bernstein 1966). Anaemia was detected by 14 days' gestation but jaundice was not apparent until shortly after birth. The majority of homozygotes die within the first week but some survive to adult life. No evidence of maternal-foetal incompatibility or haemoglobinopathy was found (Bernstein and Wolfe, cited in Russell and Bernstein 1966), but an intracorpuscular defect was revealed by the drastically reduced survival of ^{51}Cr-labelled ha/ha erythrocytes, compared to normal, in ha/ha recipients. Reduced red-cell survival was also found with heterozygous red cells, but here the haemolysis appeared to be well compensated in the animal.

10.11.3   Jaundice (ja)

This recessive form of neonatal jaundice with severe anaemia (Stevens et al. 1959) is controlled by a locus unrelated to sph and ha. The anaemia is of a severe microcytic type detectable by 14 days' gestation with jaundice apparent a few hours after birth. As in haemolytic anaemia (ha) many immature nucleated erythroid and myeloid elements appear in the circulation. A major difference in viability distinguishes ha from ja since the latter was associated with death usually within 24 hours of birth (Russell and Bernstein 1966).

A diminished red-cell survival time was found with both ja/ja and ja/+ erythrocytes in either normal or heterozygous recipients, suggesting an intrinsic intracorpuscular defect. No evidence was obtained for an immunological basis for the defect or for the presence of abnormal haemoglobins. The marrow was hyperplastic and contained a normal proportion of CFU's (Russell and Bernstein 1966).

10.11.4   Hereditary spherocytosis in the Deer mouse (sp)

Neonatal jaundice associated with excessive haemolysis due to spherocytosis has been described in the deer mouse (peromyscus) (Huestis and Anderson 1954; Motulsky et al. 1956; Huestis et al. 1956). In this autosomal recessive condition the spherocytic red cells had increased osmotic fragility and reduced survival (Anderson et al. 1960). However, afflicted animals were not excessively anaemic since compensatory erythropoiesis was evident. Transplantation studies have demonstrated the intrinsic nature of the erythrocyte defect since the haemolysis can be cured by allogeneic marrow grafting (Steinmuller and Motulsky 1967). Though similar in many respects to human spherocytosis, the latter has a dominant genetic expression.

10.12 Haemopoietic abnormalities in New Zealand mice (NZ)

NZ mice originated from a mixed mouse colony maintained at the Otago University Medical School, New Zealand. Dr. Marianne Bielschowsky developed the inbred strains NZB, NZC, NZO and NZY by brother-sister mating and selection for coat colour (Bielschowsky et al. 1959; Bielschowsky and Goodall 1970). Mice of the New Zealand Black (NZB) strain spontaneously develop an autoimmune type of haemolytic anaemia with autoantibody production and were the first reported inbred experimental animals to develop a spontaneous autoimmune disease. Autoimmune manifestations appear in certain hybrids of NZB, some developing haemolytic anaemia and in others antinuclear antibodies and a renal disease closely resembling lupus nephritis (Holmes and Burnet 1966; for review see Howie and Helyer 1968).

CFU assays in syngeneic recipients were performed on NZC, NZB, NZW and NZO mice and the NZC mice were found to be markedly deficient in spleen colony-forming ability with approximately 5% of normal numbers of CFU's detected in the spleen and 15% in the marrow (Warner, N. L. and M. A. S. Moore, unpublished observations). All other NZ strains had normal spleen colony-forming ability as did several hybrids of NZC.

The basis of defective exogenous colony-forming capacity in NZC mice appeared to be an environmental defect showing some similarity to the Sl mutation since NZC CFU's formed considerably more spleen colonies in mice of other H-2^d strains than in syngeneic recipients, and NZB CFU's also failed to form colonies in NZC recipients.

In contrast to the exogenous assay results, NZC (and NZB) mice showed 5–10-fold more endogenous spleen colonies following 650 R irradiation than did mice of many other strains. Both NZC and NZB hybrids with other strains gave normal numbers of endogenous colonies and backcross or F$_2$ tests showed that this elevated, endogenous colony formation was controlled by a single recessive gene (Warner, N. L., unpublished observations).

The inbred NZC strain also shows a high incidence of spontaneous hydronephrosis with up to 56% of males and 81% of females exhibiting some evidence of this condition. Genetic studies showed that NZC hydronephrosis was controlled by a single recessive gene, but since this was not linked to the gene controlling endogenous colony formation (Warner, N. L., unpublished observations) the basis of the abnormality in NZC colony-forming capacity was not related to abnormal renal function.

Preliminary studies have suggested NZB and NZC CFU's may be more radioresistant than in other strains, which may in part account for elevated endogenous colony formation, but other factors such as some primary autoimmune reaction within the haemopoietic system, or some secondary influence of an autoimmune process are possibly implicated.

10.13 RF mice – abnormal granulopoiesis

This strain of mouse displays a 3–5 % incidence of spontaneous, granulocytic leukaemia which increases to 40 % in males and 20 % in females following 300 R whole-body irradiation (Upton 1959). The leukaemia can be transmitted by a virus to new-born RF mice, and males show greater susceptibility, which can be diminished by oestrogen treatment (Jenkins et al. 1966). Normal untreated RFM spleens showed pronounced intrasplenic granulopoiesis (Jenkins et al. 1969a) suggesting some genetic abnormality in granulopoiesis, which may predispose this strain to the development of granulocytic leukaemia. Abnormalities in haemopoiesis in RFM mice were revealed by Jenkins et al. (1969a, b). These investigators demonstrated that endogenous spleen colonies developing in these mice were predominantly granulocytic between 6–8 days of growth, whereas in other strains erythroid colonies were most frequent (75 %). Reduction in colony number was seen between 6–8 days and appeared to be due to loss of granulocytic colonies so that, by 9 days, these were no more numerous than erythroid colonies. This loss was associated with a reduction in the number of cells in the granulocytic colonies and an increase in the numbers of free granulocytes scattered throughout the red pulp, suggesting that the colonies underwent maturation and that differentiated cells were released. Treatment of mice with oestradiol did not change the number of endogenous colonies at 6 days, but a decline in colony numbers was not observed and hence total number of colonies seen between 7–9 days was greater than in control mice. Increased IUdR and ^{59}Fe uptake was also found. The most striking effect of oestradiol was a reduction in numbers of endogenous granulocytic colonies resulting in a predominance of erythroid colonies. The depression was also seen when oestradiol treatment was combined with hypertransfusion-induced suppression of erythropoiesis.

Exogenous colonies developing in lethally irradiated RFM mice following syngeneic marrow grafting did not change in number between 6–8 days and the frequency of granulocytic colonies was much lower than seen in the endogenous situation. Such granulocytic colonies as were seen were larger and more undifferentiated than in the endogenous situation. The frequency of undifferentiated colonies was also much higher than observed in other strains (35–42%) and was similar to the frequency of erythroid colonies. Oestradiol treatment of the recipient had little effect on the number or morphology of the exogenous colonies; however, treatment of the donor reduced the number of marrow CFU's and produced an increased frequency of erythroid colonies with virtually complete absence of granulocytic colonies It is evident that an interesting abnormality in granulopoietic regulation exists in these mice and further investigation is necessary to resolve whether the defect is intrinsic to the stem cells predisposing them to granulocytic differentiation or whether it is an environmental factor due either to excessive leukopoietic stimulation or an increased splenic granulopoietic microenvironment. Experiments on *in vitro* colony-forming cells in spleen and marrow of normal, irradiated and oestradiol-treated RFM mice would provide valuable information.

10.14 Hairless mice and haemopoietic regeneration

Vacek and Davidova (1969) studied radiosensitivity and haemopoietic regeneration in the hairless BFU semi-inbred strain of mouse and compared this with normal hairy (H) mice and with inbred C57BL mice. Endogenous colonies developing after 500 R in hairless mice were 4 times more frequent than in normal hairy (H) mice and 20 times more frequent than in C57BL mice. This difference was not due to the greater radioresistance of BFU CFU's since the D_0 values for endogenous CFU's in the three strains were not significantly different. The regeneration in spleen and marrow following 300 R was more rapid in hairless mice with ^{59}Fe incorporation reaching control values by 3 days in the spleen compared to 5 days in H mice and 7 days in C57BL mice. A 15-fold greater repopulating capacity of spleen cells was also seen in the BFU hairless than in C57BL strain. Vacek and Davidova (1969) suggested that inflammatory foci frequently found in the skin of hairless mice may present a chronic non-specific stimulus to haemopoietic tissue increasing splenic haemopoiesis, stem-cell mobilisation and permitting more rapid haemopoietic regeneration.

10.15 Congenital aplasia of the thymus in the nude mouse

Pantelouris (1968) reported a congenital absence of the thymus in homozygous mice in a stock carrying the mutation nude (nu). These hairless mice died before 3 months of age with a wasting syndrome similar to that observed after neonatal thymectomy. nu/nu mice have very low lymphocyte counts and the thymus-dependent areas in all the lymph nodes and corresponding areas of spleen and Peyer's patches were greatly depleted of lymphocytes (De Sousa et al. 1969). No thymus has been found in these mice and the spleen was small, though lymph nodes were of normal size. Mice carrying this autosomal recessive mutation are apparently very difficult to breed and homozygotes are infertile. nu/nu mice showed grossly defective homograft rejection and rat skin grafts were accepted and remained healthy with union of rat and mouse epidermal layers. Second grafts of rat skin were also accepted as readily as primary grafts, and both primary and secondary grafts were retained until the animals died of wasting at 48–85 days (Rygaard 1969). Terminal loss of hair from the grafts may be due to a slow rejection or to general wasting and debilitation. Even a human xenograft of a highly differentiated mucoid-producing adenocarcinoma took and grew subcutaneously in nude mice further revealing the gross deficiency in homograft rejection displayed by these mice (Rygaard and Povlsen 1969). Preliminary immunoelectrophoretic analysis showed constantly minimal immunoglobulin values in nu/nu mice compared to the heterozygotes or normal mice. However, nu/nu mice have normal or elevated Ig values 3–4 weeks after skin grafting (Rygaard 1969). Plaque-forming cells to sheep erythrocytes, producing either 7S or 19S antibody, were drastically reduced in nude mice, but the background of plaque-forming, and rosette-forming cells was normal (Rygaard and Muller-Berat 1971). Preliminary studies by these workers have indicated that hemi-allogeneic thymus grafts increased the life span of nude mice and allowed them to reject third-party skin grafts and produce appreciable amounts of haemolytic antibody. The lesion in nude mice does not seem to be associated with parathyroid deficiency or cardiovascular anomalies, and it is therefore unlike the human 3rd and 4th pharyngeal pouch or Di George syndrome. A closer parallel may be with the Nezelof type of autosomal recessive lymphopenia with normal immunoglobulin levels, where the thymus is hypoplastic and lacks Hassall's corpuscles and lymphocytes. A careful search for a small non-lymphoid thymic anlage (possibly undescended) in nude mice, particularly at birth, may prove fruitful in this condition. Quantitation particularly of specific antibody formation and reconstitution experiments with thymic grafting must have priority in experiments on this potentially very valuable mutant.

10.16 Human thymic defects

The field of human immunological deficiency diseases has been reviewed extensively elsewhere, and various classification systems have been proposed (Gabrielsen et al. 1968; Hoyer et al. 1968a, b; Meuwissen et al. 1969; Seligman et al. 1968; Bergsma 1968). Consequently the emphasis in this chapter is directed towards an understanding of the level of the lesions in the broader context of haemopoietic development and function.

The condition of defective third and fourth pharyngeal pouch development leading to absence of thymus and parathyroids was recognised by Di George (1965). This third and fourth pharyngeal pouch syndrome, or Di George syndrome, was probably first described by Harington (1829), who noted the absence of the thymus in an infant dying at 8 days of age of convulsions. In a prophetic statement Harington wrote: 'The nature and uses of the thymus gland still lie in so much obscurity... perhaps, by the collation and placing on record this and similar examples, we may hereafter succeed in discovering the physiology of an apparatus apparently of great importance to foetal and infantile organisation.' The syndrome is additionally characterised by absence of cell-mediated immunity (homograft rejection and delayed hypersensitivity) and gross depletion of lymphocytes in the thymic-dependent areas of spleen and lymph node. Plasma cells and germinal centres are normal and circulating lymphocyte levels are not extremely low (Lishner et al. 1967; Lishner and Di George 1969). Immunoglobulin levels appear to be normal, but varying degrees of impairment of antibody formation have been described. Cleveland et al. (1968) and Kretschmer et al. (1965) reported near-normal antibody production, whereas Di George (1968) and Lishner and Di George (1969) reported no antibody formation in one patient following repeated injection with numerous antigens, though low levels of agglutinating antibody to *Candida albicans* and *E.coli* were detected and quite high isohaemagglutinin titres were found. The latter workers suggest that some cases of third and fourth pharyngeal pouch syndrome involve incomplete defects in thymic development and in such patients antibody formation is near-normal. The patients of Cleveland et al. (1968) and Kretschmer et al. (1965) did show some slight signs of cellular immunity and may therefore have had an incomplete syndrome. The observation that thymic grafting restored phytohaemagglutinin responsiveness in host lymphocytes within 4 days in a patient with third and fourth pharyngeal pouch syndrome (August et al. 1968) indicated that the child had an incomplete form of the syndrome and that residual thymic function had produced a pool of lymphoid progenitor cells that matured rapidly, possibly under the influence of a humoral factor from the grafted thymus (Lishner and Di George 1969).

Antibody deficiency in the complete Di George syndrome (Di George 1968) raises the interesting theoretical possibility that thymus-dependent cells are required for initiation of all humoral immune responses, possibly by collaborating with a second cell population (Lishner and Di George 1969). However, it should be remembered that such a complete defect has only been reported in one patient and failure of antibody formation may be secondary to some other factor, such as severe infection.

A second type of thymic deficiency was described by Nezelof et al. (1964) and is associated with presence of the parathyroids. The thymus in this syndrome is hypoplastic and embryonic in morphology with no Hassall's corpuscles or lymphocytes. This autosomal recessive condition is associated with severe impairment of cell-mediated immunity. Lymphocytes are severely depleted in thymic-dependent areas and there is extreme lymphopenia. Plasma cells and germinal centres are present and immunoglobulin levels are normal (Fulginiti et al. 1966), although antibody formation to some antigens is defective.

Breton et al. (1963) reported a rather similar form of lymphopenic thymic dysplasia which differed from the Nezelof type in that dysgammaglobulinaemia with profound deficiency in IgA and IgG was evident. The thymus in this condition was small and embryonic in type and there was associated extreme lymphopenia and lymphocyte depletion in spleen and lymph nodes. Germinal centres were present, but small and reduced in number, and there were no detectable Peyer's patches at autopsy (Hoyer et al. 1968a, b; Good et al. 1968). Nezelof (1968) was unable to detect Peyer's patches in the normoglobulinaemic condition and proposed the title 'pure alymphocytosis' for both the Nezelof type of normogammaglobulinaemia and the Breton dysgammaglobulinaemia. Matsaniotis (1968) has, however, described normal Peyer's patches in a typical case of Nezelof alymphocytosis with thymic dysplasia. The importance attached to the presence or otherwise of the gut-associated lymphoid tissue, particularly Peyer's patches, is due to the proposal that these function as a mammalian bursal equivalent (see Chapter 6). In both the Di George thymic aplasia and the Nezelof thymic dysplasia the lesion is probably due solely to defective thymic development. In the former case possibly a failure of third and fourth pharyngeal pouch ectoderm-endoderm interaction occurs and consequently the thymic anlage does not develop. In the latter condition the epithelial anlage does develop, but does not support lymphopoiesis possibly because of a failure in epithelial-mesenchymal interaction, which is necessary for normal thymic development. The Breton dysgammaglobulinaemia may be due to a defect in the epithelial environment of both the thymus and the bursal-equivalent primary lymphoid tissue, or alternatively could be a stem-cell defect preventing thymic lymphoid differentiation and restricting differentiation into immunoglobulin-producing cells.

Thymic alymphoplasia with an associated aleucocytosis was described by De Vaal and Seynhaeve (1959). Affected infants died in the first few days of life with total absence of circulating leucocytes (De Vaal and Seynhaeve 1959) or with low numbers of circulating large lymphocytes and monocytes only (Gitlin et al. 1964). The thymus was devoid of lymphocytes and Hassall's corpuscles and lymph nodes, tonsils and Peyer's patches were absent or severely depleted of lymphocytes. This syndrome was considered a form of reticular dysgenesis involving a defect in a precursor cell common to the lymphoid and neutrophil series, but distinct from the erythroid, megakaryocytic and monocyte series which were apparently unaffected. This hypothesis is unlikely in view of the evidence of a common progenitor cell for both neutrophils and monocytes and the close relationship of this cell to the progenitors of the erythroid, megakaryocytic and lymphoid series (see Chapter 3). A more plausible alternative is that these patients suffered from a primary thymic dysgenesis with a superimposed chronic graft-vs.-host reaction initiated by maternal immunocompetent cells. Kadowaki et al. (1965) demonstrated XX/XY chimaerism in infants with thymic deficiency and evidence of graft-vs.-host activity, and terminal neutropenia has been described in such cases (Miller 1968).

10.17 *Combined defects – thymic dysplasia with agamma-globulinaemia*

An autosomal recessive form of thymic dysplasia with agammaglobulinaemia was first described by Hitzig et al. (1958) and Tobler and Cottier (1958). Infants with this Swiss form of lymphopenic agammaglobulinaemia have a small embryonic thymus devoid of Hassall's corpuscles and lymphocytes, absence of germinal centres, Peyer's patches and plasma cells in peripheral lymphoid tissue and lymphopenia. Thymic-dependent areas of the peripheral lymphoid tissues exhibit extreme lymphocyte depletion. Functionally, immunological failure is almost complete with absence of homograft rejection, delayed hypersensitivity, PHA-lymphocyte transformation, and antibody formation. All immunoglobulin classes are absent or extremely depressed (Hitzig 1968; Cole et al. 1969; Gabrielsen et al. 1968).

A sex-linked form of this condition has been described by Gitlin and Craig (1963) with no cellular or humoral immunity and a severe immuno-globulin deficiency, although some variation in the depression of the different immunoglobulin classes has been reported (Hoyer et al. 1968a, b). Hitzig (1968) considered the evidence for sex-linked transmission was only suggest-ive and clinically the two groups could not be distinguished. A somewhat longer life span with the sex-linked form has been noted, but since the number of cases is small the significance of this is doubtful (Hoyer et al. 1968a, b). Hoyer supports the distinction between the two types and maintains that the sex-linked form shows less extreme lymphoid depletion and deficiency of immune responses than the autosomal form. The basis of the defects seen in the combined deficiency syndromes is unclear, but four possibilities have been considered: (1) a stem-cell defect, (2) an environmental defect common to both thymus and bursal equivalent primary lymphoid tissue, (3) an auto-immune process, and (4) a defect in a pituitary adrenal control mechanism. De Koning et al. (1969) and Good et al. (1969) have successfully treated lymphopenic sex-linked agammaglobulinaemia by haemopoietic grafting and have established persistent chimaerism with restoration of normal cellular and humoral immunity. De Koning grafted foetal thymus in addition to the bone marrow, but a thymic graft was not used by Good et al. (1969) suggest-ing that the defect resided in the stem-cell population rather than the en-vironment of the primary lymphoid organs. The problems of graft-vs.-host reactions in such grafting procedures were overcome by density-gradient separation of donor marrow to eliminate competent cells (De Koning et al. 1969) and by close histocompatibility matching of donor and recipient.

The evidence for an autoimmune basis for the condition is reviewed by De Vries et al. (1968). Although autoantibodies are not generally detectable, there is an interesting report of an autoantibody in a child with the sex-linked form (South et al. 1969). The antibody was specific for the LW (Landsteiner-Weiner) antigen, an almost universal blood-group antigen. An autoantibody with similar anti-LW activity has recently been described in a patient with Bruton-type agammaglobulinaemia (Robbins et al. 1969). The presence of autoantibody to this particular antigen in two cases with agammaglobulinaemia yet absent general antibody formation is intriguing.

Pierpaoli and Sorkin (1967, 1968) have proposed that pituitary factors influence immunological development and have suggested that the combined deficiency syndromes may have an underlying endocrinological defect. In this context, DuQuesnoy et al. (1970) have demonstrated severe lymphopenia, decreased antibody responses and graft-vs.-host activity, and general lymphocyte depletion in the Snell-Bagg pituitary dwarf mouse. This study suggested a selective defect in the thymus-dependent lymphoid system (Ig levels were normal) caused by defective thymotrophic pituitary control. The thymotrophic activity may or may not be growth hormone. Clinically, patients with immunological deficiency disease often showed growth retardation, and Gatti et al. (1969) have described an autosomal recessive lymphopenic form of agammaglobulinaemia associated with a distinctive form of short-limbed dwarfism with ectodermal dysplasia. On the other hand, there appear to be no immunological abnormalities in human hypo-pituitary dwarfism.

An intrinsic stem-cell defect is still the most plausible lesion in these conditions operating either to impair localisation of circulating stem cells within the epithelial environment of primary lymphoid tissue or impair their subsequent differentiating capacity. The association in some patients of cyclic neutropenia, granulocytopenia, terminal agranulocytosis and occasionally pancytopenia suggests the possibility of a more broadly-based stem-cell defect (Hitzig 1968).

10.18 Agammaglobulinaemia and dysgammaglobulinaemias with normal thymic development

Bruton (1952) described a sex-linked recessive agammaglobulinaemia involving all immunoglobulin classes. Intensive immunisation over long periods failed to elicit antibody formation, and germinal centres and plasma cells were absent from peripheral lymphoid tissue (Good et al. 1962). In contrast to the sex-linked combined deficiency syndrome, affected patients have an intact thymus-dependent system with normal delayed hypersensitivity, homograft rejection and circulating lymphocyte levels and no depletion of the paracortical areas of lymph nodes (Gabrielsen et al. 1968). With more precise techniques for immunoglobulin quantitation it appears that agammaglobulinaemia is a misnomer and no patient has been described who was completely devoid of gammaglobulin (Good et al. 1968). In this context therefore 'agammaglobulinaemia' is diagnosed when there is less than 100

10.20 *The Wiscott-Aldrich syndrome*

The Wiscott-Aldrich syndrome is a rare sex-linked recessive condition that
manifests as a triad of lesions: eczema, thrombocytopenia and increased
susceptibility to infections (Aldrich et al. 1954; Krivit and Good 1959).
Susceptibility to infections is associated with inability to form antibody
against certain antigens, a striking reduction in isohaemagglutinins, haemolysin to sheep red cells and agglutinin production against *E.coli* (Gabrielsen
et al. 1968; Blaese et al. 1968). Delayed hypersensitivity responses were
absent or impaired but the thymus was normal except for stress involution.
Lymphocyte levels were low and lymphocytes were deficient in peripheral
lymphoid tissue, particularly in the paracortical regions of lymph nodes.
Lymphocyte deficiency was progressive but probably secondary to reticulum
cell hyperplasia (Cooper et al. 1964, 1968a, b). The immunological deficiency
in this condition probably resides in the afferent limb of the immune system
and is probably due to an abnormality in processing of polysaccharide
antigens (Cooper et al. 1968a, b; Blaese et al. 1968). Such antigens may be
processed too rapidly to allow induction of an antibody response (Ayoub
et al. 1968). Alternatively the defect may be due to an inability to process
polysaccharide antigens, and if this is due to an enzyme defect in carbohydrate metabolism it could also account for the abnormalities of platelet
development and the pathogenesis of the eczema (Cooper et al. 1968a, b).

10.21 *Human granulocyte defects*

Defects in granulopoiesis can be considered in two categories: deficiencies in
polymorph function or deficiencies in polymorph production and/or regulation. In the former category, chronic or fatal granulomatous disease and
the Chediak-Higashi syndrome are examples of defective granulocyte
function. Chronic granulomatous disease is an inherited disorder with a
sex-modified autosomal recessive mode of inheritance (Chandra et al. 1969;
Thompson and Soothill 1970). The syndrome is associated with recurrent
suppurative and granulomatous lesions in various organs, and a normal
immunological capacity to produce antibody to bacterial and viral antigens
and normal delayed hypersensitivity and PHA responsiveness. Peripheral
blood neutrophils were defective in bactericidal capacity for staphylococci
and gram-negative organisms, although engulfment and phagocytosis of
bacteria was normal (Holmes et al. 1967, 1968; Quie 1969). Defective intra-

cellular killing may be due to defective degranulation with cytoplasmic granules disrupting less rapidly or completely than in normal granulocytes. Macrophages and monocytes in affected patients were also deficient in intracytoplasmic bacterial killing and a peculiar yellow-brown lipofucin pigment accumulated in macrophages (Quie 1969; Huber 1968). The bactericidal role of leukocyte myeloperoxidase in the presence of hydrogen peroxide has been convincingly demonstrated and, in chronic granulomatous disease, polymorphs showed depressed oxygen consumption, glucose oxidation and hydrogen-peroxide formation, which probably contribute to defective bacterial killing (Quie 1969). The specific site of lesions may be a deficiency in leucocyte reduced nicotinamide adenine-dinucleotide oxidase, which is revealed by failure of the cells to reduce nitro-blue tetrazolium during phagocytosis (Baehner and Nathan 1967; Thompson and Soothill 1970). The presence of a defect common to neutrophils, monocytes and macrophages, provides further support for the concept of a common origin of these cell types from a single progenitor cell population.

The Chediak-Higashi syndrome is an autosomal recessive condition characterised by the presence of large granules in the leucocytes (Higashi 1954) and a pronounced dilution of skin, eye and hair colour due to abnormally large melanin granules. Giant granulations or inclusions are seen in many cell types, and the defect is either in the primary synthesis of granules or in the integrity of cellular structures limited by cell membranes (Windhorst et al. 1968). Normal sized lysosomal granules arranged in concentric arrangements within leucocytes have also been reported (White 1967) and are apparently associated with cytoplasmic autophagy. The Chediak-Higashi syndrome has also been described in the Aleutian strain of mink (Leader et al. 1963) as well as in cattle (Padgett 1967) and in dogs (the grey collie syndrome; Lund et al. 1967; Windhorst et al. 1968). In the latter syndrome cyclic neutropenia was an additional complicating factor. The high susceptibility to infections seen in children and animals with this syndrome may be related to the abnormally large cell granules and their failure to lyse following phagocytosis of bacteria. However, no defect in phagocytic capacity or bactericidal action of neutrophils has been found, and the direct cause of increased susceptibility to infections is still unknown (Padgett 1967).

Defective granulocyte production is frequently associated with drug toxicity, but certain inherited agranulocytoses or neutropenias have been reported. Kostmann (1956) reviewed reports of inherited agranulocytosis and described 14 cases of an autosomal recessive defect where the marrow and blood showed an absence, or markedly diminished numbers, of granulocytes. Similar cases of this infantile genetic agranulocytosis were subsequently reported with evidence of maturation arrest at the promyelocyte or myelocyte stage (MacGillivray et al. 1964). In a more recent review Miller et al. (1968) reported eosinophilia, monocytosis and hypergammaglobulinaemia in affected infants associated with the recurrent infections and a marked monocytic response to adrenalin administration. Since eosinophilia was observed in association with neutropenia, infantile genetic neutropenia is a better description of this syndrome. The pathogenesis of the condition is unknown, but it is distinct from transitory granulocytopenia of the newborn which is due to maternal leukoagglutinins. It also differs from the neutropenia of unknown aetiology described by Lau et al. (1967), where mature forms of neutrophil granulocytes were rare in marrow, but *in vitro* marrow neutrophil maturation in the presence of autologous or homologous plasma was normal. The defect in this latter condition may be a distortion of the normal feedback mechanisms regulating leukopoiesis. In congenital neutropenia, myeloid maturation was defective *in vitro* even in the presence of normal serum and was probably the consequence of an intrinsic haemopoietic cell defect (Miller et al. 1968).

An association of pancreatic insufficiency with bone-marrow dysfunction and neutropenia has been recognised (Shwachman et al. 1964; Colebatch et al. 1965; Moller et al. 1967). Chronic neutropenia and severe infections were observed with diminished or absent exocrine pancreatic secretion, unrelated to cystic fibrosis. A possible autoimmune basis for this condition is indicated by the report of a neutrophil cytotoxic factor present in these patients, and the possibility exists of an autoantibody directed against neutrophils and pancreatic exocrine cells (Moller et al. 1967).

A possibly sex-linked recessive form of familial granulocytopenia has been reported and is characterised by an immunoglobulin abnormality, hypogammaglobulinaemia and profound neutropenia (Lonsdale et al. 1967). The marrow of affected patients showed a striking maturation arrest in the granulocytic series, but episodes of temporary recovery suggested an inhibitory influence was responsible. The neutrophils that are present showed reduced phagocytic and migratory properties, and Lonsdale et al. (1967) suggested that the condition was a variant of the impotent neutrophil syndrome.

Defects in neutrophil regulation are implicated in the aetiology of the rare, probably autosomal dominant, condition of cyclic neutropenia. This condition is nearly always apparent before the age of 10 years and is characterised by the regular disappearance of neutrophils from the circulation at approximately 20–21-day intervals (Page and Good 1956; Reimann 1963). In some affected individuals total white-cell counts do not fluctuate since the neutrophil deficiency is made up by the occurrence of compensatory mono- cytosis and also eosinophilia. Anaemia and thrombocytopenia are sometimes observed (Morley et al. 1967) suggesting the defect may not be confined to neutrophils, and for this reason Reimann (1963) suggested the alternative title of periodic myelodysplasia. Cyclic neutropenia with associated mono- cytosis has also been described in the grey collie dog (Lund et al. 1967) and in some cases of pancreatic achylia (Colebatch et al. 1965). The cause of cyclic neutropenia is not clearly understood and it has been suggested that distinctions between chronic idiopathic neutropenia and the cyclic form are more apparent than real (Morley et al. 1967). Certainly a neutrophilic cycle of 14–23 days has been described in normal healthy individuals with an oscillation between 2000 and 4000 neutrophils per mm^3 (Morley 1966), and the periodicity in cyclic neutropenia may simply be an exaggeration of this normal cycle.

If a defect in feedback regulation is operating in cyclic and in certain chronic idiopathic neutropenias, the association of compensatory monocytosis in many instances is of considerable interest and suggests that the defective regulation probably operates at or subsequent to the level of a common progenitor cell for these two lines. Studies on the differentiation of *in vitro* colony-forming cells and colony-stimulating factor levels in such patients would be most illuminating.

10.22 Human anaemias

An extensive review of this complex area of human haemopoietic ab- normalities embracing both inherited and acquired defects is beyond the scope of this monograph, and more comprehensive reviews can be found in Wintrobe (1967), Britton (1969), Dacie (1969), and Vilter et al. (1967).

The refractory or aregenerative anaemias are a group of diseases character- ised by severe anaemia, or even pancytopenia, and in many instances in- effective erythropoiesis in the presence of a hypercellular marrow. Many terms have been used to describe this group of conditions: refractory anaemia, chronic bone-marrow failure, erythrogenesis imperfecta, aregenerative anaemia, pure red-cell anaemia, refractory sideroblastic anaemia, congenital hypoplastic anaemia, pseudo-aplastic anaemia, etc. Vilter et al. (1967) recognised six categories of refractory anaemia.

In children a congenital hypoplastic form of anaemia has been reported by Diamond and Blackfan (1938). This syndrome has been called erythrogenesis imperfecta, and the initial pure red-cell anaemia may be due to an erythrocyte maturation defect possibly due to disordered tryptophane metabolism; however, moderate leukopoietic involvement has been reported.

Pure red-cell anaemia has been described in adults in association with thymoma and may possibly have an immunological basis since the condition frequently responds to cortisone and splenectomy (Jeunet and Good 1968; Dameshek et al. 1967). Patients with thymoma and agammaglobulinaemia have a high incidence of anaemia with agenesis or aplasia of the marrow erythroid series and frequently terminal aplastic anaemia. An interesting association of eosinopenia or complete absence of eosinophils, and also leukopenia has been reported in such patients (Jeunet and Good 1968). The pathogenesis of the condition is unknown and any analysis is made difficult by the variable association and temporal relationships of the various defects. Three possibilities have been considered: (a) The thymus may produce a humoral factor which suppresses erythropoiesis (Miller et al. 1965; Yunis et al. 1965). (b) An autoimmune reaction may exist and be directed against the erythroid series. Krantz and Kao (1967) have described a patient whose serum contained a material, probably antibody, which was shown by immunofluorescence to react with erythroblast nuclei. A further possibility is that an autoantibody is directed against erythropoietin in some patients. (c) A common stem-cell deficiency may exist. Dreyfus et al. (1969) described a patient with marrow hypoplasia and hypogammaglobulinaemia who did not develop thymoma until 3 years after initial diagnosis. These workers considered an autoimmune basis unlikely in this patient and favoured a defect in the stem cell common to both erythroid (myeloid) and lymphoid series.

Classic aplastic anaemia is rarely primary or inherited and is most frequently drug-induced. It has been suggested (Dacie 1963) that somatic mutations may arise following drug-induced damage to haemopoietic cells and be the origin of the abnormal stem cell in paroxysmal nocturnal haemoglobinuria. This rare disorder is probably due to a membrane defect in red cells, which allows a complement component to attack the membrane, in the absence of antibody, and induce lysis (Yachnin 1965). Excessive red-cell lysis may occur at the low pH optimum for complement function and may produce a severe haemolytic anaemia and ultimately marrow hypoplasia and hypochromia due to prolonged iron loss (Gardner and Blum 1967). A biphasic survival curve of the chromium-labelled red cells in patients with paroxysmal nocturnal haemoglobinuria and evidence for two populations of leucocytes on the basis of histochemical staining (Lewis and Dacie 1965) support Dacie's concept of a somatic mutation at the stem-cell level induced by a transient toxic effect during a phase of marrow aplasia. The resulting mutated clone may compete with and outgrow the normal population giving rise to the abnormal red cells and granulocytes (Dacie 1963).

An interesting familial pancytopenia beginning in childhood and associated with anaemia, thrombocytopenia, hyper-pigmentation, skeletal malformation and hypo-gonadism was first described by Fanconi (see Fanconi 1967 for a review). Cultures of peripheral blood lymphocytes from patients with Fanconi's anaemia exhibit a high proportion (10–70%) of mitoses with chromatid aberrations in the forms of constrictions, gaps and breaks, and a high incidence of endoreduplication. The incidence of chromosome aberrations in marrow and fibroblast cultures was much lower than in peripheral leukocytes. Chromatid lesions may be due to increased chromosomal fragility or defective lysosomal membrane function causing release of lytic enzymes and secondary production of breaks. Alternatively, chromosome damage could reflect a greater susceptibility of certain cells to infection by ubiquitous viruses well known for their ability to induce extensive chromosome breakages (Schmid 1967). The role of the chromosome abnormalities in the development of this anaemia is therefore uncertain, and an alternative primary defect in mesenchymal function has been proposed (Fanconi 1967).

Di Guglielmo (1946) reported a rare syndrome with erythroblastic hyperplasia in marrow and leukoblastic and thromboblastic hypoplasia. A severe anaemia is present in patients with this syndrome, and erythroid maturation is arrested at the erythroblast stage with a bizarre erythroblast morphology. Di Guglielmo's syndrome or erythaemic myelosis shows malignant characteristics and frequently becomes leukaemic in the terminal phase. Defects in the activity of some of the enzymes of the haem biosynthesis pathway have been reported in this condition by Steiner et al. (1963) and defective haem synthesis, and in some patients defective globin synthesis, were reported by Necheles and Dameshek (1967). Chromosomal abnormalities have also been recognised (Kiossoglou et al. 1965) and it is probable that these and the biosynthetic defects are secondary to an as yet unknown primary lesion.

Other forms of familial anaemia result from erythrocyte structural defects such as in spherocytosis and elliptocytosis which reduce red-cell survival and lead to excessive haemolysis. Hereditary spherocytosis is characterised by near-spherical red cells that are trapped and subsequently destroyed in the spleen. The condition is an autosomal dominant and the defect may involve abnormal function of a membrane enzyme, which results in increased membrane sodium permeability, osmotic swelling, secondary loss of membrane lipoprotein and consequent microspherocytosis (Jacobs 1968). Haemolytic anaemias of varying severity are found as a secondary consequence of various enzymatic deficiencies in red cells, such as defects in G-6-P-dehydrogenase, glutathione reductase, pyruvic kinase, etc. At least 12 enzymatic defects have been identified as causes of anaemia (Wintrobe 1967). Anaemia associated with the presence of certain forms of abnormal haemoglobins, such as haemoglobin-S in Sickle cell anaemia and haemoglobin C and E and other rare forms of haemoglobins, are reviewed by Dacie (1969) and Carrell and Lehmann (1969). Patients with thalassaemia, particularly in the homozygous state, also develop chronic progressive anaemia and the lesion here is an abnormality in globin synthesis probably due to a rate-controlling (operator) locus mutation leading to a marked reduction in the rate of globin peptide-chain production (see review by Weatherall 1967).

10.23 Polycythaemia

Polycythaemia vera is a primary hyperplasia of the haemopoietic tissues with red-cell counts in the range $7–13 \times 10^6$ per mm^3. The condition was first described by Vaquez (1892) and Osler (1903) as an erythroid hyperplasia, but it is now recognised that all forms of marrow haemopoiesis are involved with panmyelosis, expansion of the marrow cavity and frequently terminal leukaemia or aplasia (Britton 1969; Brodsky et al. 1968). The pathogenesis of this condition is unknown, but inherited factors appear to play a role. Millard et al. (1968) found in some patients a chromosomal abnormality resembling deletion of chromosomes of the F (19–20) group in marrow metaphases. F-group deletions were also recognised in a case of leukopenia, an anaemia of obscure aetiology and in seven cases of idiopathic sideroblastic anaemia (De Grouchy et al. 1966). These chromosomal abnormalities are probably not the primary cause of the condition but may be generated by the abnormally high cell turnover.

Patients with increased red-cell mass but without other features of polycythaemia vera have been described and classified as examples of benign erythrocytosis. Examples of this condition are primary erythrocytosis of childhood and familial polycythaemia (Russell and Conley 1964; Modan and Modan 1968). Aetiological factors are unknown, and some workers consider these patients represent the extreme end of the normal distribution of erythrocyte levels. Polycythaemia has also been reported in association with the presence of an abnormal haemoglobin-Hb-Chesapeake (Charache et al. 1966).

10.24 Conclusions

This chapter has reviewed some of the genetic defects which influence haemo-poiesis in both mouse and man, and even this incomplete catalogue of mutations serves to illustrate the complexity of haemopoietic regulation.

Haemopoietic defects can be divided into two main categories: those intrinsic to the haemopoietic cells and those which are extrinsic yet influence haemopoiesis. In the latter category are the abnormalities in haemopoietic microenvironments which lead to inhibition of stem-cell proliferation and alterations in the pattern of progenitor cell differentiation. In Figure 10.1 certain abnormalities in the microenvironment are illustrated. In the case of the primary lymphoid environment, lesions can be detected at two levels: (a) the primary inductive interaction between ectoderm and endoderm in thymic, and possibly bursal equivalent ontogeny where defects lead to thymic agenesis, (b) the secondary epithelial-mesenchymal induction required if the thymic anlage is to support lymphopoiesis. Defects here lead to thymic (and possibly bursal equivalent) dysgenesis.

Extrinsic defects in mucosal iron uptake, antigen processing mechanisms, etc., may also profoundly influence haemopoietic function. Defective production of a humoral regulator may also underlie certain haemopoietic abnormalities. Though clear examples of such defects are not yet available, both cyclic neutropenia and certain forms of pure red cell aplasia may come into this category.

The intrinsic haemopoietic cell defects may be detected at a number of levels: (a) At the stem-cell level as revealed by reduced numbers of such cells, or by their impaired proliferative capacity. (b) At the level of progenitor cell differentiation within the appropriate microenvironment. In this category, the flexed-tail anaemic mouse serves as an example in the erythroid series, and the human lymphopenic agammaglobulinaemias in the lymphoid series. This latter defect may be due to an impaired stem cell which is incapable of differentiating into a lymphoid progenitor cell within the primary lymphoid environment, or alternatively may be due to defective proliferative capacity of lymphoid progenitor cells. (c) Defects may only be manifest at the level

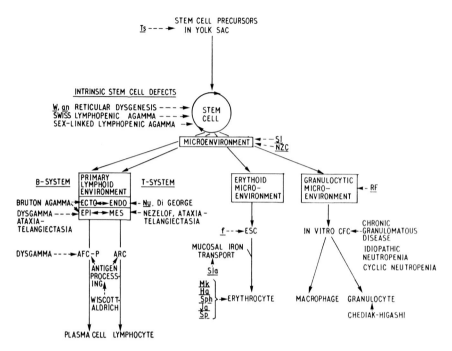

Fɪg. 10.1.   Schematic diagram showing sites of action of mutations in the mouse and man which influence haemopoiesis. Mouse gene symbols or mouse strains underlined. AFC-P = antibody-forming cell progenitors; ARC = thymus-derived antigen reactive cells; ESC = erythropoietin sensitive cells; *in vitro* CFC = *in vitro* colony-forming cells (granulocyte and macrophage progenitors); B-system = bursal equivalent system; T-system = thymic system.

of the differentiated end cell, and in this category the erythrocyte defects are the best characterised. Defects may be due to primary structural abnormalities (spherocytosis, microcytosis) enzymatic deficiencies (G-6-P dehydrogenase), haemoglobin abnormalities (Sickle cell anaemia), or control abnormalities (Thalassaemia).

Though some lesions are detected primarily at the level of the mature end cell, abnormalities may be present at earlier stages of differentiation and in other lines of haemopoiesis (e.g. paroxysmal nocturnal haemoglobinuria, polycythaemia vera, Faconi's anaemia). It is consequently unwise to be dogmatic as to the precise stage of differentiation when a defect is first manifest, and undoubtedly with more sophisticated techniques, abnormalities in stem cells and progenitor cells will be detected. On the other hand, stem- and progenitor-cell defects would not be expected to be present where mutations influence some characteristic expressed only in the differentiated state, e.g. haemoglobin.

Provided that genetic defects in haemopoiesis can be adequately classified into the above categories then rational clinical therapy can be undertaken. Marrow transplantation is potentially the most effective treatment for all conditions where the defect is intrinsic to the haemopoietic cells. In this category the lymphopenic agammaglobulinaemias have responded well to transplant therapy, and such treatment may be extended to certain forms of aplastic anaemia, neutropenia and pancytopenia as well as the haemoglobinopathies and thalassaemias. Defects in humoral regulator production, or function can conceivably be treated with purified (or semi-purified) regulators, while microenvironmental defects may be overcome by organ grafting procedures, e.g. thymus or marrow stromal grafts.

References

Aldrich, R. A., A. C. Steinberg, and D. C. Campbell, 1954, Pediat. *13*, 133.

Altman, K. L. and E. S. Russell, 1964, J. Cell. Comp. Physiol. *64*, 293.

Anderson, R., R. R. Huestis, and A. G. Motulsky, 1960, Blood *15*, 491.

Attfield, M., 1951, J. Genet. *50*, 250.

August, C. S., F. S. Rosen, R. M. Filler, C. A. Janeway, B. Markowski, and H. E. M. Kay, 1968, Lancet *2*, 1210.

Ayoub, E. M., B. A. Dudding, and M. D. Cooper, 1968, J. Lab. Clin. Med. *72*, 971.

Baehner, R. L. and D. G. Nathan, 1967, Science *155*, 835.

Bannerman, R. M. and R. G. Cooper, 1966, Science *151*, 581.

Bannerman, R. M. and P. H. Pinkerton, 1967, Brit. J. Haemat. *13*, 1000.

Bennett, D., 1956, J. Morphol. *98*, 199.

Bennett, M. and G. Cudkowicz, 1966, Fed. Proc. *25*, 296 (Abs.).

Bennett, M., G. Cudkowicz, R. S. Foster, Jr., and D. Metcalf, 1968a, J. Cell. Physiol. *71*, 211.

Bennett, M., R. A. Steeves, G. Cudkowicz, and E. A. Mirand, 1968b, Science *162*, 564.

Bennett, M., P. H. Pinkerton, G. Cudkowicz, and R. M. Bannerman, 1968c, Blood *32*, 908.

Bergsma, D., 1968, (editor), Immunologic deficiency diseases in man. Birth defects, original article series, *4*, No. 1, pub. The National Foundation – March of Dimes.

Bernstein, S. E., 1962, Science *137*, 428.

Bernstein, S. E., 1963, Proc. XI Intern. Congr. Genet, The Hague, Netherlands *1*, 186.

Bernstein, S. E. and E. S. Russell, 1959, Proc. Soc. Exp. Biol. Med. *101*, 769.

Bernstein, S. E., E. S. Russell, and G. Keighley, 1968, Ann. N.Y. Acad. Sci. *149*, 475.

Bielschowsky, M. and C. M. Goodall, 1970, Cancer Res. *30*, 834.

Bielschowsky, M., B. J. Helyer, and J. B. Howie, 1959, Proc. Univ. Otago Med. School *37*, 9.

Blaese, R. M., R. S. Brown, W. Strober, and T. A. Waldmann, 1968, Lancet *1*, 1056.

Borghese, E., 1959, Acta Anat. (Basle) *36*, 185.

Breton, A., R. Walbaum, L. Boniface, M. Goudemand, and A. Dupont, 1963, Arch. franç. Pédiat. *20*, 131.

Britton, C. J. C., 1969, Disorders of the blood. London, J. and A. Churchill Ltd.

Brodsky, I., S. B. Kahn, and L. W. Brady, 1968, Brit. J. Haemat. *14*, 351.

Bruton, O. C., 1952, Pediatrics *9*, 722.

Carrell, R. W. and H. Lehmann, 1969, Seminars in Hematology *6*, 116.

Chandra, R. K., W. A. Cope, and J. F. Soothill, 1969, Lancet *2*, 71.

Charache, S., D. J. Weatherall, and J. B. Clegg, 1966, J. Clin. Invest. *45*, 813.

Chervenick, P. A. and D. R. Boggs, 1969, J. Cell. Physiol. *73*, 25.

Cleveland, W. W., B. J. Fogel, W. T. Brown, and H. E. M. Kay, 1968, Lancet *2*, 1211.

Cole, R. B., A. Di Sousa, R. A. Good, R. A. Gatti, and J. R. Hoyer, 1969, Am. J. Diseases of Children *118*, 748.

Colebatch, J. H., C. M. Anderson, M. J. Simons, and V. Burke, 1965, Lancet *2*, 496.

Cooper, M. D., P. Chase, J. W. St. Geme, Jr., W. Krivit, and R. A. Good, 1964, J. Lab· Clin. Med. *64*, 849.

Cooper, M. D., H. P. Chase, J. T. Lowmann, W. Krivit, and R. A. Good, 1968a, Am. J. Med. *44*, 499.

Cooper, M. D., H. P. Chase, J. T. Lowman, W. Krivit, and R. A. Good, 1968b, Immunological defects in patients with Wiscott-Aldrich Syndrome. Birth defects, original article series, edited by D. Bergsma, *4*, 378.

Crandall, M. A. and T. D. Brock, 1968, Science *161*, 473.

Dacie, J. V., 1963, Proc. Roy. Soc. Med. *56*, 587.

Dacie, J. V., 1969, Seminars in Hematology *6*, 109.

Dameshek, W., S. M. Brown, and A. D. Rubin, 1967, Seminars in Hematology *4*, 222.

De Aberle, S. B., 1927, Amer. J. Anat. *40*, 219.

De Grouchy, I., C. de Nava, R. Zittoun, and J. Bousser, 1966, Nouv. Rev. Franç. Hémat. *6*, 367.

De Koning, J., L. J. Dooren, D. W. van Bekkum, J. J. van Rood, K. A. Dickie, and J. Radl, 1969, Lancet *1*, 1223.

Deol. M. S., 1961, Proc. Roy. Soc. B *155*, 78.

De Sousa, M. A. B., D. M. V. Parrott, and E. M. Pantelouris, 1969, Clin. Exp. Immunol. *4*, 637.

Detlefsen, J. A., 1923, Anat. Rec. *24*, 417.

De Vaal, O. M. and V. Seynhaeve, 1959, Lancet *2*, 1123.

De Vries, M. J., L. J. Dooren, and F. J. Clenton, 1968, Graft-versus-host or autoimmune lesions in the Swiss type of agammaglobulinemia, Birth defects, original article series, edited by D. Bergsma, *4*, 173.

Diamond, L. K., and K. Blackfan, 1938, Am. J. Dis. Child. *56*, 464.

Di George, A. M., 1965, Am. J. Pediat. *67*, 907.

Di George, A. M., 1968, Congenital absence of the thymus and its immunologic consequences: Concurrence with congenital hypoparathyroidism. Birth defects, original article series, edited by D. Bergsma, *4*, 116.

Di Guglielmo, G., 1946, Rev. d'Hémat. *1*, 355.

Dreyfus, B., B. Varet, and C. Sultan, 1969, Nouv. Rev. Franç. d'Hématol. *9*, 33.

Duquesnoy, R. J., P. K. Kalpaktsoglou, and R. A. Good, 1970, Proc. Soc. Exp. Biol. Med. *133*, 201.

Falconer, D. S. and J. H. Isaacson, 1962, Genet. Res. (Cambridge) *3*, 248.

Fanconi, G., 1967, Seminars in Hematology *4*, 233.

Fekete, E., C. C. Little, and A. M. Cloudman, 1941, Proc. Nat. Acad. Sci. (Washington) *27*, 114.

Finley, S. C., W. H. Finley, T. A. Noto, I. A. Uchida, and R. F. Roddam, 1968, Lancet *1*, 1095.

Fowler, J. H., J. E. Till, E. A. McCulloch, and L. Siminovitch, 1967, Brit. J. Haemat. *13*, 256.

Fried, W., N. Rishpon-Meyerstein, and C. W. Gurney, 1967, J. Lab. Clin. Med. *70*, 813.

Fulginiti, V. A., O. F. Sieber, H. N. Claman, and D. Merrill, 1966, J. Pediat. *68*, 723.

Gabrielsen, A. E., M. D. Cooper, R. D. A. Peterson, and R. A. Good, 1968, The primary immunologic deficiency diseases. In: Textbook of immunopathology, vol. 2, edited by P. A. Miescher and H. J. Muller-Eberhard. New York, Grune and Stratton, p. 385.

Gardner, F. H. and S. F. Blum, 1967, Seminars in Hematology *4*, 250.

Gatti, R. A., N. P. Platt, H. H. Pomerance, R. Hong, L. O. Langer, H. E. M. Kay, and R. A. Good, 1969, J. Pediat. *75*, 675.

Giedion, A. and J. J. Scheidegger, 1957, Helv. paediat. Acta *12*, 241.

Gilbert, C. and R. Hong, 1964, Amer. J. Med. *37*, 602.

Gimeno, A., H. Liano, and M. Kreisler, 1969, J. Neurological Science *8*, 545.

Gitlin, D. and J. M. Craig, 1963, Pediat. *32*, 517.

Gitlin, D., G. Vaivter, and J. M. Craig, 1964, Pediat. *33*, 184.

Good, R. A., W. D. Kelly, J. Rotstein, and R. L. Varco, 1962, Progr. Allergy *6*, 187.

Good, R. A., R. D. A. Peterson, D. Y. Perey, J. Finstad, and M. D. Cooper, 1968, The immunological deficiency diseases of man. Birth defects, original article series, edited by D. Bergsma, *4*, 17.

Good, R. A., R. A. Gatti, R. Hong, and H. J. Meuwissen, 1969, Lancet *1*, 1162.

Grewal, M. S., 1962, Genet. Res. (Cambridge) *3*, 238.

Gruneberg, H. J., 1939, Genetics *24*, 777.

Gruneberg, H. J., 1942a, J. Genet. *43*, 45.

Gruneberg, H. J., 1942b, J. Genet. *44*, 246.

Gruneberg, H. J., 1952, The genetics of the mouse, 2nd edition. The Hague, Martinus Nijhoff.

Haddad, Z. H., R. F. Allen, J. W. Towner, and M. G. Wilson, 1969, Lancet *1*, 678.

Hanson, L. A., 1968, Aspects of the absence of the IgA system. Birth defects, original article series, edited by D. Bergsma, *4*, 292.

Harington, H., 1829, London Medical Gaz. *3*, 314.

Hertwig, P., 1942, Z. Indukt. Abstamm. Vererb.-Lehre *80*, 220.

Hertwig, P., 1956, Zool. Anzeig. Suppl. *20*. 185.

Higashi, O., 1954, Tohoku J. exp. Med. *59*, 315.

Hitzig, W. H., 1968, The Swiss type of agammaglobulinemia. Birth defects, original article series edited by D. Bergsma, *4*, 82.

Hitzig, W. H., Z. Biro, H. Bosch, and H. J. Huser, 1958, Helv. paediat. Acta *13*, 551.

Holmes, B., A. R. Page, and R. A. Good, 1967, J. Clin. Invest. *46*, 1422.

Holmes, B., A. R. Page, D. B. Windhorst, P. G. Quie, J. G. White, and R. A. Good, 1968, Fatal granulomatous disease: A genetic defect of phagocytic function. Birth defects, original article series, edited by D. Bergsma, *4*, 433.

Holmes, M. C. and F. M. Burnet, 1966, Thymic changes in NZB mice and hybrids. In: CIBA Symposium on the thymus: experimental and clinical studies, edited by G. E. W. Wolstenholme and R. Porter. London, Churchill, p. 381.

Howie, J. B. and B. J. Helyer, 1968, Adv. in Immunol. *9*, 215.

Hoyer, J. R., M. D. Cooper, A. E. Gabrielsen, and R. A. Good, 1968a, Medicine *47*, 201.

Hoyer, J. R., M. D. Cooper, A. E. Gabrielsen, and R. A. Good, 1968b, Lymphopenic forms of congenital immunologic deficiency: Clinical and pathologic patterns. Birth defects, original article series, edited by D. Bergsma, *4*, 91.

Huber, J., 1968, Experience with various immunologic deficiencies in Holland. Birth defects, original article series, edited by D. Bergsma, *4*, 53.

Huestis, R. R. and R. Anderson, 1954, Science *120*, 852.

Huestis, R. R., R. S. Anderson, and A. G. Motulsky, 1956, J. Hered. *47*, 225.

Hunt, H. R. and D. Permar, 1928, Anat. Rec. *41*, 117.

Jacobs, H. S., 1968, Brit. J. Haemat. *14*, 99.

Jenkins, V. K., T. T. Odell, and A. C. Upton, 1966, Cancer Res. *27*, 454.

Jenkins, V. K., A. C. Upton, and T. T. Odell, Jr., 1969a, J. Cell. Physiol. *73*, 141.

Jenkins, V. K., A. C. Upton, and T. T. Odell, Jr., 1969b, J. Cell. Physiol. *73*, 149.

Jeunet, F. S. and R. A. Good, 1968, Thymoma, immunologic deficiencies and hematological abnormalities. Birth defects, original article series, edited by D. Bergsma, *4*, 192.

Joe, M., J. M. Teasdale, and J. R. Miller, 1962, Can. J. Genet. Cytol. *4*, 219.

Kadowaki, J., W. W. Zuelzer, A. J. Brough, R. I. Thompson, P. V. Wooley, Jr., and D. Gruber, 1965, Lancet *2*, 1152.

Kahan, D. and R. A. Reisfeld, 1969, Science *164*, 1969.

Kales, A. N., W. Fried, and C. W. Gurney, 1966, Blood *28*, 387.

Kamenoff, R. J., 1935, J. Morphol. *58*, 117.

Keighley, G. H., P. Lowy, E. S. Russell, and M. W. Thompson, 1966, Brit. J. Haemat. *12*, 461.

Kiossoglou, K. A., W. J. Mitus, and W. Dameshek, 1965, Blood *26*, 610.

Kostmann, R., 1956, Acta Paediat. *45*, 309.

Krantz, S. and V. Kao, 1967, Clin. Res. *15*, 283.

Kretschmer, R., B. Say, D. Brown, and F. S. Rosen, 1965, New Eng. J. Med. *279*, 1295.

Krivit, W. and R. A. Good, 1959, Amer. J. Dis. Child. *97*, 137.

Kunze, H. G., 1954, Folia Haematol. (Leipzig) *72*, 39.

Lau, P., J. T. Brody, and L. H. Beizer, 1967, Blood *29*, 462.

Leader, R. W., G. A. Padgett, and J. R. Gorham, 1963, Blood *22*, 477.

Lewis, J. P., L. F. O'Grady, S. E. Bernstein, E. S. Russell, and F. E. Trobaugh, Jr., 1965, Blood *26*, Am. Soc. Hematol. 8th Meeting p. 870.

Lewis, J. P., L. F. O'Grady, S. E. Bernstein, E. S. Russell, and F. E. Trobaugh, Jr., 1967, Blood *30*, 601.

Lewis, S. M. and J. V. Dacie, 1965, Brit. J. Haemat. *11*, 549.

Lischner, H. W. and A. M. Di George, 1969, Lancet *2*, 1044.

Lischner, H. W., H. H. Punnett, and A. M. Di George, 1967, Nature *214*, 580.

Little, C. C., 1915, Am. Naturalist *49*, 727.

Little, C. C. and A. M. Cloudman, 1937, Proc. Nat. Acad. Sci. *23*, 535.

Lonsdale, D., S. D. Deodhar, and R. D. Mercer, 1967, J. Pediat. *71*, 790.

Louis-Bar, D., 1941, Confin. neurol. (Basel) *4*, 32.

Lund, J. E., G. A. Padgett, and R. L. Ott, 1967, Blood *29*, 452.

MacGillivray, J. B., J. V. Dacie, J. R. K. Henry, L. S. Sacker, and J. P. M. Tizard, 1964, Acta Paediat. *53*, 188.

Margolis, F. L. and E. S. Russell, 1965, Science *150*, 496.

Matsaniotis, N., 1968, Discussion. In: Birth defects, original article series, edited by D. Bergsma, *4*, 114.

Mayer, T. C. and M. C. Green, 1968, Dev. Biol. *18*, 62.

McCulloch, E. A., L. Siminovitch, and J. E. Till, 1964, Science *144*, 844.

McCulloch, E. A., L. Siminovitch, J. E. Till, E. S. Russell, and S. E. Bernstein, 1965a, Blood *26*, 399.

McCulloch, E. A., J. E. Till, and L. Siminovitch, 1965b, The role of independent and dependent stem cells in the control of hemopoietic and immunologic responses. In: Methodological approaches to the study of leukemias, edited by V. Defendi. Wistar Inst. Symp. Mon. No. 4. Philadelphia, Wistar Inst. Press, p. 61.

McCulloch, E. A., J. E. Till, and L. Siminovitch, 1965c, Host-cell interactions in mice bearing isologous hemopoietic grafts. In: La greffe des cellules hématopoïétiques allogéniques. Colloques Internationaux du Centre National de la Recherche Scientifique, *147*, 61.

McCulloch, E. A., M. W. Thompson, L. Siminovitch, and J. E. Till, 1970, Cell. Tissue Kinet *3*, 47.

McCusick, V. A. and H. E. Croso, 1966, J. Am. Med. Ass. *195*, 739.

McNeill, T. A., 1970, Immunol. *18*, 39.

Mekor, T. and R. A. Phillips, 1969, Proc. Soc. Exp. Biol. Med. *132*, 115.

Meuwissen, H. T., O. Stutman, and R. A. Good, 1969, Seminars in Hematology *6*, 28.

Millard, R. E., S. D. Lawler, H. E. M. Kay, and C. B. Cameron, 1968, Brit. J. Haemat. *14*, 363.

Miller, D. R., B. A. Freed, J. D. Lapey, 1968, Am. J. Dis. Child. *115*, 337.

Miller, J. F. A. P., M. Block, D. T. Rowland, and P. Kind, 1965, Proc. Soc. Exp. Biol. Med. *118*, 916.

Miller, M. E. 1968, Graft-versus-host reactions in man with special reference to thymic dysplasia. Birth defects, original article series, edited by D. Bergsma, *4*, 257.

Mintz, B., 1967, Proc. Nat. Acad. Sci. *58*, 344.

Mintz, B. and E. S. Russell, 1955, Anat. Rec. *122*, 443.

Mintz, B. and E. S. Russell, 1957, J. Exp. Zool. *134*, 207.

Mirand, E. A. and T. C. Prentice, 1964, Am. Zool. *4*, 326.

Modan, B. and M. Modan, 1968, Brit. J. Haemat. *14*, 375.

Moller, E., P. Olin, and R. Zetterstrom, 1967, Acta Paediat. Scand. Suppl. *177*, 29.

Moore, M. A. S. and D. Metcalf, 1970, Brit. J. Haemat. *18*, 279.

Morley, A. A., 1966, Lancet *2*, 1220.

Morley, A. A., J. P. Carew, and A. G. Baikie, 1967, Brit. J. Haemat. *13*, 719.

Moscona, A. A., 1963, Proc. Nat. Acad. Sci. *49*, 742.

Motulsky, A. G., R. R. Huestis, and R. Anderson, 1956, Acta Genet. *6*, 240.

Nash, D. J., 1964, Mouse Newsletter *30*, 53.

Nash, D. J., E. Kent, M. M. Dickie, and E. S. Russell, 1964, Am. Zool. *4*, 404.

Necheles, T. F. and W. Dameshek, 1967, Blood *29*, 550.

Nezelof, C., 1968, Thymic dysplasia with normal immunoglobulins and immunologic deficiency: Pure alymphocytosis. Birth defects, original article series, edited by D. Bergsma, *4*, 104.

Nezelof, C., M. L. Jammet, P. Lortholary, B. Labrune, and M. Lamy, 1964, Arch. franç. Pédiat. *21*, 897.

Osler, W., 1903, Amer. J. Med. Sci. *124*, 187.

Padgett, G. A., 1967, Blood *29*, 906.

Page, A. R. and R. A. Good, 1957, Am. J. Dis. Child. *94*, 623.

Pantelouris, E. M., 1968, Nature *217*, 370.

Peterson, R. D. A. and R. A. Good, 1968, Ataxia-telangiectasia. Birth defects, original article series, edited by D. Bergsma, *4*, 370.

Peterson, R. D. A., M. D. Cooper, and R. A. Good, 1966, Amer. J. Med. *41*, 342.

Pierpaoli, W. and E. Sorkin, 1967, Nature *215*, 834.

Pierpaoli, W. and E. Sorkin, 1968, J. Immunol. *101*, 1036.

Pinkerton, P. H., 1968, J. Path. Bact. *95*, 155.

Pinkerton, P. H. and R. M. Bannerman, 1966, Blood *28*, 987.

Pinkerton, P. H. and R. M. Bannerman, 1967, Nature *216*, 482.

Pinkerton, P. H. and R. M. Bannerman, 1968, The hereditary anemias of mice. Hematologic Reviews vol. 1, Edt. J. L. Ambrus (E. Arnold Ltd., London) p. 119.

Quie, P. G., 1969, Advances in Pediatrics *16*, 287.

Reimann, H. A., 1963, Periodic diseases. Oxford, Blackwell Scientific Publishers.

Robbins, J. B., R. G. Skinner, and H. A. Pearson, 1969, New Eng. J. Med. *280*, 75.

Rosen, F. S., J. M. Craig, G. Vawter, and C. A. Janeway, 1968, The dysgammaglobuline-mias and x-linked thymic hypoplasia. Birth defects, original article series, edited by D. Bergsma, *4*, 67.

Russell, E. S. and S. E. Bernstein, 1966, Blood and blood formation. In: The biology of the laboratory mouse, edited by E. L. Green, 2nd ed. New York, McGraw Hill, p. 351.

Russell, E. S. and S. E. Bernstein, 1967, Transp. *5*, 142.

Russell, E. S. and S. E. Bernstein, 1968, Arch. Biochem. Biophys. *125*, 594.

Russell, R. P. and C. L. Conley, 1964, Arch. Intern. Med. *114*, 734.

Russell, L. B. and M. H. I. Mayer, 1957, Genetics *42*, 161.

Russell, E. S. and E. C. McFarland, 1965, Fed. Proc. *24*, 240 (Abs.).

Russell, W. L. and E. S. Russell, 1948, Genetics *33*, 122.

Russell, E. S., C. M. Snow, L. M. Murray, and J. P. Cornier, 1953, Acta Haemat. *10*, 247.

Russell, E. S., S. E. Bernstein, E. C. McFarland, and W. R. Modeen, 1963, Rad. Res. *20*, 677.

Rygaard, J., 1969, Acta Path. Microbiol. Scand. *77*, 761.

Rygaard, J. and C. N. Muller-Berat, 1971, Immune response in the congenitally athymic mice 'nudes'. Transp. Proc. (in press).

Rygaard, J. and C. O. Povlsen. 1969, Acta Path. Microbiol. Scand. *77*, 758.

Sarvella, P. A. and L. B. Russell, 1956, J. Hered. *47*, 123.

Schmid, W., 1967, Seminars in Hematology *4*, 241.

Schooley, J. C., J. F. Garcia, L. N. Cantor, and V. W. Havens, 1968, Ann. N. Y. Acad. Sci. *149*, 266.

Seeger, R. C., A. J. Ammann, R. A. Good, and R. Hong, 1970, Clin. Exp. Immunol. *6*, 169.

Seligman, M., H. H. Fudenberg, and R. A. Good, 1968, Am. J. Med. *45*, 817.

Seller, M. J., 1968a, Transp. *6*, 856.

Seller, M. J., 1968b, Nature *220*, 300.

Seller, M. J. and P. E. Polini, 1966, Nature *212*, 80.

Shearer, G. M. and G. Cudkowicz, 1967, Fed. Proc. *26*, 688 (Abs.).

Shwachman, H., L. K. Diamond, F. A. Oski, and Khaw, Kon-T, 1964, J. Pediat. *65*, 645.

Simon, D., 1960, Arch. Anat. Micr. Morphol. exp. *49*, 93.

South, M. A., K. A. Starling, and D. J. Fernbach, 1969, New Eng. J. Med. *280*, 94.

Steeves, R. A., M. Bennett, E. A. Mirand, and G. Cudkowicz, 1968, Nature *218*, 327.

Steiner, M., M. Baldini, and W. Dameshek, 1963, Blood *22*, 810.

Steinmuller, D. and A. G. Motulsky, 1967, Blood *29*, 320.

Stevens, L. C. and J. A. Mackensen, 1958, J. Hered. *49*, 153.

Stevens, L. C., J. A. Mackensen, and S. E. Bernstein, 1959, J. Hereditary *50*, 35.

Sutherland, D. J. A., J. E. Till, and E. A. McCulloch, 1970, J. Cell. Physiol. *75*, 267.

Thieffrey, S., M. Arthuis, J. Aicardi, and C. Lyon, 1961, Rev. Neurol. *105*, 390.

Thompson, E. N. and J. F. Soothill, 1970, Arch. Dis. Child. *45*, 24.

Thompson, M. W., E. A. McCulloch, L. Siminovitch, and J. E. Till, 1966a, Brit. J. Haemat. *12*, 152.

Thompson, M. W., E. A. McCulloch, L. Siminovitch, and J. E. Till, 1966b, Genetics *54*, 366 (Abs.).

Thoms, G., 1951, Wiss. Z. Martin Luther Univ. *4*, 13.

Till, J. E., L. Siminovitch, and E. A. McCulloch, 1967, Blood *29*, 102.

Till, J. E., E. A. McCulloch, R. A. Phillips, and L. Siminovitch, 1968, Aspects of the regulation of stem cell function. In: The proliferation and spread of neoplastic cells. Proc. 21st Ann. Symp. Fundamental Cancer Research, Houston, Texas. Baltimore, Williams and Wilkins, p. 235.

Tobler, R. and H. Cottier, 1958, Helv. paediat. Acta *13*, 313.

Upton, A. C., 1959, Studies on the mechanism of leukaemogenesis by ionizing radiation. CIBA Symposium on Carcinogenesis: mechanisms of action, edited by G. E. W. Wolstenholme and M. O'Connor. London, J. and A. Churchill, p. 249.

Vacek, A. and E. Davidova, 1969, Folia Biol. *15*, 197.

Vaquez, H., 1892, C. R. Soc. Biol. Paris *44*, 384.

Vilter, R. W., J. J. Will, and T. Jarrold, 1967, Seminars in Hematology *4*, 175.

Waldmann, T. A. and W. Strober, 1968, Kinetic studies of immunoglobulin metabolism in immunologic deficiency. Birth defects, original article series, edited by D. Bergsma, *4*, 388.

Warner, N. L., J. W. Uhr, G. J. Thorbecke, and Z. Ovary, 1969, J. Immunol. *103*, 1317.

Weatherall, D. J., 1967, Seminars in Hematology *4*, 72.

Weiss, L., 1967, The cell periphery metastasis and other contact phenomena. Frontiers in Biology Series *7*. Amsterdam, North Holland Publishing Co.

Weston, J. A. and S. L. Butler, 1966, Dev. Biol. *14*, 246.

White, J. G., 1967, Blood *29*, 435.

Windhorst, D. B., J. G. White, P. B. Dent, J. Decker, and R. A. Good, 1968, Defective defense associated with genetic disease of subcellular organelles. Birth defects, original article series, edited by D. Bergsma, *4*, 424.

Wintrobe, M. M., 1967, Clinical Hematology, 6th edt. Philadelphia, Lea and Febiger.

Wolfe, H. G., 1963, Mouse Newsletter *29*, 40.

Wolfe, H. G. and D. L. Coleman, 1966, Pigmentation. Biology of the Laboratory Mouse, edited by E. L. Green, 2nd Edition. New York, McGraw Hill, p. 405.

Wolff, E. and K. Haffen, 1965, Germ cells and gonads. In: Cells and tissues in culture *2*, edited by E. N. Wilmer. London, Academic Press, p. 697.

Yachnin. S., 1965, J. Clin. Invest. *44*, 1534.

Yunis, E. J., H. R. Hilgard, C. Martinez, and R. A. Good, 1965, J. Exp. Med. *121*, 604.

CHAPTER 11

General discussion

The foregoing chapters have reviewed the remarkable increase in knowledge of the haemopoietic tissues which has occurred over the past 10–15 years. It would be idle to suggest that the major problems in haemopoiesis have now been solved, for it is evident that there is still profound ignorance concerning many of the important processes which operate during haemopoiesis. What has been established, however, is a very clear picture of the basic pattern of haemopoiesis, and techniques are available which should allow much more detail to be added to this picture.

It is now apparent that the original concept of fixed populations in haemopoietic organs was mistaken. Haemopoietic cells are not generated *de novo* from structural cells of haemopoietic organs either in embryonic or adult life, and there is a continuous replacement of these populations throughout life, in all organs except the bone marrow, by new cells seeding from the blood.

The source of all haemopoietic populations has been shown to be the multipotential stem cell, a remarkable cell which has the capacity for migration throughout the body, extensive self-generation and the generation of specific progenitor cells for each of the various blood-cell classes. The multipotential stem cells originate in the yolk sac early in embryogenesis and, after migration to the embryo, sequentially establish haemopoietic populations in the liver, spleen, bone marrow, thymus and lymph nodes. More remarkable is the fact that, throughout post-natal life, multipotential stem cells regularly migrate from their primary location in the bone marrow to continuously repopulate the other major haemopoietic organs. This system provides the basis for the great proliferative reserves of the haemopoietic tissues and the great flexibility of haemopoiesis, allowing populations to build up in locations optimally situated to meet particular functional demands. The full complexity of the mechanisms controlling self-replication of stem cells is not yet understood, but it seems evident that the system is so designed as to avoid uneven de-

mands on individual stem cells which might precipitate mutations or exhaustion of replicative capacity.

The generation of specific progenitor cells from multipotential stem cells is
achieved by the induction of differentiation along a single pathway, a process
mediated by specialised fixed cell structures (microenvironments) scattered
through the various haemopoietic organs. With the possible exception of the
lymphoid microenvironments, these structures appear to allow the simultaneous self-replication of stem cells and the generation of progenitor cells,
programmed along a single pathway of differentiation. Activation of progenitor cells to commence generating specific blood cells is achieved by a
commitment process mediated, at least in some cases, by specific humoral
regulators.

While the above basic sequence occurs in all organs and for all blood-cell
classes, there are individual differences in detail, whose significance is not
yet clear. E.g., repopulation of the spleen and lymph nodes is a relatively
rapid process occurring in the mouse every 1–2 months. On the other hand,
repopulation of the thymus may not be complete and clearly occurs at a much
slower rate. Similarly, repopulation of the thymus and the non-lymphoid
elements of the spleen appears to be initiated by migrating stem cells,
whereas repopulation of the peripheral lymphoid tissue is carried out by
progenitor cells whose initial precommitment occurred either in the bone
marrow or thymus. Furthermore, there appear to be possible differences in
the manner in which the increased generation of mature cells is accomplished
in each cell class. In the erythropoietic series, the production of increased
numbers of red cells is achieved by the commitment of additional progenitor
cells, whereas in the granulopoietic series the evidence suggests that this can
be achieved either by commitment of additional progenitor cells or by
increasing the number of progeny produced by each progenitor cell.

It is clear that cell-cell interactions are of critical importance in the establishment and maintenance of haemopoietic populations. Such interactions
are necessary to create the initial haemopoietic microenvironments that
induce differentiation in multipotential stem cells, and in the lymphoid
system they continue to be important even in the collaboration of T and B
cells at a relatively differentiated level. These cell-cell interactions probably
involve the apposition of highly specific receptor sites on cell surfaces, and
future progress in analysing these interactions will depend on the development of techniques for isolating and characterising these receptors. Here
chemical analysis may be inadequate for the task, and it may be profitable
to introduce immunological methods to determine the specificity and reacti-

vity of these sites. It is of equal importance to design simple *in vitro* systems
for mimicking organ microenvironments. The present techniques of organ
culture are quite inadequate for such studies and simple cell monolayers on
diffusion membranes may serve as useful starting points.

Because of the dispersed nature of haemopoietic populations throughout
the body, humoral regulators must play an unusually important role in the
overall regulation of cell proliferation and differentiation. Good progress has
been made with erythropoietin and CSF, but numerous other regulators must
exist and await proper characterisation. It seems probable that the initial
induction step mediated by the microenvironment leads to the development
on the progenitor cell surface of specific receptor sites which restrict the
responsiveness of this cell to one specific regulator. The regulator presumably
makes contact with this receptor site which activates a sequence of cytoplasmic events leading to the initiation of structural changes and synthetic
processes which will characterise the specialised progeny of this progenitor
cell. Again the nature of these surface receptors is clearly a central issue, but
other questions can be raised. What makes one progenitor cell more responsive than another to a regulator – more receptor sites, better 'fitting' receptor
sites, or something else? Can a regulator molecule achieve derepression at the
gene level and, if so, how is this derepressed state maintained in the progeny
of the progenitor cell? Do regulators simply 'activate' a gene which was
already derepressed, but in a 'latent' state, by some non-specific intermediary
such as cyclic-AMP? The solution of many questions of this type lies in the
field of molecular biology rather than experimental haematology. It should
be emphasised here, however, that haemopoietic cells provide unique marker
systems which make these cells superior models for the analysis of fundamental problems of cell regulation.

The migration streams of haemopoietic cells in embryonic and adult life
raise questions which have long intrigued embryologists. To what degree are
such migration streams purposeful, and what activates a cell to commence
migration? In the adult animal only a small fraction of stem cells is migratory –
at least, at any one point in time. What determines the size of this fraction
and which particular cells shall be involved? Paralleling these questions are
similar ones relating to the developing haemopoietic organs. What determines that there shall be one spleen and only one? What determines its
precise location? Do the microenvironmental cells undergo inductive
differentiation in anticipation of the arrival of stem cells, and if so, how is this
regulated?

Any cell system which exhibits a high level of proliferative activity and complex patterns of differentiation, can be expected to be at high risk of developing neoplastic changes. Even the limited studies so far made on leukaemic populations have indicated that the resulting patterns of cellular deviation can be complex and highly variable. In part these abnormalities must be due to intrinsic changes within the affected haemopoietic cells, but regulatory disturgances are likely also to be involved. One of the most intriguing developments from recent *in vitro* culture work with leukaemic cells has been the suggestion that such leukaemic cells may still be responsive to regulation and these initial observations are in urgent need of exploitation.

What relevance have these advances in knowledge of haemopoiesis for the clinical management of various haematological diseases? In part the answer to this question is similar to that to the query: 'Of what use is a newborn babe?' There are, however, some immediate potential applications, granted the capacity for cell and tissue grafting to matched histocompatible recipients. Already some disease states have been characterised as being due to stem-cell deficiencies or to deficiencies in haemopoietic microenvironments. In these cases successful attempts have already been made to cure or alleviate the disease by haemopoietic cell or organ grafts. The proper understanding of the interrelationships between stem and progenitor cells, coupled with im- proved cell-separation procedures is beginning to permit cell grafting free of the formerly inevitable consequences of secondary or graft-vs.-host disease. Similarly the characterisation and ultimate synthesis of specific regulators may place powerful therapeutic weapons in the hands of the clinician faced with problems of infectious disease and leukaemia. Like the newborn babe, the prospects tend to lie in the future rather than in the present, but few medical advances are made without a preliminary understanding of basic physiological processes, and the recent advances in knowledge of haemo- poiesis represent a major step in understanding the nature and behaviour of these tissues.

Subject Index